Documentation and Reimbursement for Home Care and Hospice Programs

Prinny Rose Abraham, RHIT, CPHQ

AHIMA

AMERICAN HEALTH INFORMATION ®
MANAGEMENT ASSOCIATION

As of June 14, 2001, the Health Care Financing Administration (HCFA) became known as the Centers for Medicare and Medicaid Services (CMS). Because production of this book was already underway by the time of the name change, the reader will notice that Health Care Financing Administration and the acronym HCFA are still used throughout this book. In addition, the acronym HCPCS, formerly used to indicate HCFA Common Procedure Coding System, now stands for Healthcare Common Procedure Coding System.

Previously published in 1996 as *Documentation and Information Management in Home Care and Hospice Programs* by Susan C. Miller

ISBN 1-58426-043-2
Product No. AB101601
IPC No. 1000-801

Cheryl Smith, BS, RHIT, CPHQ, Reviewer
Carol Brockman, Project Editor
Jennifer Solheim, Copy Editor

American Health Information Management Association
233 North Michigan Avenue, Suite 2150
Chicago, Illinois 60601-5800

http://www.ahima.org

Contents

Contents

About the Author

Prinny Rose Abraham, RHIT, CPHQ, founded the Minneapolis-based hiqmConsulting in 1995. Abraham frequently works for the Corridor Group as an associate consultant. Prior to hiqmConsulting, Abraham worked for In Home Health, Inc., as a health information management manager and coordinator and as a performance improvement coordinator.

Abraham currently serves as a member of the outcomes committee for the Minnesota Home Care Association. In addition, she is a part of the editorial advisory board of the PPS Alert for Home Health. In the past, Abraham has served the Minnesota Health Information Management Association as regional president and as a member of its professional development and nominating committees. She also held a national-level position as a member of AHIMA's professional development committee.

Articles authored by Abraham can be found in various publications, including *Home Care PPS Alert, Remmington Report, Journal of the American Health Information Management Association,* and *Advance for Providers of Post-Acute Care.* In her writing, Abraham covers topics related to home health, coding, and prospective payment systems. She has also addressed these topics in presentations to various state home care associations and at AHIMA's national convention.

Abraham holds an associate's degree in Applied Science Health Information Management from the College of St. Catherine.

Acknowledgments

The original version of this book, titled *Documentation and Information Management in Home Care and Hospice Programs,* was published in 1996 under the authorship of Susan C. Miller.

AHIMA wishes to thank Margaret Morgan Stewart, RHIA, for her authorship of chapter 6 within this revised edition. AHIMA also wishes to extend thanks to the following contributors and volunteer technical reviewers:

- Ida Kay Blevins, RHIA, BS: Business manager, Home Health Services, St. Johns Hospital, Springfield, Illinois

- Carol Bovasso, RHIT: Compliance manager, Englewood Hospital Home Health and Hospice Services, Englewood, New Jersey

- Dawn Bushnell: Health information management student, St. Catherine's College, St. Paul, Minnesota

- Karen Dodd: Consultant, Compuware, Bloomington, Minnesota

- Kathleen J. Dodd, BSN, MHA: Founder, owner, and CEO, The Corridor Group, Inc. (TCG), Overland Park, Kansas, and San Francisco, California

- Michelle Dougherty, RHIA: Practice manager, American Health Information Management Association

- Barbara January, RN, BSN: Clinical services specialist in home health, Minnetonka, Minnesota

- Mary Johnson, RHIA: Health information management supervisor, Fairview Home Health and Hospice, Minneapolis, Minnesota

- Mary St. Pierre, BSN, MGA: Director of regulatory affairs, National Association for Home Care, Washington, D.C.

- Patricia Skogen, RN: Mobile director of operations, Heartland HomeCare and Hospice, Toledo, Ohio

- Cheryl Smith, BS, RHIT, CPHQ: Practice manager, American Health Information Management Association

- Paula Stearns, MSN, RN: Center for Health Services Research, Denver, Colorado

- Charles W. Tidd: President, Charles W. Tidd Associates, Inc. (a home care information management consulting firm), Newtown, Connecticut

- Tom D. Williams: Publisher, Home Care Automation Report, Fredonia, Wisconsin

In addition, Ms. Abraham wishes to personally extend her thanks to those dedicated clinicians who care for sick and dying patients and the nursing leaders who taught her about home care and hospice.

Introduction

Documentation and Reimbursement for Home Care and Hospice Programs is an extensive update of the 1996 book published under the title *Documentation and Information Management in Home Care and Hospice Programs.* This revised edition emphasizes current needs, such as the needs for high-quality, standardized data and their management; for computerization of data and information; and for state-of-the-art quality improvement programs. This book also addresses the continuing need for assistance in record documentation and management, and for maintenance and security of information and record confidentiality. This book is intended for use by health information management (HIM) professionals working in home care and hospice settings; home care and hospice administrators; and students.

Referenced throughout this publication are the requirements of the two major home care accrediting organizations: the Community Health Accreditation Program, Inc. (CHAP), and the Joint Commission on Accreditation of Healthcare Organizations (JCAHO). Medicare home healthcare and hospice requirements are also referenced. Because state home care and hospice regulations vary in scope and requirements, readers should consult their particular state's regulations for requirements.

Home care in the United States is a diverse and dynamic service industry. Within this industry, home health agencies, home care aide organizations, and hospices have come to be known collectively as home care organizations. More than 20,000 providers deliver home care services to some eight million individuals who require services because of acute illness, long-term health conditions, permanent disability, or terminal illness. Annual expenditures for home health were estimated to be $36 billion in 1999. The growth of the agencies themselves has also been dramatic. The 1880s saw the establishment of the first home care agencies. By 1963, the number of agencies totaled nearly 1,100. Today that number exceeds 20,000. And based on AHIMA's annual membership survey, 8.2 percent of respondents work in the home health setting (NAHC 2000).

According to the National Association for Home Care (NAHC) data (2000), Medicare-certified home health agencies grew more than threefold, from 1,753 to 5,983 in the time period of 1967 through 1985. But then in the 1980s, the number of Medicare-certified home care agencies leveled off to approximately 5,900 as a result of increasing Medicare paperwork and unreliable payment policies. Both of these problems led to a 1987 lawsuit brought against the Health Care Financing Administration (HCFA) by a coalition of U.S. congressional members, consumer groups, and NAHC. After the successful conclusion of the lawsuit, Medicare's annual home care benefit increased significantly and the number of agencies rose to over 10,000. Yet, once again, the number of Medicare-certified agencies has declined to 7,747 since 1997. NAHC believes the 26-percent decline is a direct result of the changes in Medicare home health reimbursement that were enacted as part of the Balanced Budget Act of 1997.

Medicare added hospice benefits in October 1983, ten years after the first hospice was established in the United States. The number of Medicare-certified hospices has grown from 31 in January 1984 to 2,288 as of January 2000. Home care and hospice growth occurred in a changing healthcare environment—a more competitive, managed care environment. This environment challenges providers to develop information management systems that encourage documentation of standardized, high-quality, and accessible data and information to support patient and family care, quality improvement efforts, strategic planning, and other essential activities. *Documentation and Reimbursement for Home Care and Hospice Programs* provides assistance in this endeavor. It also aids HIM professionals in making the transition from hospital-based to home care or hospice-based practice.

References and Bibliography

National Association for Home Care. 2000. *Basic Statistics about Home Care.* Washington, D.C.: National Association for Home Care. Available at http://www.nahc.org/Consumer/hcstats.html.

You Are Here—Annual Membership Survey Marks the Spot. 2000 (August). *AHIMA Advantage* 4(4):14.

Chapter 1

Data and Information Management

Data pertaining to the individuals who use healthcare services are collected in virtually every setting where healthcare is delivered. Data represent basic facts and measurements. In healthcare, these facts usually describe specific characteristics of individual patients. For example, the age of a patient is a data element as are the patient's gender, insurance coverage, and blood pressure. The term *information* refers to data that have been collected, combined, analyzed, interpreted, and/or converted into a form that can be used for specific purposes. In other words, *data* represents facts; *information* represents meaning.

Access to reliable data and information is critical to the delivery of home care and hospice services. Quality improvement processes are based on the use of accurate and accessible data, and managers and administrators depend on it. Clinicians need accurate and up-to-date information to make patient care and business decisions. When information is unreliable or is not available, the quality of patient care can be adversely affected.

Chapter 1 defines some essential terms and then discusses the reasons behind the need for reliable and standardized data at the provider, state, and national levels. This chapter also discusses the present status of data quality and availability in home care and hospice organizations.

Health information management (HIM) changes and the evolution of the American healthcare delivery system are having a dramatic impact on the information demands placed on home care and hospice organizations. The health information systems of every organization will need to be continuously improved to keep pace with changes in the larger healthcare environment. Improving the organization's information systems is a team effort that involves all of the organization's employees and volunteers.

Driving Forces behind the Improvement of Information Management Systems

Several key factors are driving the need for improved information management systems (IMS) in home care and hospice organizations:

- **The need to comply with federal regulations:** The Health Care Financing Administration (HCFA), through its Home Health Initiative, developed a quality-monitoring system that makes highly specific data collection and information management demands on home care providers. (Specifics of this initiative are addressed later in this chapter.) Also, the Balanced Budget Act of 1997 (BBA) and the Omnibus Budget Reconciliation

Act of 1986 (OBRA) mandated the implementation of a new prospective payment system for skilled nursing facilities, home healthcare agencies, outpatient rehabilitation services, and other outpatient services provided to Medicare beneficiaries. The prospective payment system (PPS) became effective on October 1, 2000. The PPS changed home care reimbursement from a cost-based system to a system of fixed fee reimbursement based on a patient-need classification system. The BBA bundled all services covered and paid for on a reasonable cost basis under the Medicare home health benefit, including medical supplies, into the prospective payment.

- **The need to comply with accreditation standards:** Organizations that choose to be accredited by the Joint Commission on Accreditation of Healthcare Organizations (JCAHO) must meet its management of information standards (known as IM standards) (JCAHO 2000). Home care and hospice organizations may also decide to participate in the Community Health Accreditation Program (CHAP) (CHAP 1997), whose core standards are related to information management, clinical records, and management information systems.

- **The increasingly competitive managed care environment:** To vie for managed care contracts and to survive in the current competitive healthcare environment, home care and hospice providers need data and information to document the quality, outcomes, and costs of services provided. Providers who can demonstrate that their services and outcomes are superior (through comparisons with norms or comparative data) have a competitive edge.

- **The need to improve the management of increasingly complex organizations:** As healthcare organizations become more diverse, the need for available organization- and patient-level process and outcome data and information grows. Reliable, standardized systems for data documentation are essential, as are efficient methods for sharing data and information among providers within an organization.

- **The influence of government on healthcare planning and policy:** The state and federal governments need home care and hospice information to examine such issues as access to healthcare services and the quality, outcome, utilization, and costs of services provided. Having such information is especially vital when reformed systems are introduced.

Data Quality and Availability

Despite a heavy investment in computer systems, some home health and hospice organizations continue to manually collect quality improvement data and other information. One of several challenges in revising the home health *Conditions of Participation* was the development of a standard core assessment tool. The management tool is designed to be used by providers and eventually by government agencies and healthcare consumers to compare patient indicators and outcomes across providers (HCFA 1997, 11004). HCFA made Outcome-Based Quality Management reports available to providers in early 2000.

Some data on the national level are available. An annual survey instituted in 1996 provides valuable information on home and hospice care. The National Center for Health Statistics published a summary of 1996 findings, which contains such information as length of service by diagnosis, disposition at discharge, primary diagnosis at admission, and activities of daily living. This type of information is of interest to provider organizations because it can be used for comparative purposes. Survey instruments are also included in the summary report (Haupt 1996).

The National Medical Expenditure Survey is another source for national home care utilization and expenditure data. Of the $1,113.7 billion attributed to personal health spending in 1998, 60 percent was for hospital care and physician services, and only a small fraction (3 percent) was spent on freestanding home care. Hospital-based home care is included with hospital expenditures. Total home care spending is difficult to estimate due to the limitations of data sources. The National Association for Home Care (NAHC) estimated total spending for home care at $41 billion in 1997 and $36 billion in 1999. The decline is largely the result of dramatic decreases in Medicare-financed home health. These estimates do not include spending for home care services that are not included in the national health accounts data, for example, payments made by consumers to independent providers.

The U.S. Department of Census estimated there were 19,960 home health service organizations in 1997. The Census Bureau's definition of a home health organization includes only those organizations that provide skilled services exclusively or in combination with other home health services (NAHC 2000). Medicare-certified provider data and Medicare Part A and Part B claims data provide information on Medicare home care and hospice providers nationally and on Medicare home care and hospice service provision and utilization.

Data and Information Management Initiatives

HCFA and JCAHO revised their *Conditions of Participation* and standards to focus on outcomes of care and to eliminate unnecessary procedural requirements. The challenge for revising *Conditions of Participation* and standards was to standardize assessments and develop data collection methods useful as management tools for providers. In addition, the revisions were meant to enable government agencies, accreditation and licensure, surveyors, and healthcare consumers to compare indicators and outcomes across home health organizations.

Uniform Data Set for Home Care and Hospice

In 1993, the National Association for Home Care's board of directors charged the information resources and quality assurance committee with the task of developing standardized definitions for home care and hospice data elements through a consensus conference process. The board recognized that a uniform minimum data set was a necessary first step toward achieving standardized, comparable home care and hospice data. The consensus conference was held in December 1993. In 1997, the information resources and quality assurance committee added the Outcome and Assessment Information Set (OASIS) to the uniform data set (UDS). OASIS is a group of data elements that represent core items in a comprehensive assessment for an adult home care patient. The data elements form the basis of patient outcome meaurements used for outcome-based quality improvement.

A uniform minimum data set is a minimum set of informational items that have uniform definitions and predefined categories. Uniform minimum data sets are designed to meet the essential information needs of multiple users in the healthcare system. The framework adopted to guide development of the data set for home care and hospice services was based on the U.S. Department of Health and Human Services' concept of a uniform minimum data set (UDS). The UDS is intended to meet the common data needs of multiple users, and so it will not necessarily meet the total data needs of any one organization, nor does it limit additional data collection by an organization to meet its specific information needs. The UDS addresses data documentation and collection at the organizational level and at the individual patient level. Appendix A shows the listing of all data elements with their definitions and categories. This data set will be used for future data collection efforts conducted by the NAHC. Other entities involved in home care and hospice are encouraged to use these definitions when constructing surveys and questionnaires (NAHC 2000).

Home Health Initiative and Home Care Outcome Monitoring

In 1994, HCFA began the Medicare home health initiative to identify opportunities for improvement in the Medicare Home Health Benefit. Among the primary recommendations, HCFA was advised to develop home health *Conditions of Participation* that include a core standard assessment data set and patient-centered, outcome-oriented performance expectations that stimulate continuous quality improvement in healthcare. OASIS will become part of the same information system that was designed to collect and report beneficiary-specific outcomes and provider performance across a multitude of delivery sites (HCFA 1997, HCFA 1999a).

On the basis of comments received, minor modifications were made to the Outcome and Assessment Information Set (OASIS-A2). HCFA published the Outcome and Assessment Information Set (OASIS-B1) in June 1998. OASIS is a group of data elements that represent core items of a comprehensive assessment for an adult home care patient. In addition, OASIS forms the basis for measuring patient outcomes for purposes of outcome-based quality improvement (OBQI). OASIS serves as a key component in fostering and monitoring improved home healthcare outcomes in the partnership between Medicare and the home care industry. It is also an integral part of the revised *Conditions of Participation* for Medicare-certified home health agencies. Outcome measures are the crux of OBQI, which is a systematic approach HHAs can implement and follow to continuously improve the quality of care they provide. OASIS data significantly improve each state's ability to identify areas of potential quality concerns (HCFA 1999b).

Most data items in the OASIS were derived in the context of a national research program to develop a system of outcome measures for home care. Outcome-based quality improvement and OASIS evolved over a ten-year developmental period. The core items were refined through several iterations of clinical and empirical research. Other items were later added by a group of home care experts to augment the outcome data set with selected items deemed essential for patient assessment. The goal was not to produce a comprehensive assessment instrument, but to provide a set of items necessary for measuring patient outcomes and essential for assessment, which home health agencies could augment as needed. OASIS items are used in outcome monitoring, clinical assessment, care planning, and other internal agency-level applications.

OASIS encompasses sociodemographic, environmental, support system, health status, and functional status attributes of adult (nonmaternity) patients. In addition, selected attributes of health service utilization, such as therapy utilization, are included. These different attributes should be part of a comprehensive patient assessment (HCFA 2000).

JCAHO's Management of Information Standards

Through the Management of Information Standards in JCAHO's *2001–2002 Comprehensive Accreditation Manual for Home Care* (CAMHC), a series of required processes provide a framework for home care and hospice providers to more effectively and productively manage their information. The 2001—2002 standards are functionally based, and information management (IM) is viewed as a function integral to the provision of care and services. JCAHO IM standards describe the effective and continuous improvement of information management in healthcare organizations. The organization's leaders are responsible for achieving, maintaining, and improving an organizationwide approach to information management and ensuring the education and training of staff in managing and using information. In the next section, specific JCAHO IM standards are discussed in relation to the information management system.

Information Management System

To develop and maintain a high-quality information management system (IMS) that meets the data and information needs of a home care or hospice program, strategic and continuous planning is required. Integral to this planning, and to implementation, are knowledgeable and forward-thinking leaders and educated employees who understand their roles in the IMS, as well as demonstrated leadership support for IM, including the allocation of needed resources.

This look at the IM processes that follows applies to provider organizations with manual or computer-based systems. Computerization is not a prerequisite to a good IMS, but for sorting, describing, and analyzing data, some computer assistance (such as computer-based spreadsheet or database programs) would prove beneficial to even the smallest of organizations.

System Planning

JCAHO IM standards require a thorough assessment and analysis of internal and external information needs, which will consider data and information needs among departments, services, or programs, the clinical staff, the administration, and governance structure, as well as information needed to support relationships with outside services, contractors, companies, and agencies. Leaders should seek input from staff for information needs, selecting appropriate technology, while integrating and using information systems to manage clinical and organizational information (JCAHO 2000). After an organization has identified its information needs, it identifies how the needs can be met, develops a budget with associated time frames, and plans and implements the needed system. Development of a shared vision is important to planning the IMS. Along with the vision, strategic objectives are set so that the organization can monitor the implementation and operation of its system. Some organizations may choose to plan in an incremental fashion by focusing first on a selected data need, such as clinical outcome data. Once knowledge is gained in this particular area, the organization can approach other data needs systematically. The IM plan would discuss this approach, along with plans to focus on other data needs.

JCAHO requires home care and hospice providers to plan and continuously monitor and improve IM processes. Scoring guidelines delineate the intent of the standards and give examples of compliance (JCAHO 2000). JCAHO does not mandate a computerized IMS, and so standards can be met when a manual IMS is in place. Specific planning standards include IM.1, the organization plans and designs information management processes to meet its internal and external information needs. As the standard implies, JCAHO requires diverse input into planning an IMS.

CHAP does not require an IM plan per se, but it addresses the need for information, as well as its monitoring. CHAP requires that the organization's strategic plan be based on a comprehensive external environmental assessment and internal organizational evaluation based on data and information (CHAP 1997). The following is a list of CHAP management of information systems standards:

CIV.5	An efficient and effective management information system is established and assures accountability at all levels of the organization.
CIV.5a.	A system is developed for collection of key management data (manual or automated) on a regular basis with standards identified for each element.
CIV.5a1.	The organization facilitates timely access to internal and external databases, which provide information relevant to service development or delivery.
CIV.5b.	The organization provides for security and confidentiality of management information system data.

CIV.5c.   Management data are collected on a timely basis and appropriately reviewed.

CIV.5d.   Management data are used as a basis for identification of and response to organization trends.

CIV.5e.   The organization participates in evaluation programs that provide for a comparative outcome-based performance review with other organizations providing similar services or programs.

CIV.5f.   All levels of staff are held accountable for maintaining measurable performance standards.

Initial and Continuing Assessment of Data Needs

Identifying the primary users of information is one of the first steps in defining the information needs of an organization. Users can be classified as either internal or external customers. Internal customers include the following:

- **Patient care delivery:** The needs of such individual providers as nurses, therapists, and others

- **Patient care delivery:** The needs of such consumers as patients, families, significant others, and others

- **Patient care management and support:** The needs of administrators, accountants, quality improvement managers, utilization review managers, and others

- **Patient care reimbursement:** The needs of managers, payers, and others

- **Others:** The needs of accrediting bodies, policymakers, lawyers, and others

External customers include the following:

- **Healthcare delivery:** The needs of alliances, health maintenance organizations (HMOs), hospitals, and other provider organizations

- **Management and review of care:** The needs of such organizations as peer review organizations and utilization review companies

- **Reimbursement of care:** The needs of payers, employers, and others

- **Research:** The needs of registries, research centers, and others

- **Education:** The needs of professional schools

- **Accreditation:** The needs of accrediting and licensing organizations

- **Policymaking:** The needs of local, state, and federal governments

Once the primary users of the data and information have been identified, an information needs assessment is performed to determine user needs. Interviews and surveys can pinpoint the following:

- Essential data and information needs

- The extent to which needs are being met in an accurate and timely manner

- Data sources used to meet needs and how the sources are accessed

- Positions responsible for retrieving, aggregating, analyzing, and interpreting needed data and information

External users can also be interviewed and surveyed to assess their data and information needs. But whatever methods are employed, the work sheets and survey instruments should be maintained so that documented evidence remains to support compliance with JCAHO standard IM.1, which requires such an assessment.

To assess the needs of regulatory or accrediting groups, a review can be performed of licensing and certification regulations—and, if applicable, accreditation standards—to determine required documentation and data collection. For example, in its standard CIV.1, CHAP requires the collection and monitoring of data appropriate to the complexity and scope of the organization, and cites specific data elements to be collected (CHAP 1997). JCAHO scoring guidelines for standard IM.8 give examples of specific required aggregate information that the IMS of an organization must be able to produce (JCAHO 2000). The needs of other important external users—such as payers, HMOs, or healthcare alliances—must also be determined.

It is important to try to ascertain the amount of duplication and poor communication that exists in the IMS due to manual or computer-based systems not being adequately linked to facilitate communication and sharing of patient and administrative data. Planners will also want to determine the extent to which users' needs are being met only because users have developed or purchased specialized manual or computer-based systems to meet their needs. For example, in an organization with extensive computerization of assessment and clinical information, quality improvement (QI) managers may have their data needs met, but only because they have developed their own computer-based database that requires manual data retrieval from various sources, and manual computer entry. This type of scenario would signal a need for further investigation to determine why the present system does not meet the needs of quality improvement managers and how the system can be modified to better meet their needs.

Organization leaders and IMS planners anticipate data and information needs, so that the IMS is better able to meet future demands. IMS planners in Medicare-certified home health agencies can consider the data and information needs of HCFA's Home Health Initiative. The data contained in OASIS-B1 are useful in this regard.

Figure 1.1 includes sample questions that can be used to perform an information needs assessment. These questions address the assessment of data needs as well as the broader capabilities of the IMS.

Data Capture and Collection

Four steps must be considered in the process of capturing and collecting data:

- Determination of the data set or database
- Documentation and capture of the data
- Maintenance of the confidentiality and security of the data
- Collection and retrieval of the data

Determination of the Data Set or Database

Once the user data and information needs have been systematically determined, the planners can address how the needs should be prioritized. Establishing the priority of needs helps to determine the minimum required data to be uniformly defined and documented across the range of patients and across departments and organizations. There are the data that will be routinely collected and readily accessible, in an aggregate form when applicable, to users to assist

Figure 1.1. **Sample Questions for Assessment of Organizationwide Information Management**

Assessment Question	Ratings*						Comments
Is a clinical information plan in place and is it updated as needed?	NA	1	2	3	4	5	
Does the plan include a list of all the data collected within the healthcare organization, and is the list updated as needed?	NA	1	2	3	4	5	
Are the sources for the data identified?	NA	1	2	3	4	5	
Are uniform data capture methods used organizationwide?	NA	1	2	3	4	5	
Is there a data quality manual and is it updated as necessary?	NA	1	2	3	4	5	
Is a health record maintained for every individual receiving services in the healthcare organization?	NA	1	2	3	4	5	
Are health record documentation standards followed for all types of patients?	NA	1	2	3	4	5	
Are health record documentation standards reviewed and updated periodically?	NA	1	2	3	4	5	
Does the organization follow a policy that outlines the time frames for completion of components of active health records and health records of discharged patients?	NA	1	2	3	4	5	
Do health information management professionals participate in in-service and/or continuing education activities related to health information systems, health record content, authentication of record entries, correction of documentation errors, documentation approaches, and information systems backup and disaster recovery?	NA	1	2	3	4	5	
Are health information management professionals given the opportunity to attend outside educational programs on health information systems, health record content, authentication of record entries, correction of documentation errors, documentation approaches, and information systems backup and disaster recovery?	NA	1	2	3	4	5	
Are educational activities documented in the employment files of health information management staff?	NA	1	2	3	4	5	
Are users of health information systems and reports educated regarding the confidentiality and security of, and access to, confidential systems and information?	NA	1	2	3	4	5	
Are the costs of filing supplies (such as folders, labels, chart dividers, disks) reviewed regularly and competitive prices investigated?	NA	1	2	3	4	5	
Is the filing process periodically analyzed through flow charting?	NA	1	2	3	4	5	
Is the flow of the process periodically reviewed by management and staff with a focus on process improvement?	NA	1	2	3	4	5	

Figure 1.1.   (Continued)

Assessment Question	Ratings*						Comments
Do the healthcare organization's written confidentiality policies address the central question of who may have access to what data and for what purpose?	NA	1	2	3	4	5	
Do the healthcare organization's written confidentiality policies state that disclosure of patient-identifiable data and healthcare information requires the written authorization of the patient or his/her legal representative?	NA	1	2	3	4	5	
Do the confidentiality policies encompass concerns for both primary and secondary healthcare information?	NA	1	2	3	4	5	
Is information system planning performed on a regular basis?	NA	1	2	3	4	5	
Is the organization's information system plan updated annually?	NA	1	2	3	4	5	

* NA = Not applicable; 1 = Never; 2 = Rarely; 3 = Sometimes; 4 = Often; 5 = Always

Source: Adapted from *Health Information Management Practice Standards: Tools for Assessing Your Organization.* AHIMA ©1998.

in patient care, continuing strategic management decisions, QI efforts, payer decisions, and so on. A systematic process must be agreed upon for determining the priority level of different data elements. For example, NAHC used a consensus process requiring that 100 percent of the participants would agree that they could live with a data element and its definition in developing the uniform data set. In line with the previous discussion, the data and information needed for monitoring strategic planning receive priority, as do the data and information required by payers, regulators, and accrediting bodies.

Data validity is an important concept to consider when determining data elements to include in the organization's data set. Data are documented and collected to provide information to users. Data validity refers to the degree that data reasonably represent what is being measured (O'Leary 1998). For example, if an organization wants to measure nursing workload, the planners determine which data reasonably represent workload. The conclusion may be that the average number of daily visits represents workload, but only when assessed in conjunction with such other factors as distance to patient's home, services rendered in the home, and length of a visit.

In standard IM.3, JCAHO requires that whenever possible, the organization use standard minimum data sets, data definitions, codes, classifications, and terminology throughout the organization. It also requires home care and hospice organizations to refer to externally standardized sets, definitions, codes, classifications, and available terminology when they are developing and defining their data sets. By capturing and collecting data in a uniform fashion as the NAHC data set prescribes, home care and hospice programs can compare their data and information to that of similar provider organizations.

The product of an organization's assessment and priority setting is a list of defined data elements and, when applicable, data element categories. Because individual organizations have many specific data and information needs beyond national data sets, an organization's list will probably be longer than the national list. Ideally, data elements will be retained in a computer-based database (also known as an enterprise database) from which data and information can be retrieved. An Institute of Medicine (IOM) study on regional health data networks described four desirable data and database attributes. These attributes summarize the desired outcomes of IMS planning, implementation, and continuous monitoring. These attributes include the following (Donaldson and Lohr 1994):

- Data elements must be useful (in other words, reliable and complete) and needed.

- Data must be accurate and analyzable.

- Databases should be structured to be conducive to high-quality data and information.

- Databases should have capacity for expansion and change.

Documentation and Capture of the Data

Once an organization determines and defines its minimum data set, it can then ensure that data are documented and captured in the prescribed uniform fashion. First, records and administrative forms and computer data-entry screens, and instructions for completing items on forms and screens, are reviewed to determine where and how data are currently documented. Organizations often find the same data element documented in several different locations. Short of the highly desirable method of modifying the system to reduce redundant data entry, planners can determine what data source results in the most accurate representation of the data element. The data element would then be collected from this source. When data elements are not captured in the manner defined and categorized in the data set, forms and computer data-entry screens are modified to ensure documentation congruent with the data set. Also, documentation or computer data-entry guidelines are modified.

Data quality incorporates legibility, accuracy, completeness, and meaning, each of which are explained by the following (Dick and Steen 1991):

- Completeness and meaning are addressed by development of an organizational uniform minimum data set.

- Legibility is addressed by computerization or by monitoring and providing feedback to employees and volunteers.

- Accuracy is addressed when designing the IMS.

Data accuracy refers to the degree to which data are free of errors or mistakes. In manual systems, accuracy can be improved by designing forms that encourage capture of data as defined and categorized in the data set. Computer-based systems use data-entry prompts and logic rules to reduce accuracy problems relating to missing data, out-of-range values, unrealistic changes in parameters over time, logical discrepancies and inaccurately coded diagnosis or procedure information (Donaldson and Lohr 1994; Dick and Steen 1991)

Timely data entry is also essential in ensuring accuracy. To accomplish this, management's commitment to data quality is vital. Policies are needed that enforce timely documentation, as well as systems to encourage timely data entry. JCAHO (2000) requires policies on the time frames for conducting the initial patient assessment and for completing records for discharge patients. JCAHO requires policies on completion, timeliness, and accuracy of information and communication, and health records.

Regular reviews of home care and hospice records also promote data quality by collecting information on record completeness, accuracy, and timeliness. This information can be used to assess record forms, data-entry screens, and documentation policies and to educate staff and volunteers on documentation. JCAHO requires this type of record review. In its IM standards, JCAHO requires efficient collection of complete, reliable, valid, and accurate data and states that mechanisms should be in place to monitor this (JCAHO 2000).

Maintenance of Data Confidentiality and Security

JCAHO's IM standards stress the importance of balance between the need for security and confidentiality and the needs of users for ready access to data and information. The IMS must have adequate safeguards to ensure system security and data confidentiality. System security is concerned with data loss and data misuse (Cofer 1994). By instituting safeguards against such natural disasters as floods and fires, system failures, or intentional data corruption, data loss can be addressed and effectively avoided. Health records and other data sources on paper must be properly stored to reduce the likelihood of destruction and thus reduce the likelihood of data loss. Original records should always stay inside the confines of the organization, unless a court order, subpoena, law, or regulation requires otherwise (as mandated by JCAHO). Computer-based systems must have adequate backup, as well as technology to restore the system, to reduce the possibility of data loss should hardware or software components fail (CPR Systems Evaluation Work Group 1995). Access to paper- and computer-based systems must be controlled. Only limited access should be granted to storage rooms where records are kept, with preferably a file clerk responsible for pulling needed records. Passwords (or other controls, such as fingerprints) should be required for access to computer-based systems, and that access should be restricted to the types of information that the specific user needs. The computer-based system should have recorded audit trails that document all who access the system and for what purpose.

Confidentiality relates to disclosure or nondisclosure of patient and family information (Donaldson and Lohr 1994). The protection of data and information from unauthorized access is also involved.

Collection and Retrieval of Data

Data collection and retrieval serve to continue patient care and to inform billing processes, quality monitoring, strategic planning, and other similar purposes. Home care and hospice programs face a tremendous challenge in efficiently communicating needed data and information because of the many sites of care and the diverse locations of the individual providers of care. Both the paper-based patient record and the computer-based record system are communication tools that are vital to providing high-quality patient and family care. The efficient, uniform sharing of the information on paper and in computer-based record systems is essential to the continuity of patient care. JCAHO's standard IM.5 requires transmission of timely and accurate data and information (JCAHO 2000).

The following factors should be considered when designing a new application or use of data (AHIMA 1998b):

- Accountability
- Data definition
- Standardizing collection
- Quality monitoring

"Data is driving more and more healthcare industry decision making" (AHIMA 1998b). This trend is evidenced by two initiatives to capture outcome data: JCAHO's ORYX and OASIS. Both data sets will function as benchmarks of performance improvement within and among organizations. But the raw data that each data set gathers must be collected in such a way that data quality is ensured. To do so, organizations must invest in quality technology and quality staff. Attaining quality comes under the practice of data quality management (DQM).

"DQM functions involve continuous improvement for data quality throughout the enterprise" and include the following (AHIMA 1998b):

Data application: The purpose for which data are collected
Collection: The processes by which data elements are accumulated
Warehousing: Processes and systems used to archive data and data journals
Analysis: The process of translating data into information utilized for an application

Characteristics of data quality include accessibility, consistency, currency, granularity, precision, accuracy, comprehensiveness, definition, relevancy, and timeliness (AHIMA 1998a). To meet many of the users' data and information needs, the IMS must allow data and information to be combined from various sources. JCAHO's IM.6 standard requires this capability (JCAHO 2000).

Analysis and Interpretation of Data

Data analysis involves summarizing and describing data and when relevant assessing their statistical significance. The knowledge, work force, and computer assistance available to perform data analysis vary tremendously among provider organizations. (Some helpful resources on data analysis performance are listed in the Additional Resources section at the end of this book.) User-friendly, computer-based statistical software programs are good tools for analyzing data, as are spreadsheet and database programs.

As discussed earlier in this chapter, the IM plan and the data collection timetable include the positions or departments responsible for data analysis and interpretation. Interpreting data involves coming to an understanding of its meaning for a specific application. Comparisons over time or between factors are desirable. Within organizations, comparisons over time and between entities or departments become feasible when data have been collected in a uniform fashion. When data have been documented according to a nationally recognized data set, comparisons with other provider organizations are then feasible. Information becomes more meaningful to external users such as HMOs or payers when presented in a comparative fashion, and JCAHO standard IM.10 requires such comparisons. This standard requires that home care and hospice programs share data with databases as required by law and regulations, compare their data with those found in such databases, and conduct internal organization comparisons as part of their management functions (JCAHO 2000). HCFA's outcome-based quality improvement database became available to home care providers in February 2001. Also, CHAP has developed outcome measures, and using these measures allows for organizational comparisons (CHAP 1997).

The Education Process

Leadership and employee commitment will enhance the quality of the IMS and data and information resulting from the IMS. Considering this, it is necessary that all employees be educated on IM and the organization's IMS. JCAHO's standard IM.4 states that decision makers and other individuals in the organization who generate, collect, and analyze data and information understand the principles of information management as appropriate to their job responsibilities. Along with this required education, it is important to share the vision for the IMS with employees and volunteers and to discuss the importance of each employee and volunteer in attaining this vision.

JCAHO standard IM.9 requires that the organization provide systems, resources, and services to meet its needs for knowledge-based information and literature. Authoritative and up-to-date scientific, clinical, and managerial knowledge-based information resources must be available to staff, patients, and families who need them. These resources may be accessed through computer or manually through libraries or other channels. Examples of such resources include reference materials and research data, textbooks, and practice guidelines. The organization must assess the organizational needs for knowledge-based information (JCAHO 2000).

Summary

Chapter 1 introduced IM concepts and IMS processes. This chapter and the 2001–2002 JCAHO home care IM standards challenge organizations to excel in an area that has at times received little attention. Home care and hospice provider organizations must meet the challenge of proper data and information management if they are to survive and thrive in a dynamic healthcare environment.

References and Bibliography

American Health Information Management Association. 1998a. Practice Brief: Designing a data collection process. *Journal of the American Health Information Management Association* 69(5).

American Health Information Management Association. 1998b. Practice Brief: Data quality management model. *Journal of the American Health Information Management Association* 69(6).

Blide, Leslie A. 1994. Issues in medical computer system data quality control in 1994. *Journal of Health Information Management Research* 2(2):1–9.

Cofer, Jennifer, ed. 1994. *Health Information Management.* 10th ed. Berwyn, Ill.: Physicians' Record Company.

Community Health Accreditation Program. 1997. *Standards of Excellence for Home Care Organizations.* New York City: National League for Health Care and Community Health Accreditation Program.

CPR Systems Evaluation Work Group. 1995. *Draft CPR Evaluation Criteria, Version 2.0.* Schaumburg, Ill.: Computer-based Patient Record Institute.

Dick, Richard S., and Elaine B. Steen, eds. 1991. *The Computer-Based Patient Record.* Washington, D.C.: National Academy Press.

Donaldson, Molla S., and Kathleen N. Lohr, eds. 1994. *Health Data in the Information Age.* Washington, D.C.: National Academy Press.

Foundation for Hospice and Homecare. 1991. *All About Hospice: A Consumer's Guide.* Washington, D.C.: Foundation for Hospice and Homecare.

Garbo, John J. 1994. The JCAHO and the Information and Management Systems Professional. *Journal of the Healthcare Information Management Systems Society* 8(2):23–29.

Haupt, B. J. 1996. The National Home and Hospice Care Survey: 1992 Summary. *Vital Health Stat* 13(117).

Health Care Financing Administration. 1997. Proposed Rules, Medicare and Medicaid Programs: Home Health Agencies. *Federal Register* 62(46):11004, 11007.

Health Care Financing Administration. 1998. *Outcome and Assessment Information Set Implementation Manual: Implementing OASIS at a Home Heath Agency to Improve Patient Outcomes.* Washington, D.C.: Government Printing Office.

Health Care Financing Administration. 1999a. Rules and Regulations, Medicare and Medicaid Programs: Home Health Agencies. *Federal Register* 64(15):3758.

Health Care Financing Administration. 1999b. Notices, Medicare and Medicaid Programs: Home Health Agencies. *Federal Register* 64(117).

Health Care Financing Administration. 2000. Rules and Regulations, Medicare and Medicaid Programs: Home Health Agencies. *Federal Register* 65(128).

Joint Commission on Accreditation of Healthcare Organizations. 2000. *2001-2002 Comprehensive Accreditation Manual for Home Care.* Oakbrook Terrace, Ill.: Joint Commission on Accreditation of Healthcare Organizations.

Metzger, Jane B., et al. 1994. Implications of the JCAHO Information Management Initiative for Information Systems. *Healthcare Information Management* 8(2):23–29.

National Association for Home Care. 2000. *Basic Statistics about Home Care.* Washington, D.C.: National Association for Home Care.

OASIS Overview. Cited March 2001. Health Care Financing Administration Web site. Available at www.hcfa. gov/medicaid/oasis/hhoview.htm.

O'Leary, M. R., et al. 1998. *Lexicon: Dictionary of Health Care Terms, Organizations, and Acronyms for the Era of Reform.* 2nd ed. Oakbrook Terrace, Ill.: Joint Commission on Accreditation of Healthcare Organizations.

Shaughnessy, P. W., et al. 1994. *Measuring Outcomes of Home Health Care.* Denver: Centers for Health Policy and Services Research.

Chapter 2

Record Documentation and Review

Accurate, up-to-date health records are essential for providing high-quality hospice and home care. As discussed in chapter 1, well-designed and -documented records capture the minimum, uniform data that both internal and external users need. This chapter provides information and guidance in designing health record forms and documentation and in reviewing policies and procedures for home care and hospice programs.

Chapter 2 begins by discussing documentation challenges, considerations when developing policies and forms, and general documentation guidelines. Guidelines pertaining to specific issues, basic record elements, types of services provided, and record review follow. Because Medicare pays for much of home and hospice care, a section of this chapter is devoted to Medicare documentation requirements. A valuable resource to put the theories in this chapter into practice, JCAHO's *2001–2002 Comprehensive Accreditation Manual for Home Care* contains a crosswalk between the Medicare *Conditions of Participation for Home Health Agencies,* hospice, and the federal standards of the Health Care Financing Administration (HCFA). Administrators and HIM professionals can use these crosswalks to determine documentation needs. Refer to actual standards and regulations to ensure completeness when developing organization policies and procedures or record forms.

Documentation Challenges for PPS and OASIS

Home health providers are overwhelmed by the burden of documentation for the prospective payment system (PPS) and Outcome and Assessment Information Set (OASIS). A recent General Accounting Office study revealed that among surveyed agencies, start-of-care visits last 40 minutes longer when collecting OASIS data and that tasks related to data submission (including supervisory review; entering, rechecking, and correcting OASIS data; and batching and transmitting the data) took almost 50 additional minutes (OASIS 2001). In the following sections, specific challenges are explained that contribute to the lengthiness of these visits.

Burdens of Documentation

For patients to whom OASIS applies, Medicare COP 484.55 requires that the comprehensive assessment must be completed in a timely manner, consistent with the patient's immediate needs, but no later than five calendar days after the start of care. Item M0090 on the OASIS data set reflects the final date the qualified clinician completed the actual patient assessment. This is usually the date of the last home visit made to complete the comprehensive assessment but may reflect a date subsequent to the onsite visit when the qualified clinician needs to follow up with the patient's family or physician in order to complete an OASIS clinical data item. The agency has seven additional days from the date that the patient assessment is completed to encode, enter, edit, check, lock, and export the data for future submission to the state survey agency.

Every month, agencies must electronically report all OASIS data collected on all applicable patients in a format that meets HCFA electronic data and editing specifications. OASIS data on non-Medicare and non-Medicaid patients receiving skilled services must be reported once the masking requirement is effective. Agency software must mask non-Medicare and non-Medicaid OASIS data so that the patient-identifiable information remains anonymous, except to the reporting home health agency (HHA). At that time, HHAs using software developed by private vendors must use software that appropriately masks non-Medicare and non-Medicaid records for all assessments in a similar manner to the functionality provided by the Home Assessment Validation Entry (HAVEN) software.

Medicare COP 484.20 requires OASIS data collection by a qualified clinician as part of the comprehensive assessment at start of care, resumption of care, follow-up, transfer to inpatient facility with or without discharge, discharge to community, and death at home. Encoding of OASIS data items must be complete and locked in order to accurately compute the information (health insurance prospective payment system [HIPPS] code) necessary for billing Medicare patients under the PPS (HCFA 2000b).

HCFA has maintained that once providers are familiar with the OASIS items, OASIS data collection imposes a minimal burden above what providers were previously collecting to assess their patients. Providers using health records with integrated OASIS items indicate that after using OASIS approximately five times, the time required beyond the routine patient assessment to complete the OASIS decreases from 15 to 2.5 minutes (HCFA 1997). HCFA has adjusted home care costs by $0.12 per visit or $4.32 for each 60-day episode to collect, enter, edit, and audit OASIS data (HCFA 2000a).

As the experiences of home care and hospice providers make evident, the paperwork burden is not abating. The need for accountability and the health record data and information continue to increase. Considering this, home care and hospice organizations are addressing the paperwork burden by implementing more efficient documentation systems. But the process for reducing the time needed for documentation is complex and time-consuming. Computerizing the record alone is no panacea for reducing the documentation burden. Gains in productivity can arise from computerization or even a new manual system when organizations plan carefully through an assessment of needed data, revised processes, staff education, and monitoring of the effectiveness of the new system.

Regardless of whether an organization's health record is manual or computerized, efficiency can be gained through well-designed forms and data-entry screens that are logically sequenced and discourage redundant data entry. The forms found in appendices E through M serve as examples, and along with the guidance provided in this chapter, they can be used as starting points to develop or revise existing forms.

Provider Organization Service Diversity

Provider organizations now offer more diverse services to their patients, either directly or through written agreements with other organizations. This diversity affects documentation needs and requirements. Intensive home care services are now common, including infusion services, ventilator support, home dialysis, and pain management. The physician house call is also becoming more common, especially in conjunction with home care services (Rothkopf 1992). The policies, procedures, and practices of a provider organization reflect the care, reimbursement, and legal documentation considerations unique to different types of service provisions. This chapter highlights some of these considerations, as well as the crosswalks contained in the 2001–2002 JCAHO manual.

This chapter also addresses the following major categories of services:

- Homemaker and chore services

- Durable medical equipment (DME)

- Clinical respiratory

- Pharmaceutical and infusion therapy

Many types of organizations may provide these services (JCAHO 2000):

- HHAs offering skilled, intermittent care

- Hospice programs providing home, inpatient, and bereavement services

- Private-duty agencies providing nursing or other care at home

- Intravenous therapy companies providing parenteral nutrition, antibiotics, and other therapies in the home

- Organizations providing pharmaceutical products and clinical monitoring to patients in the home

- Home medical equipment companies providing equipment and patient instruction in the home

- Organizations providing personal care and support services

- Rehabilitation organizations providing therapy services in the home

- Organizations providing clinical respiratory services in the home

This wide array of services and organizations leads to the next discussion: communication and timeliness of documentation in a diverse home and hospice care environment.

Communication and Timeliness of Documentation

To offer well-coordinated care, an individual care provider needs ready access to information on the care and services that all disciplines and organizations provide to patients. In addition, providers need information on patients' response to care, and any changes in care plans and goals.

The possibility of inadequate transmission of treatment-related information among home care staff and between home care programs and other organizations providing patient care is a negligence risk. This risk is equally high for hospice programs, perhaps more so when hospices contract for inpatient or skilled nursing facility services. Maintaining timely communication can be challenging, because physicians, the actual care setting, and many individual care providers are physically distant from the home care or hospice organization. The health record serves as one vehicle for communication. Other communication vehicles include computer terminals, telephones, and facsimile machines. In addition to serving as a vehicle for communication, the health record contains evidence of continuing communication. The home care and hospice program also is obligated to provide information to patients and their families (Haddad and Kapp 1991).

Timely health record documentation affects communication and the coordination of care. An organization's policies address the time requirements for incorporating OASIS, encounter information, and signed orders into the health record. Healthcare practitioners should record their findings at the point of care or within 24 hours of an encounter to adequately support patient care. State laws frequently define timeliness, especially in relation to signatures on physician's orders. Failure to obtain signed orders in accordance with policies and state laws puts an organization at a liability risk and raises red flags for payers and surveyors. Additionally, Medicare and some third-party payers cannot be billed unless signed orders are present.

Home care and hospice organizations must go to great lengths to promptly incorporate documentation and signed orders into paper-based health records, and it may be difficult to meet state requirements for timely documentation. Computer-based record systems can make it possible for care providers to document at the point of care on hand-held or laptop computers brought to the patient's home and to transmit current patient information to the organization's centralized computer through modems in the individual caregiver's home. Such computer systems are becoming increasingly common in the home care and hospice settings. Computer networks to physician offices are also needed, so that information can be efficiently shared and orders can be signed electronically. This application is currently far less common.

Consistent and Complete Documentation

A litmus test for an accurate and up-to-date health record is whether an alternative care provider can review the record on any given day and obtain a clear, consistent picture of the patient's status, care plans and goals, and the care and services recently provided. Although passing this litmus test takes some effort, the alternative could be incomplete and inconsistent documentation that might lead to serious problems involving care, legal, reimbursement, licensure, and accreditation issues. Timely documentation and reference-based, up-to-date documentation policies, procedures, and practices promote completeness and consistency in documentation. Also, ongoing record reviews that monitor record completeness and consistency can target problem areas needing improvement.

Because home care and hospice programs have come under increased scrutiny during investigations for Medicare fraud, incomplete or inconsistent documentation poses particular legal concerns (Harrison and Cole 1994). Section 1128B of the U.S. Social Security Act prohibits obtaining money from the federal government to which one is not entitled, by submitting inaccurate information, by overutilizing services, or by falsifying the information provided (Foster and Kazon 1992). Billing for services not provided may be alleged under this prohibition when documentation does not agree with claims that have been submitted. For example, documentation may not be present for services provided or documentation of a patient's status may not be consistent. Complete, consistent documentation that includes dates of service provided and signatures of providers goes a long way toward avoiding (and when necessary, defending against) fraudulent claim allegations. Complete records also protect an organization from unsubstantiated lawsuits and judgments.

Development of Documentation Policies and Procedures

Specific and clear documentation policies and procedures result in health records that reflect evidence of care and service provision in keeping with community standards. Policies and procedures guide the practice and documentation of a home care or hospice organization. When based on community standards and reimbursement regulations, policies and procedures also define what disciplines can and cannot do and give directions on how to perform a particular responsibility, including documentation. For example, a policy and procedure would delineate who notifies a physician of a change in a patient's condition, when this notification is necessary, and how this notification should be conveyed and documented.

A discipline's professional practice standards reflect community standards. Such standards define a discipline's scope and practice. Professional practice standards are developed and published by such professional organizations as the American Nurses Association (ANA), National Association of Social Workers, American Occupational Therapy Association, American Physical Therapy Association, and the American Speech and Hearing Association. The ANA has standards for home health nursing practice. States have practice acts or statutes that define professional practice for nurses and other disciplines. CHAP and JCAHO standards, as well as federal and state regulations, also reflect community standards. These standards and regulations may be referenced in a court of law even when an organization has chosen not to be accredited or Medicare certified. JCAHO standards (2000) require numerous documentation policies and procedures.

Up-to-date, standard operating procedures that are monitored for compliance help to ensure high-quality, consistent care and legally protect the individual provider and the organization. Policies and procedures that are consistently reviewed and updated to reflect changes in community standards, laws, organizational structure, and technology are an organization's key to risk management (Harrison and Cole 1994).

Health Record Documentation Guidelines

Several guidelines are essential to health record documentation. Incorporating these guidelines into documentation policies, procedures, and practices can support high-quality care and service provision. Also, these guidelines address reimbursement, licensure, and accreditation requirements and can help avoid negligence. The term *professional services* pertains to home healthcare, hospice, clinical respiratory, and pharmaceutical and infusion therapy services. The phrase *all patient services* refers to these professional services, as well as DME and home chore services. The guidelines follow:

1. There is a health record for every patient and family served.

2. There are written documentation policies and procedures, and staff education on these policies and procedures. Policies address documentation regarding patient's rights, consent for care, do not resuscitate orders, and advance directives.

3. There is a standardized format for health record documentation.

4. A unit record is maintained for each patient. This record includes all admissions to the program, transfer forms, summaries or copies of records received from the transferring facility, and documentation by the attending physician and all organizations and disciplines involved in the patient's care, including volunteers, chaplains, and contracted staff.

5. All documentation is legible and written in black ink, or typewritten and electronically signed, then stored or printed.

6. Written program policy delineates authority to make entries in the health record.

7. Documentation is complete and includes patient assessment, plans for care, care provided, and response to care, including patient status changes. Communication with patients, families, team members, and attending physicians is documented.

8. Documentation is consistent. Discrepancies are discussed and reconciled. Documentation in the health record indicates this reconciliation.

9. Documentation reflects observations and is objective and nonjudgmental. Sensitive information is verified prior to inclusion in the health record. When hospice care is not being provided, information other than basic demographic information regarding family members should not be documented unless it affects a patient's care.

10. Documentation includes correct grammar and spelling. Healthcare professionals use appropriate professional language.

11. Any person making an entry in the record dates and signs the entry, complete with his or her credentials. This includes flow sheet entries. Program policy determines when initials may be used to authenticate an entry and when electronic signatures are acceptable.

12. Because volunteer documentation within the hospice record has the same legal implications as any other hospice record documentation, training in this activity is part of volunteer orientation and continuing education. The volunteer coordinator, team supervisor, or nurse reviews and initials volunteer documentation prior to its incorporation into the health record.

13. Required documentation is completed within 24 hours of when the service was provided, and it is filed in the health record in a timely manner as outlined in organization policy or by state regulations. Program policy and procedure determines when and how important information is to be promptly conveyed (immediately or within 24 hours of service) to other team members or organizations involved in the patient's care. When a patient dies or is discharged from care, the health record is completed (including required summary, documentation, and signatures) within seven days. When a family member or significant other is discharged from bereavement follow-up, bereavement documentation is completed, which includes required summary, documentation, and signatures, and is incorporated in the health record within seven days.

14. Documentation justifies the level of care and services being provided. In this regard, documentation is complete and accurate and addresses the need for the level of care or service provided.

15. Documentation is specific. When drawings or photographs enhance a narrative description, they can be used.

16. Program policy delineates documentation required on incident reports and in the health record when an incident occurs. It is recommended that incident reports be filed separately from client records.

17. Procedures are developed for ongoing health record review to ensure that all documentation is received in a timely manner with appropriate follow-up as necessary.

18. The documentation policy includes an explanatory legend or designated reference defining any abbreviations or symbols that will be used in the health record. Each abbreviation or symbol has only one meaning. The program's interdisciplinary staff approves the explanatory legend.

19. Because the health record is a legal document, no form can be removed or destroyed after it has been filed within the record. Inactive records, however, may be destroyed in a controlled manner in accordance with an approved agency retention schedule.

There is no obliteration of entries by erasures, whiting-out, pasting over, or other methods. The proper method of error correction in the health record is as follows:

a. Draw one single line through the entry in such a way that the written information underneath may still be read.

b. Write "error" or "mistaken entry" and initial and date the correction.

c. Write the correct information near the entry or where the correct information is placed.

20. There is no embellishment of record documentation. If subsequent additions to documentation are desired, they are labeled as such and include the date (and time, when appropriate) of entry. Computer-based record systems prevent the alteration or loss of data and retain an account of any communications to and from the system.

Home Care and Hospice Legal Issues

In home care and hospice, patient's rights, advance directives, do not resuscitate orders, and issues related to the withholding of life-sustaining treatment are at the fore of pertinent legal issues. To avoid pitfalls, organizations should review written policies, procedures, and organization-specific documentation requirements carefully for redundancy. At the time of publication, it is unclear how HIPAA requirements will affect critical legal documents.

Patient's Rights

Home health organizations have a responsibility to inform patients of their rights with respect to care provided. Patients whose data will be collected and used by the federal government must receive a notice of their privacy rights. The health record provides evidence that patients are fully informed consumers, actively involved in their care. The protection and promotion of patient and family rights and responsibilities in home care and hospice programs is addressed by CHAP and JCAHO standards, as well as by Medicare home care and hospice *Conditions of Participation*.

The Omnibus Budget Reconciliation Act of 1987 (OBRA) requires organizations receiving Medicare and Medicaid funds to document that home care and hospice patients are informed of their rights and that they agree to their care plans. To inform them of their rights, patients are provided with a bill of rights. This form can be used as is or modified to reflect state licensure requirements, any new accreditation standards, and/or reference to hospice instead of home care. The crosswalk between JCAHO standards and the Medicare *Conditions of Participation* outlines documentation requirements.

Medicare regulation COP 484.10 confirms a patient's right to be informed and to participate in planning care and treatment, and the right to be informed, in advance, about the care to be furnished, and of any changes in the care plan. The home health agency (HHA) must advise the patient in advance of the disciplines that will furnish care and the proposed frequency of visits. The HHA must advise the patient in advance of any change in the plan of care before the change is made. The patient has the right to participate in the planning of care. The HHA must advise the patient in advance of the right to participate in planning the care or treatment and in planning changes in the care or treatment (HCFA 2000b).

The OASIS database is subject to the requirements of the Federal Privacy Act of 1974. The privacy act allows the disclosure of information from a system of records without an individual's consent if the information is to be used for a purpose that is compatible with the purposes for which the information was collected. However, under patient's rights regulations, the HHA must provide the patient with a written notice of the collection of OASIS information in advance of furnishing care to the patient.

Determining care includes the right of a patient to refuse treatment, which the U.S. Supreme Court supported in *Cruzan vs. Director of the Missouri Department of Health* (1990). In the Cruzan decision, the court affirmed both the right of a patient to refuse medical treatment and the status of artificial tube feeding as medical treatment. The decision affirmed a patient's right to refuse both life-sustaining treatment and life-saving treatment (Brent 1994).

Patient Self-Determination Act of 1990

In 1990, OBRA's Patient Self-Determination Act was enacted. It requires home care and hospice organizations receiving Medicare and Medicaid funds to inform patients of their rights under state law to make advance decisions concerning medical care by activating advance directives. Advance directives are instruments patients can use to clarify treatment choices in the event that they are no longer capable of doing so. State laws recognize different types of advance directives. Two common types are living wills and durable powers of attorney. A home care and hospice organization's written policies and procedures on advance directives should reflect required documentation, including the following (Brent 1994):

- A discussion with the patient regarding the presence of advance directives

- Provision of written information to the patient on state laws and the organization's advance directive policies

- Medical orders to carry out the patient's wishes

- The physical presence in the record of the advance directive itself

When an existing advance directive is not filed in the health record, documentation explains the reason why, such as patient refusal. The crosswalk between the JCAHO standards and the Medicare *Conditions of Participation* outlines documentation requirements.

Do Not Resuscitate Orders

A do not resuscitate (DNR) order is a physician's order documenting a patient's (or a substitute decision maker's) desire for no resuscitation attempts. Although a DNR order results from a desire expressed in an advance directive, it does not replace the need for that directive. In hospice care cases, routine care only orders (or consent for care that indicates routine care only) do not substitute for a specific DNR order. Prior to writing a DNR order, a discussion should take place between the attending physician and other team members, the patient, and the next of kin or significant other. The health record contains documentation of the content and outcome of this discussion, and the record must also be clearly flagged to indicate the presence of a DNR order. This is especially important in the hospice inpatient setting. If the DNR form is missing, there is a risk of resuscitating a person in error.

In relation to other life-sustaining measures, "do not" orders in home care and in hospice are necessary (Haddad and Kapp 1991). "Do not" orders include such orders as "do not hospitalize" and "do not treat." These orders should also be documented and flagged, as appropriate. When hospices document routine care only orders to cover "do not" orders, policy must clearly reflect the meaning of the routine care only orders, and their meaning should be conveyed to the patient and/or family.

Hospices as well as other healthcare providers need to develop mission statements reflecting their care philosophies. These mission statements must be shared with patients and their families or significant others. The sharing of an organization's care philosophies should be documented, especially in relation to DNR orders, "do not" orders, and philosophies regarding other life-sustaining measures. JCAHO standards and Medicare home care and hospice regulations require that patients and their families be informed of healthcare providers' care philosophies.

Written policies and procedures on DNR orders, "do not" orders, and the withholding or withdrawing of other life-sustaining treatment should specify the documentation required and reflect an organization's care philosophies, review of legal requirements, and input from legal counsel. State laws vary significantly regarding DNR orders and the withholding or discontinuance of other life-sustaining treatment. Organizations should be cognizant of their state laws, as well as the legal climate surrounding them.

Nursing Care and HIM

Understanding nursing diagnosis, classifications, and the nursing process is critical to effective health information management, process, and documentation design. Standardizing data and care protocols begins with selecting a classification system that categorizes patient populations. Nursing is an information-intensive profession, and nurses are experts in the diagnosis and treatment of human responses to illness, prevention of illness, and health promotion. But, typically, they are not experts in information management other than for the purposes of diagnostic and treatment decision making. Most practicing nurses are not aware that several nursing classification systems exist, nor are they aware of the multiple benefits of such systems. Thus, HIM professionals, as experts in information management, have a collaborative role to play in working with nurses in areas such as computer-based health record system selection and multidisciplinary documentation (such as critical paths and Care Maps™). For instance, the HIM professional is well-equipped to address issues related to data reliability and validity, as well as other issues related to the multiple uses of collected data. In some institutions, the HIM professional may also function within the healthcare team as the expert on vocabulary issues related to computer-based health record systems. In such a capacity, he or she shares information about national efforts and related issues with other team members. The HIM professional also has the potential to act as a consultant to quality management teams in designing reliable and valid strategies to prospectively or retrospectively collect chart data (Bakken 1998).

The provision of home healthcare is a multidisciplinary effort. In this era of numerous requests for data and information from multiple accrediting, governing, and quality monitoring agencies, it is vital that the HIM professional be aware of classification systems and related national efforts, beyond those that are physician-centric in nature, such as ICD-9-CM and CPT. Without reliable and valid data concerning the contributions of the entire healthcare team, it is impossible to engage in the practice of evidence-based healthcare delivery (Bakken 1998).

Nursing Diagnoses and Classifications in Home Health and Hospice

Because nurses are central to the provision of home and hospice care, home care and hospice documentation systems must accommodate the documentation of nursing diagnoses and the nursing process. Nursing diagnoses are a means of classifying those actual, potential, or possible problems that a nurse can independently and legally assess and treat. Nursing diagnoses differ from medical diagnoses and nursing problems in that they classify the independent nursing process. A licensed physician must make a medical diagnosis, as well as order the treatment for the diagnosis. A nurse may identify and assess a nursing problem such as potential aspiration, but if the aspiration actually occurs, a licensed physician must order the treatment for it. However, a nursing diagnosis, such as knowledge deficit, can be independently identified and treated by the nurse.

The nursing profession has developed a number of classification systems. Nursing classifications have been developed to describe the nursing process, to document nursing care, and to facilitate aggregation of data for comparisons at the local, regional, national, and international levels. As opposed to other healthcare classification systems such as ICD-9-CM or CPT, the nursing systems have not been widely used for reimbursement purposes. Therefore, many HIM professionals may be unfamiliar with their contents. The ANA has played a leadership role in activities related to nursing data sets and classification systems. The ANA established the Steering Committee on Databases to Support Clinical Nursing Practice (SCD) to monitor and support the development and evolution of the use of multiple vocabularies and classification schemes.

There are five ANA-recognized nursing classifications: the North American Nursing Diagnosis Association (NANDA) taxonomy, the Omaha system, the Home Health Care Classification, the Nursing Interventions Classification (NIC), and the Nursing Outcome Classification (NOC). (See table 2.1.) Three of the five systems include nursing diagnoses, three systems include nursing interventions, and three systems include outcomes. Thus, it is up to the individual organization to select the single system or set of systems that it will implement. All of the ANA-recognized systems have been successfully deployed in both manual and computer-based documentation systems. Factors that organizations take into account in making the selection include the setting for which the system was designed, access issues such as cost and copyright, ability to represent nursing data at a sufficiently granular level, and ease of implementation, particularly in computer-based systems.

As opposed to classification systems such as ICD-9-CM, in which the codes are most often assigned through abstraction methods after the episode of care is complete, the nursing classification systems are used directly by the nurse during the course of care. In addition to the granularity of the five nursing systems, there are other issues affecting the ease of implementing the nursing classifications in computer-based systems. A recent analysis showed that none of the ANA-recognized systems met the Computer-based Health Record Institute's (CPRI) features of classification systems that support implementation within a computer-based health record (Bakken 1998).

The Nursing Process and Health Record Documentation

The nursing process includes the following five steps: assessment, diagnosis, planning, implementation, and evaluation (Humphrey and Milone-Nuzzo 1991). As reflected in the ANA Standards of Nursing Practice, nursing involves the following processes:

- The collection of patient health status data
- The derivation of nursing diagnoses based on these data
- The development of care plans with goals, priorities, and nursing approaches or measures based on nursing diagnoses
- The implementation of planned nursing interventions
- The continual assessment of goal achievement

Based on continuing evaluation, nursing strategies are modified to facilitate goal achievement or progress, when applicable (Iyer and Camp 1991).

Table 2.1.   Classification Systems Recognized by ANA

Classification	Nursing Diagnoses	Nursing Interventions	Nursing Outcomes	Settings	Access
North American Nursing Diagnosis Association (NANDA)	128 nursing diagnoses classified into nine patterns Example: Altered family processes			Across the continuum of care	Copyright North American Nursing Diagnosis Association; written permission required for use
Nursing Interventions Classification (NIC)		433 nursing interventions classified into six domains and 27 classes Example: Bowel incontinence care		Across the continuum of care Example: University of Iowa Hospitals, long-term care, school nursing	Copyright Mosby-Year Book, Inc.; price negotiated for electronic implementation
Nursing Outcome Classification (NOC)			193 outcomes classified into six domains and 24 classes; each outcome has a set of indicators scaled 1–5 Example: Caregiver well-being	Across the continuum of care	Copyright Mosby-Year Book, Inc.; price negotiated for electronic implementation
Omaha System	40 problems classified into four domains with two sets of modifiers Example: Communication with community resources	62 targets with four categories of interventions (health teaching, guidance, and counseling; treatments and procedures; case management; surveillance) Example: Target = Rest/sleep, which can be modified by any of the four intervention categories	Five-point Likert scale for three outcomes related to specific diagnoses Example: Caretaking/parenting rated on three scales (knowledge, behavior, and status)	Predominantly community-based settings Example: Visiting Nurses of Omaha; Penn Nursing Network; Nightingale Tracker	Public domain
Home Health Care Classification	145 diagnoses classified into 20 care components; diagnoses include NANDA plus additional diagnoses developed for the home care environment Example: Knowledge deficit of therapeutic regimen	160 nursing interventions classified into 20 care components with four types of qualifiers (assess, care, teach, manage) Example: Wound care-Teach	Three qualifiers for the nursing diagnoses to predict the outcome (improved, stabilized, deteriorated) Example: Improved acute pain	Predominantly home care settings, but has been demonstrated to have utility for hospital setting	Public domain

Source: Bakken Henry et al. 1998.

Health record documentation must reflect all elements of the nursing process. The problem-oriented health record system allows for documentation of the nursing process. A discussion of this system follows, and its components are addressed in the remaining documentation guidelines. Another feasible addressed in the following section is documentation via critical paths.

Critical Paths in Home Care

Critical paths emanate from process management, also referred to as quality improvement or performance management. The underlying tenets of process management are that the process is key to the results or outcome and that people alone cannot change a result or outcome because they are but one element of the process (Spath 1993). A critical path defines the essential functions believed to be important for delivery of care to a specific patient category, as well as the optimal sequencing and timing of these functions (Coffey 1992).

Critical paths are case management tools; thus, teams can develop them to provide care to a particular category of patient, such as the hospice patient who requires pain management. The JCAHO will begin scoring pain assessment and management standards to the rights and ethics (RI) chapter in 2001.

The use of critical paths in healthcare is becoming popular, especially in conjunction with computerized documentation systems. Using critical paths affects the design of a documentation system, because documentation of the identified critical functions and expected outcomes is most often accomplished through structured assessments, care plans, flow sheets, and clinical notes. The structured documentation used with critical path systems facilitates process and outcome monitoring. It may also reduce the paperwork associated with documentation and improve the consistency of care and its documentation. However, with this improved consistency comes the potential problem that care and its documentation may become too standardized and, thereby, lose touch with individual concerns. HCFA, in particular, has voiced concern about standardized (or *canned*) care plans and now requires hospices to individualize any of the standardized care plans they use so that they reflect the specific needs of the patient and caregiver. If an organization decides to use critical path documentation or standardized care plans, users must be cognizant of the concerns about standardization and address it in documentation policies, procedures, and practices. Because critical path documentation systems streamline documentation, it is also important that the supporting documents and protocols for the paths be filed and readily available to organization employees, as well as to surveyors.

Several groups are developing critical paths and accompanying documentation systems for use in home care. (See appendix H.) Visit forms contain the nursing assessment, the intervention and education to be performed, and the expected patient outcomes. There is also space for recording other interventions, education, and outcomes, and for documentation of the reason for a variance when expected outcomes are not met. In addition, other forms for documenting the care episode may include the assessment form, the identification page, the care plan page, the blank visit form, the copath form, and the path variance report.

Problem-Oriented Health Records and the Flow of Information

The problem-oriented health record system comprises four basic elements: the database, problem list, care plan, and progress notes. Many home care and hospice organizations include the problem list in the care plan instead of maintaining it separately. With the problem-oriented system, database information is used to formulate the problem list (see appendix G). Care plans address each problem on the problem list in terms of care to be provided and changes in that care. Clinical progress notes document the care that was given, observations, and the status or an aspect of the problem. Figure 2.1 illustrates the flow of documentation when using a problem-oriented record. Line A shows the documentation flow when the observation/assessment that was documented in clinical/progress notes necessitates a change in the care plan. Line B shows the documentation flow when an observation/assessment that was documented in clinical/progress notes necessitates a reassessment and/or activation, reactivation, or resolution of a problem on the problem list. The arrows running through the center indicate that any change in the problems requires a change in the care plan. Changes in care plans are then reflected in the care documented in clinical/progress notes. (Different formats for recording clinical notes are discussed later in this chapter in the clinical notes/visit documentation section.) A discharge summary summarizes the entire care episode.

The Health Record Database

The information provided upon referral is essential when determining whether a patient is suitable for admission to home care or hospice. Organizations develop admission criteria for determining the appropriateness of a patient's admission. These criteria depend on the types of care and services provided and on the care philosophies of the organizations. In hospices, typical criteria include a terminal prognosis, the inappropriateness of curative treatment, a patient's desire for palliative treatment, and, depending on hospice philosophy, the availability of a willing and

Figure 2.1. Flow of Documentation Using a Problem-Oriented Record

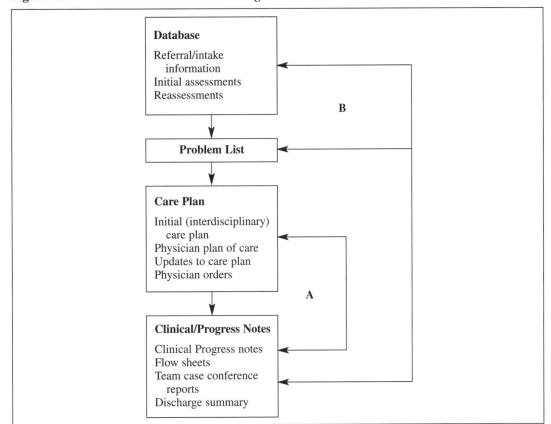

able caregiver. Four general categories govern admission criteria: medical stability (with the exclusion of hospice patients), desire for home care (or hospice), the suitability of the home environment, and financial resources (Haddad 1987).

The Office of Inspector General (OIG) monitored all Medicare beneficiary access to HHAs in 1999. In 1999, the OIG concluded that there appears to be no widespread problem with placing Medicare hospital patients with HHAs. The OIG will continue to study the impact of the PPS on access to care and the quality of care (Gibbs Brown 2000). Many HHAs use select OASIS questions to prescreen potential referrals. The OIG work plan increases the importance of documenting referrals not admitted.

The health record database originates with intake/referral data, and these data form the basis for initial care planning. Intake personnel commonly receive referral data via telephone or facsimile. Some organizations have nurses working in hospitals to assist in discharge planning and admitting patients to home or hospice care. Accurate referral data are a result of such early collaborative efforts, which are vitally important for continuity of care, especially in cases where patients are receiving clinical respiratory or pharmaceutical/infusion therapy.

Data that intake personnel receive via telephone are notoriously poor, especially diagnosis data, which are often incomplete. The ideal method for providing patient referral information is the electronic sharing of information, which will become more common as home care and hospice organizations develop links with managed care organizations or healthcare networks. Faxing is also an efficient and preferred method of sending data from healthcare facilities, because the resulting data are more accurate and complete (Wilde 1992).

COP 484.55 states that the initial assessment visit must be held either within 48 hours of referral or within 48 hours of the patient's return home or on the physician-ordered start-of-care date. In the absence of a physician-specified start-of-care date, the initial assessment visit is conducted within 48 hours of the referral. When the physician specifies a start-of-care date, this supersedes the 48-hour time frame. The intake or clinical record documentation must specify a start-of-care date.

The following are recommendations for the content of referral and intake data in home care and hospice. The crosswalk between JCAHO standards and the Medicare *Conditions of Participation* outlines these documentation requirements:

A. For professionally related home care services, the initial data should include:

1. **Admission/referral/general information:**

   a. Patient-identifying information and social data
   b. Name, address, and telephone number of next of kin or significant other
   c. Emergency contact
   d. Referral source
   e. Attending physician identification
   f. Reimbursement information

2. **Initial clinical information.** The following information should be received from the attending physician, referral source, and/or patient or family, and documented prior to the first home visit:

   a. Admitting diagnosis(es), principal and other
   b. Surgical procedures related to home care admission
   c. Significant history and presenting problems, including the patient's social and emotional status, activity limitations, and limitations to healthcare access
   d. Allergies

e. Initial medication and treatment orders including type and frequency of services to be provided and the supplies and equipment needed, in the form of verbal orders until signed orders are received

f. Any dietary restrictions

g. Patient's living arrangements

h. Availability of able and willing caregiver

i. Other agencies involved in care

B. For hospice patients, the initial data should include:

1. **Admission/referral/general information:**

a. Patient-identifying information and social data

b. Name, address, and telephone number of next of kin or significant other

c. Primary care person's name, when applicable

d. Referral source

e. Physician identification

f. Referral information

g. Any other information that standards/regulations require

2. **Initial clinical information.** The following information should be received from the attending physician (directly or through approved personnel) and documented prior to admission:

a. Admitting diagnosis(es), principal and other

b. Prognosis

c. Current medical findings, including present physical, social, and emotional status of the patient

d. Allergies

e. Pain status

f. Initial medical and treatment orders, including medications

g. Input in establishing, and concurrence with, tentative treatment plan

h. Any dietary restrictions

i. History and physical examination

j. For Medicare hospice patients, physician certification of a life expectancy of one year or less

k. Any other information that standards/regulations require

C. **Nonmedical services.** The following information should be received regarding home chore services or durable medical equipment (DME) with no professional services provided:

1. Client-identifying information, including client's name, address, and telephone number

2. Demographic and social information, including sex, birthdate, race, ethnicity, marital status, and usual living arrangement

3. Emergency contact

Documentation of a patient's physical limitations (such as blindness) is also desirable, so that any problems with delivery of services can be anticipated.

Within 10 days, written transfer information, including transfer discharge summaries and other pertinent portions of the clinical record, should be received from the transferring facility.

Home Care and Hospice Assessment Information

Although the initial assessment may begin in the hospital or long-term care facility where the patient is referred, it more commonly begins on the first home care visit or admission to hospice. The type, content, and comprehensiveness of the assessment should correspond to the types of care and services to be provided. It is essential to include the suitability of a home environment in the assessment, as well as any safety measures that are needed, especially relating to the placement of DME and the provision of infusion therapy. It is also essential to assess the ability of a patient and family to use the equipment provided (JCAHO 2000). In addition, an assessment should include the availability of an able and willing caregiver, living arrangements, and family composition. These data, together with an assessment of activity and functional limitations, help to determine the extent of required support. Nonhospice home care also uses this information to begin to plan for home care discharge.

Before comprehensive assessments, which include collection of OASIS data items, are conducted, the HHA must tell patients about OASIS and explain their rights with respect to the collection and reporting of OASIS information. These rights include the following:

- The right to be informed that OASIS information will be collected and for what purpose

- The right to have the information kept confidential and secure

- The right to be informed that OASIS information will not be disclosed except for legitimate purposes allowed by the Privacy Act

- The right to refuse to answer a specific question

- The right to see, review, and request changes on their assessment

A standard notice to patients that explains these rights in plain language was published in the *Federal Register* on June 18, 1999, and is available in English and Spanish on the OASIS Web site (www.hcfa.gov/medicaid/oasis/oasishmp.htm). HHAs must present and explain this required notice to beneficiaries before their initial OASIS assessment (HCFA 2000b).

When professional home care services are provided, the assessment becomes more comprehensive, documenting the presence as well as the absence of problems. The OIG 2001 work plan includes a determination on how assessment information helps to establish the case-mix adjustment used in determining the level of Medicare payment to an HHA for a particular patient (Gibbs Brown 2000). (See appendix E for a comprehensive assessment form.) The crosswalk between JCAHO standards and the Medicare Conditions of Participation outlines documentation requirements specific to service type provided.

Medicare COP 484.55 requires a comprehensive assessment of patients. Each patient must receive, and an HHA must provide, a patient-specific, comprehensive assessment that accurately reflects the patient's current health status and includes information that may be used to demonstrate the patient's progress toward achievement of desired outcomes. The comprehensive assessment must identify the patient's continuing need for home care and meet the patient's medical, nursing, rehabilitative, social, and discharge planning needs. For Medicare beneficiaries, the HHA must verify the patient's eligibility for the Medicare home health benefit, including homebound status, both at the time of the initial assessment visit and at the time of the comprehensive assessment. The comprehensive assessment must also incorporate the use of the current version of OASIS items, using the language and groupings as specified by the secretary.

The comprehensive assessment includes the collection of OASIS data items by a qualified clinician, such as a registered nurse, physical therapist, occupational therapist, or speech language pathologist.

For Medicare patients, there are additional requirements. Agencies are expected to conduct an assessment that accurately reflects the patient's current health status and includes information to establish and monitor a plan of care. The plan of care must be reviewed and updated at least every 60 days or as often as the severity of the patient's condition requires. The requirement to conduct a drug regimen review applies to all patients serviced by the HHA.

Federal regulations require a comprehensive assessment, with OASIS data items integrated, for all patients who receive skilled services except for those patients who are under age 18, receiving maternity services, receiving only housekeeping or chore services, or receiving only personal care services. This includes Medicare, Medicaid, managed care, and private pay patients accepted by the HHA. It also includes Medicaid patients receiving services under a waiver program.

Subsequent updates on the comprehensive assessments must be conducted at certain time points during the admission. These updates must include certain data items in the current OASIS data set. OASIS data items are not meant to be the only items included in an agency's assessment process. They are standardized health assessment items that must be incorporated into an agency's own comprehensive assessment tool. For therapy-only cases, the comprehensive assessment should incorporate OASIS data items with other assessment data that the HHA currently collects for therapy patients, as opposed to simply adding them at the beginning or end (HCFA 2000b).

For hospice care, a patient and family assessment is performed. This involves a psychosocial assessment of patient and family needs, including adaptive and coping abilities. A spiritual assessment is also performed. This may be included on a psychosocial assessment form or on a separate assessment form. Although a spiritual assessment does not address spirituality in strictly religious terms, its content depends greatly on the community being served (Miller 1985). As is made evident in the context of the preceding discussion, the assessment of needed bereavement support begins on hospice admission.

When a hospice patient is experiencing pain, a pain assessment is performed to document the effectiveness of pain medication. As discussed earlier, the content of assessment forms for particular categories of patients may conform to data items indicated by a critical path, with opportunity for individualization. A large number of home care and hospice organizations record pain assessment data electronically via hand-held devices or laptop computers.

The following are recommendations for the content of initial assessment data for home care and hospice patients. The crosswalk between JCAHO standards and the Medicare *Conditions of Participation* outlines specific documentation requirements.

A. For professional home care services, the initial assessment data should include the following information:

   1. The health record documents the following initial nursing assessment information:

      a. Diagnoses and problems
      b. Past medical history and present illness
      c. Review of systems
      d. Present medications and treatment
      e. Activities of daily living and functional limitations
      f. Patient care requirements, including equipment and supplies needed

       g. Dietary and nutritional information

       h. Suitability of the patient's residence and safety measures required to protect the client from injury

       i. Composition of household and relevant information regarding the family and caregiver

2.   When skilled nursing is required, the home care nursing staff obtains the initial nursing assessment on the first day of admission; when skilled nursing care is ordered later during admission, the assessment is obtained at the first skilled care visit. Be aware that some states require a nursing assessment even when skilled nursing care is not provided. The record should also include documentation of the initial clinical evaluations of other disciplines or services that may have been involved in care of the patient (for example, physical therapy, occupational therapy, and pharmacy).

3.   Relevant X ray, pathology, laboratory, or other test findings are documented.

B.   For hospice patients, it is recommended that initial assessment data include the following information:

1.   The hospice record includes the following relevant information:

       a. Diagnoses

       b. Past medical history

       c. Review of systems

       d. Present treatment

       e. Activities of daily living

       f. Functional limitations

       g. Patient care requirements

       h. Dietary or nutritional information

       i. Pain assessment

       j. Psychosocial assessment

       k. Spiritual assessment

       l. Safety measures required to protect the patient from injury

       m. Equipment needed in the home

       n. Suitability of the patient and family residence

       o. Relevant information regarding the primary caregiver

2.   The appropriate hospice clinical staff obtains the initial assessment on the first day of admission or on the first home visit. The record should also include documentation of the initial clinical evaluations of other disciplines involved in the care of the patient (for example, physical therapy, occupational therapy, and pharmacy).

3.   Relevant X ray, pathology, laboratory, or other test findings are documented.

4.   A problem list, based on the initial assessment, is documented.

C.   When nonmedical services are being provided, such as homemaker/chore services or DME with no professional service provision, assessment information is much more limited than in the preceding cases. Referencing JCAHO (2000) requirements is recommended in these instances.

Home Health Plans of Care

In this section, the term *plans of care* refers to the Medicare-required home health plans of care that are documented on form HCFA-485. Plans of care may also be referred to as *physician's orders.* A description of care plans follows.

Based on the problems and needs identified during assessment and documented on the problem list, care plans are comprehensive and include documentation of care or services to be provided by all disciplines, independent contractors, organizations, and volunteers. JCAHO requires that an organization design the process, including required documentation, for care planning, review, and when necessary, revision. A policy for care plan review and revision must exist (JCAHO 2000). Care plans include goals and objectives, as well as indicating the person/discipline responsible for implementing the plan(s), frequency of services to be provided, and the medications prescribed. Hospice care plans are interdisciplinary. Record documentation reflects the participation of patients, physicians, and pharmacists in care planning (JCAHO 2000). The crosswalk between JCAHO standards and the Medicare *Conditions of Participation* outlines care plan documentation requirements.

For home care reimbursement purposes, form HCFA-485 is used to document the physician's plan-of-care orders. The physician uses form HCFA-485 to certify the patient's need for home health service. Most home health agencies have computer-based applications to assist them in completing form HCFA-485 and in tracking the need for recertification, which is required every 60 days. The crosswalk between the JCAHO standards and the Medicare *Conditions of Participation* outlines documentation requirements for home care and hospice.

When a Medicare-certified hospice contracts with an inpatient facility, the inpatient care must be based on the interdisciplinary care plan of the hospice. The hospice maintains control of the care, and this must be made evident in the health record. Policies and procedures and contracts define the relevant information to be shared among providers so gaps in care are prevented and the hospice record documents all services provided. Procedures should provide for written and oral communication among hospice team members and inpatient care providers throughout the inpatient care episode.

Standardized care plans and protocols are available for specific service provision and for medical and nursing diagnoses. Any standardized care plans that are used must be individualized for each patient and caregiver. When critical paths are used, standardized or structured care plans may also be used for documentation.

Regardless of an organization's Medicare certification status, a care plan conforms to the physician's plan-of-care orders. The care plan is based on the nursing initial assessment, as well as the initial assessments of other disciplines involved in the care of the patient. An interdisciplinary care plan is recommended, but separate discipline care plans may be documented when they are filed together in the health record.

Following are recommendations for the content of interdisciplinary care plans for professional home care and for patients. The crosswalk between the JCAHO standards and the Medicare *Conditions of Participation* lists specific requirements that pertain to these matters.

A. For professional home care services, interdisciplinary care plans should include the following information:

    a. Identified patient problems

    b. Expected outcomes, long- and short-term goals

    c. The dates the expected outcomes were met

    d. Plans and interventions, including medications prescribed and required medical equipment to be provided to meet the identified goals

    e.   Discipline responsible for carrying out plans and achieving goals

    f.   Signature of the nurse or care coordinator for the patient

1. Verbal orders are appropriately documented and then signed by the attending physician when an additional discipline enters the care plan, or when a change occurs in care management.

2. The care plan undergoes an interdisciplinary review, even when separate discipline care plans may be documented. The service providers and, whenever possible, the attending physician, perform this review. When care services were provided through contractual agreement, persons who provided these services also participate in care plan review.

3. Care plan reviews are individualized to each client, but occur at least every 60 days. They are documented in case conference minutes or elsewhere in the health record. (See case conference summary form in appendix I.) Care plan changes are also documented.

4. The record clearly reflects coordination of care planning between all disciplines, paraprofessionals, organizations, and other care providers, as well as between the organization, the attending physician, and the patient.

B. For hospice patients, it is recommended that the interdisciplinary care plan include the following information:

1. Within one week of admission, an interdisciplinary care plan is developed for each patient and family. This plan conforms to physician orders and is based on clinical information in the initial database and problem list. The care plan documents the following:

    a.   Identified patient and family problems and needs

    b.   Identified goals that are realistic, achievable, and measurable

    c.   Care and services to be provided to meet identified goals, including medications prescribed and required medical equipment

    d.   The signature of the attending physician and team coordinator for the patient and family

2. Verbal orders are appropriately documented and then signed by the attending physician when an additional discipline enters the care of the patient and family or when a change in care management occurs.

3. The planned frequency of interdisciplinary care plan review is documented. Although they are individualized to each patient, reviews occur no less than every two weeks after admission. Care plan changes are documented, and when appropriate, there is documentation of new orders signed by the attending physician.

4. Record documentation should include the findings and conclusions of team case conferences (see case conference summary in appendix I).

5. Continuing discussions among the attending physician and members of the interdisciplinary team is documented.

C. When nonmedical services are provided, the health record contains documentation of the services to be performed. The JCAHO standards should be referenced for additional guidance.

Physician's Orders and Plans of Care

As indicated by the type of care service provided, the health record includes legible, complete, signed, and dated physician's diagnoses and therapeutic orders. The person authorized to accept the orders must record, date, and sign all verbal or telephone orders, and then the attending physician must countersign and date the orders within the time period specified in organization policy and required by state regulations. The crosswalk between the JCAHO standards and the Medicare *Conditions of Participation* contains specific JCAHO and Medicare requirements on these matters. When pharmaceutical care is provided, the pharmacist reviews every prescription before dispensing medication and verifies verbal orders which he or she did record and for which there are questions (JCAHO 2000).

Current regulations require a physician-signed plan of care before an HHA can bill for payment. However, HCFA views the initial percentage payment as a request for anticipated payment (RAP) rather than a Medicare claim for home health PPS purposes. The first percentage payment under home health PPS does not require a physician-signed plan of care before submission. The RAP for the episode may be submitted based on verbal orders. In order to request anticipated payment for the initial percentage based on a physician's verbal orders, a copy of the plan of care with all physician's verbal orders—in writing with the date of receipt by the registered nurse or qualified therapist responsible for furnishing or supervising the ordered services—must be completed and immediately sent to the physician for signature. The RAP may be submitted when the HHA has a signed referral prescribing the physician's detailed orders for services and the patient's condition. Signed orders must be obtained as soon as possible and before the claim for services is submitted for the final percentage payment of each episode. The claim for the final percentage payment requires a signed plan of care prior to billing.

The RAP will be canceled and recovered unless the claim for the episode is submitted within 60 days from the end of the episode or the issuance of the anticipated payment. This split-percentage payment approach helps alleviate cash flow concerns but increases the need for timely signed orders.

Clinical and Progress Notes

For this discussion the term *clinical note* refers to a note documenting care services provided, and *progress note* refers to a summary note. A progress note may be documented upon any transfer between hospice care levels, on discharge, or when physicians or others need summary information.

Clinical Notes and Visit Documentation

Clinical and visit notes are designed to give a clear, comprehensive picture of the patient's continual status, the care being provided, and the response to that care. Policies, procedures, and forms can ensure that documentation is entered efficiently into the record and that such important aspects of care as supervision of care and patient and family education are documented. Documentation incorporates conversations with physicians, pharmacists, relatives, and others who have an impact on patient care.

When nonmedical services are being provided and there is no professional service provision, a checklist may be used to document the services provided. The crosswalk between the JCAHO standards and the Medicare *Conditions of Participation* outlines other important items for DME providers to document.

When professional services are provided, visits by licensed certified staff are documented in a signed and dated clinical progress note or flow sheet entry, which includes the following information:

- A description of the patient's physical and psychosocial signs and symptoms or changes in signs and symptoms

- Any treatment, service, or medication rendered and the patient's reaction

- Any changes in the patient's condition or the patient's and family's psychosocial status

- Any patient and family instruction given, as well as patient and family demonstration or verbalization of knowledge of instructions given

- Plans for future visits

See appendix K for a sample form used to record a skilled nursing visit.

When flow sheets are used to document interventions or progress toward care goals, clinical notes are then used to record supplemental information such as assessment of findings, interventions, and plans; telephone conversations; and nursing supervisory visits. When flow sheet documentation uses a coding system, a legend should appear on the form.

The Home Care and Hospice Advisory Committees recommended that all clinical notes be filed chronologically (referred to as *integrated*) rather than by discipline or service. For cases where integrating the clinical notes is not feasible, the committees recommended that the clinical notes should at least be filed in the same section of the patient's record, as opposed to being filed in a separate record or in a separate section of the record. It was also recommended that notes written by different disciplines be distinguished from one another through color coding or a similar system. However, some home care and hospice programs have found that filing care plans and notes by discipline can be more efficient, especially when discipline-specific information must be retrieved for fiscal intermediaries. Whatever file order is adopted, the end product should be a health record that can readily provide a clear, consistent picture of the patient's status, care plans, and goals, as well as the care and services provided by all the disciplines and services.

There are various systems for documenting clinical notes. The narrative note is unstructured and usually is not indexed, although problem numbers or titles may accompany it. The subjective/objective assessment plan (SOAP) system breaks documentation down into four major divisions. However, each note does not have to contain documentation for each division. The major divisions are described as:

- **S**ubjective: Input by the patient or family about problem(s) (for example, onset, duration, severity, current symptoms, current medication use)

- **O**bjective: Information from examination, observations, laboratory tests, and other sources

- **A**ssessment: Interpretation by the individual provider of the subjective and objective data; identification of problem(s) and patient's current medical, psychosocial, and functional status

- **P**lan: Course of action for problem(s) described, including information given to patient and/or family, plan of care and problem management, and plan for follow-up (This category, or a separately labeled category or narrative note, should also contain documented interventions and instruction, as well as an assessment of client reaction to interventions and/or demonstration/verbalization of instructions that have been given.)

Three other charting systems exist: SOAPIE, PIE, and FOCUS (Iyer and Camp 1991). A variation on the SOAP system, the SOAPIE system separates intervention and evaluation from plan:

- Intervention: Interventions and instructions

- Evaluation: Assessment of patient reaction to interventions and/or demonstration/ verbalization of instructions

In conjunction with critical paths or standardized protocols for care, charting by exception (CBE) is common (especially in organizations with computer-based systems). When using a CBE system, protocols based on standards of practice outline essential assessment, interventions, and expected outcomes in relation to clinical problems, diagnoses, or services (such as wound care and catheter irrigation). Flow sheet documentation is used to indicate accomplishment of the protocol, and documentation substitutes for other types of clinical notes. When using CBE, narrative, SOAP, or SOAPIE, notes are used only to document changes or revisions in problems or care plans, exceptions to the protocol or to expected outcomes, evaluation of expected outcomes, or a discharge summary (Burke and Murphy 1988). With reimbursement considerations in mind, home care and hospice programs using CBE are advised to supplement flow sheet documentation with other narrative, SOAP, or SOAPIE notations.

Medication Administration

The comprehensive assessment must include a review of all medications the patient is currently using in order to identify any potential adverse effects and drug reactions, including ineffective drug therapy, significant side effects, significant drug interactions, duplicate drug therapy, and noncompliance with drug therapy. This requirement applies to all patients being serviced by the HHA, regardless of whether the specific requirements of OASIS apply. This includes over-the-counter drugs. If the qualified clinician determines that the patient is experiencing problems with his/her medications or identifies any potential adverse effects and/or reactions, the physician must be alerted. Drugs and treatments ordered by the patient's physician and not documented on the care plan should be recorded in the clinical record. The label on the bottle of a prescription medication constitutes the pharmacist's transcription or documentation of the order. Such medications are noted in the patient's clinical record and listed on form HCFA-485. This is consistent with acceptable standards of practice (HCFA 2000b). The individual medication record may serve as the record of receipt and disposition of all controlled drugs to meet hospice *Conditions of Participation* (HCFA 1994).

When authorized home care or hospice staff administers medications, the action is documented in the health record, as well as any beneficial effects and presumed adverse drug reactions. When pharmaceutical and infusion therapy services are provided, patients are continually monitored for medication effectiveness and actual or potential medication-related problems. This is a collaborative process involving the pharmacist, and documentation will show evidence of this collaboration. The health record provides evidence that conclusions and findings of medication monitoring are communicated to all healthcare professionals involved in the patient's care (JCAHO 2000). When pharmaceutical services are provided, pharmacy records are filed with health records (JCAHO 2000). The American Society of Health-System Pharmacists has developed educational materials on the health record and the pharmacist's record documentation.

Volunteer Documentation

Volunteers are defined in 42 CFR 418.3 as hospice employees who facilitate compliance with the hospice core services requirement. The hospice uses volunteers, in defined roles, under the supervision of a designated hospice employee. The hospice must provide appropriate volunteer training consistent with the specific tasks that volunteers perform. The interdisciplinary group conducts an assessment of the patient's and caregiver's need for a volunteer. Volunteers must be used in administrative or direct patient care roles. Agencies must document the roles assigned to that hospice's volunteers. Hospices use volunteers to supplement the care being provided by the paid staff who work directly with patients and their family members, both in the patients' homes and the inpatient setting. Hospices must document the cost savings of volunteers, which must include the identification of necessary positions occupied by volunteers, work time spent by volunteers, and estimates of the dollar costs that the hospice would have incurred if paid employees occupied the positions. Hospices must document a continual level of volunteer activity and expansion of care and services achieved through the use of volunteers, including the types of services and the time worked (HCFA 1994).

In hospice settings, volunteers write notes after each visit and include them in the hospice record using separate volunteer documentation forms. The volunteer coordinator or nurse team coordinator reviews the volunteer's notes and initials them before they are filed. Volunteer's notes include the following information:

- New issues, special concerns, or significant changes observed in the patient or family since last contact

- The volunteer's response and interventions to changes/concerns at this contact

- The volunteer's plan for next contact

- The request for special consultation/contact from other staff when needed

Home Health Aide Documentation

Agencies must provide enough home health aide services to meet the needs of the patient. Home health aides who are employees of the home care or hospice, as well as aides used by the agency hospice under an arrangement or contract, must meet the personnel qualifications specified by the *Conditions of Participation*. Home health aides are selected on the basis of such factors as a sympathetic attitude toward the care of the sick; ability to read, write, and carry out directions; and maturity and ability to deal effectively with the demands of the job. They are closely supervised to ensure their competence in providing care. A registered nurse provides written patient care instructions and monitors the services provided by the home health aide. This nurse also visits the patient's residence at least once every two weeks if aide services are provided, in order to assess aide services and relationships and determine whether goals are being met. The onsite visit need not be made while the aide is furnishing services.

Home health aide services should be adequately documented in the health record, including nursing orders for the home health aide and an assignment sheet, flow sheet, and narrative notations documenting services rendered. The nurse or therapist should also include documentation of coordination with the aide and continuing supervision of the aide's services. (See appendix K.)

It is recommended that home health aides record the services they provide in a checklist format. Aides should document short narrative notes only when reporting unusual occurrences (for example, changes in the condition of the patient and phone calls) or when state regulations require it.

Dietary and Nutritional Information

Health record documentation should reflect, as appropriate, the patient's nutrient intake, dietary instructions to the patient and family, and demonstration or verbalization from the patient and family of dietary instructions given. A diet history and nutritional evaluation by a dietician will be completed when appropriate as defined in organization policy. The crosswalk between 1999–2000 JCAHO standards and the *Medicare Conditions of Participation* outlines documentation requirements when nutritional care is provided.

Justification of Hospice Skilled Care Levels

Employees in Medicare-certified hospices must be conscientious when documenting a patient's need for inpatient and continuous home care and the actual provision of services. To be considered continuous by Medicare, home care must be provided for at least 8 hours in one 24-hour period (for example, 12 a.m. to 11:59 p.m.), and care must be predominantly skilled nursing care. Continuous care is initiated during periods of crisis (such as severe pain, hemorrhaging, and imminent death) or when active palliation or management of acute medical symptoms is needed. Record documentation must describe the crisis and include the date and time it occurred. In conjunction with this, the patient's care plan is revised to reflect the changes in the problems and care provision. During continuous care, an extensive nursing note is written at least hourly, and it is signed with the date and time, as are all record notations during this period. When inpatient care is required, a medical crisis such as "symptoms out of control" is documented. On admission and continuously throughout the inpatient care period, documentation reflects the patient's need for acute care. As with continuous care, the interdisciplinary care plan is modified to reflect new or exacerbated problems, as well as changes in care provision. The hospice furnishes a copy of the patient's plan of care to the inpatient provider and specifies the inpatient services to be furnished.

Short-term inpatient care may be provided in a Medicare hospice inpatient unit. The Medicare conditions for each of these providers of service apply to all patients regardless of payment source, unless a specific exception is provided in the regulations. Services provided in an inpatient setting must conform to the hospice patient's written plan of care and must be reasonable and necessary for the palliation of symptoms or the management of the terminal illness. General inpatient care may be required to adjust and monitor the patient's pain control or manage acute or chronic symptoms that cannot be provided in another setting. Inpatient admission may also be furnished to provide respite for the patient's family or other persons caring for the individual at home. Respite care is the only type of inpatient care that may be furnished in a nursing facility. The hospice is accountable for all hospice services provided under arrangement at nursing facilities. The hospice furnishes the inpatient provider a copy of the patient's plan of care and specifies the inpatient services to be furnished. The hospice health record includes a record of all inpatient services and events and a copy of the discharge summary (HCFA 1994).

Progress Notes and the Discharge Transfer Record

Upon a patient's discharge or death, a summary is documented. This report includes the following information:

- Admission and discharge dates and type of discharge

- Care and support provided by each discipline

- Status of goal attained upon discharge or death

- When discharged alive, the status of the patient and the reason for discharge

- Discharge diagnoses or problems

- Any unmet needs and referrals for continuing care

- For hospice settings, time (if known) and place of death, as well as plans for bereavement follow-up

Home care or hospice organizations may also include other outcome monitoring information on their discharge summaries. OASIS data are collected and completed by the qualified clinician when a patient transfers to an inpatient facility with or without discharge, discharge to community, or death at home. Agencies may take up to seven calendar days after the date of completion of the comprehensive assessment to enter (encode) the OASIS data into their computers using HAVEN or HAVEN-like software. The day the clinician completes the assessment is day zero for purposes of calculating the seven-day window. Encoding of all OASIS data items must be complete, or locked, in order to accurately compute the information (health insurance prospective payment system [HIPPS] code) necessary for billing Medicare patients under the prospective payment system.

When hospice patients are transferred between home and inpatient care, a transfer note is created. The documentation summarizes the patient's status, care, and support being provided, as well as the reason for transfer.

For Medicare-certified home health agencies, a discharge summary that includes a patient's medical and health status at discharge must be made available to the patient's attending physician, and physicians must be informed of this availability. The discharge summary may be incorporated into the routine summary reports already furnished by the physician (HCFA 2000b).

HCFA Forms 485–487 may be used as a progress note or a summary report. Notations should be appropriately labeled and should provide an overall, comprehensive view of the patient's total progress and current summary report including social, emotional, and behavioral adjustments relative to the diagnosis; treatment; rehabilitation potential; and anticipated outcomes toward recovery or further debilitation. Medicare regulations do not dictate the frequency with which progress notes must be written.

Bereavement Documentation

Bereavement counseling services are often provided to the family and caregivers after a patient's death. Counseling is provided on the basis of an assessment of the family's and caregiver's needs, the presence of any risk factors associated with the patient's death, and the ability of the family and caregivers to cope with grief. The supervisor of bereavement services may be the interdisciplinary group social worker or other professional with documented evidence of training and experience in dealing with grief. Documentation for bereavement counseling does not necessarily have to be contained in the clinical record, but it must be maintained by the hospice in an organized, easily retrievable manner.

The hospice record includes an initial and follow-up bereavement assessment of the family and significant others that documents the physical and emotional status of the family and significant others. (See sample forms in appendix L.) It is recommended that the initial bereavement assessment be completed at the team meeting following the patient's death. The bereavement follow-up assessment is completed within four weeks of the patient's death. Subsequent bereavement assessments are completed as deemed necessary by the hospice bereavement staff and as stated in hospice policy. Notes are written after each bereavement visit. These notes document the general emotional and physical status of the family and significant other at that visit, any counseling that was performed or follow-up action taken, and any changes in plans (see the crosswalk between JCAHO standards and the Medicare *Conditions of Participation* for specific requirements).

On discharge from bereavement follow-up, a summary is written. This summary includes appropriate information regarding services provided to the family and significant other and the status of the family and significant other during the last bereavement contact.

The Medicare Hospice Benefit

It is essential that health information managers working in hospice know what makes a patient eligible for the Medicare hospice benefit and how to document provision of care. Most hospice reimbursement hinges on meeting those requirements.

Medicare Hospice Benefit and Documentation of Eligibility

Medicare coverage for hospice care began with enactment of section 122 of public law 97-248, the Tax Equity and Fiscal Responsibility Act of 1982 (TEFRA). The *Code of Federal Regulations* (CFR 1997) defines the Medicare hospice benefit and documentation requirements. Interpretive guidelines provide additional guidance on required documentation. Throughout this section, definitions and requirements have been abstracted from these sources.

Patients must elect hospice care from a Medicare-certified hospice to be eligible for Medicare reimbursement. When patients elect hospice care, they waive their rights to Medicare reimbursement for treatment of their principal (terminal) diagnosis and related conditions outside of care provided by the designated hospice, by another hospice provided under arrangements made by the designated hospice, or by the individual's attending physician when that physician is not an employee of the designated hospice or receiving compensation from the hospice for those services. An individual can revoke the Medicare hospice benefit and then reelect the benefit after revocation. An individual can also elect to change the designated hospice program. Election, revocation, and reelection of the Medicare hospice benefit—as well as change of the designated hospice—must be documented in the health record, and that documentation should clearly show that the patient or the patient's legal representative was well-informed.

Patients can elect the hospice benefit at any time, the order listed below or at different times. The periods consist of the following:

1. An initial 90-day period

2. A subsequent 90-day period

3. A subsequent extension of an unlimited number of 60-day periods when the patient is certified terminally ill with a six-month prognosis if the disease runs its normal course

To be eligible for the hospice benefit, a patient must have a physician-certified terminal illness. A written certification must be obtained for each of the four periods in the preceding list, and the certification must indicate a life expectancy of six months or less if the terminal illness runs its normal course. The health record should contain evidence of this certification.

Medicare hospice fiscal intermediaries are beginning to conduct focused medical reviews of hospice claims. One area these intermediaries are questioning concerns the validity of the terminal certification of some patients. Some cases of long lengths of stay and patients with chronic diagnoses have led to this questioning.

To prevent denials, coding personnel are advised to use the most specific diagnosis codes and to ensure that the terminal diagnosis is always listed as the principal diagnosis. All complications of chronic conditions should be documented and coded as appropriate. Also, health record documentation on admission and throughout a hospice episode must support a patient's terminal status. When a claim is selected for medical review, it is recommended that copies of all health record documentation, including the admission assessment, be submitted to a fiscal intermediary for review (HAA 1994).

The Hospice Association of America (HAA), in conjunction with HCFA and the National Hospice Organization, has developed guidelines on screening hospice patients who have illnesses other than cancer for admissions and recertifications. Guidelines address determining a patient's prognosis, what to look for, and what to document (HAA 1994).

Provision of Care under the Medicare Hospice Benefit and Documentation

Medicare has defined four general hospice care levels and has assigned different reimbursement rates to each:

1. Routine home care

2. Continuous home care

3. Inpatient respite care

4. General inpatient care

A hospice must maintain management control of a patient's care, regardless of the treatment setting, and the health record must contain evidence of this control. According to Medicare regulations, hospices that cannot provide inpatient care directly must contract with an inpatient care provider. The crosswalk between the JCAHO standards and the Medicare *Conditions of Participation* contains specifics regarding contract and documentation requirements.

Hospice regulations require an interdisciplinary group to plan and provide or supervise the care and services provided to patients and families. This group includes at least the following hospice employees:

• A doctor of medicine or osteopathy

• A registered nurse

• A social worker

• A pastoral counselor or another type of couselor

The team in the preceding list establishes and revises an interdisciplinary care plan (specifics regarding care plan requirements can be found in the crosswalk between the JCAHO standards and the Medicare *Conditions of Participation*). The care plan becomes the basis for team decision making and can be considered the map for team interventions (Tierney and Wilson 1993).

Medicare requires that volunteers be used in administrative or direct patient care roles. In many hospices, volunteers provide services and support to the patient, family, or significant other. Volunteers are considered members of the interdisciplinary team.

A summary of the advice regarding documentation and the hospice Medicare benefit included in this chapter follows:

- The health record must contain evidence that the interdisciplinary team plans and manages a patient's care across all settings of care.

- The health record must contain evidence that hospice interdisciplinary care continues when a patient is admitted for inpatient hospice care.

- Health record documentation must justify the level of hospice care the patient is receiving. When the status of a patient changes, requiring continuous home care or inpatient care, clinical notes must document this change, and the care plan must be revised to indicate any new problems or changes in plans.

The Medicare Home Care Benefit

Successful health information managers working in home health often refer to the *Home Health Agency Manual* (HIM 11). Referencing the HIM 11 is key to understanding how the Medicare home care benefit drives documentation requirements for patient care, home health certification and plan of care form 485, Medicare home care surveys, and the prospective payment system. The following sections describe some of those requirements.

The Medicare Home Care Benefit and Documentation of Eligibility

Medicare certification of Part A home care providers includes the home health agency. Because Medicare Part B providers (that is, DME, pharmacy, and others) are considered vendors, they are not certified. The *Home Health Agency Manual* defines the Medicare home care benefit and documentation in relation to such. Interpretive guidelines provide additional directions concerning required documentation. Throughout this section, definitions and requirements have been abstracted from these sources (all other sources are referenced).

To be eligible for Medicare-reimbursed home healthcare, a Medicare beneficiary must meet the following conditions:

- The beneficiary is confined to home.

- The beneficiary is under the care of a physician, who establishes and approves the plan of care for the individual.

- The beneficiary needs intermittent, skilled nursing care, physical therapy, speech therapy services, or continuing occupational therapy.

Home Confinement

Patients should be essentially homebound. This does not mean that the patient must be bedridden, but leaving home must present considerable difficulty and be infrequent and of short duration unless for medical reasons. The reason(s) for homebound status and the fact that the patient is homebound must be recorded on form HCFA-485, on the comprehensive assessment, and periodically in the clinical notes. Documentation regarding homebound status should be descriptive. Why is a patient homebound? What happens when a patient walks too far? When the patient visited the doctor, what type of assistance was provided? Nursing and therapy documentation should be congruent, not conflicting. OASIS items MO350-MO380 and Life System Profile items MO640-MO820 should also support the patient's homebound status.

Home Health under the Care of a Physician

The beneficiary's physician is responsible for signing the home health certification form HCFA-485 upon the initiation of any plan of care. Upon the completion of every 60-day episode during which the patient received continuous home healthcare from the same home health agency, the beneficiary's physician is responsible for home health recertification. The home health prospective payment system did not change the plan of care. It remains the beneficiary's physician's responsibility to develop a plan of care based on his or her intimate knowledge of the medical condition of the home health patient. The plan of care developed in consultation with the agency staff covers all pertinent diagnoses, mental status, types of services and equipment required, frequency of visits, prognosis, rehabilitation potential, functional limitations, activities permitted, nutritional requirements, medications and treatments, safety measures to protect against injury, instructions for timely discharge or referral, and any other appropriate items.

The patient's physician approves the patient's plan of care and certifies the need for home health services by signing a home health certification and plan of care, form HCFA-485. Upon the completion of every 60-day episode if the patient continues to receive continuous home healthcare from the same home health agency, the beneficiary's physician is responsible for recertification of the plan of care (United Government Services 2000).

Skilled Services Requirement for Benefit Eligibility

The patient must require skilled services. The three required skilled services include intermittent skilled nursing care, physical therapy, and speech therapy. To qualify for home care, *intermittent skilled nursing* is defined as a recurring need for nursing care less than five times a week, unless required more often for a finite and predictable period of time. Patients receiving one of these three services are also eligible to receive medical social services and occupational therapy; the occupational therapy may be continued if required after other skilled services have been discontinued.

The skilled care being provided must be reasonable and necessary. Foster and Kazon (1992) note that to deem care not reasonable or necessary, a fiscal intermediary's decisions must be based on the individual patient's health status and medical need as reflected in his or her plan of care and health record. Even though intermediaries have edit screens to detect questionable claims, the information from these screens cannot be the only reason for denying coverage, and documentation must also be reviewed.

According to HCFA, reimbursable skilled nursing care consists of services that are reasonable and necessary to the treatment of illness or services that must be performed by or under the direct supervision of a licensed nurse if the safety of the patient is to be ensured and the desired result achieved. Following are general categories of reimbursable skilled services include:

- Observation and assessment when significant changes in the patient's condition could occur that would require the skills or evaluation of a skilled nurse and that may result in changes in the client's plan of treatment or in possible institutionalization

- Teaching and training activities that require nursing skills or knowledge

- Performance of skilled procedures such as the insertion and sterile irrigation of catheter, intravenous and intramuscular injections, and wound care

- Management and evaluation of the care plan

The *Home Health Agency Manual* (HIM 11), Section 203 (HCFA 1989 and updates), includes additional discussion regarding coverage for skilled care services, as well as for other reimbursable services. Documentation throughout the record must continually confirm the need for and provision of skilled services.

Once a patient begins receiving one of the skilled services described in the preceding material, he or she qualifies for other reimbursable services. These other services include medical social services provided to patients under direction of a physician, part-time or intermittent home health aide services, medical supplies (other than drugs or biologicals), and durable medical equipment available from the agency. Recent changes to Medicare home care regulations allow medical social services of a brief duration to be provided to families of patients.

Intermittent or Part-Time Home Care Benefits

For coverage of home care benefits, skilled nursing and aide services must be provided on an intermittent or part-time basis. HIM 11 defines the terms *intermittent* and *part-time* in detail.

Home Health Certification and Plan of Care

Form HCFA-485, Home Health Certification and Plan of Care, is designed to meet regulatory requirements for the physician's plan of care. It also documents a physician's certification and recertification that a patient needs home health services and meets the Medicare requirements for receipt of home health services. HIM 11 offers detailed instructions on how to complete this form. The agency must receive a completed and signed form before the final claim for each episode can be submitted to the Medicare fiscal intermediary. The patient's physician must review, update, and recertify the plan of care at least every 60 days. Fiscal intermediaries may request a hard copy of form 485, but it need not be submitted with the bill, which is submitted by most agencies electronically. (See appendix J for an example of form HCFA-485.)

Medicare Home Care Surveys

Medicare home care surveyors use medical, nursing, and rehabilitative care indicators to determine the quality of a patient's care and the scope of the home health agency services provided to the client. These surveyors use the HCFA Home Health Functional Assessment to document data from home care record reviews and patient visits. During a standard Medicare survey an agency's admission volume determines the number of records to be reviewed, and surveyors review a stratified sample of clinical records. Based on record review, employee interviews, and home visits to patients, Medicare surveyors make their conclusions about the following areas:

484.10	Patient's rights
484.11	Release of patient-identifiable OASIS information
484.12	Compliance with federal, state, and local laws; disclosure and ownership information; and accepted professional standards and principles
484.14(g)	Coordination of services
484.18	Acceptance of patients, plans of care, and medical supervision
484.36	Home health aide services
484.48	Clinical records

Partial or extended Medicare surveys can focus on:

484.14	Organization, services, and administration
484.16	Group of professional personnel

484.30	Skilled nursing services
484.32	Therapy services
484.34	Medical social services
484.38	Qualification to furnish outpatient physical therapy or speech therapy

Home health agency deficiencies per agency increased 26 percent between the first six months of 1997 to the first six months of 1999. Nearly one-fourth of citations fell within 484.18, Acceptance of patients, plan of care, and medical supervision. The most frequently cited G-tag was G158, Care follows a written plan (Gibbs Brown 2001).

COP 484.20(a) guidelines instruct surveyors on presurvey and onsite survey activity related to OASIS data collection. Before the survey, surveyors check with the state OASIS education or automation coordinator and review OASIS data management reports to determine whether encoding is completed within seven days after completing the OASIS data set. Onsite, surveyors check to see if the HHA is transmitting its own data or has an arrangement with an outside entity acting on behalf of the HHA to electronically submit OASIS data to the state agency. If so, surveyors confirm that a written contract exists that describes the arrangement the HHA has with the outside entity to enter and transmit OASIS data on behalf of the HHA. Surveyors determine the process for encoding and locking OASIS data being readied for transmission to the state. When questions are raised through interview or record review, surveyors review the HHA's policies regarding encoding time frames. New HHAs seeking initial certification must apply for appropriate state and federal HHA identification and passwords and be able to demonstrate compliance with collecting, completing, encoding, and reporting OASIS data for all applicable patients in an electronic format that meets HCFA specifications prior to the initial survey (HCFA 2000b).

Home Health Prospective Payment System

A 60-day episode is the unit of payment for home health prospective payment system (PPS). The episode payment is specific to an individual beneficiary. A 60-day episode begins with the first Medicare billable visit as day one and ends on and includes the sixtieth day from start-of-care date. The next continuous episode recertification period begins on day 61 and ends on and includes day 120. The 60-day episode payment covers one individual for 60 days of care regardless of the number of days of care actually furnished during the 60-day period, unless there is an intervening event.

The 60-day episode amount is case-mix adjusted for each patient using the OASIS developed by HCFA as part of the required home care assessment. The system combines twenty-three data elements to measure case-mix across three domains: clinical severity factors, functional status, and service utilization factors. Key data elements and their respective values were identified for each dimension to create a case-mix system that included eighty severity categories or home health resource groups (HHRG). HHRGs are a case-mix classification system in which patient characteristics and health status information gathered from the OASIS assessment in conjunction with projected therapy use during the 60-day episode are used to determine payment. After obtaining physician orders, the HHA submits a request for anticipated payment based on the current OASIS-based case mix, and receives 60 percent of the estimated case-mix adjusted episode payment.

At the end of the 60-day episode, the HHA submits a final claim for the beneficiary and receives the remaining 40 percent of the estimated case-mix adjusted episode payment. Each final claim must represent the actual utilization during this period, in line item detail. An initial and final bill must be submitted for each episode period. If care continues at the same provider for a second episode, the initial payment for the second episode will not be made until the final claim for the first episode is received.

An episode may end before the sixtieth day if the patient is transferred, discharged, or readmitted. Such cases call for a partial episode payment adjustment, which takes into account key intervening events in a patient's care defined as a beneficiary-elected transfer to a different agency or a discharge and return to the same HHA. In such situations, a new 60-day episode clock begins for purposes of payment. When a new 60-day episode begins, the original 60-day episode payment is proportionally adjusted to reflect the length of time the beneficiary remained under the agency's care before the intervening event. The prorated payment is the partial episode payment adjustment. The new 60-day episode interrupting the original episode requires an OASIS assessment and physician's certification signature of the plan of care.

If a patient experiences an unanticipated change in condition during a 60-day episode and the change is significant enough to justify a different payment level or change in the plan of care, the episode payment may be adjusted. In such situations, the early part of the episode is paid proportionally at one rate and the latter part at an adjusted rate. Physicians are required to provide and assign change orders in the plan of care to accommodate the patient's significant change in condition. This type of adjustment does not restart the 60-day episode clock.

Under the PPS, an agency is paid for a 60-day period of care without regard to the amount of services it provides in a 60-day period. As with hospital diagnosis-related group payments, the agency has incentive to provide care efficiently by using as little resources as possible to provide care for the patient (United Government Services 2000).

Home Care Medicare Reimbursement Documentation Guidelines

Whether federally or privately funded, insurance programs employ specific guidelines to determine patient eligibility for home care benefits. When a home care organization accepts a client for care, it also assumes the responsibility for documenting that the client meets the eligibility guidelines at the time of admission and throughout the period of time that the client receives care. Failure to do so can lead to additional costs for the agency should claims be denied.

Medicare is the largest single payer for home care services. In 1997, Medicare spending accounted for about 40 percent of total estimated home care expenditures. Other public funding sources for home care include Medicaid, the Older Americans Act, Title XX social services block grants, the Veterans' Administration, and Civilian Health and Medical Program of the Uniformed Services (CHAMPUS). Private insurance accounted for only a small portion of home care payments. Slightly more than one-fifth of home care services is financed through out-of-pocket payments. HCFA projects that Medicare's share of home care services will decline through 2008 as Medicaid's share increases (NAHC 2000). Clearly, it would serve the best interests of home care organizations to become familiar with the requirements of the various third-party payers and design their documentation systems so that they not only facilitate the provision of high-quality care but also ensure documentation of specific information required for reimbursement.

Documentation of the initial agency contact must establish that the client is eligible for services that are reimbursed by the third-party payer and that the professional caregiver rendered a necessary service during the contact. Many third-party payers will only reimburse for conditions of an acute nature. The assessment must give a clear picture of the patient's status before the onset of the acute illness, report the date of onset of the acute illness, and describe the patient's limitations that resulted from the illness and that make it necessary for home care services to be provided.

Third-party payers require that professional services be provided under a plan of care that a physician has established. The plan of care, which documents physician's orders, should reflect an accurate diagnosis and list treatments and services to be provided. Also, the plan of care should indicate the frequency and duration expected for each treatment modality. Subsequent documentation should note that services have been provided within the bounds of the plan of care and any subsequent physician's orders. The third-party payer has no obligation to reimburse for services that are provided that have not been specifically ordered or were provided more frequently or for a longer duration than ordered. It is well to note that the services provided must be appropriate to the patient's diagnosis(es). For example, when physical therapy services are ordered, the patient's diagnosis(es) must reflect that the client has a problem that requires the services of a physical therapist.

Homebound status must be established during the initial visit. The Medicare Home Health Agency Manual (HCFA 1989) states that, by definition, homebound status is retained when the patient can leave home only with some difficulty for medical appointments or for occasional other purposes. Continuing documentation substantiates this homebound status.

It is also important for the professional caregiver to document any care given during the initial visit to the client. Most third-party payers will not reimburse a visit made for assessment purposes alone. If the nurse assessed a healing wound during an initial assessment and then changed the dressing, the assessment and change of dressing must be documented.

Documentation language is important. The third-party payer wants to see that the client is receiving the care that the skilled professional is trained to give, and so record documentation shows that the care has been provided. Need-based charting is a must. Each entry must stand alone in its ability to demonstrate that a problem or need existed, that it was within the realm of reimbursable services, that intervention was taken by a skilled professional, and that the effects of the intervention taken were assessed. Instead of simply saying that a leg wound was dressed, nurses must describe the wound, the amount and type of drainage, any odor, and the diameter and depth. Documentation must also indicate specifically what kind of wound dressing was used, the client's response to the procedure, the client's understanding of his or her role in the care of the wound, and, finally, the plan for future visits.

Because of the need for detailed, specific documentation, it has become increasingly important that the format of the record expedite documentation of these factors. But some third-party reviewers have not been receptive to forms that use a checklist format to facilitate documentation on flow sheets.

The professional caregiver must be acutely aware of how entries in the record are documented. Simple remarks such as "walks with walker" may signify to the reviewer that the patient is no longer homebound when the caregiver may have meant that the patient requires the use of a walker to ambulate from the bed to the living room or that the patient continues to be unable to ambulate without the assistance of a walker. Specific statements about the extent to which the client is able to ambulate are also important in documenting homebound status: for example, the caregiver could state that the patient is unable to ambulate more than 10 feet without stopping to rest.

Care should be taken to avoid making premature judgments about the client's condition. For example, if the nurse on the second visit finds that the client's blood pressure is within normal limits, a statement such as "blood pressure stable on medication" could indicate to the reviewer that the client no longer requires nurse visits. The nurse would be better advised to record that the client's blood pressure is responding to diet and medication intervention and then go on to describe what continuing needs for nursing care are present. On the next visit, documentation could reflect that the client is continuing to respond to diet and medication intervention. As a general rule, it will be easier to convince a reviewer to acknowledge that a problem continues to be present when the caregiver focuses on what else needs to occur in order for the client to be ready for discharge, rather than on progress made to date.

Ambiguity can also cause denial of a benefits claim, because the reviewer does not have enough information to substantiate that skilled care was given. For instance, if the nurse were seeing a newly diagnosed diabetic patient and wanted to indicate that diet was assessed and instructions were given on specific food exchanges during the visit, documentation should specifically reflect these details rather than simply stating that the diet was reviewed and food exchanges discussed. Most third-party payers will not reimburse for reviews and discussions; however, they will pay for assessments and instructions.

At the time of discharge, the record should include the skilled services that were rendered on the final day of care. If the client no longer needed assistance to ambulate, then a question could arise as to whether the client continued to be homebound and in need of home health-care. It could be argued that such details are trivial and foolish. However, claims have been denied because documentation lacked details.

The burden of proof lies with the home care organization. Although an organization has the right to appeal a claim denial, such appeals are costly in terms of delays in receiving reimbursement and in the staff time required to complete the paperwork involved. Potential denials are best avoided by following the rules and providing details up front. Denials should be categorized and reported by reason so that corrective action may be taken. Medicare regional home health intermediaries can provide quarterly cumulative denial data. Audit and billing activities should be set up accordingly.

A final point about charting for reimbursement is that documentation must be timely, or payment may be jeopardized. An organization can better accomplish this task by following two steps. First, the organization must be aware of paperwork submission deadlines for services payment, and, second, the organization must share this information with the staff who submit claims for reimbursement.

Quantitative Record Review Guidelines

Quantitative record review should be conducted at regular intervals. Routine quantitative record review of all hospice and home care records ensures that the required documentation is present, accurate, consistent, and timely.

The quantitative record review described in this section differs from the qualitative home care clinical record review that Medicare requires. Clinical record review may focus on completeness, but it also examines quality and utilization of services. Requirements call for it to be completed only quarterly on a sample of health records.

Trained staff or health information management professionals, known as registered health information technicians (RHITs) and registered health information administrators (RHIAs), often perform quantitative record review. Health records should be reviewed on admission, on discharge, and on a regular basis every 30 to 60 days. Monitoring processes should ensure timely documentation of the services provided and the timely signature of physician's plans of care and orders. Policies and procedures should address the process of record review, as well as administrative mechanisms for ensuring staff compliance in completing records.

The fact that the Medicare PPS is reimbursed on the basis of the home health resource group is not a reason to skip the review of Medicare documentation. The OIG's compliance program guidance addresses the importance of accurate documentation of care reflected in charges. The reason for this is that annual updating and calculation of norms for the PPS are driven by actual charges. As with compliance, tracking actual charges makes good business sense; it helps the organization measure its efficiency in resource utilization. For compliance purposes, all documentation that serves as the basis for the generation of a bill for patient care should be reviewed. This type of review is different from the type of review that occurs for coding purposes. Documentation monitoring, performed concurrently, ensures that the documentation reflects the full extent of the care provided. At a minimum, the following types of documentation should be monitored concurrently:

- Documentation generating charges (especially higher dollar amounts like infusion care)

- Documentation for any physician charges

- Documentation for ancillary service billing

The HIM department should manage documentation monitoring. However, it is important to involve expert clinical staff when necessary. This not only validates the process, but also involves more of the organization's staff in the compliance process. Clinical staff expertise may be needed for some parts of the review or for the clinical record review process required by Medicare *Conditions of Participation* (Krouth 2000). (See appendix M for a sample home care record review form.)

A software program can be used to tally the review results, which are then forwarded to the performance improvement (PI) committee. The PI committee informs those responsible for the results when a problem is identified. Part of JCAHO's assessment of an ongoing record review process will be determining whether problems were identified and corrected. For this reason, it is important to demonstrate that action was taken. Copies of PI minutes are good pieces of evidence. In addition, agencies should review about 5 percent of their discharges. For example, if an agency discharges 1,000 patients each quarter, the ongoing record review should include 50 records each quarter, or about 17 records per month (Ongoing 2000).

Hospice Inpatient Record Review

All hospice inpatient records should be reviewed shortly after admission to and on discharge from inpatient care. In cases where patients are inpatients for extended time periods, the records should also be reviewed every 30 to 60 days. Shortly after the admission of the patient, the health record is reviewed for the following information:

- Dates and signatures on all documents

- Patient's name on all documents

- Correct filing of all documents

- Referral information

- Patient and family identification data

- Properly completed consent forms

- Patient's rights documentation

- Advance directives

- Do not resuscitate (DNR) and other applicable "do not" orders

- Required assessments

- Current physical examination

- Interdisciplinary care plan

- Copies of documents from transferring facility

- Other documents as required by an individual hospice

On discharge of the patient and on an ongoing basis, the health record should be reviewed for the following information:

- Date and signature on all documents

- Patient's name on all documents

- Correct filing of all documents

- Updated care plans

- Team case conference documentation

- Clinical/progress notes

- A discharge summary to include discharge diagnosis and the applicable bereavement assessments

Home Care Record Review

Clinical record review is a concurrent process at home health organizations. Records are reviewed for completeness, timeliness, and accuracy at admission, as visits are made, and at discharge. In addition, home health organizations must have a tracking process to ensure the prompt return of physician's plans of care and orders.

Admission Review

Shortly after a patient's admission to home care or hospice, the health record should be reviewed for the following information:

- Dates and signatures on all documents

- Patient's name on all documents

- Correct filing of all documents

- Referral information

- Patient identification data

- Properly completed consent forms and service agreements

- Documentation of provision of patient's rights and advance directive information

- Copies of advance directives, when applicable

- Required comprehensive initial assessments

- Signed physician plan of care and physician orders

- Care plan for each discipline providing service and/or for each type of service being provided (interdisciplinary for hospice)

- Copies of documents from transferring agencies

- Other documents as required by an individual organization

Discharge and Ongoing Review

On discharge and on an ongoing basis (every 30 to 60 days), the home care health record should be reviewed for the following information:

- Date and signature on all documents

- Patient's name on all documents

- Correct filing of all documents

- Team case conference documentation (interdisciplinary for hospice and interdisciplinary preferred for other providers)

- Updated and signed plans of care and orders by attending physician

- Updated care plans for all disciplines providing service and for each type of service being provided (interdisciplinary for hospice)

- Clinical progress notes, home health aide notations, or volunteer documentation for each visit made

- Home health aide supervisory visits by a nurse or therapist

- Evidence of review of volunteer notes

- Discharge summary documenting care and support provided by each discipline, whether goals were met, discharge type, discharge medical and health status and reason for discharge when patient is discharged alive, unmet needs and plans for follow-up care, discharge diagnoses and problems, admission and discharge dates; and, for hospice, applicable bereavement assessments

Visit Documentation Review

To ensure that records are complete, many home care and hospice providers monitor visit documentation. The HIM professional or trained staff can accomplish visit reviews by documenting visits against visit itineraries or schedules. To ease the review process, individual providers can attach or consolidate clinical notes to their itineraries and provide this documentation to review personnel for verification before filing. Alternatively, review personnel can be presented with itineraries and schedules to check against handwritten or typed notes before filing. When the notes are computer based, the review personnel can compare itineraries and schedules against the computer-based documentation. A computer-based system also makes it possible to routinely check schedules against clinical progress note documentation. Visit documentation review should be included in routine processes, so that the review does not delay the filing of clinical progress notes.

Physician's Documentation Review

Home care organizations can rely on the mail or fax to obtain required signatures from physicians on plans of care and orders. It is recommended that a system be put in place to monitor the timeliness of signatures and to follow up when signatures are late. When problems persist even with a monitoring system, the entire process should be reviewed to determine how to better achieve timeliness. Although the organization has little control over the behavior of physicians, it does have the power to reduce its own time lags. A monitoring system should address the following points:

- Physician's offices should be notified about any items not returned within a specific time period.

- Staff must confirm that the orders were sent to the correct physician at the correct office before resending orders for signature.

- Establishing trends in delinquent orders by physician group will allow the organization to determine whether some referral relationships continually put the agency at financial or compliance risk.

- Agency managers should know how many claims are on hold due to unsigned orders.

The following methods can be used to monitor return of plans and orders from physicians:

- Copies of mailed or faxed documents are kept in a tickler file by order date. Upon return of the signed order, the tickler file copy is pulled and appropriately destroyed. A specified time frame is established to review and resend orders.

- A manual or computer-based log of unsigned documents is maintained, in which attempts to retrieve signed orders are logged. A review of report details helps identify delinquent signatures.

- Home health order-generating software that includes documentation tracking modules may be employed. Some software systems even allow document tracking through bar codes and bar code readers.

According to Mary St. Pierre, director of regulatory affairs for the National Association for Home Care, "the largest percentage of home health claim denials is for failures to obtain physician orders in a timely manner" (St. Pierre 1999, 52). But in addition, lack of detail, errors, and omissions can result in payment denials. Most times, it is this inattention to detail, not failure to obtain orders and the physician signature, that leads to noncompliance issues. Examples include (St. Pierre 1999, 52):

- Verbal orders are received prior to service delivery, but the agency fails to document the verbal order date on the order form and the physician signs the form after services have been initiated. . . .

- Orders are signed by the physician's nurse or physician assistant, rather than by the physician. . . .

- Orders are signed by the physician but not dated, and the agency fails to record the date the orders were received on the order form. . . .

- Medical treatments are offered, but the order does not specify which discipline is to perform the treatment. . . .

- The frequency of visits is not specified for each discipline. . . .

- A verbal change of orders to add services or increase visit frequency is received after sending the recertification plan of care to the physician for signature. . . .

St. Pierre recommends that agencies avoid technical errors and claim denials by establishing "a series of audits to ensure that orders are received and properly documented prior to billing for services" (St. Pierre 1999, 52).

Summary

Chapter 2 presented documentation challenges and offered management guidelines for specific issues. Health information managers must continually review records to confirm that their standard record content meets all applicable home care and hospice rules, regulations, and standards.

References and Bibliography

Anderson, Kathryn L. 1992. Deceptive documentation in home healthcare nursing. *Home Healthcare Nurse* 10(6):31–35.

Bakken Henry, Suzanne, Judith J. Warren, and Rita D. Zielstorff. 1998. Nursing data, classification systems, and quality indicators: what every HIM professional needs to know. *Journal of the American Health Information Management Association* 69(5):48–53.

Beauchamp, T., and J. Childress. 1983. *Principles of Biomedical Ethics.* 2nd ed. New York City: Oxford University Press.

Brent, Nancy J. 1994. Protecting the AIDS patient's right to make treatment decisions. *Home Healthcare Nurse* 12(2):10–11.

Brown, Louise M., and G. Kay Rousseau. 1990. Resuscitation status begins at home. *American Journal of Nursing*:24–26.

Burke, L., and J. Murphy. 1988. *Charting by Exception.* New York City: John Wiley and Sons.

Byock, Ira. 1990. The rights of patients to forego treatment. *American Journal of Hospice and Palliative Care* 7(2):16–17.

Code of Federal Regulations, Title 42, Volume 2. 1997. Revised. Washington, D.C.: Government Printing Office.

Coffey, R. J., et al. 1992. An introduction to critical paths. *Quality Management in Health Care* 1(1):45–54.

Cruzan v. Director, Missouri Department of Health, 497 US 261 (1990).

Daniel, Denise, and Rita Fulmer. 1992. The documentation dilemma: an integrated solution. *Home Healthcare Nurse* 10(6):41–44.

Falcom, Carol B. 1992. *Home Health Claims Editor.* Alexandria, Va.: St. Anthony Publishing.

Foster, Hope S., and Peter M. Kazon. 1992. Legal aspect of intensive home health-care services. *Intensive Homecare.* Baltimore: Williams and Wilkins, pp. 9–61.

Fox, Leslie Ann, et al. 1987. *The Record That Defends Its Friends.* Chicago: Care Communications.

Gibbs Brown, June. 2000. Department of Health and Human Services Office of Inspector General, Work Plan Fiscal Year 2001, pp. 6–7.

Gibbs Brown, June. 2001. Department of Health and Human Services Office of Inspector General, Semiannual Report, April 1, 2000–September 30, 2000, p. 31.

Gulla, James P. 1993. Family assessment and its relation to hospice care. *American Journal of Hospice and Palliative Care* 10(4):30–34.

Haddad, Amy Marie. 1987. *High Tech Home Care: A Practical Guide.* Rockville, Md.: Aspen Publishers.

Haddad, Amy Marie, and Marshal B. Kapp. 1991. *Ethical and Legal Issues in Home Health Care.* East Norwalk, Conn.: Appleton and Lange.

Harris, Marilyn D. 1994. The laws and regulations make us do it. *Home Healthcare Nurse* 12(4):68–69.

Harrison, Burgess A., and David Cole. 1994. Managing risk to minimize liability. *Caring* 13(5):26–30.

Health Care Financing Administration. 1989. *Home Health Agency Manual.* Washington, D.C.: U.S. Government Printing Office.

Health Care Financing Administration. 1994. Appendix M: Hospice survey procedures and interpretive guidelines, Rev. 265. In *Medicare State Operations Manual Provider Certification.* Washington D.C.: Government Printing Office.

Health Care Financing Administration. 1997. Proposed rules. *Federal Register* 62(46):11060.

Health Care Financing Administration. 1999. Notices, Medicare and Medicaid programs: home health agencies. *Federal Register* 64(117).

Health Care Financing Administration. 2000a. Rules and regulations. *Federal Register* 65(128):41180–41183.

Health Care Financing Administration. 2000b. Appendix B: Interpretive guidelines for home health agencies. In *Medicare State Operations Manual Provider Certification.* Washington, D.C.: Government Printing Office.

Health Care Financing Administration. 2000c. Transmittal 21. In *Medicare State Operations Manual Provider Certification.* Washington, D.C.: Government Printing Office.

Hospice Association of America. 1994. Region IV hospices face new claims review edit and new policy regarding limitation of liability. *Hospice Forum* 9(13):1–2.

Hueber, Emily A., and Patricia A. Harrison. 1991. *The Home Care and Documentation Guide.* Gaithersburg, Md.: Aspen Publishers.

Humphrey, Carolyn J., and Paula Milone-Nuzzo. 1991. *Home Care Nursing: An Orientation to Practice.* Englewood Cliffs, N.J.: Prentice-Hall.

Illinois Homecare Council. 1995. Medicare to pay physicians for oversight of care plan. *Council Communicator*:3.

Iyer, Patricia W., and Nancy Hand Camp. 1991. *Nursing Documentation: A Nursing Process Approach.* St. Louis: Mosby-Year Book.

Joint Commission on Accreditation of Healthcare Organizations. 2000. *2001–2002 Comprehensive Accreditation Manual for Home Care.* Oakbrook Terrace, Ill.: Joint Commission on Accreditation of Healthcare Organizations.

Krouth, Mary. 2000. Monitoring content and quality of documentation. *HIM Connection 2000* 2(43):2–4.

Lee, Doris S., Mary Lynn McPherson, and Ilene H. Zuckerman. 1992. Quality assurance: documentation of pain assessment in hospice patients. *American Journal of Hospice and Palliative Care* 9(1):38–41.

Mengel, Norma S. 1989. A model home health clinical record system. *Home Healthcare Nurse* 7(4):19–21.

Miller, Susan C. 1985. Hospice medical record documentation and management: opportunity for improvement. *Topics in Health Record Management*:13–22.

Miller, Susan C. 1987. *Documenting for High-Quality, Reimbursable Home Care. Quality and Home Health Care: Redefining the Tradition.* Oakbrook, Ill.: Joint Commission on Healthcare Organizations.

Miller, Susan C. 1992. The dynamics of home care—an update. *LTC Spectrum* 5(2):8–10.

Miller, Susan C. 1993. HIM professionals in home care: they must march to the beat of a different drummer. *Journal of the American Health Information Management Association* 64(10):42–45.

Monica, Elissa Della, and Joan Yuan. 1988. Documentation in home care: skilled observation. *Home Healthcare Nurse* 6(1):39–40.

National Association for Home Care. 2000. Basic statistics about home care. www.nahc.org/Consumer/hcstats.html.

OASIS adverse event reports may incorporate recert, SCIC data. 2001. *Eli's Home Care Week* 10(9):70.

Ongoing record review: one hospital's pathway to success. 2000 (November). *Medical Records Briefing* 15(11):1–3.

Peters, Donna Ambler. 1988. Quality documentation-quality care. *Caring* 7(10):30–32, 34.

Rice, Robyn. 1994. Conceptual framework for nursing practice in the home. *Home Healthcare Nurse* 12(2):51–53.

Rothkopf, Michael M. 1992. Concept and scope of intensive homecare. In *Intensive Homecare.* Baltimore: Williams and Wilkins.

Saba, K. V., and Alan E. Zuckerman. 1992. A new home health classification method. *Caring* 11(10):27–34.

Sontag, Mary-Ann. 1992. Hospice values, access to services, and the Medicare hospice benefit. *American Journal of Hospice and Palliative Care* 9(6):17–21.

Spath, Patrice L. 1993. Critical paths: a tool for clinical process management. *Journal of the American Health Information Management Association* 64(30):48–58.

St. Pierre, Mary. 1999. Lack of physician's orders is the no. 1 compliance problem. *Journal of Health Care Compliance* 1(5):52, 63.

Tamborlane, Theodosia A. 1994. Prohibited practices and safe harbors—a legal quagmire. *Caring* 13(5):32–34, 36–37.

Tierney, Jeanette, and Damien Wilson. 1993. The effect of the Medicare regulations on hospice practice: enhancing staff performance. *American Journal of Hospice and Palliative Care* 10(2):26–31.

Tierney, Jeanette, and Damien Wilson. 1994. Hospice care versus home health care: regulatory distinctions and program intent. *American Journal of Hospice and Palliative Care* 11(2):14–22.

United Government Services. 2000. Medicare Memo-2000-5.0, p. 10.

Wilde, Donna J. 1992. Home health agency computer systems: current status and future directions. *Journal of the American Health Information Management Association* 63(12):82–85.

Williams, Richard W. 1991. A letter to hospice board members: billing, reimbursement and other mystic arts. *American Journal of Hospice and Palliative Care* 8(4):7–12.

Chapter 3

Quality and Performance Improvement

A number of methods for improving the quality of healthcare services and the performance of healthcare organizations have been developed over the past decades. Today, accreditation programs and healthcare organizations recognize the value of looking at quality from a systems perspective. The emphasis of modern quality management methods is on improving processes. The basic assumption is that mistakes and errors are usually the result of systematic problems in organizational processes rather than an outcome of substandard performance by specific individuals.

Various methods of quality and performance improvement are used today, but all of them emphasize the cyclical nature of process improvement activities. Continuous quality improvement (CQI) and total quality management (TQM) are familiar terms in healthcare organizations, especially hospitals and large hospital systems, although TQM is less common today than it was in the 1990s.

Quality and performance improvement activities enhance HIM performance, create resource economies, and improve patient care. This chapter begins with a general discussion of CQI. Then it discusses performance improvement activities specific to health information management in hospice and home care programs.

Continuous Quality Improvement

CQI is a refinement of TQM concepts. Underlying the CQI philosophy is a belief in the willingness and ability of people to achieve high performance levels when they are equipped with effective tools and processes. CQI embraces a participative management style in which employees are given a voice in the organization's management and its process improvement system.

TQM was originally developed by industrial engineers and is based on the work of three quality improvement pioneers: W. Edwards Deming, Joseph M. Juran, and Philip B. Crosby. In the 1960s, Avedis Donabedian applied the TQM philosophy then used in the manufacturing sector to healthcare services. He was the first to advocate the improvement of healthcare from four perspectives: structure, process, outcome, and cost. Today, every model of healthcare performance improvement (PI) recognizes the importance of these four factors.

Continuous quality improvement focuses on the processes that lead to desirable performance outcomes. By focusing on processes, a healthcare organization can achieve improvements that benefit all of the organization's customers—patients, visitors, employees, managers, and medical staff. CQI is similar to more traditional methods of quality management in that it is based on the monitoring of actual performance in comparison to preestablished standards. It is different in that it defines quality in terms of meeting the needs and expectations of internal and external customers. It is also different in that it follows a continuous cycle of monitoring and improvement.

Traditional quality management programs focused on quality assurance and quality control, which were based on the identification of problems attributable to mistakes and errors in judgment made by individuals. Quality control established standards that assumed that a certain level of error was acceptable; for example, a standard might stipulate that action would be taken if the postsurgical infection rate exceeded a certain percentage of surgical cases. In general, traditional quality management programs took action after serious problems occurred or when external factors required change.

In contrast, CQI is a ongoing process, and PI is a permanent way of working. No level of error is considered acceptable, and so the organization systematically looks for opportunities to improve its processes and services. When a problem does occur, the problem is treated as an opportunity for improvement rather than as a mistake for which someone must be punished.

CQI includes the following cyclical, organizationwide activities (Elliott 2000, p. 5):

- Ongoing performance monitoring

- Identification of critical performance measures (also called quality standards or quality indicators)

- Measurement of organizational performance against performance measures

- Analysis and comparison of internal performance data with external information

- Identification of performance improvement opportunity

- Implementation of improved process

- Ongoing performance monitoring

When variation is discovered through the results of continuous monitoring or when unexpected events suggest performance problems, members of the organization analyze the results and decide whether there is an opportunity for improvement. When an opportunity for improvement is identified, the individuals closest to the performance process form a team to study the opportunity. Many performance problems can be solved by providing additional education and training. Other improvement opportunities may require the team to develop new processes or procedures or to redesign current processes or procedures that are not producing the desired outcomes. The PI team follows five basic steps in planning process improvements:

1. Research and define performance expectations for the process (for example, determine the customer's needs).

2. Design or redesign the process or educational intervention to satisfy the improved expectations.

3. Implement the improved process or educational intervention.

4. Document and communicate the team's findings.

5. Analyze and compare internal data on the outcomes of the improvement and compare with external data and fine-tune the process improvement.

The organization continues to monitor the outcomes of the process and compare outcomes data against performance expectations. Quality standards and performance measures (these tools are sometimes called quality indicators) can be based on federal and state licensing and credentialing requirements, accreditation standards, national clinical practice guidelines and protocols, and/or internal procedures and processes.

Existing Quality Requirements

Home care and hospice programs that elect to seek accreditation through the Community Health Accreditation Program (CHAP) or the Joint Commission on Accreditation of Healthcare Organizations (JCAHO) and those electing Medicare certification must meet the performance improvement requirements of these groups. Organizations in states with licensing regulations that require quality management must also meet state requirements.

Community Health Accreditation Program Improved Performance Standards

CHAP standards emphasize the need for healthcare organizations to establish an organizational structure that supports a consumer-oriented philosophy and consistently provides for high-quality services and products. CHAP standards also stress the need for organizations to possess adequate resources and a strong potential for long-term viability (CHAP 1997). The organization's focus on quality must be reflected in its strategic plans, staff orientation and development programs, and quality commitment (CHAP 1997).

CHAP standards require planned efforts to ensure continuous quality improvement. In addition, the organization must develop quality improvement measures and monitoring processes for the following factors (CHAP 1997):

- Client outcome data
- Client satisfaction assessment
- Clinical record reviews
- Peer reviews
- Program evaluations

The standards address the required content of the quality improvement plan and specifics regarding expectations for monitoring. The standards also require that organizations document evidence illustrating how the organization used quality improvement results in service planning and problem resolution. Evidence should also show that the organization's quality improvement efforts resulted in actual improvements (CHAP 1997).

JCAHO Performance Improvement Standards

JCAHO standards are statements of the performance expectations that, when followed, lead to positive outcomes (O'Leary 1994). Performance expectations for each function are addressed in the *Accreditation Manual for Home Care*. JCAHO standards on improving organizational performance provide a framework for improving the functions addressed in the manual (JCAHO 2000). The framework for PI emphasizes quality and focuses on the common causes of problems and processes. Although the JCAHO's standards do not require CQI per se, they do require a process in which planning, design, measurement, assessment, and improvement focus on and lead to PI. A brief discussion of the requirements for each of these components follows. The standards themselves should be referenced for specifics.

Planning Standards

Standards require evidence of a planned, systematic, and organizationwide approach to PI (JCAHO 2000). Planning must address the processes for conducting PI and ensure that multiple services and staff are involved in planning efforts. Collaboration among disciplines and services should be evident in PI efforts, and contracted services should be included in planned PI activities (JCAHO 2000).

Design Standards

Design standards address the concept of building quality in at the front end of the process, and thus they focus on the design of new processes. Design standards require that the design of new processes take into consideration the following factors:

- The organization's mission, vision, and plans

- Needs and expectations of patients, staff, and others

- Up-to-date sources of information related to designing processes, such as practice guidelines or parameters

- Performance of the processes and their outcomes in other organizations, such as information from reference databases

Measurement of Performance

Performance measurement is considered to be at the heart of all PI activities. Through evaluation of measurement data, home care and hospice organizations address the need for improved processes. JCAHO requires certain measurements to be conducted systematically for the following factors:

- Processes and outcomes

- Performance of processes pertaining to the functions addressed in the accreditation manual

- Quality control activities in at least the following areas, where applicable:

    —Clinical laboratory services

    —Equipment provided to patients

    —Equipment used in providing care

    —Pharmacy equipment and preparations

Data for measurement can be collected to focus on issues chosen as priorities for improvement and to judge the stability of a particular process or the predictability of a particular outcome (as known as continuous measurement). Performance measurement of the functions addressed in the accreditation manual must be continual and focus on processes that meet the following characteristics (JCAHO 2000):

- Affect a large percentage of patients

- Place patients at serious risk when not performed well, or when performed when not indicated, or when not performed when indicated

- Have been or are likely to be problem prone

Assessment of Measurement Data

JCAHO requires organizations to have a systematic process in place for assessment of measurement data. This assessment should incorporate the use of statistical quality control techniques. The assessment should also incorporate internal and external comparisons of organization process and outcome data over time. External comparisons include comparison to sources such as practice guidelines, data from other organizations, and reference databases. Home care and hospice organizations are advised to obtain JCAHO input on the expected level of compliance regarding required comparisons, because the 2001–2002 scoring guidelines acknowledge that current systems and resources do not adequately support the comparisons required by the standards (JCAHO 2000).

JCAHO standards require that intensive assessment be performed when undesired variation in performance occurs. This variation may be represented by an important single event (the JCAHO uses the term *sentinel event*), such as a blood transfusion reaction, or by a significant variation from either the standards or comparative performances of other organizations. Also, organizations may choose to perform intensive review to further improve performance. JCAHO requires intensive assessment when any of the following sentinel events occur: confirmed transfusion reactions, significant adverse drug reactions, or significant errors related to medication use. When systematic data assessment reveals that an individual's performance presents an opportunity for improvement, the person responsible for patient services ensures that steps for assessing and improving competence are followed (JCAHO 2000).

PI Process

The last component of JCAHO's improving organizational performance standards concerns the PI process itself. Standards require the PI process to be systematic and standardized throughout the organization. Because every opportunity for improvement cannot be addressed, the standards require organizations to establish criteria for determining organization improvement priorities. The standards specify considerations that the criteria should address. They also specify operational issues that must be considered when designing or improving an activity, as well as the planning, measurement, and assessment that must occur before an improved process is fully implemented (JCAHO 2000).

Medicare *Conditions of Participation* for Home Care

The Omnibus Budget Reconciliation Act of 1987 (OBRA) had a major impact on the delivery of home healthcare services. The revised *Conditions of Participation* focused on the health and safety of patients and emphasized patient's rights and the competency of home health aides. Initially published in the *Federal Register* in 1989, the *Conditions of Participation* were revised in 1990, 1991, and 1995. In 1999, HCFA added a new condition on comprehensive assessment and the Outcome and Assessment Information Set (OASIS). In 2000, HCFA revised some conditions as part of the final rule for the prospective payment system (PPS). The interpretive guidelines define the conditions and provide surveyors with direction for the survey process. The guidelines were originally published in the *State Operations Manual* in 1991 and revised in 1993, 1997, and 2000. This section addresses the most current Medicare *Conditions of Participation* in place at the publication of this text.

The Home Health Initiative

Chapter 1 discusses the Health Care Financing Administration's (HCFA) home health initiative and its primary goals. The revised *Conditions of Participation* for home health agencies (HHAs) include requirements for an internal quality improvement system based on OASIS data. Chapter 1 also discusses the HCFA- and Robert Wood Johnson Foundation-funded work on home care outcome measures. These outcome measures are both global and focused on specific patient groups (Shaughnessy 1994). Monitoring clinical progress and financial exposure by episode under the PPS is a challenge requiring effective, time-efficient reviews week after week. (See table 3.1 and figure 3.1.)

The Outcome and Assessment Information Set-A (OASIS-B1) is intended to support home care assessment and outcome monitoring. OASIS gave regional home health intermediary (RHHI) auditors a new audit tool. The RHHI Outcomes and Assessment Information Set Verification (ROVER) protocol is an automated accuracy protocol used to assist in the medical review of home health claims submitted by HHAs that are paid under the HHA PPS. According to Program Memorandum A-00-99, ROVER uses health records to verify that the information contained on an HHA-completed OASIS reflects the condition of the patient and the services actually delivered during a particular episode in time. The protocol is a laptop-based software program that guides medical review staff through a review of information in the clinical record. Through the protocol, the reviewer can document whether the case-mix OASIS items have been validated by the information contained in the record. The end products are

Table 3.1. PPS Episode Monitoring

Risk	Criteria	Frequency	Level	Review (%)
High	Complex comorbidities and/or treatments; history of hospitalization; selected diagnoses, for example wound; unfavorable home situation; planned loss	Weekly	Clinical and finance directors	10
Medium	Neither high nor low	Every 2 weeks	Clinical supervisor and financial analyst	30
Low	Straightforward treatments; expected revenue exceeds planned cost by%	Every 3 weeks	Case manager with a short report to the clinical supervisor	60

Source: Tidd, Charles W. 2000 (November/December). The First 60 Days of PPS: Effective Episode Monitoring. *The Remington Report.* Reprinted with permission from *The Remington Report.*

Figure 3.1. The Daunting Arithmetic of Episode Monitoring

Episode Monitoring for Every 100 Active Patients	
To review **every** episode	You must review, on average
every week	**20** cases per day
every **2** weeks	**10** cases per day
every **3** weeks	**6.7** cases per day
every **4** weeks	**5** cases per day

Source: Tidd, Charles W. 2000 (November/December). The First 60 Days of PPS: Effective Episode Monitoring. *The Remington Report.* Reprinted with permission from *The Remington Report.*

twofold, resulting in a recommended home health resource group (HHRG) classification based on the input data and a reporting database containing information from the reviews. Therefore, the information gained by the use of the ROVER applies not only to data verification but also to intermediary data analysis and provider education.

Case-Mix and Adverse Event Reports for Outcome-Based Quality Management

HCFA recommends a two-stage outcome-based quality improvement process. The first stage, outcome analysis, includes collecting needed OASIS data; processing, editing, and transmitting data; and reviewing risk-adjusted outcome reports. The second stage, outcome enhancement, includes targeting outcomes for enhancement, evaluating the care for targeted outcomes, and developing a plan of action to change care.

HCFA prescribes the following quality management process:

1. Review each report

2. Prioritize adverse event outcomes

3. Conduct review of care

4. Identify problematic care

5. Develop plan to change care

6. Implement the plan

7. Monitor the plan

8. Determine whether change made a difference

Agencies should prioritize adverse events and outcomes with the highest incidence and then investigate those most clinically relevant to their organization. After reviewing comparison charts and listing the clinical actions expected to prevent adverse events, HHAs can design chart audit tools. By using record review findings, HHAs can refine subsequent investigations and identify both appropriate and problematic care.

HCFA warns HHAs against assuming that change will happen. Instead, HHAs should develop improvement plans to change the care that is provided. As part of a plan, an HHA states the care delivery expectations, implements the plan, and then monitors the care provided. HCFA also encourages HHAs to incorporate monitoring plans into other record activities and determine what positions should receive monitoring results. Only then can HHAs expect incremental changes.

State survey agencies will review case-mix and adverse event reports periodically. Reports may also be used during the survey process under COP 484.52, agency and program evaluation; policy and administrative review; and clinical record review.

The *Conditions of Participation* for Medicare-certified HHAs requires an annual evaluation of the agency's overall program and a quarterly clinical record review. Patient care services are identified as one component of the agency's total program that must be included in this evaluation. The use of the case-mix and adverse event outcome reports to review and improve patient care delivery is congruent with these program evaluation components. It is also anticipated that state survey agencies will incorporate the adverse event outcome reports into the off-site presurvey preparation and actual on-site survey. Specific adverse event outcomes and their potential incorporation in the survey process are included in this section.

Home health regulations require agencies to have written policies requiring an annual evaluation of the agency's overall program. The evaluation assesses the extent to which the agency's program is appropriate, adequate, effective, and efficient. Results of the evaluation are reported to and acted upon by those responsible for the operation of the agency and are maintained separately as administrative records. As part of the evaluation process, the policies and administrative practices of the agency are reviewed to determine the extent to which they promote patient care that is appropriate, adequate, effective, and efficient. Mechanisms are established in writing for the collection of pertinent data to assist in evaluation (COP 484.52a). On a quarterly basis, appropriate health professionals who represent the scope of the program review a sample of both active and closed clinical records to determine whether established policies are followed in furnishing services directly or under arrangement. There is a continuing review of clinical records for each 60-day period that a patient receives home health services to determine adequacy of the plan of care and appropriateness of continuation of care (COP 484.52b).

The agency is expected to have policies and administrative practices in place to promote patient care that is appropriate, adequate, effective, and efficient. Further, it is noted that mechanisms are established in writing for the collection of pertinent data to assist in evaluation. The investigation of adverse event outcomes provides evidence of the agency's review of potential problems in care provision. When problems in care provision are discovered, the development and implementation of the improvement plan demonstrates the agency's goals of overcoming or minimizing existing problems. The use of a chart audit tool for the adverse event outcome investigation provides evidence of the collection of pertinent data to assist in evaluating patient care. Utilizing the adverse event outcome investigation partially addresses this standard. Agency policies and procedures must address how reports are incorporated into the program evaluation.

Quarterly record review is required to determine whether established HHA policies are being followed in the provision of care. Two aspects of the adverse event outcome report investigation address this standard. It is expected that the chart audit tool used to investigate the adverse event outcomes will incorporate any relevant HHA policies for care provision. Similarly, the monitoring of clinician compliance with new or revised care practices should incorporate relevant HHA policies. When the investigation process is conducted in a phased manner, the adverse events can be investigated and monitored on a quarterly basis. In this way, the associated record review is incorporated into an HHA's current quality monitoring requirements. The investigation of adverse event outcomes becomes part of the HHA's overall quality monitoring program. Although these reports represent many HHAs' first exposure to the use of outcomes for quality improvement activities, the utility of the reports for the HHA's overall quality monitoring program is clear. The benefit to patients is also evident as agencies focus on continuously improving the quality of care they provide. These early steps in outcome-focused quality improvement will lay the foundation for the HHA-level activities to be conducted in response to the risk-adjusted outcome reports expected in 2002.

Both state survey agencies and HHAs have access to the adverse event outcome reports. State survey agencies review available reports prior to going onsite as part of their presurvey preparation. The reports help surveyors identify areas of focus during the on-site survey. Surveyors expect HHAs to use the information in the reports to improve patient outcomes. Surveyors assess the HHA's use of the reports for quality monitoring, including how the HHA addresses systemic issues that may be present, in an effort to reduce the incidence of similar adverse events in the future. For example, surveyors may review the specific patient situations included in the adverse event outcome reports to determine whether any events might have been prevented. Another focus of the surveyor's review may be to determine whether any of the adverse event outcomes was due to noncompliance with the *Conditions of Participation* on the part of the HHA. HHAs are strongly encouraged to take advantage of the information presented in their reports for their ongoing quality-monitoring program (HCFA 2001).

Medicare *Conditions of Participation* for Hospices

The Medicare *Conditions of Participation* for hospice quality assurance read as follows:

A hospice must conduct an ongoing, comprehensive, integrated, self-assessment of the quality and appropriateness of care provided, including inpatient care, home care and care provided under arrangements. The findings are used by the hospice to correct identified problems and to revise hospice policies if necessary. Those responsible for the quality assurance program must—

- Implement and report on activities and mechanisms for monitoring the quality of patient care;
- Identify and resolve problems; and
- Make suggestions for improving care.

Surveyors examine structures and processes contributing to the quality of hospice services. The principal survey focus is the outcome of the hospice's practices in implementing hospice requirements and the effect of the hospice's services on the patients. Home visits must be made to a sample of Medicare and Medicaid hospice patients during a hospice survey when the surveyor determines that home visits are required to verify that the hospice complies with all conditions and standards. The hospice self-assessment should include all provided services and the patients' and caregivers' responses to those services. It should also include those services that might have been provided but were omitted. Special attention should be given to the ability of the hospice to deal with symptom management, pain control, stress management, continuity of care, and inpatient care. Suggestions for improving care and any problems identified in providing hospice care should receive the appropriate consideration from the hospice management or governing body (HCFA 1994).

Interpretive guidelines contained in HCFA's operations manual indicate that a hospice must establish a system to evaluate the care and services provided as well as services that might appropriately have been provided but were not. The governing body should support the quality assurance program, and it should encompass critiques by the patients' families, monitoring of staff performance, and an annual program evaluation of the hospice's total operation. There should be annual studies of at least the following areas:

- Symptom management
- Stress management
- Continuity of care
- Inpatient care

A representative of the governing body must be involved in the annual program evaluation, as should representatives from the various disciplines and representatives from home care inpatient services. Throughout the process, a reporting mechanism to the governing body is required (HCFA 1994).

Home Care or Hospice CQI Program Implementation

An organization should consider strategic planning and initiatives from organizational leaders before implementing a home care or hospice CQI program. Integration of planning strategies creates a critical mass for change and gives employees a sounding board for suggestions and complaints. The following sections describe this integration.

Strategic Planning

Planning is the process of determining a desired outcome and defining a course of action to achieve this outcome. Planning is performed at many levels in an organization. The mission is the driving force behind all planning. From the mission a strategic plan is developed by the organization as a whole. Then specific objectives and goals are set at the overall organization level and the individual level. Finally, these objectives and goals are used to develop daily, weekly, and monthly plans and schedules (Cofer 1994).

Visionary Leadership

The organization's governing body is ultimately responsible for the quality of care and services provided. The president or CEO of the hospice or home care program provides CQI strategic planning leadership as well as leadership for the entire CQI effort. JCAHO expects leadership to establish PI expectations, plans, and priorities, and manage the PI process.

It is leadership's responsibility to develop a quality vision statement. A vision statement describes the organization's dream of what it wants to be (Melum and Sinioris 1992). Its formulation should incorporate organizationwide employee participation. The vision statement drives CQI because the vision is communicated to all employees and translated into an organization's goals and actions (Melum and Sinioris 1992). A vision statement is inherently linked to an organization's mission statement. The following are the five fundamental values recommended for a quality vision statement (Melum and Sinioris 1992, 17):

- Excellence and continuous improvement
- Employees
- Continuous learning
- Customers
- Community

Based on these values, a vision statement for an organization offering home and hospice care and services would read as follows:

> *Apple and Orange Home Care and Hospice program will be recognized as the home care and hospice provider and employer of choice by anticipating community and customer needs and by meeting those needs with a full range of high-quality, continually improving services that meet or exceed customer expectations.*

Plan Development

A CQI plan provides a blueprint for the quality activities of an organization. A plan documents the result of a strategic planning process—a process that should incorporate customer input and involve employees throughout the organization. Guidelines for the strategic planning process include the following (Gaucher and Coffey 1993):

- Development of broad organizational goals and the means to achieve them

- Assignment of responsibility and creation of resources to assist in meeting the responsibilities

- Development of an education curriculum to support the required changes and creation of a reward and recognition process to reinforce the new behaviors

- Development of an evaluation process to review performance against goals

By using the preceding guidelines and CHAP and JCAHO accreditation requirements, an organization can create a framework for CQI planning and documentation. A CQI plan is not a JCAHO requirement, but evidence that planning has occurred is required. Also, the CQI plan may globally address the monitoring activities while a separate document may contain the details regarding indicators, data sources and collection, assessment, and other information.

Planning for Quality and Performance Management

Like other programs in healthcare organizations, the quality/performance management program should be founded on regularly updated strategic and operational plans. To be effective, the quality/performance management plan should also be rooted in the organization's overall mission. Specifically, the quality/performance management plan should include the following elements:

- A mission statement that describes the program's purpose and and broad objectives and reflects the organization's overall mission

- A vision statement that describes the program's future aspirations and reflects the organization's overall vision for the future

- A list of the program's strategic goals, which describe the desired outcomes of the program, developed by organization's quality/performance improvement committee or council

- A description of the organizational structure for the program, which includes a list of positions and their scope of authority and responsibility

Best described and illustrated in an organizational chart, the quality/performance management structure may be simple in small organizations but quite complex in large multifacility networks or healthcare corporations. The composition of the organization's quality councils or committees should also be illustrated as appropriate. The description of the structure should include a discussion of the administration's and governing board's role in quality management, including their responsibility for approving the quality/performance management plan. In addition, the plan should include a description of the information management and financial resources needed for effective quality/performance management.

Planning should also address the program's educational goals and strategies both for initial training in CQI processes and for continuing education activities. The educational methods to be used should be detailed as well as the specific behaviors and values to be fostered (for example, customer service and mutual respect). The plan should also detail recognition processes and other methods for reinforcing positive behavior and attitudes.

Planning for quality and performance improvement should begin with an analysis of the population served by the organization as well as the scope and types of services the organization provides and the types of staff needed to perform the services. Planning should identify the services and aspects of care that are most relevant to the overall quality of services provided. In most organizations, the services that have the highest volume or the highest level of risk or are the most prone to problems are emphasized. The processes for monitoring the most important aspects of care are also detailed, for example, risk management, infection control, peer review, and utilization management. Any aspects of care that are monitored by licensing, certification, or accreditation organizations are also identified as especially important.

Specific quality indicators are identified for monitoring and evaluating important dimensions of performance (JCAHO 1991, 1994), including the following:

- Efficiency

- Appropriateness

- Availability

- Timeliness

- Effectiveness

- Continuity

- Safety

- Efficacy

- Respect and caring

The section of the plan that discusses monitoring and evaluation activities should include a description of the data elements and information needed. CHAP (1997) requires generic sources that include client outcome data, client satisfaction assessment, and clinical record reviews. As discussed in chapter 1, many of the data elements needed for indicator measurement are documented and collected as part of patient care documentation. For example, outcome data such as the satisfactory management of a patient's pain are routinely documented in the health record.

The plan should also spell out the processes for quality assessment and the positions responsible for conducting assessment activities. The reasons why a more intensive assessment might be triggered via specified performance thresholds or standards should also be addressed. CHAP (1997) standards specifically require the documentation of assessement standards and criteria in the performance improvement plan.

The organization's quality/performance improvement plan should also discuss how the program's findings are to be communicated throughout the organization. The plan should also document the process to be followed in improving performance. The plan should also emphasize the confidentiality of CQI materials to ensure the privacy of patients, providers, and staff.

Measurement

The next evolution in JCAHO involves the integration of performance measurement into the accreditation process. An organization must consider its mission and strategic plan for improving performance before determining what is important to measure about the clients for whom the organization provides care.

Through a measurement process, attributes are given quantitative values. For example, a patient's cognitive status can be measured using the Mini–Mental State Examination assessment tool. The assessment findings result in a quantitative measurement, or score. Scores are useful for determining status and for making comparisons, but only when the scores reflect a reliable measurement process and when they are a valid representation of the phenomena being measured. A reliable measurement process obtains the same result when subsequent measurements of something thought to be static are taken. In contrast, valid measurement accurately quantifies the attribute being measured. For example, the Mini–Mental State Examination is valid because it quantifies a patient's cognitive status, and it is reliable because consistent measurement has been demonstrated using this assessment tool.

In CQI, indicators are used to measure the performance of a process or outcome. In relation to this measurement, the concepts of reliability and validity are important. The indicator chosen must accurately represent a facet of quality, such as efficiency, appropriateness, or timeliness, for the aspect of care or service being monitored. The measurement process, including the data source used for measurement, must also be consistent and reliable. Consider the following example:

> **Example:** The following indicator will be used by Apple and Orange Home Care and Hospice Program to monitor the functional area of management of information, and, specifically, the problem-prone aspect of obtaining signatures on verbal orders. The organization is monitoring this indicator because a customer, the state's Department of Health, has cited it as a problem. Also, it is an aspect that the program wishes to continuously improve.

> **Indicator:** Verbal change orders are signed by physicians within the time frame required by state law.

> **Measurement source:** Discharge records are reviewed to determine if verbal orders are signed within the state's time requirement.

> Assessment of reliability and validity of the measurement finds the indicator to be valid, because it can quantify a dimension of performance—in this case, timeliness—relevant to the management of information. But the program finds the reliability of the measurement process to be problematic because signature dates are often incomplete or illegible. Guesses regarding illegible dates result in unreliable data, and missing dates contribute no data to the measurement process. The program decides that its manual verbal order tickler system would be a better data source for indicator measurement since the system tracks the return of signed orders. Weekly scanning of this file proves to be a reliable measurement of verbal orders not signed within the required time frame. Through process improvement, the program plans to address the problem of missing and illegible dates on verbal orders.

Standardization is another important consideration in identifying and designing indicator measures. The use of standard uniform indicators allows an organization to compare its performance with other similar organizations. Uniform indicators result when diverse organizations collaborate in developing indicator measures or when nationally developed and tested indicators, such as OASIS, are used across delivery systems.

The ORYX Initiative

ORYX is the name of JCAHO's initiative to integrate performance measures into the accreditation process. The ORYX initiative requires organizations to collect quarterly performance measurement data and submit the information via their selected vendors to JCAHO. JCAHO introduced its ORYX initiative in 1997. ORYX integrates outcomes and other performance measurement data into the accreditation process. The goal is to provide a continuous, data-driven accreditation process that focuses on the actual results of care (performance measurement) and is more comprehensive and valuable to all stakeholders. JCAHO strives for its primary mission—improvement of the quality of care provided to the public—through the provision of healthcare accreditation and related services that support PI in healthcare organizations. The ORYX initiative is the critical link between accreditation and the outcomes of patient care, allowing JCAHO to review data trends and patterns and to work with organizations as they use data to improve patient care. ORYX performance measures supplement and help guide the standards-based survey process by providing more targeted bases for the regular accreditation survey, continuously monitoring actual performance, and guiding and stimulating continuous improvement in healthcare organizations.

Home health organizations with an average annual census of 120 patients or more, accredited prior to January 1, 2001, were required to select and participate in a performance measurement system. The organizations chose six clinical or perception-of-care measures by December 31, 2000, and began data collection on January 1, 2001. They selected measures most relevant to their patient populations and strategic measurement objectives. The resulting data were reported by the performance measurement system to JCAHO by July 31, 2001.

Selecting or participating in a performance measurement system was optional for home health organizations with an average annual census of less than 120 patients or organizations undergoing their initial survey in 2001. However, these organizations must choose six measures that are most relevant to their patient populations and strategic measurement objectives. They may select measures from existing performance measures. Sources may include listed performance measurement systems, the professional literature, internally developed measures, or measures from professional associations. Measure selections should be reported to JCAHO on a standardized reporting form.

Surveyors will assess organizations' use of selected measures in their PI activities during the on-site survey process. Organizations will be expected to demonstrate, for each measure, the ability to collect data reliably, conduct credible analyses of the data, and initiate appropriate system and process improvements. In the future, eligible organizations will be expected to select and enroll in a listed performance measurement system when core measures relevant to their services are identified.

Performance Measurement Data

During 2001 and 2002, JCAHO surveyors will assess how home care organizations have integrated and used ORYX performance measurement data in their performance improvement activities. During the PI interview, surveyors will ask organization leaders what process was used to select performance measures, how ORYX data have been integrated into internal PI activities, and what results emerged from these activities. ORYX initiatives were designed so that expectations would increase over time. The initial phase of the ORYX initiative offers accredited healthcare organizations significant flexibility by allowing them to select the performance measurement system and individual measures that best serve their strategic measurement goals. More than 15,000 performance measures from nearly 300 performance measurement systems have already been cataloged in JCAHO's database as part of this initiative.

The next phase of the ORYX initiative includes the identification of specific core performance measures and the opportunity for listed systems to embed some, or all, of these measures in their own systems. Core measures will be grouped into measure sets. In time, measure sets may include clinical performance, client perception of care, health status, and administrative or financial measures. The initial core measures will focus primarily on clinical performance. In the future, JCAHO intends to create a balanced set of measures applicable to all types of healthcare organizations. The identification and use of core measures will allow comparisons of processes and outcomes of patient care among healthcare organizations across the country, regardless of which performance measurement system the organization has selected. JCAHO will gradually transition core measure sets into ORYX requirements (JCAHO 2000).

Important Aspects of Care and Measurement Indicators

The following sections provide a framework for determining important aspects of care and measurement indicators. Home health organizations must evaluate their scope of care and services, obtain patient or customer input, and integrate measurements into other quality activities. Examples of important aspects of care and measurement indicators are provided.

Scope of Care and Services

Developing a profile of the organization's scope of care and services—the staff providing the care and services and the patient population—is the first step in determining the important aspects of care and their measurement indicators. Care and services provided through contracts or arrangements are included in this profile. Development of the profile provides a systematic means to ensure that all areas of care and service delivery are considered when developing a CQI program. An example of a partial profile for the hypothetical Apple and Orange Home Care and Hospice Program follows (see table 3.2).

Table 3.2.   Scope of Care and Services for Apple and Orange Home Care and Hospice Program

Program	Staff Providing Services	Patients/Clients
Home Care		
Skilled nursing services	Registered nurses	Primarily elderly with comorbid illnesses receiving Medicare benefit
Physical therapy	Physical therapists	Same as above
Occupational therapy	Occupational therapists	Same as above
Hospice Program		
Hospice interdisciplinary team services including volunteer services	Registered nurses Social workers Medical directors (physicians) Pastoral care counselors Volunteers	Primarily elderly terminally ill receiving Medicare benefit 10%–15% are nonelderly with an AIDS diagnosis
Bereavement services	Social workers Volunteers	Primarily elderly spouses of deceased 10%–15% are nonelderly partners/parents of deceased patients with AIDS diagnosis

Patient or Customer Input

Because CQI is a customer-driven process, obtaining customer input is essential when determining the aspects of care and services to be monitored, and the indicators to be used. Input from internal and external customers should be obtained and evaluated. Internally, anyone who depends on the outcome of a particular process is a customer of that process. For example, billing personnel are internal customers concerned with the completeness and quality of reimbursement-related documentation. An external customer for the same process would be the Medicare fiscal intermediary, whose rejected claim provides feedback regarding the completeness and quality of reimbursement-related documentation. Another external customer would be the patient, because nonpayment of potentially covered services due to poor documentation ultimately affects the patient. Other external customers include patients' families, referring physicians, managed care organizations, other third-party payers, accrediting organizations, and regulatory agencies. Essentially, the internal and external customers of an organization are the same persons and groups as the users of an organization's data and information. PI leaders should look to strategic initiatives when internal and external needs conflict.

Undoubtedly, the patient and family are the most important customers of home care and hospice services. It is critical, therefore, to routinely obtain patient and family input. This input proves useful in determining the aspects of care and services that are important to patients and families, and in monitoring how the organization is performing relative to patient and family expectations. It is important to give patients a clear definition of quality because their expectations may differ from the expectations of home care staff or from quality standards. On the one hand, a study published in the magazine *Caring* showed that elder home care clients, while revealing agreement on many quality themes, placed the most importance on the relationship with providers and sought control over care and caregiver continuity to ensure safety and independence (Wilson 1994). Nurses, on the other hand, emphasized the quality themes of medical outcomes and compliance of the client. A study by CHAP (1994), in which consumer-oriented outcome measures for home care were developed, also found differences in definitions of high-quality home care between home-care consumers and staff. In the CHAP study, input from focus groups led to the project's approach to quality as defined by a partnership between client and provider (CHAP 1994).

Numerous approaches can be used to obtain patient and family input, including focus groups, satisfaction surveys, and systematic reviews of patient- or family-initiated input such as commendations and complaints. The JCAHO book *Understanding the Patient's Perspective: A Tool for Improving Performance* (1995a) describes how a CQI program can obtain patient input and use it. This book also contains case studies on how four healthcare institutions used patient input. According to JCAHO, organizations should consider the following items when designing a process to obtain patient input (JCAHO 1995b):

- The patient groups serviced by the organization

- The important clinical and organization functions that affect patients

- The dimensions of performance that affect patients in each function

- The possible methods for gathering and using patient input

Integration of Quality Activities

An organization staff familiar with the traditional components of quality monitoring and review (including quality assurance, risk management, infection control, utilization review, clinical record review, and program evaluation) may be confused by the concept and implementation of CQI. The introduction of CQI does not mean an elimination of existing quality-control and -review mechanisms. In larger organizations, it does not even mean an elimination of such existing departments as infection control, risk management, or quality assurance. However, CQI does involve a different organizational approach to quality, as it encompasses and spans all of the preexisting quality programs of an organization. How this is accomplished in terms of organizational structure depends on the particular organization, but all staff and departments performing quality activities should have an integral part in the planning and the implementation of CQI in any organization.

Much vital quality monitoring is being performed through preexisting quality activities. Because such monitoring has often been in response to regulatory requirements, it must continue to occur. For example, pending changes in the Medicare Home Care *Conditions of Participation,* Medicare-certified home health agencies must continue to perform quarterly clinical record reviews. For Medicare-certified hospices, annual studies of continuity of care must continue, per regulations at the time of publication.

An examination of an organization's existing quality activities provides information for identifying the important aspects of care and services to be monitored, as well as measurement indicators to be used. How existing monitoring can adapt to a CQI approach is demonstrated by the following example. The example reflects an extensive process change, but provides a graphic illustration of the difference between some existing quality activities and measurement, assessment, and improvement using CQI.

Example: Apple and Orange Home Care and Hospice Program reviewed its process for quarterly clinical record reviews, as required by Medicare to ensure that established policies are followed in providing services, to determine how this process could be improved and integrated into the CQI program. Previously, a sample of active and closed records was reviewed by a group of professionals representative of all the home care services that the organization provided. A record review form asked such questions as: Were patient services adequately coordinated? Were any of the services that were used past the point of need? Did the patient have any unmet needs?

The organization found that the review met regulatory requirements, but it did not contribute valid and reliable data on whether established policies were being followed. In addition, the measurement process was extremely subjective, and it was neither standard nor reference based.

To improve the measurement process, the organization first reviewed the CQI plan identifying the care processes that affected the largest number of patients, placed patients at risk, or were problem prone. After extensive investigation and preparatory work, the organization then implemented documentation via critical pathways for these processes, using as a basis an existing system for documentation of home care critical pathways. A new indicator measurement process was instituted. Health record personnel now routinely review those forms that document care provided via critical pathways, to check for any care pathway deviations. The same group of professionals who previously performed record review conducts a quarterly assessment of a summary of deviations that were found. Significant deviations from care pathways trigger more intensive review of the relevant critical pathway process, and this review could determine that a need exists for improvement in the care pathway process.

Examples

Based on the customer input and requirements discussed throughout this chapter, home care and hospice organizations identify important aspects of care to be monitored and the indicators to be used for measurement. Because organizations will not have the resources to monitor all important aspects of care, a method should be in place to prioritize the aspects to be monitored. In accordance with requirements, there should be process and outcome indicators that reflect the following aspects:

- **Sentinel events:** Transfusion reactions, emergency care for wound infections, and other events with the potential to injure the patient

- **Aggregate rates:** Percentage of significant others satisfied with bereavement support, percentage of orthopedic patients who show functional improvements, equipment breakdown rates, percentage of health records with complete assessments within 48 hours of admission, and other rates

- **Means, medians, or modes of aggregate data:** Average waiting time for initial home care contact, average number of months on oxygen by diagnosis, average days to obtain physician signatures on verbal change orders, and other numbers

The following example shows an indicator measurement that a home care and hospice organization might perform. The example is not intended to be comprehensive. It draws from *Measuring Outcomes of Home Health Care* (Shaughnessy 1994), as well as other sources.

> **Example:** Apple and Orange Home Care and Hospice Program begins its CQI program, based on customer input and other assessed information, with the following monitoring. Figures 3.2–3.5 present Medicare home care services and three important aspects of care. Figures 3.6–3.9 present Medicare hospice services and two important aspects of care.

Indicator Data Collection and Organization

The collection of indicator data requires decisions to be made regarding desired sample size and frequency of collection. Ideally, the IMS, regardless of the extent of computerization, has been designed so that much of the data required for continuing quality monitoring is being routinely documented. Data categories summarized for rates, such as the reasons for patients' discharges, should also be documented in the health record using the same categories.

Figure 3.2.   Medicare Home Care Services

Important Aspects of Care

- **High volume**
  —Cardiac conditions
  —Diabetes mellitus
  —Orthopedic conditions

- **High risk**
  —IV/infusion therapy
  —Open wounds/lesions

- **Problem prone**
  —Continuity and care coordination
  —Signatures on verbal change orders

Indicators for Measuring Important Aspects of Care
The organization, in choosing indicators, has integrated some of the developed tested indicators (Shaughnessy 1994).

Figure 3.3.   Important Aspect of Care: Cardiac Conditions

Quarterly-Calculated Aggregate Outcome Rates

Desirable outcomes   **Undesirable outcomes**

- Improvement or stabilization in: - Acute care hospitalization for any reason
  —Main meal preparation   - Patient's death within two months
  —Management of oral medications   - Emergent care for cardiac condition
  —Housekeeping   - Emergent care for pulmonary problems
  —Dyspnea
  —Fluid retention
  —Activity level/tolerance
- Discharged to independent living

Other Indicators/Data

Indicators

- Whether patient met agency goals
- Patient satisfaction with care (including education received)

Other data

- Discharge reason by category
- Average expenditures per patient for home care services
- Average visits by discipline per patient

Data Sources

- Record review of critical pathway documentation for patients with cardiac conditions
- Routinely collected data through organization's computerized information management system
- Patient satisfaction survey data

Note: Critical pathway documentation is already routinely monitored by health record personnel to collect data for the agency's quarterly clinical record reviews, so collecting this data will not create an extensive, additional burden.

Figure 3.4.   Important Aspect of Care: IV/Infusion Therapy

Quarterly-Calculated Aggregate Outcome Rates

Desirable outcomes   **Undesirable outcomes**

- Improvement or stabilization in: - IV-catheter-related infection
  —Ability of patient to manage equipment   - Medical side effects, circulatory overload, IV-catheter-related infection

  —Ability of caregiver to manage equipment - Medication noncompliance, side effects, toxicity, anaphylaxis

- Discharge to independent living   - Emergent/urgent hospitalization within two months

Sentinal Events

- Circulatory overload
- Anaphylaxis

Other Indicators/Data Indicators

- Whether patient met agency goals
- Patient satisfaction with care (including education received)

Other data

- Discharge reason by category
- Average expenditures per patient for home care services
- Average visits by discipline per patient

Data Sources

- Record review of critical pathway documentation for patients receiving IV/infusion therapy
- Routinely collected data through the organization's computerized information management system
- Patient satisfaction survey data

Figure 3.5.   Important Aspect of Care: Continuity and Care Coordination

Quarterly-Calculated Aggregate Rates

- **Desirable outcomes**

    —Patient is satisfied with the continuity of caregivers providing care
    —Patient, when applicable, is satisfied with the discharge and transfer information provided

- **Desirable processes**

    Health record contains documentation of:
    —Care and services provided through contract services
    —Communication with physician when a change occurs in patient's condition, suggesting a needed care
      plan change
    —Communication between therapist and assistant
    —Communication between disciplines/providers of care
    —Communication with contracted providers
    —Evidence that a summary/progress report is forwarded to physician at least every 62 days
    —Evidence that patient is informed in a timely manner of need for planning for discharge or transfer

Data Sources

    Record review and patient satisfaction survey

Figure 3.6.   Medicare Hospice Services

Important Aspects of Care

- **High volume**

    —Pain management
    —Other symptom management
    —Volunteer services
    —Bereavement counseling

- **High risk**

    AIDS patients

- **Problem prone**

    Continuity and care coordination between home and inpatient care stress management

Figure 3.7.   Important Aspect of Care: Pain Management

Calculated Aggregate Rates

Desirable outcomes

- Improvement or stabilization in:
    —Pain interfering with activity
    —Perceived level of pain
- Patient satisfaction with pain management
- Family satisfaction with the patient's pain management

Data Sources

- Record reviews
- Patient satisfaction survey
- Family satisfaction surveys

Figure 3.8.   **Important Aspect of Care: Continuity and Care Coordination between Home and Inpatient Care**

Calculated Aggregate Rates

Desired outcomes

- Patient satisfaction with continuity of care between home and inpatient care
- Family satisfaction with continuity of care between home and inpatient care

Desired Processes

The home care record contains documentation reflecting that:
- The hospice interdisciplinary care plan was provided to the inpatient setting
- The patient and family continued to receive interdisciplinary hospice services while the patient was in the inpatient setting
- The care and services were provided to the patient and family while the inpatient was in an inpatient setting

Data Sources

- Record reviews
- Patient satisfaction surveys
- Family satisfaction surveys

Figure 3.9.   **Other Routine Monitoring**

Other Sentinel Events

- Confirmed transfusion reactions
- Significant adverse drug reactions
- Significant errors related to medication use

When a computerized system allows the systematic retrieval of data, the sample size can be large because automated data retrieval requires virtually no additional time for larger sample sizes. When data must be manually collected, or when observation, interviews, or surveys are used for data collection, practicality dictates that a sample be chosen. Sample size should be large enough so that meaningful interpretations of the data can occur. Since the complexity of sample selection varies with the size and complexity of the organization, some organizations may wish to consult experts for help in selecting and determining meaningful samples. One good sampling methodology for most organizations involves the random sampling of groups of patients who are being monitored, known as stratified random sampling. In the case of the preceding example a 20 percent random sample could be taken of cardiac patients, orthopedic patients, and so on. This sample may be chosen by using a systematic random sampling process that starts with a random number to select the first patient and then chooses every fifth patient from lists of active patients with cardiac diagnoses, orthopedic diagnoses, and so on.

The percent sample that needs to be taken varies with the volume of patients who are being provided with care and services. With larger volumes, a smaller percentage needs to be sampled. For meaningful statistical comparisons to occur between periods, it is recommended, whenever possible, that the sample size be at least thirty.

When data collection is performed manually, decisions will have to be made regarding what persons will collect, organize, and display the data. This could be a diverse collection of individuals, depending on whether record data or survey/observation data is being collected. Indicators and their measurement tools, which incorporate standards or criteria, must be designed so the process of data collection remains objective. Data collection from health records and logs should not require any clinical judgments; thus, it is not essential for clinicians to retrieve such data (clinical expertise becomes important when interpreting assessed data and in improving clinically related processes). A decision must be made concerning whether data collection will be concurrent or retrospective. Keeping CQI philosophy in mind, concurrent monitoring is recommended in most instances.

Data Assessment

Routinely collected data should be assessed at periodic intervals, but at least quarterly. According to CQI methodology, assessment of statistical control precedes other types of assessment. This means that before a measurement can be relied upon to elicit meaningful information about problems in the underlying process, the data must be systematically assessed to determine if the process is in statistical control. Statistical control is attained when the measurement does not show wide variations over time. Measurements that show wide variations reflect a process that has been affected by special cause problems, or outliers. These special causes may include poor performance of a particular employee, inadequate education of staff, and similar issues. Special causes represent about 6 percent of the process problems. In CQI, the goal is to improve the overall process that contributes to 94 percent of the variation in processes. So, when wide variation exists, the goal becomes eliminating this variation so that the process is in control. Traditional quality assurance does this when it identifies problems pertaining to cases that do not meet criteria.

A measurement that reflects a process once it is in control will provide a more stable result. This is not to say that the result will be acceptable to an organization, but only that special causes do not affect the result.

Example: Apple and Orange Home Care and Hospice Program is monitoring the time required for physicians to sign verbal change orders. When initial monitoring began, the monthly means ranged from fourteen to twenty-three days—a wide variation. The agency determined that two physician groups were extremely late in signing orders. Corrective measures specific to these physician groups were initiated. Subsequent to this corrective action, the means now range from twelve to fifteen days. Because the state where the agency is located requires verbal change orders to be signed within fourteen days, the averages are not acceptable to the organization, so it will now begin the PI process to improve the processes affecting the time required to obtain signatures on verbal orders.

Control charts are used to determine whether processes have excessive variation. Basically, a control chart is used to plot averages or a rate over time. When plotting an average over time, lines are drawn on the chart to show the data points representing three standard deviations above and below the overall mean. Individual averages that exceed these data points reflect a process that is out of control. JCAHO requires the use of control charts and other systematic methods when assessing data (JCAHO 2000).

As discussed earlier, organizations should conduct internal and external data comparisons. Benchmarking is a methodology used to continuously improve performance. With external benchmarking, organizations can compare their results to high-performing organizations in an effort to further improve performance.

To further understand the meaning of data, intensive assessment can be performed. Criteria should exist to trigger when intensive assessment should be performed. According to JCAHO (1994), intensive assessment should be triggered by a sentinel event, a significant variation from standards, comparisons with other organizations, or an organization's desire to further improve. One conclusion to draw from intensive assessment might be that process improvement is warranted.

Performance Improvement

Numerous models exist for implementing quality or PI processes. These models represent approaches similar to the systems analysis and design approaches that may be more familiar to readers. Generally, the models address the following factors:

- The need to involve individuals who are knowledgeable about the process

- The need to identify the reasons for process variation

- The need to plan and improve the process

- The need to monitor and assess the new process

- The need to implement the new process after it has been determined that the process actually results in improved outcomes

JCAHO (2000) requires organizations to adopt a single, organizationwide model for use in implementing PI. Here are some available models (Gaucher and Coffey 1993):

- Hospital Corporation of America's FOCUS-PDCA

- The Juran Institute's Juran's Journey

- Organizational Dynamics' FADE

- Analog Devices' Seven-Step Problem-Solving Model

- Qualtec's Seven-Step QI Process

- The University of Michigan Medical Centers' seven-step process, ROAD MAP

When an organization puts PI into place, the work on improving processes falls to teams trained in CQI. Small organizations may not find the use of such teams to be practical. Other organizations may simply find it undesirable. In any case, the groups responsible for improving processes should be familiar with the process under consideration as well as with the organization's approach for improving performance.

CQI Program Review

The effectiveness of an organization's CQI program should be reviewed annually. This review should consider the vision and mission of the organization, and the objectives and goals of its CQI program. The review may result in changes in the CQI plan.

Confidentiality of CQI and OASIS Data

The Federal Privacy Act of 1974 and the Health Insurance Portability and Accountability Act (HIPAA) require that the organization's policies and procedures related to data collection be made available to the public. The information given to the public should describe the reasons for collecting OASIS data and quality, what will be done with the data, and who will have access to the data in a patient-identifiable identifiable format. The legislation also puts into place certain processes that protect patient-identifiable data from unauthorized use and disclosure. Provisions of the Privacy Act as they relate to the collection of OASIS data are described in detail on the OASIS Statement of Patient Privacy Rights (see appendix C). HCFA instructed state surveyors to verify that the HHA has established a mechanism to ensure confidentiality of OASIS data whether in hard copy or electronic format before and after transmission to the state agency.

Surveyors interview agency administrators or system administrators about knowledge and application of rights to add, edit, or otherwise modify encoded OASIS data, assign passwords, to ensure that only specified staff have contact with assessment information, and the actions taken when an employee with access to the system leaves HHA's employment. If possible, surveyors may observe security of the OASIS data-entry location and observe if the computer screen is logged off or password protected when not attended. If applicable, surveyors can review vendor contracts for provisions protecting confidentiality of OASIS data and determine what systems are in place to ensure confidentiality throughout the transmission process. If the HHA has branches, surveyors may ask how OASIS data are protected and kept secure during transfer from the branch to the parent agency. If the HHA contracts out OASIS encoding and reporting, surveyors want to know what systems are in place to ensure that the contracted vendor maintains confidentiality of OASIS data.

Summary CQI information is often released to customers to demonstrate an organization's performance in relation to customer expectations. But organizations must recognize when monitoring data or information that they could become targets of legal scrutiny. There have been cases where the courts have determined quality-monitoring materials to be discoverable, meaning that the data can be brought before a court of law. Considering this, it is recommended that these guidelines be followed:

- No information about specific patients, families, employees, volunteers, or physicians should be included in CQI minutes or final reports.

- When a coding system is used to identify individual patients or providers, the appropriate designated organization employee should hold the key to this system secure.

- Worksheets containing patient- or family-identifiable patient or family data should be destroyed after the data have been verified and final results summarized.

- Access to computer files containing CQI data should be controlled (see chapter 5 for methods).

- Computer printouts should not contain identifiable patient or family data, and printouts should be maintained in a confidential manner according to organization policy.

Summary

By heeding the information and suggestions found in the references used in this chapter, home care and hospice organizations can establish or enhance quality monitoring systems to further improve the care and services provided to patients and their families. These techniques can help an organization develop an IMS that supports the organization's need to excel in a competitive, customer-driven environment.

References and Bibliography

Beacon Health. 2000. *The Conditions of Participation and Interpretive Guidelines: A Reference Manual for Home Health Agencies.* Mequon, Wis.: Beacon Health.

Cofer, Jennifer, ed. 1994. *Health Information Management.* 10th ed. Berwyn, Ill.: Physicians' Record Company.

Cofer, Jennifer I., and Hugh P. Greeley. 1992. *Quality Improvement Techniques for Medical Records.* Marblehead, Mass.: Opus Communications.

Community Health Accreditation Program. 1993. *Standards of Excellence for Home Care Organizations.* New York City: National League for Health Care and Community Health Accreditation Program.

Community Health Accreditation Program. 1994. *In Search of Excellence in Home Care.* New York City: National League for Health Care and Community Health Accreditation Program.

Community Health Accreditation Program. 1997. *Standards of Excellence for Home Care Organizations.* New York City: National League for Health Care and Community Health Accreditation Program.

DeCosmo, B. 1994. Transforming QA to QM: one agency's approach. *Caring* 13(7):9, 11, 64.

Elliott, Chris, et al. 2000. *Performance Improvement in Healthcare: A Tool for Programmed Learning.* Chicago: American Health Information Management Association.

Fazzi Associates. 2001. National PPS design project issues findings. *Minnesota Home Care Alert* 1(1):14–15.

Gaucher, E. J., and R. J. Coffey. 1993. *Total Quality in Healthcare: From Theory to Practice.* San Francisco: Jossey-Bass Publishers.

Health Care Financing Administration. 1994. Appendix M: Hospice survey procedures and interpretive guidelines, Rev. 265. *Medicare State Operations Manual Provider Certification.* Washington, D.C.: Government Printing Office.

Health Care Financing Administration. 2000. Appendix B: Interpretive guidelines for home health agencies. *Medicare State Operations Manual Provider Certification.* Washington, D.C.: Government Printing Office.

Health Care Financing Administration. 2000. Appendix M: Interpretive guidelines for home health agencies. *Medicare State Operations Manual Provider Certification.* Rev. 265. Washington, D.C.: Government Printing Office.

Health Care Financing Administration. 2000. Transmittal 21. *Medicare State Operations Manual Provider Certification.* Washington, D.C.: Government Printing Office.

Health Care Financing Administration. 2001. *Quality Monitoring Using Case Mix and Adverse Event Outcome Report, Implementing Outcome-Based Quality Improvement at a Home Health Agency.* Washington, D.C.: Government Printing Office.

Joint Commission on Accreditation of Healthcare Organizations. 1991. *Quality Improvement in Home Medical Equipment: A Practical Guide for Development and Implementation.* Oakbrook Terrace, Ill.: Joint Commission on Accreditation of Healthcare Organizations.

Joint Commission on Accreditation of Healthcare Organizations. 1993. *The Measurement Mandate: On the Road to Performance Improvement in Health Care.* Oakbrook Terrace, Ill.: Joint Commission on Accreditation of Healthcare Organizations.

Joint Commission on Accreditation of Healthcare Organizations. 1994. Improving organizational performance. *1995 Accreditation Manual for Home Care: Volume II—Scoring Guidelines.* Oakbrook Terrace, Ill.: Joint Commission on Accreditation of Healthcare Organizations.

Joint Commission on Accreditation of Healthcare Organizations. 1995a. *Understanding the Patient's Perspective: A Tool for Improving Performance.* Oakbrook Terrace, Ill.: Joint Commission on Accreditation of Healthcare Organizations.

Joint Commission on Accreditation of Healthcare Organizations. 1995b. Using Patient Input in a Cycle for Performance Improvement. *Journal on Quality Improvement:*87–96.

Joint Commission on Accreditation of Healthcare Organizations. 2000. *2001-2002 Comprehensive Accreditation Manual for Home Care.* Oakbrook Terrace, Ill.: Joint Commission on Accreditation of Healthcare Organizations.

Joint Commission on Accreditation of Healthcare Organizations. December 2000. http://www.jcaho.org.

Longo, D. R., and D. Bohr, eds. 1991. *Quantitative Methods in Quality Management.* Chicago: American Hospital Publishing.

Maturen, V. L., and K. Zander. 1993. Outcomes management in a prospective pay system. *Caring* 12(6):46–53.

Melum, M. M., and M. K. Sinioris. 1992. *Total Quality Management: The Health Care Pioneers.* Chicago: American Hospital Publishing.

Miller, R., and J. Lazar. 1995. Public reporting of performance measures in home care. *Journal on Quality Improvement* 21:3, 105–15.

O'Leary, D. S., and P. M. Schyve. 1993–1994. The role of accreditation in quality oversight and improvement under healthcare reform. *The Quality Letter* 5(10):11–14.

O'Leary, M. R., et al. 1998. *Lexikon: Dictionary of Health Care Terms, Organizations, and Acronyms for the Era of Reform.* 2nd ed. Oakbrook Terrace, Ill.: Joint Commission on Accreditation of Healthcare Organizations.

St. Pierre, M., and H. Dittbrenner. 1995. HCFA's Home health initiative: The first comprehensive reassessment of the Medicare home health benefit. *Caring* 14(3):22–27.

Shaughnessy, P. W., et al. 1994. *Measuring Outcomes of Home Health Care.* Denver: Centers for Health Policy and Services Research.

Shaughnessy, P. W., K. S. Crisler, and R. E. Schlenker. 1995a. *Medicare's OASIS: Standardized Outcome and Assessment Information Set for Home Health Care.* Denver: Centers for Health Policy and Services Research.

Shaughnessy, P. W., K. S. Crisler, and R. E. Schlenker. 1995b. *Outcome-Based Quality Improvement: A Manual for Home Care Agencies on How to Use Outcomes.* Denver: Centers for Health Policy and Services Research.

Shaughnessy, P. W., K. S. Crisler, R. E. Schlenker, and A. G. Arnold. 1995c. Outcome-based quality improvement in home care. *Caring* 14(2):44–49.

Tidd, Charles W. 2000. The first 60 days of PPS: effective episode monitoring. *The Remington Report.*

Wagner, D. M. 1992. Quality indicators: an approach to quality improvement in home healthcare. *Journal for Healthcare Quality* 14:3, 8–10.

Wilson, A. A. 1993. Bridging cost and quality through patient outcome measurement. *Caring* 12(6):40–44.

Wilson, B. 1994. *Perceptions of Quality Homecare Among Nurses and Elderly Clients.* Published abstract. Gerontology Society of America, 47th Annual Scientific Meeting.

Chapter 4

Health Record Management

This chapter will cover the health record management principles that home care and hospice organizations can employ to develop or modify their health records systems. This discussion will cover automation and the computer-based health records (CPR), as well as key diagnostic and procedural coding guidelines and minimum recommended statistics that all home care and hospice organizations should maintain. Finally, this chapter concludes by discussing the health information management (HIM) professionals and their associated roles in health record management in home care and hospice organizations.

Numbering of Records

Organizations may assign an identification number to the patient's health record at the time of admission. The number should be assigned from a table of numbers, which is maintained manually or electronically and consists of the following elements:

- A chronological listing of all assigned numbers

- The names of patients to whom the numbers were assigned

- A listing of the numbers yet to be assigned

A six-digit number is commonly used, which for most organizations ensures a sufficient supply of numbers for many years to come. If an organization files its health records by number, the assigned record number must appear on the health record folder and on all health record forms.

When a home care or hospice organization is inpatient-based, the record numbers that the inpatient facility has assigned should be used. Organizations that are Medicare-certified may want to add an identifier, such as an H, to an inpatient facility's record number so the home care or hospice record documentation can be easily identified. When filing such records, the identifier would not affect the file location.

It is recommended that an organization choose between two different numbering systems: serial-unit or unit. In a serial-unit system, a new number is assigned each time a patient is admitted to the home health agency (HHA). If the records are filed numerically, the record information from previous admissions is incorporated with the new folder. The new record number is recorded on the previous record folder, which is then filed in the previous file location, in order to direct staff to the new file location. In a unit system, a number is assigned at the time of the patient's first admission. The patient keeps this number regardless of the number of admissions and regardless of whether the admission is for inpatient or home care. A unit numbering and record system results in one comprehensive record per patient with a consistent record number.

It is important to keep in mind that in hospices the number assigned should be used for hospice episodes of care that relate only to the patient's terminal illness and bereavement follow-up. When a patient's family member is admitted at a later date for other care, a different number should be assigned and the family member's record and patient index card should be cross-indexed to the hospice patient or family number, a separate system explained next.

When home care or other services are provided to families, a family numbering system may be useful for these organizations. With this system, one number is assigned to the family while a subnumber is assigned to each family member. Subnumbers identify each family member's relationship, such as head of household, spouse, or child.

Example:

Family Record Number	**126012**
Mother (Head of household)	01-126012
Spouse	02-126012
Child 1	03-126012
Child 2	04-126012
Child 3	05-126012

By assigning family numbers and filing folders numerically, information on all family members can be easily retrieved without filing all family information in one folder. However, this system can be administratively cumbersome, as frequent number changes will be required in cases of marriages, divorces, emancipation of minors, or other situations.

Record Form Sequencing

To ease retrieval of information from health records, an established filing sequence is recommended. The filing sequence may be different for active health records (patient or family still receiving care) and inactive health records (patient or family discharged from care).

Active Records

The needs of the home care or hospice organization determine the filing sequence for the active records. For example, forms that are referred to frequently, such as care plans and clinical notes, can be placed in the front of the record. All records should follow the determined filing sequence to facilitate quick information retrieval. Dividers that label types of record documentation (for example, care plans, clinical notes, and laboratory reports) can help to facilitate quick information retrieval but also increase filing time. Beneath each divider, information is filed in reverse chronological order. Several companies manufacture printed dividers that home care and hospice programs will find appropriate for this system. Examples of active filing sequences are provided for skilled home healthcare, hospice, pharmacy/infusion therapy, and support/nonskilled home care.

Skilled Home Healthcare

1. Physician's orders
2. Assessment(s)
3. Medications/intravenous solutions
4. Care plan
5. Nursing notes
6. Rehabilitation
7. Home health aide
8. Medical social work
9. Labs
10. Miscellaneous

Hospice

1. Interdisciplinary care plan
2. Assessment(s)
3. Medications/intravenous solutions
4. Case conferences
5. Nursing notes
6. Home health aide
7. Medical social work
8. Spiritual
9. Volunteer
10. Labs
11. Bereavement
12. Miscellaneous

Pharmacy/Infusion Therapy

1. Physician's orders
2. Care plan/medication profile
3. Assessments/intake
4. Clinical notes
5. Home documentation/inventory
6. Labs
7. Pharmacy record
8. Miscellaneous

Support/Nonskilled Home Care

1. Referral information/orders

2. Assessment/follow-up

3. Care plan

4. Homemaker/home health aide

5. Nursing supervisory notes

6. Social work

7. Miscellaneous

Active records can be kept in loose-leaf binders, with rings on either the top or the side, or in traditional file folders. Loose-leaf binders are more durable than file folders, but they require more filing space. The number of active patients, the space available for the filing of active records, the efficiency of use, and staff preferences will determine the type of folder selected.

There are two basic methods of filing records: centralized and decentralized. In a centralized filing system, all information about a patient is funneled into a single file held in a central location.

Centralization has the following advantages:

- There is less duplication of effort to file loose sheets.

- There is less overall space and equipment.

- A composite record containing all available information is a greater help to clinicians than one scattered in several places.

- Record control and security are easier to maintain.

In spite of obvious advantages, circumstances may make it expedient to decentralize records either temporarily or permanently. In a decentralized filing system, certain records, such as incomplete charts, are filed in a separate location. Decentralization may be justified when a home health organization operates from several sites; this system also requires less transportation and time.

Inactive Records

Inactive records are often organized in file folders with a two-prong fastener at the top, preferably on both sides of the folder. Folder durability depends on the frequency of usage and length of time inactive records will be kept, as defined by the record retention policy. Folders should be designed with a long, extended tab to allow documentation of a patient's name and, when applicable, the health records number. A felt pen is recommended for writing the name and number on a folder because typewritten labels often become detached. Color-coded folders facilitate filing and retrieval as well as help in locating filing errors.

Forms in inactive records are most commonly filed in chronological order. Examples of inactive filing sequences are provided for home healthcare and hospice (see figures 4.1 and 4.2).

Figure 4.1. Home Healthcare Filing Sequence

Left-Hand Side	Right-Hand Side
Form HCFA-485 (Plan of care/physician's orders) Verbal/interim orders Other HCFA forms submitted Other billing information Correspondence	Face sheet/information form Discharge summary Referral forms Assessments Initial care plan and updates Team case conference reports Clinical/progress notes (integrated) Disease, generic or discipline flow Sheets (by category) Home health aide care plan(s) Home health aide flow sheets Medication treatment form(s) Special reports (lab, X-ray, and other reports) Home care information/instructions Miscellaneous • Consents for care • Service agreements • Authorizations for release of information • Patient's bill of rights • Certificate of death • Autopsy report • Records/reports from other healthcare providers

Figure 4.2. Hospice Filing Sequence

Left-Hand Side*	Right-Hand Side
Bereavement assessment and follow-up Bereavement visits—notes	Face sheet/identification information Referral or transfer information Discharge summary or information Initial assessment Care plan and reviews Progress notes Special reports (lab, X-ray, and other reports) Doctor's orders Miscellaneous • Consents for care • Consents for release of information • Certificate of death • Autopsy report • Records from other facilities/providers

*Folders with fasteners on both sides cost more compared to folders with fasteners on one side alone. If the latter are purchased, bereavement documentation should be distinguished by some other means.

Filing Systems

Health records can be filed numerically, alphabetically, or by a non-numeric color coding system. Numeric filing is generally considered the most efficient filing method. However, a small HHA or hospice may determine that an alphabetic or color-coded alphabetic filing system works best for their purposes. When an organization is choosing a filing system, it should consider the volume of present and anticipated records to be stored, the filing space available, the frequency of record retrieval, the volume of loose material to be filed, and the cost of the system.

If an organization is large enough to include a record employee or record department, it is probably large enough to maintain a numeric or a color-coded alphabetic system. When organizations or individual branch offices provide 50,000 or more visits a year, a terminal or middle-digit numeric filing system can reduce filling errors, especially when using color-coded folders.

Numeric Filing

The three primarily recognized numeric filing methods are straight numeric, terminal digit, and middle digit. Under the straight numeric filing method, folders are filed consecutively using the entire number. For example, 001275 follows 001274 follows 001273. Under terminal and middle digit filing methods, health record numbers are broken down into sections (for example, 00-00-01). In the terminal digit system, records are filed by the last two numbers, then the middle two numbers, and finally the first two numbers. An example of the sequencing follows:

46-52-02	98-05-26	98-99-30
47-52-02	99-05-26	99-99-30
48-52-02	00-06-26	00-00-31
49-52-02	01-06-26	01-00-31

Though terminal digit filing is the most widely used filing system in healthcare facilities, some organizations do make use of the middle digit filing system. In this system, records are filed first by the middle two digits, then the left two digits, and finally, the right two digits. An example of the sequencing follows:

56-78-96	57-78-00	99-78-98
56-78-97	57-78-01	99-79-99
56-78-98	99-78-96	00-79-00
56-78-99	99-78-97	00-79-01

Issues of expansion are addressed by all three methods. The straight numeric filing method only requires space at the end of the file for expansion. A terminal or middle digit system requires that space be left for expansion throughout the files; 25 percent is recommended.

Alphabetic Filing

Some small organizations, or small branches of larger organizations, may prefer to file alphabetically. Loose material filing may be faster with alphabetic filing because knowledge is not required of the health records number, which is often not recorded on loose material. Alphabetic filing is not recommended when record storage requires more than two three-drawer filing cabinets because of the increase in filing errors.

Color-Coding Record Folders

Color-coding refers to the use of color on folders to prevent misfiles. Color bars in various positions around the edges of folders create blocks of color in various sections of the file. A break in the color block within a file section signals a misfiled record. Color-coding is most effective when used in conjunction with terminal digit filing; however, it can be used with alphabetic filing.

The entire folder may also be colored and signify the right-hand primary digit or first letter of the last name. In setting up a color-coding system, it is generally advisable to limit color-coding to two or three digits or characters. Color-coded folders may be purchased from commercial firms, or employees of the health information department may apply colored bands or tabs to the folders.

Changing Filing Systems

When converting from an alphabetic to numeric filing system, it is recommended that all active health records be converted by a specified date. In addition to the date, HHA staff would assign a health record number and a numeric folder to each patient admitted. For readmitted patients, the records of their previous admission(s) would be pulled and combined with the new admission record. A charge-out would be placed in the file location of the previous record folder and annotated with the client's record number. Those records with numeric folders would be filed in a designated section of the files. Eventually, all of the records in the alphabetic filing section will be brought forward for new admissions or purged for microfilming, storage, or destruction. Throughout this process of change, the space for the numeric file shelves would be continually increased, while the space for the alphabetic file shelves would be continually decreased.

This same conversion process can be performed gradually if an organization wishes to change from alphabetic filing to color-coded alphabetic filing, or from straight numeric filing to terminal digit filing. A total conversion can take place at the time when an agency or record department may be moving, or when new file shelving is being purchased, thus eliminating the need for maintaining two separate sets of files. When changing from an alphabetic to a color-coded alphabetic system, all records must be transferred to color-coded folders. The same folders can be used when changing from a straight numeric to a terminal digit filing system, but an agency may want to purchase color-coded adhesive numbers to code the side tabs of the folders.

Filing Equipment

The health information departments of hospices and HHAs need sufficient space and equipment to store patient health records so they are easily accessible when requested. Adequate filing equipment, lighting, temperature control, supplies, and attention to safety in the file room all contribute to the productivity of filing clerks. The following sections discuss shelving, file guides, and outguides.

Shelving

Records can be filed in filing cabinets or in open filing shelves. Open shelving is preferable because it is less expensive, saves space (approximately half as much floor space as file cabinets), and makes record retrieval faster. For small home health agencies, open shelving can be placed along a wall, using minimal space. When more than one row of open shelving is needed, aisle space of 30 inches minimum between file units is recommended to meet fire codes and to allow adequate space for filing and retrieval of records. If file cabinets are being used, an aisle space of 54 to 60 inches is needed. Movable file units on tracks are available as handy spacesavers if only one aisle is needed. However, tracked file units should only be used for inactive records since access is limited to one aisle at a time.

Standard open-shelf file sections are 36 inches long and up to eight shelves in height. The standard file drawer is 26 inches deep. The amount of filing equipment required is determined by:

1. Measuring the linear inches of current inactive records

2. Projecting the number of linear inches that will be needed for the number of years planned to retain records

3. Determining the linear inches of filing space provided by a particular filing unit

4. Adding the results of steps 1 and 2 and dividing by the result of step 3 to determine number of units needed

The filing capacity of filing units varies. Check with the manufacturer to obtain the filing capacity of a particular filing unit.

Example:

Present inactive records	200 linear inches
Projected inactive records	500 linear inches
(100 linear inches per year $\times$ 5 years)	
Total linear inches files must accommodate	700 linear inches
Filing capacity of a file unit (with 5 shelves)	180 linear inches
Filing units needed	4
(700/180 = 3.8)	

It is important that safety be ensured in the filing area. Sprinkler systems must be evaluated and fire extinguishers placed conspicuously. Employees should receive preparatory training in the event of fire or other disaster.

File Guides and Outguides

File guides facilitate record retrieval and filing because they direct employees to file locations. Guides extend from the files so employees can easily determine where a filing section begins (for example, where the S-section and the Sch-section begin, or where the 01s and the 05-01s begin). The number of file guides needed depends on the number of records stored, the thickness of the records, the activity of the records, and the organization's needs. Generally, agencies with thicker or more active records should place guides more frequently throughout the files.

When determining the number of guides that need to be ordered, an organization should first decide the guide-to-record ratio, and then, divide the desired number of records per guide into the number of records being maintained. Once the number of guides needed is determined, the organization must decide how to label and place the guides throughout the files. Guiding will vary throughout an alphabetic file: for example, more guides will be needed for Ss and fewer for Qs. For straight numeric filing, guide numbers will become larger as the numbers assigned to patients are larger. Guides will be distributed equally throughout terminal digit files, and because the files expand equally, guides remain the same even when volume increases. It is essential that guides be constructed of durable material and extend out from files so they remain clearly visible.

When any record leaves the file area, it should be charged out to its new location by using an outguide. An outguide and a completed requisition slip are used to directly record the file name, the file number, the date the charge-out occurred, and the new record location. The completed requisition slip is placed in a pocket or holder on the outguide. Like file guides, outguides should be constructed from a durable cardboard or plastic material. An outguide made of colored material is easily visible in the files, which can expedite the refiling of records. Stand-alone or networked chart tracking systems using bar coding technology are recommended for large and active file rooms.

Record Retention

An organization must decide how long to maintain inactive records in hard copy on its premises. Ideally, this decision should be made when designing the record system because it affects the storage space required. When making this decision, an organization must consider the following:

- Legal requirements (the statute of limitations and any state laws requiring specific record retention periods)

- Regulatory or accrediting requirements (when appropriate)

- Patients' ages (in relation to the statute of limitations)

- Patient care needs (that is, the readmission rate within a specified time period)

- Research and teaching needs

- Costs of inactive storage, microfilming, optical storage, and destruction of records

An organization may decide to maintain agency discharge records for 10 years, but to maintain them on-site in hard copy for only two years. At the end of the two years, the records would be sent to commercial storage, or to a basement or branch office storage space where they would be maintained for an additional eight years. Alternately, an organization may decide to microfilm discharge records after two years and then maintain the microfilm indefinitely. Optical disk storage using imaging technology offers another storage option.

Once a decision is made regarding how long and in what manner to maintain records, the organization should formulate a record retention policy. As part of this policy, procedures should be written, approved, and updated as necessary. Agencies using point-of-care systems must ensure that electronically maintained records meet the organization's retention policies. Destruction methods should be reassessed annually on the basis of current technology, accepted practices, and availability of timely and cost-effective destruction services.

Inactive paper-based and computer-based records require the same level of protection as active records. Obsolete paper-based records and duplicate paper printouts should be shredded, pulped, burned, or pulverized to ensure confidentiality. They should never be thrown into the garbage or sent to a recycling center in a legible format. Computer disks, billing tapes, electronic documents, and printed copies of billing forms that include patient identifiable information should be protected from unauthorized access and appropriately destroyed when they are no longer needed. Magnetic degaussing is the preferable method for destroying computerized data.

Commercial Storage

Some agencies may opt for commercial storage of records. This convenient method allows easy retrieval of the hard copy client record for readmissions or other purposes. Since commercial storage may be cheaper than microfilming, it should be investigated as an alternative, especially if an agency plans to destroy records when allowed by legal requirements.

Microfilming

Microfilming reduces the required in-house file space by 98 percent, and the result adds up to savings in file equipment. A microfilm or microfiche reader/printer machine produces microfilm images that can be viewed on a screen, and, when needed, printed to paper. Microfilmed records allow HHAs and hospices to meet legal requirements for record retention without maintaining records in hard copy.

Microfilming can be done in-house or by an outside company. A variety of methods are available for maintaining microfilm, including rolls, cassettes, microfilm jackets, or microfiche. Although rolls are the cheapest method, they present two disadvantages: the inability to update individual records due to the sequential filming of the records and inconvenience of reviewing records.

Microfilm on cassettes is also an inexpensive method, and since the film is easier to feed, reviewing is less inconvenient. In addition, special indexing equipment can be purchased, allowing staff to directly access a patient's record on microfilm cassette. However, like microfilm rolls, the sequential filming of microfilm cassettes does not allow individual record updates.

Though the most expensive microfilm method, microfiche is nevertheless easy to review. More importantly, updating individual records is possible because each sheet of microfiche contains only one health record. On of the best options is microfilm in jackets, which costs approximately half as much as microfiche, and also can be updated, as each jacket contains only one health record. In addition, unit records can be kept by maintaining microfilm on microfiche or in microfilm jackets.

When deciding among these various microfilm options, organizations need to weigh the financial cost against the need for easy record viewing and retrieval for studies and readmissions. To choose between in-house or outside microfilming, a cost-benefit analysis should be performed of the cost of in-house labor and equipment versus the costs of outside processing.

To prepare records for microfilming upon a client's discharge, all staples from the record should be removed. The patient's name (and number, if applicable) should be visible on every form in the record, and no form of documentation should obscure another form of documentation (for example, notes filed in a shingled fashion must be laid flat).

Optical Storage-Based Document Imaging System

The optical storage-based document imaging system, also known as the electronic filing cabinet, is viewed as a replacement for microfilm systems (Brandt 1994a). This recent technology, developed for permanently archiving discharge records, electronically scans records onto optical disks for storage and retrieval. According to an AHIMA workgroup study, optical storage-based document imaging systems can be a cost-effective alternative for storing the health records of patients. The same group cautioned, however, that this system's cost-effectiveness must be evaluated for each particular setting and application (Brandt 1994a). The cost-effectiveness of these systems is debatable: some professionals view microfilming as a less expensive alternative when record storage is the sole purpose. Investment in an optical storage-based document imaging system may be justified in cases where stored record images must be frequently retrieved and retrieved simultaneously by different users (Hassig 1991). Commonly, hospitals justify such an investment due to their lack of readily available inpatient discharge records for ambulatory care, billing, audits, and other areas. However, this is not the case for many home care and hospice programs, which do not cite the availability of discharge records as a frequent problem. In fact, in home care and hospice programs, frequent, simultaneous access is needed for active records, and applications addressing this need are more desirable than systems intended solely for storage purposes. One large home care and hospice organization introduced a health records document imaging system to support payroll, billing, and health record functions. The system reduced backlogs, increased efficiency, and led to a reduction in storage and retrieval staff (Vetter 1995).

Purging of Files

At least annually, agencies should remove records for microfilming, storage, or destruction. To do this, agencies must know how long records have been inactive. The period of record inactivity can be easily observed as long as each record folder has been marked upon discharge with the most recent year of client activity. Marking of the folders can be accomplished by writing or stamping the year on the record folder, by applying a sticker with the year printed on it to the folder, or by circling the year on a folder that has been preprinted with the applicable years. Agencies are discouraged from filing records by discharge year, because two or more sets of files must be maintained and the year of discharge would have to be known to retrieve a record or to file any material into a record.

Organizations that destroy inactive records after a specified number of years rather than sending them to permanent commercial storage or microfilming them must ensure that minors' records are kept until the age of majority and the statute of limitations are reached, which vary by state. For example, in a state with an age of majority of twenty-one and a six-year statute of limitations, the records of a seven-year-old minor treated in 1995 could not be destroyed until the year 2015 (twenty years later). The record folders of minors should be flagged in some manner, and each minor's date of birth should be written on the outside of the folder. When pulling the record for destruction, such indicators will alert employees to the status of the statute of limitations.

Master Patient Index

Maintenance and retrieval of health information depend on the quality of indexes and registers. An index is anything that serves to guide, point out, or otherwise facilitate reference. A register is a formal or official recording of items, names, and actions. Today, indexes and registers are computerized in most home care organizations (Cofer 1994).

A master patient index is a listing of all patients who have ever been admitted for care or service. The index serves as a ready reference to patient information and the health records number. It should be kept permanently, since it provides information after a record has been destroyed. Also, the index will verify a patient's episode of care even if a record cannot be located or has been destroyed. For each patient admitted to an agency, the index includes at least the following information:

- Patient's full name

- Patient's record number

- Patient's address

- Patient's date of birth

- Patient's admission and discharge dates

In a hospice setting, the index would also include the next of kin's or significant other's name, address, telephone number, and bereavement discharge date. Organizations may also wish to include the name of the patient's attending physician and the patient's Medicare number and/or social security number.

Many home care and hospice computer systems can produce a master patient index; these indexes, however, may not include all necessary information and all discharged patients. For example, a system may only index active patients and patients discharged in the last six months. With a computerized patient index, an organization and its computer vendor can modify the system so that it contains all necessary information and incorporates all discharged patients.

Coding Diseases, Problems, and Procedures

The ICD-9-CM classification system is used to organize healthcare data for easy and meaningful retrieval. The following sections discuss coding of diseases, problems, and procedures.

Coding Guidelines

There are no official home care or hospice guidelines for diagnostic and procedure coding. Outpatient coding guidelines seem to apply best to home care, but organizations rely primarily on fiscal intermediary feedback to determine what are acceptable and unacceptable coding practices. Resources such as *St. Anthony's Home Health Claims Editor: A Guide to Medicare Billing* (Falconer 1992) contain tips for coding for Medicare reimbursement, as well as possible intermediary edits for medical review. Shared next are selected guidelines from this publication, as well as guidelines that home care and hospice projects have developed.

Principal Diagnosis

For Medicare reimbursement purposes, the home care principal diagnosis is the diagnosis most related to the current plan of care. The principal diagnosis may or may not be related to the patient's most recent hospital stay, but must relate to the services that the home care provider has rendered. If more than one diagnosis is treated concurrently, the diagnosis that represents the most acute condition and requires the most intensive services is considered the principal diagnosis. The ICD-9-CM guidelines dictate that certain specific principal diagnoses are only to be used when a specific secondary diagnosis is present. After the implementation of the HH PPS, the principal diagnosis must match on the physician-certified plan of care, the OASIS, and the Uniform Billing Form-92 (UB-92). For subsequent certification periods, a new principal diagnosis and code are recorded when the principal diagnosis changes.

In Medicare hospice situations, the principal diagnosis is the primary cause of the hospice patient's admission. A sign or symptom should be listed as a principal diagnosis only when the specific cause cannot be identified, and when there are no other diagnoses responsible for the patient's admission. For patients with cancer, the primary site should be coded first, except in the following instances:

- When the primary site is unknown, code secondary site(s) and then 199.1 for unknown primary

- When the primary site has been removed, code secondary site(s) and then the appropriate ICD-9-CM V code for history of malignant neoplasm of site

- When the terminal condition is related specifically to a secondary site rather than the primary site

According to the National Association for Home Care's (NAHC) Uniform Data Set for Home Care and Hospice (see appendix A), a medical diagnosis is one that affects the care provided by the home care organization as defined by ICD-9-CM codes. The principal diagnosis is the diagnosis most responsible for the admission of the patient as a client for home care service. Other coded diagnoses are all other diagnoses that affect the care provided by the home care organization. When indexing patients according to principal and other diagnoses, the use of NAHC's definition of principal and other diagnoses is recommended.

V Codes

V codes are located in the Tabular List of the ICD-9-CM codebook in the section titled Supplementary Classification of Factors Influencing Health Status and Contact with Health Services. V codes should not be used when the acute diagnosis code is more specific to the exact nature of the patient's condition. V codes are not acceptable as the principal diagnosis or the first secondary diagnosis. However, they could be recorded in item 21, Orders for Discipline and Treatments. The ICD-9-CM coding guidelines should be followed in assigning an appropriate V code (HCFA 2000). Hospice settings can especially benefit from using V codes for this purpose because V codes can be used to code such psychosocial problems as family problems, housing problems, economic problems, and the like. V codes are not used on OASIS.

Other Diagnoses and Problems

NAHC's Uniform Data Set for Home Care and Hospice (see appendix A) defines *other diagnoses* as any diagnoses aside from the principal diagnosis that affect the care provided by the home care organization. For Medicare reimbursement, other pertinent diagnoses are all conditions that coexisted at the time that the plan of care was established that developed subsequently or that affect the treatment of care. Diagnoses are excluded when they relate to an earlier episode that has no bearing on the current plan of care. However, diagnoses can be changed to reflect changes in the patient's condition so long as they match the diagnoses listed on the OASIS and the UB-92 and conform to the ICD-9-CM coding guidelines. When listed, the diagnoses should appear in an order that best reflects the seriousness of the patient's condition and justifies the disciplines and services provided. However, there may be exceptions to this rule, dictated by ICD-9-CM coding sequencing requirements. For example, if a principal diagnosis exists that dictates the utilization of a specific secondary diagnosis, then the agency should list this secondary diagnosis first in the list of other pertinent diagnoses. These coded diagnoses should relate to the current episode of care and have a bearing on the current plan of treatment (HCFA 2000). It is suggested that secondary and other pertinent diagnoses be recorded in the order that best reflects the seriousness of the patient's condition and further justifies the home health services provided (HCFA 2000).

A hospice, in addition to coding a diagnosis, may also decide to code a symptom when it represents an important care problem such as pain. ICD-9-CM has codes for specific pain sites, as well as a single code for generalized pain.

Procedure Coding

NAHC's Uniform Data Set for Home Care and Hospice (1998) defines *surgical procedure* as any surgical procedure that affects the care provided by the home care organization as defined by ICD-9-CM or CPT codes. Using form HCFA-485, Medicare-certified agencies are required to record the ICD-9-CM code pertaining to the surgical procedure most relevant to the home care provided.

Coding Quality

Accurate coding became more important in the home care and hospice setting with the increase in capitated payment for services and the implementation of the home health prospective payment system (HH PPS). With these payment systems, diagnostic codes are integral to payment and to providing information to payers on costs, lengths of stay, outcomes, and other information for specific patient groups. Since the implementation of HH PPS, HHAs have struggled to ensure ICD-9-CM coding accuracy for OASIS MO234 and MO240. Therefore, HHAs must answer these questions:

- Who maintains coding references and tables?

- How does one prevent the use of diagnosis codes in M0230 that cannot be used as a primary home care diagnosis?

- Who assigns codes?

- Who is responsible for coding oversight and education?

- What should be done when HCFA's coding guidelines contradict reimbursement rules?

Technology can enhance clinical coding, but it can also bring its own problems. Many software vendors do not deliver the annual coding updates for their ICD-9 coding tables on time. Often these tables do not include the entire library of diagnosis codes with descriptions and inclusion and exclusion notes. HHAs must therefore analyze their individual coding problems and search for the best solution. Agencies that designate only one person to assign all codes may impede their ability to meet the OASIS and request for anticipated payment timelines. The American Health Information Management Association (AHIMA) reports a 10 to 15 percent shortage of coding professionals. AHIMA expects that number to increase to 30 percent due to ambulatory payment classification coding requirements.

Web-based application service providers offer HHAs the opportunity to hire remote coders. Coding software gives users all of the features of the ICD-9-CM codebook in a convenient electronic format. By visiting the AHIMA Interactive Learning Campus (www.ahima.org), agencies can assess staff coding skills and receive online training in ICD-9-CM coding. The American Hospital Association (AHA) can be tapped for free coding advice. Coding consulting firms offer quicker response times than AHA but for a subscription fee. And as a reminder, agencies should check home health reimbursement rules before applying any coding advice they receive (Abraham 2000c).

Accurate Data and Appropriate Payments

Reporting a patient's diagnosis can be a complex process. Coders must wade through a number of possible diagnostic codes, avoid codes that only serve to increase reimbursement, and distinguish between what is and what is not a primary code. A major responsibility for the coding professional is understanding and following coding guidelines. Disregard for proper coding can only lead to reimbursement denials and accusations of fraud (Opus 2000, 1).

Payment of services in the home health PPS is determined by OASIS information. Most times within home health settings, it is not an HIM professional but a nurse or other staff member who assigns codes. Individuals who do not have HIM credentials are often unfamiliar with the ICD-9-CM codes and guidelines needed to complete the OASIS. In addition, they are unaware of the need to obtain physician's documentation to support the reported codes. Absence and lack of physician's documentation does not permit the coder "to use the patient's perception of [his] diagnoses to decide what [code] to assign" (Opus 2000, 2). It is just as much the coder's responsibility to track down and obtain physician's documentation as it is to assign and report codes.

In most cases, the physician's documentation will list multiple diagnoses for a single patient, thereby complicating the coding task. The OASIS allows only one primary diagnosis code and a maximum of five secondary diagnoses. The task of properly sequencing the diagnoses falls to the coder, who can increase the likelihood of determining an accurate sequence by taking the following questions into consideration (Opus 2000, 3–4):

- Which diagnosis represents the most acute condition being treated?

- Which diagnosis requires the most clinical and/or technical skill?

- Which diagnosis requires the most resources or the greatest number of services?

To decrease the possibility of inaccurate coding, codebooks and physician's documentation should always be employed. Never use cheat sheets or pick lists. Coders in home care and hospice must also be aware that adding diagnostic codes solely to increase reimbursement goes against compliance standards and can be deemed fraudulent. Without proper coding and supporting documentation, agencies can face penalties greater than the denial of reimbursement. To ensure accurate coding, an agency must do the following (Opus 2000, 3):

- Train the individual(s) responsible for coding and employ at least one coding professional or consultant

- Maintain and use updated references, such as codebooks, not pick lists and cheat sheets

- Review and understand coding guidelines and the OASIS form

Coding Audits

Ultimately, reimbursement to the provider depends on the content of the health records and how the information in that record is coded. Health records must support the diagnosis submitted to payers for reimbursement. Conducting regular coding audits in which health record documentation is checked against the codes is crucial to ensure compliance with Medicare and other payers. Noncompliance is the first priority of the Department of Health and Human Services' Office of Inspector General (OIG) and other federal investigators. The primary focus of investigations is checking for correct reimbursement for Medicare patients. To date, every settlement has turned on the accuracy of the ICD-9-CM and/or CPT codes reported for reimbursement. The HIM department manages and maintains the data on which most compliance investigations are based, including coding and abstracting, storage and retrieval, and ensuring completeness of the health records, as well as auditing and monitoring all of these functions.

The OIG recommends that providers perform audits of coded data on an annual basis. In addition, compliance guidance suggests that monitoring should be performed on a regular basis. In all 300 coding compliance settlements involving healthcare providers, the OIG has required the provider to perform annual coding audits. The audits, it is believed, serve two important purposes. First, they ensure that any errors or pattern of errors are identified. This allows the provider to return any overpayments to Medicare or other payers. Second, the audits serve as ongoing oversight (Krouth 2000).

Initiating coding audits in a formal way can be intimidating for some organizations. For this reason, organizations should openly discuss the issues of auditing and educate all employees from the top down. The education of administration, key managers, and the governing board is important in achieving full support for auditing. The following are benefits of health record and coding audits (Russo 2000):

- Improved operational efficiency

- Mitigated damages in the event of an investigation

- Additional protection against certain legal exposures

- Improved overall data quality

- More reliable data for outcome-based quality management reporting and research purposes

- Improved relations between HIM and professional staff

- Correct reimbursement

- Better relations among all departments and functions involved in the reimbursement process

HCFA issued a data quality alert in *Quality Monitoring Using Case Mix and Adverse Event Outcome Report* (HCFA 2001):

> A high percentage of patients with contagious/communicable conditions should serve as a "red flag" of potential data quality problems to an agency. If an agency is surprised at the large percentage of its patients with contagious/communicable conditions, it is appropriate to check the ICD codes that have been entered into OASIS, particularly as responses to M0190 or M0210. If two-digit surgical procedure codes are erroneously entered in response to these items, the data entry software may recognize them as three-digit codes signifying contagious communicable diseases (if data entry staff mistakenly enter a leading zero). An erroneously large number of patients are thus coded as having contagious communicable diseases. (An example of this problem is the two-digit surgical procedure code for joint repair, 81, erroneously recorded in response to M0190; if this is entered as 081, the data transmitted to the State system will reflect the medical diagnosis of "other typhus," which is an uncommon home care diagnosis.) Agencies with a statistically significantly large percentage of patients with contagious/communicable diseases thus are advised to investigate further for the possible presence of this type of error.

Coding Policies

When organizations implement coding policies and guidelines, they help to ensure consistent and accurate coding. Guidelines address the coding of principal and secondary diagnoses, as well as to what extent problems and symptoms should be coded. When developing coding guidelines, organizations will want to consider reimbursement guidelines, along with how they intend to use coded information. For example, if the organization desires to collect information on a particular problem or assess the management of it, the guidelines should state that the problem will always be coded.

Codebooks and Resources

The coding staff must always make use of the most recent edition of the ICD-9-CM codebook. Codebooks and tables must be updated each October with the changes to existing codes, which are published in errata form. Any cheat sheets (listings of frequently used diagnoses with their codes) should also be updated annually to include the published errata material. Many vendors offer encoder computer software that can be helpful for coding diagnoses and procedures. Home care and hospice programs may find such software products to be good tools, although they have been developed primarily for hospital inpatient coding. It is essential to annually update software products with the coding updates, which the vendor should offer. *Coding Clinic,* published by the Central Office on ICD-9-CM of the AHA, provides sound coding guidance.

Coding Personnel

To code diagnoses and procedures, it is necessary to develop a working knowledge of anatomy, physiology, and medical terminology, along with an understanding of the characteristics, terminology, and conventions of ICD-9-CM coding. Employing the skills of a credentialed HIM professional ensures accurate coding. These professionals carry one or more of the following credentials: registered health information technician (RHIT), registered health information administrator (RHIA), and certified coding specialist (CCS). They can perform the actual coding or monitor the coding quality performed by others.

Using noncredentialed coders is not advised, but, when absolutely necessary, it is recommended that they attend two or more coding training programs. AHIMA and its affiliated state associations offer information about available coding training. AHIMA also publishes an annual resource directory that offers many coding training resources as well as opportunities for education in medical terminology.

Statistics

Program statistics can be calculated using routinely collected data. The utilization-related data listed next are included in NAHC's Uniform Data Set for Home Care and Hospice (see appendix A), and they can be used to compute some key statistics. To ensure comparability of calculated statistics, the data set definitions should be used when collecting the relevant data.

- Unduplicated patient or client census

- Duplicated patient or client census

- Number of nonadmissions

- Length of stay

- Units of service per discipline

- Number of days per level of hospice care

Once collected, the preceding data can be used to compute monthly and yearly statistics. For the census and nonadmission data in the preceding list, totals would be divided by days in the period to obtain a daily average, or by the months in a year to obtain a monthly average. Note that NAHC's census definition differs from the definition of census provided in the AHIMA's *Basic Healthcare Statistics for Health Information Management Professionals* (Youmans 2000). The AHIMA definition is the one used in most institution-based healthcare settings: "the number of inpatients present in the healthcare facility at any given time." NAHC defines *census* in the following ways:

Unduplicated patient/client census: Number of individuals receiving service from an organization during a given period of time counted only once, regardless of the number of services, frequency of admission, or payer source.

Duplicated patient/client census: The total number of admissions during a given period of time regardless of the number of individuals involved. For example, the same individual admitted more than once during a reporting period would be counted each time that individual is admitted.

Formulas for other commonly used definitions follow.

Average daily census: The average daily census provides information on the number of patients, and families when applicable, receiving services on any given day. This average is useful in assessing work load and monitoring work load over time. The data for this statistic are obtained by collecting a daily count of active patients and families when applicable. The daily counts are totaled for a month or a year and then divided by the days in the period.

Hospice programs may also want to calculate an average daily census for families in bereavement follow-up using the following formula:

$$\frac{Total\ daily\ count\ of\ active\ patients\ or\ families\ in\ period}{Days\ in\ period}$$

The statistics presented next use the data defined by the NAHC data set (see appendix A). These statistics can be calculated monthly and yearly.

The average length of stay (based on discharges) refers to the NAHC data set (see appendix A) for the definitions of admission, discharge, and length of stay.

$$\frac{Sum\ of\ lengths\ of\ stay\ of\ patients\ discharged\ in\ period}{Number\ of\ discharges\ in\ period}$$

Note: Include admission and discharge day in length of stay.

Average number of visits per patient by discipline (based on discharges) refers to the NAHC data set (see appendix A) for the definitions of service utilization items.

$$\frac{Total\ visits\ made\ by\ a\ discipline\ to\ patients\ discharged\ in\ period}{Total\ patients\ discharged\ in\ period\ who\ received\ services\ from\ the\ discipline}$$

$$\frac{Total\ units\ of\ service\ provided\ by\ a\ discipline\ to\ patients\ discharged\ in\ period}{Total\ patients\ discharged\ in\ period\ who\ received\ services\ from\ the\ discipline}$$

Average number of total days of inpatient care and home care received by hospice patients or families may be computed separately for routine and continuous home care days, and for respite and general inpatient care days.

$$\frac{Sum\ of\ hospice\ inpatient\ days\ of\ care\ for\ each\ patient\ discharged\ or\ who\ died\ in\ period}{Number\ of\ patients\ discharged\ or\ who\ died\ in\ period}$$

Note: The day of discharge from inpatient care is counted as a hospice home care day unless the patient died on that day. A separate statistic may be computed for respite inpatient care days and for general inpatient care days.

$$\frac{Sum\ of\ hospice\ home\ care\ days\ of\ care\ for\ each\ patient\ discharged\ or\ who\ died\ in\ period}{Number\ of\ patients\ discharged\ or\ who\ died\ in\ period}$$

Note: Count both the home care admission and discharge day. A separate statistic may be computed for routine home care days and for continuous home care days.

Hospice programs may also want to collect data on the average length of stay in bereavement follow-up. A formula for this follows.

Average length of stay in bereavement follow-up is based on families or significant others discharged from bereavement follow-up. Upon discharge, the number of days in bereavement follow-up is calculated. The admission date to bereavement follow-up is the day after a patient's death, and the discharge date is when bereavement services were discontinued for all patient family members or significant others. Both days are counted in the length of stay.

$$\frac{\textit{Sum of total days in bereavement follow-up of a patient's family or significant others discharged in period}}{\textit{Number of patient families or significant others discharged from bereavement follow-up in period}}$$

Note: Bereavement follow-up days begin on the day following a patient's death.

Prospective Payment System Performance Measures

The Ground Point Zero project is a national effort to have a cross-section of home care leaders recommend practice strategies for agencies to best manage under PPS. The measures presented in figure 4.3 represent the minimum number recommended. While those involved in the process recognized that agencies may and should add others, they also agreed to keep the

Figure 4.3.   Prospective Payment System Performance Measures

1. Number of referrals by diagnosis
2. Referral source satisfaction
3. Percent of cases accepted by intake that become admissions
4. Percent accuracy of home health resource groups (HHRGs) upon review of the OASIS assessment, plan of care and clinical notes segmented by clinician
5. Percent of RAPs submitted within 48 hours of assessment
6. Increased revenue derived from clinical review of OASIS and plan of care development
7. Benchmarked clinical outcomes (OASIS or other clinical tools)
8. Benchmarked patient satisfaction
9. Revenue versus expense by HHRG and overall
10. Average cost per visit by discipline
11. Average cost per episode
12. Average case-mix weight for non-LUPA episodes
13. Average number of visits by discipline for non-LUPA episodes and for LUPA episodes
14. Percent of first episodes that are LUPAs
15. Percent of episodes involving 10 or more therapy visits
16. Financial performance and utilization by discipline by diagnosis
17. Financial performance by case manager
18. Percent claims denied
19. Days out for accounts receivable
20. Average case-mix weight for second, third, and additional non-LUPA episodes
21. Percent of LUPAs for second, third, and additional episodes
22. Number of outlier episodes and average outlier payment and cost/episode
23. Average number of episodes/patient/year
24. Average number of visits by discipline for non-LUPA and LUPA episodes by episode number
25. Average cost/episode and performance by HHRG for second, third, and additional non-LUPA episodes

Source: Adapted from Fazzi, Robert A.; Wright, Kathleen; and Agoglia, Robert V. 2000 (October [Cited January 2001]). 3M National Ground Point Zero Project: Final Report. Available at http://www.fazzi.com/REPORT.PDF.

number manageable and realistic. Most measures come into play during service delivery and discharge. The rationale behind each measurement and the full report can be accessed on the Fazzi Associates Web site: www.Fazzi.com.

Computerization

Since the mid-1990s, the vast majority of home care agencies have made use of some form of automation to support back office administrative functions such as patient registration, claim preparation, and receivables management. HCFA's electronic transaction processing initiative for claims, remittance, and funds transfer was the primary driver behind the expanded use of computerized information systems during the first half of the decade. Declining hardware costs and expanded use of low-cost local area networking technology also contributed to growth during this period. Automation was achieved through the following means:

- Implementation of PC-based stand-alone systems

- Use of service bureaus or local management companies

- Direct entry of data into Medicare fiscal intermediary systems

This period also saw expanded use of clinical automation systems, such as plan-of-care preparation and patient charting, and introduction of the industry's first serious point-of-care data capture products. By 1997, virtually all software products offered to the home care market included some clinical capabilities, and the majority of agencies were using computers to prepare their HCFA 485's. Point-of-care automation gained a foothold in the marketplace during the 1994–97 period, with an estimated 15–20 percent of clinicians using computers in the field to prepare clinical documentation.

Further automation of administrative and clinical functions ceased in 1998 as a result of HCFA's interim payment systems. Agencies, which earlier had room under HCFA's cost caps, stopped making system purchases. Software vendors began to curtail new product development, and some closed their doors entirely.

However, implementation of Medicare's PPS has unleashed another round of industry automation. Purchasing activity has picked up since early 2000 as agencies replace the old back-office systems that used dated technology. Interest in point-of-care computing has increased dramatically as executives begin to recognize the value of automating clinical record-keeping functions (Williams 2001).

In 1985, a national survey of HHAs, conducted in conjunction with the W. K. Kellogg Foundation-funded home care project, found that only 55 percent (140) of the agencies that responded to the survey used a computer to assist with administrative/clinical data needs (Miller 1985). Of these, 13 percent or less had computerized information systems for specific clinical functions, such as care plans, physician orders, and patient assessments. Only 4 percent had computerized progress notes. Also in 1985, the extent of computerization varied by agency size, with 95 percent of the agencies that reported annual visits of 50,000 or more having some form of computerization (Miller 1985).

Multiple computerized information system applications are essential if home care and hospice programs are to meet information system needs. Systems must address the following categories:

- Clinical/documentation

- Human resource management

- Accounting/billing

- Other

"Other" includes the functional needs that are unique to such specific home care entities as infusion therapy and durable medical equipment.

Integrated information systems (a single vendor system with modules to address diverse functional needs) are available, and many organizations purchase them. However, it is common and often necessary for organizations to purchase several information system products to meet diverse functional needs and/or the different needs of such organizational entities as Medicare home care, IV therapy, and Medicare hospice. In fact, purchasing diverse products is a popular approach to meeting information system needs. Typically referred to as open systems architecture, this approach allows an organization to purchase top-of-the-line computer products that fill a niche in providing individual departments with the utmost functionality to meet their needs. This approach makes it essential for diverse products to be interfaced so necessary data can be delivered from and between these systems (Zielstorff 1995). Although interface engines allow for this linkage, the lack of home care data and communication standards creates difficulties when diverse systems try to share data. But the sharing of data should become easier in the future, considering the work being done to develop a uniform home care data set and a home care application protocol for electronic data exchange (Infiorati 1995).

Availability and Use of Computerized Applications

Each fall since 1994, the newsletter *Home Care Automation Report* (HCAR) has conducted an annual market update to get a sense of where the home care information technology market is headed. A software matrix (see appendix R) based on HCAR's summary of a 2000 survey of 59 vendors is now available. While HCAR does not validate vendor claims regarding software capabilities, it examines the vendors and their products in the HCAR *Buyer's Guide*. They also produce a yearly vendor satisfaction survey.

At the 2000 NAHC Annual Meeting, industry professionals witnessed the debut of several products and services utilizing Web-based technologies, which capitalize on the Internet. Many vendor exhibits focused on new point-of-care devices, additional PPS-related products, expanded outsourcing alternatives, and the growing interest in telemedicine. NAHC offered a number of seminars and workshops sponsored by the Home Care Information Technology Council (HITC), which put on seven 90-minute events that addressed HIPAA, disaster preparedness, point-of-care automation, new products, wireless communications, networking technologies, and project planning (Williams 2000). Currently, not one computer system is capable of fulfilling all of these information needs.

The Computer-Based Health Records

A 1991 report from the Institute of Medicine defined a computer-based patient health record (CPR) as an electronic patient health record that resides in a system specifically designed to support users by providing accessibility to complete and accurate data, alerts, reminders, clinical decision support systems, links to medical knowledge, and other aids (Cofer 1994).

The CPR vision is that of electronic, lifelong (longitudinal) health records. Standardized data items and content would be contained in this record, and all the care settings would share them; CPRs would be available to other users as the need for information arose. Many groups are working to achieve this vision, with the Computer-based Health Records Institute (CPRI) as one of the leaders. The technology is available that would make such systems a reality, but barriers still stand in the way. Two major barriers are: (1) the lack of approved and universally accepted data exchange, vocabulary, and content standards, and (2) concerns regarding system reliability and security (Dick and Steen 1991).

Much work is being conducted to eliminate these barriers (Blair 1994). In their absence, longitudinal health records that would be initiated and updated in the patient's home might be possible (Rockwell and Pion 1994). Patients themselves would be responsible for much of the data entry. Ideally, patients would have access to their own record data, as well as to education and outcome data so that informed consent might truly be achieved.

The Institute of Medicine's vision of longitudinal health records incorporates a system with linkages to secondary databases both to provide data to clinical/registry databases and to access knowledge sources/databases (Dick and Steen 1991). Such records would assist with clinical decision making. Although pioneering work is being done on some interactive home care systems with decision support features, home care and hospice applications are limited.

Criteria for Computerization

The Systems Evaluation Group of CPRI (1995) has developed some criteria that can be referenced by organizations with a goal of developing a true CPR. Many home and hospice programs electronically collect and store portions of a patient's record while the patient is active, but, usually, paper records are also printed. Few if any organizations permanently store entire health records electronically. A CPR that contains decision and knowledge support is truly a vision for home care and hospice programs. The automated clinical records that home care and hospice offer are not CPRs, according to the Institute of Medicine's definition.

Needs Assessment and Planning

Chapter 1 examined the assessment of information management system (IMS) needs as well as the planning of the IMS. IMS assessment and planning identifies what data are to be collected and by whom, and how data are to be captured (or collected), analyzed, used, stored, shared, and accessed. Integral to this assessment and planning is the determination of the extent of computerization that the organization needs and desires. The decision that is reached will vary according to the size and complexity of the organization.

Functional and technical criteria are important considerations when assessing computerized information system needs. Functional criteria address what tasks the system can perform, while technical criteria concern how functions are performed (Duffy and McLendon 1991). Some examples of functional criteria include the ability of a system to incorporate clinical alerts or reminders, to allow for creation of custom reports, or to format screens or printed information in a way desired by a particular user group. As for technical criteria, some examples include the technologies used to secure and protect access to confidential data, and the extent to which a system incorporates industry standards for electronic messaging and in defining data (CPR Systems 1995).

Acceptance and use of a computerized IS are crucial to its success. Many systems fail or are underused because of user resistance. The source of this resistance is multifaceted. In the planning phase, organizations must decide on the functional and technical capabilities that will be necessary to meet IMS needs, and they must determine what system features will enhance acceptance by staff. In research with physicians, involvement of physicians in a system's planning and implementation increased the likelihood of the system's success (Metzger and Drazen 1993). A successful system is also associated with its fit into clinical processes; the clinical process should not have to conform to a computerized information system, in fact, the opposite should occur (Metzger and Drazen 1993). Some important design criteria that influence the acceptance of an information system include the following (Metzger and Drazen 1993):

- System availability (timeliness of system access and response)

- Ease of use (how intuitive a system is)

- Data entry (ease of entry compared to pen and paper entry)

- Data retrieval (how quickly data can be accessed and to what degree display can be customized)

- Prompts, alerts, and reminders (to what extent they are present and pertinent to decision making-hit rates of 30 to 50 percent)

CPRI has developed one resource that is useful in planning for a CPR as well as for other, more limited, computerized information system applications. The resource, Draft CPR Project Evaluation Criteria, Version 2.0, contains criteria considered essential to a CPR. According to the CPR Systems Evaluation Work Group (1995), the evaluation criteria can be used as a framework for describing and evaluating CPR systems projects. The criteria are nonprescriptive; they are guiding principles that serve as a framework for the system development process. The criteria are grouped into four categories: management, functionality, technology, and impact. The CPR Systems Evaluation Group (CPR Systems 1995) describes these categories as follows:

Management: This section addresses strategic planning, implementation, operation, and evaluation processes guiding the CPR systems project.

Functionality: This section focuses on the CPR systems' users and their information needs, the process for identifying and prioritizing functional requirements, and evidence that user needs are being met.

Technology: This section is directed to the technical design of the CPR system, security and data integrity, use of standards and system performance.

Impact: This section looks at quantitative results concerning the impact of the system on access to needed information for direct care, research, and other purposes, and on the processes and outcomes of care delivery.

The Guide to Successfully Automating Your Home Organization: An Information Systems Management Source Book, a publication by Thomas D. Williams, offers guidance that is specific to home care providers on planning for successful automation. This publication includes criteria for establishing IS goals and objectives, and for reviewing business processes (Williams 1995c).

Organization Processes Improvements

The need to critically examine home care and hospice documentation processes has been emphasized throughout this book. Chapter 3 discussed this need in the context of continuous quality improvement (CQI). Assessment and improvement of existing processes before they are computerized is essential for benefits to be realized. Without this assessment and improvement, an organization's computerized system is simply a manual system that becomes automated. If the manual system was inefficient and unable to meet user and customer needs, then the automated equivalent will likely have the same limitations. For example, while the introduction of hand-held computers for point-of-care data entry can improve communications, it will most likely not produce gains in efficiency and the availability of data items when the same assessment forms and procedures are simply automated. Without process improvement and education, clinicians would still operate as they did under a manual system. Instead of completing forms or dictating notes after leaving the home care setting, they would be manually recording assessment visit information while in the setting, then entering it via the hand-held computer after leaving the setting. Clearly, increased efficiency would not be the result of such a scenario.

Examination and improvement in processes is a critical component of CQI, and it is referred to as process reengineering (Davis 1994). (Process reengineering is not to be confused with organizational reengineering, when organizations reexamine their structure and all their processes to totally rethink how they operate [Brandt 1994b].) Process reengineering begins with an assessment and understanding of the process that must be improved, followed by a critical examination of customer needs in relation to the process. Then, the process is redesigned to consistently meet customer needs and add value to the process. To add value, the steps in the process are evaluated to determine if they are necessary in relation to the value provided to the customer. Steps are added or deleted based on this evaluation. In the CQI tradition, the redesigned steps are followed by the creation of standards, a design to prevent system failures, documentation of the new system, and, then, a specification of personnel to be involved in the process, along with a recognition system for quality performance (Brandt 1994b).

Choosing the System

Computer vendors face the challenge of a rapidly changing home care and hospice environment, as well as new technologies and emerging electronic communication and record content standards. Often, established systems do not possess the functionality/leading-edge characteristics that organizations need. Systems with the desired level of functionality are often in the development and testing phase. Those organizations who have performed strategic planning and developed an information management plan will find their decision capabilities enhanced when choosing the best approach for their organization (Blair 1994). In other words, when strategic planning is used to map the direction of an organization, the best choice to accomplish the planned goals is more readily apparent.

Historically, the home care information systems market has been slanted toward vendors, and contracts have been drafted from the perspective of the vendor (Williams 1995a). But this has been changing as the number of home care and hospice organizations has grown, as organizations have become more sophisticated purchasers of information systems software, and as competition between vendors has increased (Williams 1995a). Home care and hospice organizations are now in a better position to demand more from information system vendors and their products.

To begin to evaluate available information system software, organizations should first identify software vendors by reviewing home care, hospice, and computer industry publications, and by talking to staff at computerized organizations. Once vendors are identified, the needs of the organization should be compared with the software that each vendor makes available. At this point, it is recommended that organizations prepare a written request for proposal to be sent to identified vendors. Organizations can reference numerous publications for specifics regarding requests for proposal. Generally, the written request for proposal provides vendors detailed, written information about an organization's functional and technical requirements of the desired computer applications, training and implementation requirements, financial considerations, and the organizational profile: size, provider type, organizational structure, reimbursement source(s), and other details. Based on this information, vendors will be able to develop a proposal that will be specific to the needs of organizations (Waters and Murphy 1983).

Requests for proposal also solicit information about vendors' financial status, the length of time they have been involved in the home care and/or hospice computer business, the diversity of their business, their installation process, and the support they provide to clients, along with a listing of former clients and references. This information is especially important to home care and hospice organizations because there has been much attrition among home care vendors in the last few years and many vendors are new (Williams 1995d).

Once vendors submit proposals, the organization evaluates the proposals against established criteria. Organizations may wish to assign some weights to the desired features that are based on the preestablished priority of needs. A grade would then be assigned to each feature of the proposals, to reflect how well the vendor meets the described need. Assigned weights would then be multiplied by assigned grades to determine a total score for each feature, and these totals would be added up to arrive at a total score for each vendor's proposal. At this point, some vendors may be eliminated because they simply cannot adequately meet the needs of the organization.

After determining whether a vendor or not can meet the functional and technical needs of the organization, the qualified vendors' track records (obtained from reference checks of present and former customers, and/or by making site visits), the cost of the system, the company's research and development program, and financial status are then evaluated. An organization must be able to feel confident that a vendor will still be in existence in case software needs to be modified down the road, and that a vendor will remain proactive when facing the continually changing home care and hospice data and information system needs.

Finally, a contract between the chosen vendor and the agency is signed. The contract outlines the responsibilities of both the organization and the vendor. The continuing support and training that the vendor will provide must be clearly delineated, as should the specifics relating to installation.

System Conversion

Conversion begins once the computer software and hardware are selected and a date for availability has been received from the vendor. Planning for the conversion addresses equipment installation, the need for new floor plans, furniture needs, staff training needs, the training materials required, and any new policies and procedures that the new system should have in place. When conversion planning is undertaken, the organization will have already negotiated with the vendor any specifics regarding the installation, and the training and support that the vendor will provide. Vendors often offer user manuals and formal training on system use. Even when vendors provide training, in-service education for agency staff is conducted to teach employees about any changes in policies and procedures that will result from the conversion to computerization. Organizations determine which employees need training, what information needs to be conveyed to employees, who needs to convey that information, and how close training should be scheduled to the actual conversion date.

When organizations plan for the final conversion to a computerized information system, they should determine the order in which the applications will be implemented, whether parallel (both automated and manual) processing will occur, and the personnel that will be needed to implement the conversion. When several computer applications are being installed (that is, billing, scheduling, and clinical documentation), organizations may wish to stagger the implementation so that any problems encountered with hardware and software relating to one application can be worked out before implementing another. Also, until the problems are resolved, an organization may decide to have parallel processing for a specified period of time.

Initiatives and Technology

OASIS, ORYX, outcome-based quality management (OBQM), and PPS regulations added pressure to an already paperwork-burdened industry. OASIS regulations require different comprehensive assessments at different times. Agencies revised their manual data collection forms, though having the right form at the right time proved problematic. Logically linking OASIS data to care planning and treatment was difficult. Agencies choosing stand-alone data entry tools, such as HAVEN software provided by HCFA, increased paperwork redundancy and added support staff for data entry and tracking OASIS timelines. All agencies must implement outcome-based quality improvement to meet conditions of participation. JCAHO requires outcome-based performance improvement planning to meet their standards. Home health PPS rules incorporate an unlimited number of 60-day episodes; split payment at start of care and end of episodes; case-mix adjustments; and prorated payments when more than one agency is involved. (HCFA's key PPS billing documents can be viewed at www.hcfa.gov/medicare.) These multiple forces drive providers towards different types of technology.

Solutions for Mobile Work Forces

For HHAs that revised their manual data collection forms to meet OASIS regulation requirements for various comprehensive assessments, maintaining the myriad of forms proved unwieldy. Linking OASIS data to care planning and treatment using hard copy was difficult. Further, these additional manual forms increased paperwork redundancy, and extra support staff were needed to track the assessments and their accompanying forms, as well as implement changes after the results were accrued.

In addition to OASIS requirements, the home health prospective payment rules allow for an unlimited number of 60-day episodes, and require split payment at the start of care and end of episodes, case-mix adjustments, and prorated payments when more than one agency is involved. Both JCAHO standards and federal *Conditions of Participation* require HHAs to implement outcome-based quality improvement programs. In considering the large mobile work force that HHAs employ, it is clear that implementing these new requirements using manual forms alone has proven nearly impossible. Thus, HHAs are progressively moving towards new technologies to assist in documentation and assessment.

Computerized Point-of-Care Charting

Computerized charting solutions were born from the home health industries desire to reduce indirect cost and standardize care and documentation. Point-of-care documentation links intake, assessments, and orders to care provided, saving agencies personnel time and promoting compliance with regulatory requirements. Computerized OASIS charting automatically chooses the correct OASIS assessment with links to scheduling, care planning, and orders. Automated extract programs batch the OASIS data for transmission to state survey agencies. Furthermore, some software vendors providing OASIS and ORYX solutions offer Web-enabled systems. HHAs subscribe to service bureaus to access comparative outcome data from Web-based reporting sites. Providers trying to predict PPS resource utilization can purchase software that forecasts patient outcomes using a comparison database of matching patient histories. HHAs can also use third-party report writing software to track compliance, complete statistical reports, and demonstrate outcomes.

Scanning and Bar Coding Solutions

Scanned documentation used to collect and report home health data reduces capital dollars, training time, and technical support costs. Most agencies will not invest in laptop or pen-based computers for home health aide services, so vendors used optical mark or character recognition scanners to penetrate the home care market. Agencies can track medical supply inventory, reduce data entry errors, and track physician orders with bar coding applications.

Telemedicine

Telemedicine allows agencies to provide care to, monitor, and educate patients using live audio, video, and medical peripherals, such as telephonic stethoscopes, vital sign equipment, glucose meters, and pulse oximeters. Clinicians conduct video visits from a central station located at the agency. Measurement data uploads from peripherals and creates the documentation. Providers get real-time data of the patient's condition, concerns, and compliance with treatment protocols. A small moveable video camera with a special lens provides a clear focus for close-up shots. Patients are evaluated visually and verbally, then detailed measurements are taken. With high-resolution video, clinicians can view wounds, dressings, glucose meter measurements, and pulse oximeter readings. Telemedicine visits can supplement home visits for chronically ill, homebound, or high-cost patients, in turn reducing clinic, emergency department, and hospital visits. Patient stations are small, durable, lightweight, self-contained units. However, HCFA's telemedicine policy for home health confirmed in writing that telecommunication contacts with patients by HHAs cannot count as visits. Private payers may reimburse telemedicine services.

Telephony Software

Home health uses telephony software and the patient's phone to capture arrival, departure, and task information from home care visits. HCFA approved telephony as a source of billing information for home care agencies. Telephony eliminates many paper records, makes auditing visits easier, and expedites billing. The computer answers phone calls made from the patient's home and stores data entered by phone. Agency office staff view and download data from Web-based sites for analysis, billing, and payroll. Visit data exports to existing billing and payroll systems. Agency employees make short calls at the beginning and end of each visit. Long-distance charges are billed using toll-free numbers. Personal identification numbers secure the call. Telephony systems provide electronic validation of care plans. Agencies can quickly determine tasks that were skipped or not authorized. Telephony systems also record information about absent and refused visits. HHAs can use the Internet to find staff if needed to deliver patient care updates. Telephony reduces the time to reconcile visit and payroll documentation from a period of three to ten days to one day. Transaction-based pricing with minimal sign-on fees makes these systems affordable.

Alternative Methods of Care and Noncovered Services

The potential for video cameras, pill dispensers, and glucose monitors, as well as other care devices that communicate electronically with HHAs, is appealing to all parties involved in home health care. PPS provides strong financial incentives for HHAs to adopt technologies that provide the same or higher quality of care. HHAs are also considering the use of such technology by nutritionists or registered dietitians in an effort to reduce the total cost of episodes provided by these disciplines. However, in the Final PPS Rule (see appendix O), HCFA states, "There is nothing to preclude an HHA from adopting telemedicine or other technologies that they believe promote efficiencies, but those untested technologies will not be specifically recognized and reimbursed by Medicare under the home health benefit."

Medical reviewers work from utilization benchmark statistics based only on services specified on claims. An HHA that reduces its visits by substituting telemedicine for visits or by substituting noncovered services for covered services runs a higher risk of being flagged for review. These agencies may appear to be underutilizing when compared to averages comprised predominantly of HHAs using only the traditionally covered services. However, if these noncovered services go underreported, HCFA will not recognize the cost of alternative methods of care or noncovered services when it rebases the PPS rates. Future rates would then be based on systematically understated costs. The more HHAs innovate, the more this gap would increase. To manage alternative methods of care and noncovered services, HHAs must develop activity and discipline codes, definitions, and units of measure. When used, alternative methods of care and noncovered services must be included in care plans. Staff must code and track these activities accurately. Management must be able to identify the episode in which these methods and services are used in order to evaluate their clinical and cost effectiveness. When preparing for medical review, these methods and services should be reported by episode (Tidd 2001).

Emerging Health Records Technology

Virtual health records, which are stored on the Web, could give integrated delivery networks with home health components the secure and timely record access needed to manage critical care paths seamlessly. Healthcare enterprise portals could provide home care organizations that have multiple sites with a central copy of medical and coverage information. Agency branches could use the Internet and private networks to pick up copies of the software and email systems to send verbal orders to physicians for signature. Hospitals, clinics, and physician offices can submit patient referrals by completing electronic forms. Patients use agency Web sites to complete satisfaction surveys. Primary care givers seeking to pay privately for respite can use online auctions to bid for services.

Agencies struggling to improve quality care without adding training costs use computer-based training solutions. Home care requires highly trained professionals mandated by law to complete continuing education courses. Computer-based training applications could expand to patient education as more patients get on-line. This training can eliminate travel time and expense while providing uniform instruction and current content. A few vendors offering home care applications offer computer-based training on the Web or on CD-ROM. Among respondents who are more satisfied with their vendors, innovative Internet use was often mentioned as a plus. On-line technical support, customer-only chat rooms, and Web-based training sessions were frequently mentioned as ways to cement vendor and customer relationships. Implementing new technology often reduces home health visit productivity for three to six months. Vendors are competing by trying to speed up promised cost savings. Training options include teleconferencing, remote one-on-many Internet training sessions that bring users up to speed using live customer data and on-line multimedia tutorials. The industry's largest vendors cannot move from legacy-based DOS, UNIX, MUMPS, PICK, and other platforms to Windows fast enough.

Agencies piloting virtual visits using personal digital assistant computers, Web-TV, small video cameras, and video taping equipment, said patient acceptance of this technology and equipment impedes progress. Some patients cannot hold the camera steady for close-up wound care shots. Setting up the equipment in homes gets complicated when patients have cable TV, multiple phone lines, and add-on phone services like call waiting. Nurses often must call for additional technical support. Telemedicine research and pilot projects often add rather than decrease paperwork requirements.

Hand-held full tablet display devices are popular point-of-care tools because they are small, light, unobtrusive, and fit home health job requirements. However, the lack of universal standards for clinical data prevents vendors from integrating text within the enterprise. Every provider uses different terms for the various aspects of home health care. The open architecture of hand-held electronic organizers made it easy for several vendors to market OASIS data collection tools. Using hand-held and laptop computers together with fold-down keyboards helps users overcome portability and data storage obstacles. A small software company is experimenting with integrating speech recognition software into its back-office product. Clinicians record visit notes on a hand-held portable recording device, then transfer notes onto a laptop or office PC after the visit.

Investor and Minimalist Approaches

Under prospective pay, providers must balance cost against the need to streamline information. No one home care package meets every information need. Agencies choose either an investor or a minimalist approach. Client server software with a distributed relational database allows multiple clinicians to chart access while clinical support staff at the agency can triage care coordination calls, change physician orders, and process new referrals. Giving care providers easy access to information promotes better clinical and financial decisions.

Automated physician signature tracking is critical to timely billing under PPS. Delinquent signed orders can seriously impede agency cash flow. Most clinical documentation systems include automated physician order tracking. Physician communication software works independently of packages that produce treatment plans and interim orders. Modem software automatically sends scanned physician orders to physician offices. The software tracks transmissions between the agency and physician office. Physician offices can send and receive from any agency that has the software. The software also tracks the time physicians spend reviewing orders. HCFA approves electronic signatures for physician orders if applications meet security and authorship requirements. Similar results can be replicated with facsimile transmission software packages interfaced to database software and imaging systems. Most systems can be operated by the home care agency or contracted to vendors or third-party firms. In the end, technology can resolve problems for home health providers and create opportunities for HIM.

Vendors and Results

Vendors look for evidence that automation reduces home care cost and improves care outcomes to justify return on investment. Securing investment returns requires redesigning work, especially in traditional HIM practices. Often the return on investment comes from moving health information processes from traditional paper record management to managing data integrity. Health information managers working in home care must shift their thinking so that the following objectives are achieved:

- Reengineer health record reviews to monitor electronic work flow

- Convert HIM systems from filing paper to monitoring data

- Separate quantitative from qualitative analysis

- Design concurrent and prebilling audit methods

- Use query software to design exception reports that focus on high volume, cost, variation, and risk analysis

- Develop strategies to assure data integrity, beginning with the 23 OASIS data elements used to determine HHRGs

Future Advances

The future of computerized home care and hospice information systems promises to be exciting. Rapid advances in technology and available systems will allow a greater sharing of information between provider organizations and team members. These advances will also allow patients and families to become more active members of their treatment team. Although hand-held, point-of-care computer systems are now functional, future improvements will heighten their functionality and allow for wireless communication. The technology behind hand-held computer systems is still young, and handwriting recognition still poses too much of a challenge for performing data entry and data query. In addition, the availability of voice recognition, which would provide an extremely user-friendly interface, in hand-held devices is still further down the road. It is predicted that many of the technological advances needed in hand-held devices will be available to the healthcare industry within five to six years, or possibly sooner due to the competitive pressures in healthcare (Palmer 1995).

The following advances are currently in use, and expected to become even more widespread in the near future:

- The development of standardized data repositories containing data of all providers who contract with a managed care organization or as part of a healthcare network

- A seamless sharing of information between diverse computer applications such as Medicare home care, hospice, and IV therapy information systems

- A seamless sharing of information between diverse individual and organizational providers

- Prospective capture of quality improvement and outcome data

- Automated point-of-care data entry

- A more extensive home care and hospice CPR that incorporates critical pathways and care protocols

The home care and hospice clinical information systems of the future will support clinical decision making and provide linkages to knowledge databases. In the long term, these care settings will see interactive communication with patients that will enable the electronic capture of patient data, historical and continuing assessment via electronic interviews, and electronic provision of information to patients (Rockwell and Pion 1994). Home and hospice care will grow to be part of an electronic lifetime record that all healthcare providers will share with each other.

HIM Professionals and Record Management

AHIMA's annual membership survey reported that 8.2 percent of respondents work in the home health setting (AHIMA 2000). Home health administrators find that supervisor-level job descriptions no longer meet the HHAs' higher-level HIM needs. For example, at one agency, inadequate supervision caused the discontinuation of an automatic facsimile program for signature tracking. In a second example, monitoring, investigating, and resolving exception reports about bad transmissions was inadequately staffed. Designing processes that integrate many servers and applications requires system-level thinking. HIM practitioners can advise HHAs as providers struggle with data comprehensiveness, consistency, currency, accuracy, accessibility, timeliness, and relevancy.

HIM professionals assist organizations to develop and implement sound record and information management policies and practices. AHIMA credentials two levels of HIM professionals relevant to HHAs: the registered health information administrator (RHIA) and the registered health information technician (RHIT). To become credentialed, both RHIAs and RHITs are required to pass a national examination. To maintain the credentials, they must earn continuing education credits. The following subject areas are studied by both RHIAs and RHITs:

- General education

- Medical sciences, including the language of medicine, structure and function of the human body, and disease process

- Organization of the healthcare industry

- Systems and processes for collecting, maintaining, and disseminating health-related information

- Computer concepts and microcomputer applications

- Computer applications in healthcare

- Laws, regulations, ethics, and standards affecting HIM

- Classifications, nomenclatures, and reimbursement systems

- Data analysis and presentation

- Clinical quality assessment and improvement

RHITs also study supervisory principles and practices, while RHIAs study these additional areas:

- Management theory, principles, and practices

- Systems analysis, systems design, and project management concepts

- Healthcare financial management

- Statistics, research, and evaluation methods

RHIAs are fully qualified in the planning and management of IMSs, as well as in the analysis of data that those systems generate. As an administrator, the RHIA designs the health records management system of the organization and also plays an integral role in designing its IMS. RHIAs can also code and index diagnoses, compile statistics, and abstract records for quality indicator monitoring. Also, many RHIAs are responsible for the overall administration of quality management programs in healthcare settings.

RHITs are specialists who are fully trained in assembling, analyzing, abstracting, and maintaining health records. RHITs also code and index diagnoses and operations, compile statistics, and abstract records for quality indicator monitoring. They are often responsible for supervising many of the day-to-day functions of the HIM department, and, in some organizations, they serve as department managers.

Reports from HIM professionals indicate that their knowledge and skills are often underused by home care and hospice organizations. Reports from home care and hospice organizations indicate that recruiting HIM professionals is often difficult. AHIMA has established domains, subdomains, and task competencies (see appendix P) that contain the verified entry-level competencies of RHIAs and RHITs, and the knowledge and skills that are expected of new practitioners. Organization administrators may find that a review of these documents proves useful in understanding the capabilities of RHIAs and RHITs.

Summary

Well-thought-out and -designed health record numbering and filing systems ensure that the health record is available at all times. Centralized records with terminal digit filing will improve record retrieval. The space required for filing health records grows rapidly, and it is impractical to use valuable space for records that are seldom used. Periodic surveys should be made by the information management department head to review the types and frequency of chart retrieval requests. Results of these surveys can assist in making decisions regarding storage space, retention schedules, and miniaturizing.

An understanding of systems theory and computer technology is critical for health information managers working in home health organizations. Designing health record systems or computerizing the health record requires not only knowledge of existing health record content, data sources, system analysis techniques, and components of computer systems, but an open attitude and ability to think creatively.

References and Bibliography

Abraham, Prinny Rose. 2000a. Boosting efficiency in home health record systems. *Journal of the American Health Information Management Association* 71(4):63–64.

Abraham, Prinny Rose. 2000b. Home Health Wireless Solutions. Presentation at the American Health Information Management Association 72nd National Convention, Chicago.

Abraham, Prinny Rose. 2000c. The first 60 days of PPS: Challenges and solutions for health information and billing departments. *The Remington Report.*

American Health Information Management Association. 2000. You are here: annual membership survey marks the spot. *AHIMA* Advantage 4(4):14.

Batsford, Catherine. 2000. Evaluating your record storage. *HIM Connection 2000*:2–4.

Blair, Jeffrey S. 1994. Clinical information systems: putting them in perspective. *Journal of the American Health Information Management Association* 65(10):30–32.

Brandt, Mary. 1994a. Optical storage-based document imaging technology and the computer-based health records. *Journal of the American Health Information Management Association* 65(10):47–48.

Brandt, Mary. 1994b. Reengineering: Starting with a clean slate. *Journal of the American Health Information Management Association* 66(1):61–63.

Braunstein, Mark L. 1993. The electronic patient records solution. *Caring* 12(7):30–33.

Braunstein, Mark. 1999. Hand held technology. *ADVANCE for Health Information Executives.*

Cofer, Jennifer, ed. 1994. *Health Information Management.* 10th ed. Berwyn, Ill.: Physicians' Record.

CPR Systems Evaluation Work Group. 1995. *Draft CPR Project Evaluation Criteria, Version 2.0.* Schaumburg, Ill.: Computer-based Health Records Institute.

Davis, Elaine R. 1994. *Total Quality Management for Home Care.* Gaithersburg, Md.: Aspen Publishers.

Dick, Richard, and Elaine B. Steen, eds. 1991. *The Computer-Based Health Records: An Essential Technology for Health Care.* Washington, D.C.: National Academy Press.

Dougherty, Michelle. 2000. ICD-9-CM coding issues. *The Remington Report*:40–43.

Duffy, Phil, and Kelly McLendon. 1991. Understanding computers or some of the things you always wanted to know about computers . . . but were afraid to ask. *Journal of American Medical Records Association* 62(8):37–51.

Easley, Beth. 2000. Coding audits are crucial to compliance. *HIM Connection* 2(41):2–4.

Falconer, Carol B., ed. 1992. *St. Anthony's Home Health Claims Editor: A Guide to Medicare Billing.* Alexandria, Va.: St. Anthony Publishing.

Fazzi, Robert A., Kathleen Wright, and Robert V. Agoglia. 2000. 3M National Ground Zero Project, Final Report. http://www.fazzi.com/index_files/report.pdf.

Grebin, Burton. 1994. Interview. *The Remington Report*:5–6.

Grzybowski, Darice M. 1994. Paper to paperless, and the paper in-between. *Journal of American Health Information Management Association* 65(10):44–46.

Hassig, Jim. 1991. What do optical disks have in store for medical records: fad or fiction. *Healthcare Informatics* 8(10):42–48.

Health Care Financing Administration. 2000. Transmittal A-00-71. In *HCFA Program Memorandum on Medical Review of Home Health Services.* Washington, D.C.: Government Printing Office.

Health Care Financing Administration. 2001. *Quality Monitoring Using Case Mix and Adverse Event Outcome Report: Implementing Outcome-Based Quality Improvement at a Home Health Agency.* Washington, D.C.: Government Printing Office.

Illinois Hospital Association. 1994. *Home Care Constituency Section Data Report.* Naperville, Ill.: Illinois Hospital Association.

Infiorati, Meg E. 1995. Grappling with information-sharing strategies. *Caring* 14(8):88–91.

Metzger, Jane B., and Erica L. Drazen. 1993. Computer-based record systems that meet physician needs. *Healthcare Information Management* 7(1):22–31.

Miller, Susan C. 1985. Home care project survey data: part II. *Journal of the American Medical Record Association* 56(12):25–28.

National Association for Home Care. 1995a. *Uniform Data Set for Home Care and Hospice.* Washington, D.C.: National Association for Home Care.

National Association for Home Care. 1995b. A directory of vendors and services. *Caring*:96–97.

Opus Communications. 2000. Correct coding means accurate data, appropriate payments. *PPS Alert for Home Health* 1(7):1–4.

Palmer, Laurie. 1995. Close at hand: hand-held electronics point toward a health information revolution. *Journal of the American Health Information Management Association* 66(6):32–34.

Pion, Ron, and Tom Rockwell. 1994. Communication Technologies: Homeward Bound. *The Remington Report.*

Rockwell, Marshall, and Ron Pion. 1994. Medicine in the year 2005: a step into the future. *The Remington Report*:7–10.

Russo, Ruthann, and Joseph J. Russo. 2000. *Coding Compliance: A Practical Guide to the Audit Process.* Marblehead, Mass.: Opus Communications.

Tidd, Charles W. 2001. Alternative methods of care and non-covered services: a PPS ticking time bomb. *Home Care Alert* 1(1):1–2.

Vetter, Elizabeth. 1995. Automating payroll, billing, and medical records: using technology to do more with less. *Caring* 14(8):63–65.

Waters, K. A., and G. F. Murphy. 1983. *Systems Analysis and Computer Applications in Health Information Management.* Gaithersburg, Md.: Aspen Publishers.

Wilde, Donna J. 1992. Home health agency computer systems: current status and future directions. *Journal of the American Health Information Management Association* 63(12):82–85.

Williams, Thomas D. 1995a. Information technology for home care: a promising future. *Caring* 14(8):9–19.

Williams, Thomas D. 1995b. Special HHBR Report: Ninth Annual Home Care Computer Exposition. *Home Health Business Report.* Los Altos, Calif.: Staffing Industry Analysts.

Williams, Thomas D. 1995c. *Guide to Successfully Automating Your Home Organization: An Information Systems Management Source Book.* Los Altos, Calif.: Staffing Industry Analysts.

Williams, Thomas D. 1995d. Special HHBR Report: Selecting Information Technology for Home Healthcare. *Home Health Business Report.* Los Altos, Calif.: Staffing Industry Analysts.

Williams, Thomas D. 1997. *Buyer's Guide to Home Health Automation.* 2nd ed. Fredonia, Wis.: Stonyhill Publications.

Williams, Thomas D. 2000. *Home Care Automation Report, Annual Market Update.* Fredonia, Wis.: Stonyhill Publications.

Williams, Thomas D. 2001 (January 12). Personal communication with the publisher of *Home Care Automation Report.*

Youmans, Karen G. 2000. *Basic Healthcare Statistics for Health Information Management Professionals.* Chicago: American Health Information Management Association.

Zielstorff, Rita D. 1995. Capturing and using clinical outcome data: implications for information systems design. *Journal of the American Medical Informatics Association* 2(3):191–96.

Chapter 5

Confidentiality of Health Records

Every home care and hospice program has policies and procedures for maintaining the confidentiality of patient information and releasing it. In addition to having these policies and procedures documented, each organization develops a means to ensure that employees, volunteers, and contracted staff follow these policies and procedures. Policies and procedures incorporate applicable state and federal laws, as well as the requirements of accrediting and regulatory agencies. The Joint Commission on Accreditation of Healthcare Organizations (JCAHO) specifically requires that there be a policy on confidentiality and release of information (JCAHO 2000).

Chapter 5 serves as a guide to developing or revising policies and procedures for the maintenance, disclosure, and redisclosure of health information home care and hospice settings. The final rule on electronic transaction and code sets was published for the Health Insurance Portability and Accountability Act (HIPAA) in 2000. Compliance begins October 2002. HIPAA establishes standards for the electronic exchange of administrative and financial healthcare transactions in order to improve the efficiency and effectiveness of the healthcare system. The Congress' intention with HIPAA is to encourage electronic commerce in healthcare and to simplify processes. Especially important for home health agencies (HHAs) and hospices are the guidelines for handling patient data relating to the human immunodeficiency virus (HIV) and the acquired immunodeficiency syndrome (AIDS). Many of the forms referred to in this chapter can be found in appendix S.

It is crucial that readers stay abreast of HIPAA rules as they are released. Readers must review state and federal laws for any specific statutory requirements, and they should also obtain appropriate legal advice. Many of the component state associations of the American Health Information Management Association (AHIMA) have published comprehensive legal manuals that address state-specific concerns. This information can be obtained directly from each state's association.

Regardless of who uses it or how it is used, patient information must never be disclosed or used in an unauthorized manner by healthcare professionals, and patients, families, and significant others must be assured of this. Without this guarantee, patients have every right to withhold critical information that could affect the quality and outcome of care, as well as the reliability of the information itself.

Meeting the needs for patient information required for internal and external users, while protecting patients from unauthorized, inappropriate, or unnecessary intrusion into the highly personal data in their records, is a mounting dilemma. Computerization of a patient's clinical record (or parts of a record) makes even more information available, but the advent of technology need not herald a loss of individual privacy. A balance must be maintained between the needs of society for health information and the rights of individuals to be free from unwarranted intrusion into their personal lives.

Health Insurance Portability and Accountability Act

Compliance with the privacy standards of HIPAA requires the home health organization to examine and document its privacy policy and procedures to meet the specific requirements of the standards. The organization's privacy policy and procedures should address the appropriate handling of confidential information as it is collected and maintained in all media and information-communication systems, e-mail systems, telephone and paging systems, clinical and record systems, paper-based health record systems, financial databases, master patient indexes, statistical reports, and image systems. The new federal privacy standards apply to virtually every kind of patient-identifiable healthcare information.

Standard transactions are those complying with the rule. Standards have been adopted for eight administrative and financial healthcare transactions:

1. Health claims and equivalent encounter information

2. Enrollment and disenrollment in a health plan

3. Eligibility for a health plan

4. Healthcare payment and remittance advice

5. Health plan premium payments

6. Health claim status

7. Referral certification and authorization

8. Coordination of benefits

A group health plan or individual health plan with a maximum of $5 million in annual receipts is considered a small health plan and has until October of 2003 to comply. Standards for the first report of injury and claims attachments will be adopted later.

Effects on Home Care

HIPAA requires compliance by all health plans, all healthcare clearinghouses, and any healthcare provider who chooses to transmit any of the named transactions in electronic form. An HHA must comply with the electronic standard for that transaction even if an agency performs an identified business function on paper. The Health Care Financing Administration (HCFA) will phase out its free software starting in 2004, one year after HIPAA electronic transaction standards take effect. HCFA now provides claims submission software and Home Assessment Validation and Entry (HAVEN) software to transmit the Outcome and Assessment Information Set (OASIS) data to the state. After the HIPAA transaction standards are in place, there will no longer be Medicare-specific electronic formats and, therefore, no obligation for regional home health intermediaries (RHHIs) to make free software available.

Electronic data interchange (EDI) is the electronic transfer of information, such as claims, in a standard format between payers and providers. EDI should streamline home health billing as it allows entities within the healthcare system to exchange medical, billing, and other information and to process transactions in a fast and cost-effective manner. With EDI, handling and processing time is substantially reduced when compared to paper, and the risk of lost paper documents is eliminated. EDI can eliminate the inefficiencies of handling paper documents, which will significantly reduce administrative burden, lower operating costs, and improve overall data quality.

HIPAA Final Rule

The proposed HIPAA electronic standards rule included an exception for person-to-computer transactions (in other words, interaction between server to browser, direct data entry, faxback, and others). This exception was eliminated in the final rule. HCFA explained,

> Although we recognize there are no X12N standards for these interactions, there are standard elements and data content. Therefore, those transmissions must use the adopted standard data elements and data content. The "direct data entry" process, using dumb terminals or computer browser screens with data directly keyed by a provider into a health plan's computer, would not have to use the format, but the data content must conform. If data is entered outside the health plan's system, to be sent later, it must be sent using the full standard (DHH 2000).

The proposed rule mentioned that the secretary of Health and Human Services has authority under HIPAA to adopt standards for paper transactions as well. But in the final rule, the secretary chose not to do so. Critics of the proposed rule wondered if not including paper would influence healthcare providers to revert to paper transactions in an attempt to avoid the final rule requirements.

The final rule eliminated the exception for transactions delivered within a corporate entity (such as transaction from a hospital to its own home care agency). All transactions now must be standardized when they fall under final rule definitions.

Modifications to Adopted Standards

The final HIPAA electronic transactions rule distinguishes between maintenance and modifications of standard transactions. Maintenance is those activities necessary to support use of a standard adopted by the secretary. These include technical corrections to an implementation specification and enhancements or expansion of a data code set. Such changes could be nonsubstantive or error corrections. Public comment and notification is required as part of the normal standards development process accredited by the American National Standards Institute, and so a new regulation would not be required. Modification is a change to a standard or an implementation specification adopted by the secretary through regulation. The language of the proposed rule was revised in the final rule to state that a health plan may not delay a transaction or otherwise adversely affect, or attempt to adversely affect, the person or transaction on the basis that it is a standard transaction.

The final rule names the NCPDP telecommunication standard 5.1 and batch equivalent, instead of X12N standards, for the following retail pharmacies transactions:

- Eligibility for a health plan
- Healthcare payment
- Remittance advice

HIPAA is an information technology-intensive mandate. HIPAA's proposed security standards require health plans, healthcare clearinghouses, and healthcare providers to use the security standards to develop and maintain the security of all electronic individual health information. Each qualifying healthcare entity must maintain documentation demonstrating the development, implementation, and maintenance of appropriate security measures that include, at a minimum, the requirements and implementation features set forth. Entities must maintain documentation demonstrating that these measures have been periodically reviewed, validated, updated, and kept current.

The mandate recommends the creation of security standards for nine administrative and financial healthcare transactions. All healthcare organizations that employ electronic transmissions or that do business with other organizations that employ them, are subject to the security standards as they apply to the nine transaction areas. There are four categories of security measures that must be put into place. Each touches upon information systems, directly or indirectly, and carries a documentation mandate.

Administrative Procedures

HIPAA-proposed security standards state that there must be documented, formal practices to manage the selection and execution of security measures to protect data and manage the conduct of personnel in relation to the protection of data. Two requirements are associated with the mandate:

- **Certification:** a technical evaluation of the system that can be performed by the agency or through contract with an external accrediting agency

- **A chain-of-trust partner agreement:** an agreement between healthcare businesses to protect the integrity and confidentiality of the data exchanged (the agreement must be backed up by a documented system for effecting that protection)

In addition to these requirements, HIPAA asks for a contingency plan, routinely updated, for responding to a system emergency. The plan must include data backup, disaster recovery, emergency mode, and operation, testing, and revision procedures for each of these. The report of the plan must include a written analysis of application criticality on a hierarchical scale. Once agencies have written and tested their disaster plans, they must establish formal, documented policies and procedures for information access control, including internal audit. Agencies must track system activity such as logins, file accesses, and security incidents. Security programs must ensure that all personnel who have access to any sensitive information have appropriate clearances, including supervision and oversight of maintenance personnel, a record of access authorizations, and established personnel clearance procedures.

Information systems security includes documentation of all components of security, security testing procedures, hardware and software inventories, and virus checking. Security incident procedures must include report and response procedures, password management issues, removal of user accounts upon terminations, periodic security reminders, and user education. Elements outside of information technology are key returns, lock changes after terminations, and sanction policies.

Physical Safeguards

Physical computer systems and related buildings and equipment must be protected from fire and other natural and environmental hazards, as well as from intrusion, to guard data integrity, confidentiality, and availability. HIPAA recommends that agencies develop formal, documented policies and procedures that govern the receipt and removal of hardware and software into and out of the office. Written policies should cover how agencies secure offices, whether the agency is the only occupant, record maintenance, need-to-know procedures for personnel access, visitor procedures, and testing and revision procedures. Guidelines regarding workstation use and the security of workstation locations should also be included. This section also emphasizes the need for security awareness training, in which all employees, agents, and contractors must participate. Training should be customized to each job description and focus on issues regarding the use of health information and responsibilities regarding its confidentiality and security.

Technical Security Services

Technical security services and the following category, technical security mechanisms, are aimed directly at provider information technology departments and personnel. Providers are required to see to access control, which includes a procedure for emergency access, a choice of context-based, role-based, or user-based access and encryption. Accompanying access control is the need to audit access. While there are several network-auditing applications available, both third-party and network operating system-provided suppliers are prohibitively expensive for small-to-medium-sized agencies. This could signal the creation of a new market category consisting of a service bureau or outsourcing arrangement, or simply less expensive versions of existing software.

HIPAA also demands data authentication, "a method to corroborate that data has not been altered or destroyed in an unauthorized manner." In this instance, HIPAA offers suggestions for how an organization might do this: use of a check sum, double keying, a message authentication code, or digital signature. Other suggestions extend to automatic logoff parameters, unique user identifiers, biometric identification, PIN, telephone callback, tokens, or passwords.

Technical Security Mechanisms

Technical security mechanisms cover processes to prevent unauthorized access to data that are transmitted over a communication network. It starts with integrity controls, "a security mechanism which measures the validity of the information being electronically transmitted or stored." HIPAA demands message authentication, a security mechanism that verifies that the message received matches the message sent, to ensure that sensitive transmissions are not easily intercepted, or, as an alternate security measure, encryption.

HIPAA concludes with a description of a state-of-the-art network security system, requiring providers to install an alarm system that can sense abnormalities and either send an alert or restart the system. It also calls for a method to irrefutably identify authorized users, programs, and processes, deny access to unauthorized parties, and report automatic events. These four categories of specific mandates do not exhaust the security section of HIPAA. They merely lay down basic requirements to which all healthcare providers must adhere. None of the requirements in any categories can be effectively accomplished without at least the involvement, if not the leadership, of an agency's information technology department (Williams 2000b).

Administrative Security Procedures

The primary goal of HIPAA is to improve healthcare information dissemination and health insurance coverage continuity in order to combat waste, fraud, and abuse within health insurance and healthcare delivery. However, privacy can be compromised with improved information dissemination, and so the act includes a lengthy proposal instructing healthcare providers to ensure system security. Administrative simplification privacy and security final rules were published on December 28, 2000, with an implementation date of April 14, 2001. The proposal's description of its own purpose is to deny and limit the circumstances in which an individual's protected health information may be used or disclosed by others. HIPAA proposes to make the use and exchange of protected health information relatively easy for healthcare purposes and more difficult for nonhealthcare purposes. Five comprehensive titles address these issues:

Title I:	Health Care Access, Portability, and Renewability
Title II:	Preventing Health Care Fraud and Abuse, Administrative Simplification, Medical Liability Reform
Title III:	Tax-Related Health Provisions
Title IV:	Application and Enforcement of Group Health Plan Requirements
Title V:	Revenue Offsets

Although all of these provisions are of great concern and importance to the healthcare industry as a whole, title II, subtitle F, Administrative Simplification, is of prime significance to home healthcare information systems (Williams 2000c).

Electronic Signatures

HIPAA's proposed security rule does not require organizations to use electronic signatures, but it imposes strict standards if an organization does use them. They must be digital signatures based on cryptographic methods of originator authentication, computed with a set of rules and parameters that allow for the verification of the signer's identity and the integrity of the data. The method employed by the healthcare entity must include the following features:

- **Message integrity:** The assurance of unaltered transmission and receipt of a message from the sender to the intended recipient

- **Nonrepudiation:** Strong and substantial evidence of the message signer's identity and of message integrity, sufficient to prevent a party from successfully denying the origin, submission, or delivery of the message and the integrity of its contents

- **User authentication:** The provision of assurance of the claimed identity of the entity

If agencies elect to use electronic signatures, they may also use any of the following implementation features:

- Ability to add attributes

- Continuity of signature capability

- Countersignatures

- Independent verifiability

- Interoperability

- Multiple signatures

- Transportability

Sources of electronic signature technology can be found within and beyond the home care software vendor community.

In addition to amending administrative simplification, Congress was directed to enact privacy legislation within 36 months of HIPAA being signed into law. Since Congress failed to enact privacy legislation by August 1999, development of final regulations falls to the Department of Health and Human Services. Privacy rules limit the circumstances in which an individual's protected health information may be used or disclosed, while still providing for the relatively easy exchange of health information for healthcare purposes. Final rules will appear separately for various HIPAA provisions, with compliance required twenty-four months after each publication.

Covered entities must have authorization before using or disclosing individuals' protected health information for any purpose not otherwise recognized by this rule. A central aspect of the proposal is the principle of minimum necessary disclosure. Each provider must assess its own needs, and devise and implement privacy policies appropriate to its size, its information practices, and its business requirements. HHAs can expect, therefore, to have a contract with any business partner with whom they share protected health information. Business partners are then subject to the same privacy requirements as the covered entity. Individual patients have the right to request a covered entity to restrict the protected encounter information from further use or disclosure. However, covered entities do not need to agree to such a request. Individuals also have the right to access their protected health information. Individuals can request an accounting of disclosures of the protected health information for purposes other than treatment, payment, and healthcare operations.

The HIPAA privacy rule also gives individuals the right to request an amendment or correction of protected health information that is inaccurate or incomplete. Individuals can also receive a written notice of information practices from covered entities. HIPAA requires agencies to designate a privacy official who will develop and implement basic administrative procedures to protect identifiable health information and patient privacy rights, and a privacy training program for employees. The training should include information systems, network access, and passwords. It must also extend to everything from termination procedures and key and lock management, to how to appropriately handle conversations about individual patients. Since privacy can be breached either intentionally or accidentally, safeguards must be implemented to prevent misuse of individually identifiable health information. Covered entities must provide some means for individuals to lodge complaints about information practices and develop a system of sanctions for employees and business partners who violate the entity's policies or procedures. Organizations must also maintain documentation of their policies and procedures for complying with the rule.

Home Care Automation Report publishers recommended the following HIPAA preparation (Williams 2000c):

1. Educate yourself and your senior managers
2. Assign a privacy czar
3. Establish a HIPAA task force to oversee implementation
4. Assess your current status by reviewing all policies and procedures associated with release of information, security, confidentiality, information systems, applications, and network
5. Compare your current status to the requirements
6. Develop a detailed compliance plan and assign responsibilities and time frames
7. Determine if you will need outside resources, security, and technology consultants
8. Determine budgetary requirements
9. Communicate with assigned HIPAA specialists within your IS vendors
10. Develop new policies and procedures, and test and implement needed technology changes

Data Collection

Primary health data and information are collected and stored for patient care on paper, computer-based media, or other media. To support patient care, this information must be complete, accurate, and confidential. Examples of primary health information include reports generated by nurses (such as referral forms, assessments, clinical notes, and other reports) as well as reports generated by other providers of care and services.

Secondary health data and information are abstracted from the primary record. Provider organizations and legitimate external parties use this material for many purposes. Federal and state regulations, accrediting agencies, and third-party payers may require the dissemination of these data. Examples of secondary health information include disease indexes, quality assessment reports, and merged clinical and financial reports.

When patient data are collected through interviews, observation, testing, or review of existing documentation, it should be done in a setting that ensures maximum privacy and protects the information from unauthorized individuals. Security procedures should be followed at all times to prevent unauthorized access and to ensure the integrity of data, regardless of the medium in which they are kept. An organization's procedures should define who is authorized to enter health information into a patient's record.

Maintenance and Security

The following sections focus on the various aspects of maintenance and security of information documented in the patient's health record. The range of issues discussed includes responsibilities of the organization, staff, contractor, and vendor, as well as security.

Organizational Responsibilities

The organization must always make health information available for patient care. The organization is responsible for the data in its possession, and it must safeguard the data against loss, defacement, tampering, and unauthorized use or disclosure. There are inherent risks associated with maintaining the integrity and confidentiality of both paper-based and computer-based information. For example, an inadequately trained staff may inadvertently alter, release, or lose data. Fires or floods can destroy records, and vandals and computer hackers have been known to break into files or data banks.

Staff Responsibilities

An organization's policies and procedures must describe the responsibility of individual employees and volunteers in maintaining confidentiality, as well as the consequences of unauthorized use or disclosure. In addition, organizations must educate their employees and volunteers about these issues. AHIMA recommends that home care and hospice programs have employees, independent contractors, students, and volunteers sign a nondisclosure agreement at the time of their employment or assignment. Signing the nondisclosure agreement should be a condition of employment or assignment for all employees, independent contractors, and volunteers who will have access to confidential information as part of their employment. In addition, AHIMA recommends that each employee, student, or volunteer sign a nondisclosure acknowledgement on an annual basis, to remind these individuals of their continuing responsibility.

Providers of care and services must exercise caution at all times to protect the confidentiality of health information. Patient confidentiality can be easily and unintentionally breached through casual conversations in public places, or by reviewing or documenting a patient's record in a public place.

Contractor and Vendor Responsibilities

In some cases, an organization hires outside contractors to provide such home or hospice care or information management services as statistical processing, photocopying, transcription, storage and retrieval, microfilming, scanning, destruction, information system support, or computer outsourcing. The facility must take reasonable steps to protect information held by these contractors and their employees against theft, loss, tampering, unauthorized destruction, or other unauthorized access. In such instances, a contractor/vendor nondisclosure agreement comes into play. If employees of the contractor or vendor will have on-line access to the facility's information system, the agreement should specify which employees have this capability.

When the facility signs an agreement with the contractor, the contractor becomes responsible for the actions of its employees. Generally, the facility need not obtain individually signed agreements from each of the contractor's employees. But if particularly sensitive information is involved, each employee of the business who will have access to the information may be required to sign a separate nondisclosure agreement. Alternatively, the business could be asked to provide copies for its employees of the signed statements it has on file.

If the vendor will have possession of data (as is the case with computer outsourcing), the agreement with the vendor should require that data be returned in a usable form upon termination of the agreement.

Security

A qualified healthcare professional should supervise manual and electronic files where health information is maintained, and access to those records should be restricted to authorized personnel. Policies and procedures should specify methods for maintaining and securing both primary and secondary records, regardless of the media in which they are kept. Each organization should identify sensitive information and establish user protocols and corresponding levels of security. Higher levels of protection must be afforded information identifying individual patients or healthcare professionals. Whenever possible, internal users should be encouraged to use the original clinical record, rather than reproduce it. When multiple part forms or copies are used to facilitate home care visits, policies and procedures should be written and monitored to protect the confidentiality of this information. These policies and procedures should include the following:

- Copies shall be kept in secured briefcases and shall not be kept in car trunks overnight
- Copies of one patient's record shall not be taken into the home of another patient
- Notes shall not be written in public places, and record copies shall remain in briefcases while in public places
- Maintenance of record copies in the homes of employees shall be discouraged
- Record copies shall be obtained from employees and destroyed upon the death of a patient or the discharge of the patient/family

When record facsimiles are used to facilitate home care visits, care providers should keep only the following information:

- The most recent care plan
- The medication profile
- Initial assessment information
- Updated information for a seven-day period

Medicare interpretive guidelines suggest that when portions of a clinical record are maintained in the homes of patients, the patients or their caregivers should be informed regarding the means for protecting the confidentiality of these records. Because home record folders can be carried by patients to their doctors or to an inpatient facility, the folder should contain a statement similar to the following:

> This is a partial record. A complete original record is maintained at [insert name here] home health organization.

When home records are maintained, policies and procedures should be developed to address the documentation of sensitive or confidential information (HCFA 2000a).

A secure computer system meets the following criteria:

- Does not allow unauthorized users access to information

- Maintains the continuing integrity of data by preventing alteration or loss

- Verifies the source of data to ensure its authenticity and retains a record of communications to and from the system

- Remains available to users and recovers completely, rapidly, and effectively from unanticipated disruptions or disasters

As discussed in chapter 1, data security measures must be implemented to guard computer-based records against accidental or intentional disclosure, loss, or unauthorized access. Such data security measures should include the following characteristics:

- Physical controls over access to the system inputs and outputs, such as unique passwords, key cards with access codes, fingerprints, voiceprints, or retinal patterns for user identification, audit trails and automatic monitoring of electronic transactions, automatic log off, and the use of locks and badges

- A security system that controls access by defining authorized users and defining data access on a need-to-know basis

- 24-hour-a-day user support

- Strictly enforced policies prohibiting the sharing of passwords, key cards, and access codes

- System ability to recognize any attempt at access that goes beyond the usual course of business, along with audit trails and continuous monitoring of who accesses information and what information is accessed

- Vendor contracts that identify specific protections and dates of implementation

- Documented maintenance requirements, procedures, and logs

- Back-up systems, such as an alternate power source and off-line data storage

- Documented instructions to users describing data access procedures during scheduled and unscheduled downtime

- Documented disaster recovery procedures

Record Retention

The length of time required for maintaining health information generally depends on the purpose for which it is being kept. In developing record retention policies, providers should consider their own clinical, scientific, business, and medicolegal needs, as well as external requirements. AHIMA recommends that records on adult patients be maintained for at least ten years after the patient's last date of service, unless state law requires otherwise. Unless otherwise specified by state law, records on minor patients should be maintained until the patient reaches the age of majority (as defined by state law) plus the length of time the state's statute of limitations on malpractice runs. The Community Health Accreditation Program requires that client records be retained at least five years for adults and five years beyond the age of majority for minors (1997). JCAHO requires that organizational policies and procedures address the length of time that home care record information is being retained, and that this information should be in accordance with applicable laws and regulations (1998). Medicare regulations require that client records be retained for five years after the month that the records' applicable cost report is filed with the intermediary, unless state law stipulates a longer period of time (HCFA 2000a). These regulations also require that policies provide for retention, even if an HHA discontinues operations.

Disclosure of Health Information

It is generally accepted that the organization that creates a physical record in the delivery of care and services also owns it. Records should be removed from the organization's control and safekeeping only in accordance with a court order or subpoena. However, the organization's ownership does not imply that the organization has a right to use, disclose, or withhold information in clinical records at will. Patients generally have a qualified property interest in the health information contained in their records, although the limits of this interest vary by state.

To ensure consistent compliance with the organization's policies and procedures pertaining to it, disclosure of health information should be made only by those appropriately trained and qualified to do so. AHIMA recommends that the responsibility for disclosure of health information be centralized under the direction of the provider's HIM professional. Employees responsible for information disclosure must be carefully trained and supervised to ensure their consistent compliance with the organization's policies for disclosure. A statement that prohibits use of the information for other than the stated purpose, and requires destruction of the information after the stated need has been fulfilled, should accompany any disclosure of health information to external requesters.

Classification of Information

Health information is generally classified in one of two categories: nonconfidential and confidential. Nonconfidential patient-identifiable information includes information considered to be common knowledge, such as the patient's name, verification of admission, verification of home care or hospice services, and dates of service. Out of respect for their patients' right to privacy, many healthcare organizations make it a policy to not release any information about their patients to the public, neither their names nor the fact that they are being treated. Some patients may request that their names be withheld during treatment and that they be assigned a pseudonym. Each organization should develop policies and procedures about disclosure of this information, while taking into consideration its patient population and state laws.

Confidential patient-identifiable information includes information on the patient's clinical condition, past and present diagnoses, and treatments. Clinical information is considered privileged communication, thus any information exchanged between a patient and the physician is considered strictly confidential and is protected under law. Patient-identifiable clinical information that is part of financial records, billing systems, and secondary records, such as statistical reports, must be afforded the same protection as the source records.

Confidential patient-identifiable information also includes nonclinical information, which is not protected as privileged communication but by the patient's right to privacy. In general, confidential patient-identifiable information includes demographic data (patient's age, address, and marital status) and administrative data not related to the patient's diagnosis or treatment (such as the patient's next of kin).

Information on the business and clinical operations of home health operations may be considered confidential even when it does not include patient identifiers. For example, information pertaining to the professional performance of employees should be treated as confidential and protected by the organization's security program. Sensitive personal information about employees and medical staff, such as references to psychological profiles, substance abuse, and alternative lifestyles, should receive special protection to prevent unauthorized access.

Authority of Disclosure

The following people have authority to grant authorization for disclosure of health information:

- The patient, if she or he is a competent adult or an emancipated/mature minor

- A legal guardian or parent on behalf of a minor

- The executor of the estate or an individual appointed by the probate court, if the patient is deceased

A minor is one who is under the age of majority prescribed by state law. Some states declare minors emancipated or mature when they meet one of the following requirements:

- Married

- Self-supporting and living away from home

- Declared legally emancipated by a court of law

- Unmarried and pregnant

- On active duty with the United States Armed Forces

- At least sixteen years old and living independently from parents or guardian

If a minor meets state requirements for emancipation or maturity, he or she may authorize disclosure of health information. State laws should be consulted when determining the rights of minors in individual states.

If a patient is incompetent or otherwise unable to authorize disclosure, the following individuals may serve as the patient's legal representative, in order of priority:

1. Legal guardian or attorney ad litem

2. Agent named in a directive, durable power of attorney for healthcare, or other durable power of attorney

3. Next of kin, in the following order:
   a. Spouse
   b. Adult son or daughter
   c. Father or mother
   d. Adult brother or sister

State laws should be checked for any deviation from the preceding order.

Minimum Requirements for Acceptable Authorization

Disclosures of patient-identifiable information to parties outside the organization for purposes not related to patient care always require the written permission of the patient or the patient's guardian or legal representative. Home health organizations should also consider external requests for information about their medical staff and employees very carefully. All disclosures of confidential information should include a statement prohibiting redisclosure and requiring destruction of information after the purpose for the disclosure has been fulfilled. It should be noted that the patient has the right to revoke the authorization for disclosure at any time.

When an employee did not observe the signing of the authorization document, the signature of the patient should be compared with a previously signed document in his or her clinical record to ensure its authenticity. In case of a discrepancy, the patient should be contacted to verify that release of the requested information was indeed authorized. If electronic authentication is used, a system must be in place to identify each individual authorizing disclosure. The signed authorization from the patient or the patient's legal representative should be maintained with the patient's paper clinical record, along with a notation stating what information was disclosed, on what date, and the name of the employee who made the disclosure. In cases of computer-based records, other mechanisms must be considered that will maintain these authorizations.

Revocation of Authorization

The patient or the patient's legal representative has the right to revoke authorization to disclose information at any time. A revocation should be issued in the same manner that an authorization for disclosure was made. For a written authorization, a revocation of authorization should be submitted in writing to the organization, and it should be maintained with the patient's clinical record. If the patient or the legal representative of the patient is unable to submit revocation in writing, an oral revocation may be accepted, and the person accepting the revocation should document it. If authorization was given via computer, it may be revoked in the same manner. Revocation of authorization does not affect any health information that was disclosed before the organization received the notice of revocation, or any disclosure made for the purpose of obtaining payment for services that were provided in reliance on the authorization.

Disclosure Requirements to Specific Individuals and Entities

Medicare *Conditions of Participation* standard 484.10(d) covers the patient's right to confidentiality of clinical records maintained by the HHA, which must advise the patient of its policies and procedures regarding disclosure of clinical records. Protecting the confidentiality of OASIS information as described in COP 484.11 is twofold; the HHA has a responsibility to keep OASIS information confidential and HCFA has a responsibility to keep it confidential once it has been transmitted to the OASIS state system. Under the *Conditions of Participation,* the HHA is required to maintain confidentiality of OASIS data while it is used for patient care. In addition, the HHA may not release data without the consent of the patient for any reason other than to appropriately deliver care. If the HHA contracts with a vendor to transmit OASIS data, a written agreement that addresses the confidentiality of those data must be in place. Violations of data confidentiality by an entity under contract with the HHA are the responsibility of the HHA and would constitute noncompliance. Ultimately, the HHA is responsible for compliance with the confidentiality requirements and is considered at fault if the contractor does not meet the requirements (HCFA 2000b).

Accreditation and Licensure Surveyors

The organization's accreditation surveyors and federal and state licensure surveyors can have limited access to health information to ensure compliance with standards or regulations for health information management. Authorization from the patient or the legal representative of the patient is not required in such cases, provided that the survey reports do not identify any individual patient.

Attorneys

A valid subpoena or written authorization from the patient or the legal representative of the patient is required for release of health information, unless the attorney represents the healthcare provider. Some states do not authorize attorneys to issue subpoenas for health information. State laws vary widely regarding disclosure of health information in response to a subpoena. Organizations should obtain legal advice when developing policies and procedures for response to subpoenas.

Courts of Law

State statutes define the power to issue subpoenas, and that power varies from state to state. For the most part, attorneys, government boards, and commissions, judges, and clerks of court may issue subpoenas. When a court of proper jurisdiction issues subpoenas and court orders, they should be honored in person, by deposition or interrogatory, and they should be accompanied by a copy of the clinical record or designated portions of it. Health information disclosed in response to a subpoena or court order does not require authorization from the patient or the patient's legal representative. Information relating to alcohol or drug abuse may not be disclosed in response to a subpoena. Instead, disclosure must be authorized by a court order granted after application showing good cause for the disclosure. Under certain circumstances, if a subpoena is irregular or is in conflict with federal or state laws, the organization may make a legal motion to quash the subpoena and negate the need to comply with it. The legal counsel of the organization should be consulted in cases involving unusual subpoenas or those requesting information that is not usually released before any action is taken in response.

Employers

In order to obtain records, employers must have written authorization from the patient or the patient's legal representative, unless otherwise authorized by law. For example, in the case of worker's compensation claims, state law may give the employer the right to access health information without authorization from the patient or the patient's legal representative. HIM professionals should review state laws to ensure compliance with them.

Family Members

Family members of a patient may access that patient's health information only with written authorization from the patient or the patient's legal representative. In the case of hospice bereavement records, a family member may request access to, or copies of, bereavement records pertaining exclusively to him or her. Information should not be released when a family member requests copies of hospice records that also contain information about the patient or other family members, and when the patient or another family member does not consent to release copies of these records. When facing such requests, the hospice should obtain legal counsel.

Federal, State, and Local Government, and Voluntary Welfare Agencies

Organizations that fall within this category include schools, human services departments, disability determination, social service agencies, Internal Revenue Service, Public Health Service, Vocational Rehabilitation, and Social Security Administration. Written authorization from the patient or the patient's legal representative is required, unless disclosure is otherwise authorized or required by law.

Funeral Homes

Some states hold funeral homes responsible for completion of death certificates. In these cases, information regarding the time of death, cause of death, and attending physician's name and address may be disclosed to the funeral home without authorization from the patient's legal representative.

Health Departments

Health departments include city, county, or state agencies, such as communicable disease control, tuberculosis control, or bureau of vital statistics. Health information within the reasonable scope of these agencies' authority may be released to their authorized representatives without authorization of the patient or the patient's legal representative.

Individual Care and Service Providers

Individual care and service providers (including volunteers) may have access without patient authorization to the health information they need to perform their jobs. It is important that access be granted only on a need-to-know basis. The organization's policies and procedures should designate—by assignment, job category, or title—the employees or volunteers that may have access to health information in the course of performing their duties. Healthcare professionals should not have access to the records of their family members or patients not under their care, unless they have written authorization from the patients or the patients' legal representative.

Healthcare providers disclose necessary health information to subsequent providers to facilitate care transfers. For most disclosures, such as health information submitted with bills, providers may send only the minimum information needed for the purpose of disclosure. However, for purposes of treatment, healthcare providers need to be able to transmit fuller information to other providers. HIPAA gives providers full discretion in determining what personal health information to include when sending patients' health records to other providers for treatment purposes. Disclosures occur verbally, or by sending copies from the first provider to the second. COP 484.48 states, "if a patient is transferred to another health facility a copy of the record is sent with the patient" (HCFA 2000a). Conversely, hospitals, long-term care facilities, clinics, and rehabilitation agencies have similar legal and regulatory requirements.

Insurance Companies and Third-Party Payers

For insurance companies and third-party payers to receive health records, written authorization is required from the patient or the patient's legal representative. For some third-party payers, the insurer's health insurance contract contains a preauthorized consent for disclosure of any information necessary to pay a claim requested by the third-party payer. Such third-party payers include Blue Cross/Blue Shield, Civilian Health and Medical Program of Uniformed Services (CHAMPUS), Medicare, and Medicaid. This practice is convenient and expedient for third-party payers but requires patients to authorize the disclosure of information before the information is collected, thus presuming the patient's ability to make an informed decision.

HIM professionals should exercise caution in disclosing information based upon a contractual release, as the patient may not have authorized such disclosure. For example, in family coverage, the policyholder signs the authorization for disclosure. If the patient is the policyholder's spouse, the patient then has not signed the contractual authorization covering release of information.

Law Enforcement Officials

Officials include city, county, and state police, the Federal Bureau of Investigation, and the Central Intelligence Agency. Nonconfidential information may be released when the healthcare facility is provided with positive proof that a bona fide law enforcement agent is requesting the information. Confidential information should be released only with written authorization of the patient or the patient's legal representative, or in compliance with a subpoena or court order, in accordance with state law.

Medical Examiner and Coroner

If conducting a postmortem examination on a patient, a medical examiner may have access to the patient's health information without authorization from the patient's legal representative.

Patients

Most states allow a patient or the patient's legal representative to examine and obtain copies of the patient's hospital records, although some states grant patients the right to review their hospital records only after discharge. Less clear are the rights of access to health records maintained by physicians and other individual healthcare providers. AHIMA believes that the patient or the patient's legal representative should have access to health information, unless otherwise prohibited by state law. Health information may be disclosed to the patient or the patient's legal representative upon written request and presentation of proper identification. In the case of psychiatric records, the patient's physician should be contacted prior to disclosure. Patients should be permitted to review their records without charge. Questions regarding treatment, prognosis, or other clinical matters should be referred to the attending physician. Patients who request copies of records may be charged a reasonable fee to cover the cost of accessing and copying the record.

HIPAA privacy standards spell out the circumstances under which patients may amend information pertaining to their care. If the patient or the patient's legal representative is disputing information documented in the record, they should discuss the issue with the healthcare practitioner who made the entry in question. If the healthcare practitioner agrees that the entry contains an error, he or she should make the correcting entry in the patient's record. When correcting paper records, a single line should be drawn through the entry containing the error, the correct data should then be recorded, and, finally, the individual making the correction should sign and date it. The original entry must never be obliterated. For errors corrected in a computer-based record, the system should preserve both the original entry and the amendment, as well as the identity of the person making the amendment.

If the healthcare practitioner does not agree that a correction is warranted, he or she should discuss the matter with the patient or the patient's legal representative. She or he may make a separate statement in writing or electronically, disputing the information and offering an amendment. Such a statement should be filed with the record or made part of it, and then included with any future disclosures.

The Federal Privacy Act (5 USC Section 552a) was designed to give individuals some control over information the federal government may collect about them. This act also applies to healthcare facilities that the federal government operates (such as the Veterans Administration, Public Health Service, and Department of Defense facilities). Key provisions of the act include the following:

- The individual has the right to know that identifiable, personal information is available in a record system, and to know how that information is used.

- The individual has the right to access the information, have a copy made of all or any portion of it, and to correct or amend the records.

- The information may not be used for any purpose beyond that for which it was collected.

- No information may be disclosed to any person or another agency, without the written consent of the individual to whom the information pertains. Disclosure is permitted with authorization for certain routine uses.

Under the new HIPAA privacy standards, individual patients may request that healthcare providers restrict the use or disclosure of protected patient information. Although providers are not required to comply with such requests, they are required to inform individual patients about the consequences of such restrictions; for example, a patient's health plan is unlikely to process an incomplete claim for reimbursement. Home health organizations will be required to inform patients of the entity's privacy practices, and any communications stating these practices must be separate from the consent and authorization forms used by HHAs. The information may take the form of a brochure, pamphlet, or posted notice.

Research

The organization's policies and procedures should define the extent to which physicians and other healthcare practitioners may access health records for study and research. An institutional review board may make health information available to researchers who provide written evidence of approval of their projects. Authorization from the patient or the patient's legal representative is not required, as long as the articles, papers, or other products of the research do not identify specific patients. The researcher must share responsibility for protecting the confidentiality of health information and ensuring its availability for patient care. Identifiable patient data maintained by the researcher should be destroyed when no longer needed.

Worker's Compensation Carriers

In many states, worker's compensation laws give the insurance carrier, the patient's employer, worker's compensation representatives, and the industrial accident board the right to access health information without authorization from the patient or the patient's legal representative. HIM professionals should discuss state law with legal counsel before developing a policy to handle disclosure in worker's compensation cases.

Methods of Disclosure

As the HIPAA privacy and security final rules are published, continued advances in technology are increasing the automation of disclosures. In this fast moving atmosphere, it is important that home health organizations understand the data that must be transferred, the manner of transfer, and the law, accreditation, or professional practice standards that govern transfer.

Mail

Mailing copies of a patient's health information to a legitimate requester is the most common method of disclosure. Documents should be securely sealed in an envelope that is marked with the organization's return address.

Facsimile Machine

Though facsimile (fax) machines offer a means of immediate exchange of written health information, their use opens up the potential for loss of patient privacy if confidential information is misdirected or handled improperly upon receipt. Because of this, AHIMA recommends fax transmittal of health information only when the original paper record or mail-delivered copies will not meet the needs of immediate patient care. Routine disclosure of information to insurance companies, attorneys, or other nonhealthcare entities should be conducted through regular mail or messenger service.

Disclosure by fax requires adherence to the following procedures:

1. A cover letter accompanies each disclosure, and the letter contains the following information:
   a. Date and time of transmission
   b. The sending facility's name, address, telephone number, and facsimile number, and the sender's name
   c. The receiving facility's name, address, telephone number, and facsimile number, and the authorized receiver's name
   d. Number of pages sent, including cover letter
   e. Statement regarding redisclosure
   f. Statement regarding destruction
   g. Instructions for authorized receiver to verify receipt of information

2. Contact by telephone verifies that the authorized receiver is available before transmission begins.

3. Specific information disclosed on the cover letter is noted and the original cover letter is filed with the health record.

4. The transmission verification report generated by the fax machine verifies that the information was transmitted to the receiver's number. If the information was sent to a wrong number, a request is faxed to the incorrect number, explaining the misdirected information and requesting return of all documents. An incident report about the misdirection is then completed and forwarded to the facility's risk manager.

Due to their nature, certain types of health information are considered so sensitive that they should not be faxed. Such information includes, but is not limited to, abortion, HIV and AIDS, patients who wish to remain anonymous, mental healthcare, and sexually transmitted diseases.

Telephone

Information should be disclosed over the telephone only in urgent cases involving continued patient care. In such cases, the call should be returned to verify the identity of the individual to whom the information was disclosed. Documentation of such disclosure, including date, time, requester's name, address, telephone number, explanation of the need for urgent disclosure, and name of the individual making the disclosure, should be maintained with the patient's record.

Electronic Transmittal

In home health organizations, patient-identifiable information is exchanged routinely via electronic channels between healthcare organizations and third-party payers. In recognition of this fact, the federal government has launched several initiatives related to electronic transmission of confidential healthcare information. HIPAA was legislated to facilitate the electronic transmission for reimbursement-related information, and at the same time protect the privacy of healthcare consumers. In addition to claims processing, home health organizations use Internet-based electronic channels to exchange patient-identifiable information for a number of other purposes. Caregivers and administrative and clerical staff may exchange messages via electronic mail (e-mail) to discuss unusual cases or to seek advice from physicians. Moreover, the Internet hosts multiple health-related sites that feature discussion groups for consumers and clinicians. Many computer-based health record systems house extensive clinical data repositories linked directly to the Internet.

Home health organizations using telemedicine use Internet-based electronic channels together with information systems and multimedia communications technology to provide a forum through which clinicians and patients can exchange information in real-time interactions. Real-time electronic transmission of health information across state lines creates new challenges. State laws protecting the confidentiality of healthcare information are inconsistent, but the standardized security provisions of HIPAA may make it easier for telemedicine providers to collaborate across the United States. In all cases, providers should ensure that patients are fully informed of potential threats to their privacy and that the patients or their legal representatives have signed written consent forms prior to telemedicine encounters.

Like the disclosure of confidential information in paper-based media, the disclosure of electronic, patient-identifiable information and multimedia images to legitimate users outside the organization requires the written permission of the patient or her or his legal representative. The information released should be limited to only the information needed to fulfill the purpose of the authorized request. Organizations should establish a rigorous information security infrastructure that includes policies and procedures, staff training and awareness programs, and system architecture that protects the confidentiality and integrity of electronic transmission of confidential health information. An organizational risk assessment should consider all applicable accreditation standards and federal state laws and regulations. All confidential text, voice, and image files, and other health record and patient-identifiable information transmitted over the Internet, should be encrypted to protect from unauthorized access and alteration. Appropriate security technology, such as firewalls and transmission protocols, should be employed.

Human Immunodeficiency Virus and Acquired Immunodeficiency Syndrome

The legal requirements surrounding the health records of AIDS patients vary by state. They can also be extremely complex. Home health organizations should consult legal counsel before developing specific policies and procedures on the confidentiality and release of AIDS-related information, especially any release of information without the patient's written consent. Home health organizations should not create special handling or storage procedures for the health records of HIV-positive patients because handling or storage systems based on HIV status may actually call attention to the records of these patients and place them at greater risk of unauthorized access. Home health organizations should implement clear policies and procedures on the disclosure of health information related to HIV status and AIDS. Such policies should be monitored continuously to ensure consistent compliance.

Home health organizations should manage information on HIV-positive healthcare workers according to guidelines outlined by the Centers for Disease Control and state and federal mandates. The healthcare worker's right to privacy must be balanced against the risk of disease transmission to patients, employees, and others. When questions arise, the organization's legal counsel should be involved in resolving related questions.

Redisclosure of Health Information

Frequently, an organization's records may contain information about a patient from another healthcare provider. Such information is sent with patients who are transferred or referred to a facility for treatment, continuing care, or support. If information from another facility is used in the patient's assessment or care, the receiving facility should maintain that information permanently with the patient's clinical record. If the patient brings copies of prior health information, such copies should be returned to the patient upon request. If this information was used in the patient's assessment or care, the facility should keep a copy of it with the patient's record.

A facility may redisclose health information from another facility without authorization from the patient or his or her legal representative if it is urgently needed for the patient's continuing care. If time permits, authorization from the patient or his or her legal representative should be obtained prior to redisclosure to a third entity. If a patient requests access to health information from another facility, the facility possessing the information should disclose it to the patient upon written request, unless otherwise prohibited by state law. Unless state law requires otherwise, no other redisclosure should be made. In response to a subpoena or other request, the healthcare provider should not disclose information from another facility, with the exception of outside test results that have been made part of the organization's record.

When information from health records is provided to authorized external users, this information should be accompanied by a statement that does the following:

- Prohibits use of the information for other than the stated purpose

- Prohibits disclosure by the recipient to any other party without written authorization from the patient or the patient's legal representative unless such information is urgently needed for the patient's continuing care or otherwise required by state law

- Requires destruction of the information after the stated need has been fulfilled

Responsibility to the Patient and Public

Patients are generally unaware that their health information is subject to a full range of uses and that policies exist to govern the disclosure of that information. Typically, they take notice only of personal health information that affects their immediate concerns, such as planning their healthcare, protection of legal interests, or applications for life insurance. Such issues as utilization management, quality management, research, facility planning, licensure, accreditation, and certification are unfamiliar to most patients. Few patients are aware of the amount of information disclosed to third parties.

Current philosophy places new emphasis on patient involvement in healthcare. As providers assume active roles as educators, so patients may become active participants in their healthcare, and so too must HIM professionals assume an active role in educating patients and the public. From HIM professionals, patients can learn about the various uses of health information and the following rights:

- Restrict or limit dissemination of identifiable health information

- Access health information

- Know the facility's policies and procedures regarding disclosure, access, and amendments

Medicare home care regulations (HCFA 2000a) require home care organizations to inform patients of their policies and procedures concerning clinical record disclosure and to document in a patient's clinical record that this disclosure occurred.

Summary

The health information manager working in the home health or hospice setting must be familiar with general statutes and regulations governing health records as well as state-specific statutes and regulations. In addition, the health information manager must actively participate in the development and enforcement of the organization's policies regarding privacy and security. HIPAA privacy and security standards mandate staff training and documentation of staff training activities. The specific training requirements are similar to current Medicare compliance rules.

References and Bibliography

American Health Information Management Association. 1993. Lawyers, ethics, and the misdirected fax. *In Confidence* 1(3):7–9.

American Health Information Management Association. 1993. AMA: Some HIV privacy rights survive death. *In Confidence* 1(4):8–9.

American Psychiatric Association. 1993. AIDS policy: guidelines for inpatient psychiatric units. *American Journal of Psychiatry* 150(5):853.

Anonymous. 2001. News and analysis on reimbursement, finance, law, research, and technology. *Eli's Home Care Week* 10(7):55.

Brandt, Mary D., and Jennifer Carpenter. 1999. Practice brief: Managing health information relating to infection with the human immunodeficiency virus (HIV) (updated). *Journal of the American Health Information Management Association.* Chicago: American Health Information Management Association.

Brandt, Mary D., and Gwen Hughes. 2001. Practice brief: Facsimile transmission of health information (updated). *Journal of the American Health Information Management Association.* Chicago: American Health Information Management Association.

Cofer, Jennifer, ed. 1994. *Health Information Management.* 10th ed. Berwyn, Ill.: Physicians' Record Company, pp. 35–36, 604, 612.

Community Health Accreditation Program. 1997. *Standards of Excellence for Home Care Organizations.* New York City: National League for Health Care/Community Health Accreditation Program.

Health Care Financing Administration. 2000a. Appendix B: interpretive guidelines for home health agencies. In *Medicare State Operations Manual Provider Certification.* Washington, D.C.: Government Printing Office.

Health Care Financing Administration. 2000b. Appendix M: survey procedures and interpretive guidelines, Rev. 265. In *Medicare State Operations Manual Provider Certification.* Washington, D.C.: Government Printing Office.

Health Care Financing Administration. 2000c. Transmittal 21. In *Medicare State Operations Manual Provider Certification.* Washington, D.C.: Government Printing Office.

Joint Commission on Accreditation of Healthcare Organizations. 2000. *2001–2002 Comprehensive Accreditation Manual for Home Care.* Oakbrook Terrace, Ill.: JCAHO.

Russell, D., and G. T. Gangemi. 1991. *Computer Security Basics.* Sebastopol, Calif.: O'Reilly and Associates.

U.S. Department of Health and Human Services. 2000. FAQ: What Are the Major Differences between the Proposed Rule and the Final Rule? Office of the Assistant Secretary for Planning and Evaluation Web site. http://aspe.os.dhhs.gov/admnsimp/faqtxdif.htm.

Waller, Adele A. 1997. Legal aspects of computer-based health records and record systems. Appendix B in *The Computer-Based Health Record: An Essential Technology for Health Care.* Revised ed. Washington, D.C.: National Academy Press.

Waller, Adele A., and Deborah K. Fulton. 1993. The electronic chart: keeping it confidential and secure. *Journal of Health and Hospital Law* 26(4):104–9.

Williams, Thomas D. 2000a. *Home Care Automation Report: HIPAA Final Rule Released.* Fredonia, Wis.: Stonyhill Publications.

Williams, Thomas D. 2000b. *Home Care Automation Report: HIPAA Security Update: Compliance Will Be Tough.* Fredonia, Wis.: Stonyhill Publications.

Williams, Thomas D. 2000c. *Home Care Automation Report: Move HIPAA to Top of Your To-Do List.* Fredonia, Wis.: Stonyhill Publications.

Williams, Thomas D. 2001d. *Home Care Automation Report: HIPAA Breaking News—Final Privacy Regs Start Compliance.* Fredonia, Wis.: Stonyhill Publications.

Chapter 6

Home Health Prospective Payment System

Margaret Morgan Stewart, RHIA

In October 2000, Medicare began reimbursing all home health agencies (HHAs) under a prospective payment system (PPS). This new system replaces the pre-Balanced Budget Act system based on costs as well as the interim payment system that had been in place since October 1997. This new PPS is designed to promote efficiency and help prevent waste and abuse within the home health payment system.

Between 1990 and 1997, home healthcare expenditures grew from 2.9 percent to nearly 9 percent of all Medicare payments. The earlier cost-based system was creating growth in home health spending, due in large part to the lack of incentives to provide care efficiently. Previously, HHAs have been paid based on the costs of providing care, which was only subject to a per visit limit. Thus, the more visits HHAs provided and the greater the cost increases, the greater the payments to those HHAs. The old system encouraged abuse, as evidenced by the increase in per-beneficiary visits, which more than doubled from 36 in 1990 to 80 in 1997.

The interim payment system, which was mandated by the Balanced Budget Act of 1997 and was replaced three years later with the PPS, was based on the lowest of reasonable costs, an aggregate cost limit per visit, or an aggregate cost limit per beneficiary. Such limits removed incentives to provide unnecessary visits in order to increase payment. Under the PPS, HHAs are now paid a predetermined base payment that may vary per each 60-day episode of care depending on the patient's severity of illness and home health needs. The services that will be reimbursed include home health aide visits, skilled nursing visits, supplies, medical social services, and therapy. Key points of the PPS include the following:

- Medicare will reimburse HHAs for each 60-day episode of care as long as the patient remains eligible and the services are medically necessary.

- Beneficiaries who have greater home healthcare needs will warrant higher payment rates to their HHAs.

- National payment rates will be used that range from $1,100 to $5,900 for each 60-day episode of service. Payment is determined by the intensity of care provided. Data documented from patient assessments (which is already a requirement for all Medicare-participating HHAs) will be used to support payment rates. Payment rates are also adjusted by area wage differences.

Margaret Morgan Stewart, RHIA, authored chapter 6. Stewart is the owner and president of Morgan-Stewart Consulting, based in Atlanta, Georgia, and she is a past president of AHIMA.

- In cases where the patient's care results in unusually high home healthcare costs, outlier payments will be made for a portion of the amount of costs beyond the set threshold.

- The Health Care Financing Administration (HCFA) will pay 60 percent of the initial episode payment up front when an HHA first accepts a new Medicare patient, in order to streamline the approval process and ensure adequate payment. HHAs will receive the remaining 40 percent of payment at the end of that initial episode of care. The episodes of care that follow will be paid based on equally divided payments between the beginning and end of those episodes of care.

- Patients who have a significant change in their condition during an episode of care will have an adjustment made to their payment rate.

- HHAs will get a partial episode payment for a beneficiary-elected transfer or a discharge and return to the same agency that warrants a new clock for payment. When a new sixty-day episode begins, the original sixty-day payment is proportionally adjusted to reflect the time the beneficiary remained under the agency's care before the intervening event.

- HHAs and suppliers will be paid separately for durable medical equipment if it is medically necessary.

- HCFA will perform extensive reviews to assess errors or trends within this new payment system as well as ensure the quality of patient care is maintained.

Coding for Home Health Services

The PPS for Medicare home health services has changed greatly as of October 1, 2000. The following are key points describing the changes made in the new payment system:

- Payment is now made on the basis of a prospective amount.

- The secretary of the Department of Health and Human Services determines a new unit of payment.

- The new unit of payment reflects case-mix and wage adjustments.

- Cost outliers are allowed.

- Proration of the payment is required when a beneficiary chooses to transfer from one HHA to another within an episode.

- Services are to be recorded in 15-minute increments on claims.

- Physician identifiers (UPINs) for prescribing physicians must appear on claims.

- Periodic interim payments have been eliminated for HHAs.

- Consolidated billing is now required by HHAs for all services and supplies for patients under a home health plan of care.

Billing Requirements

As of October 1, 2000, all HHAs must bill all services delivered to homebound Medicare beneficiaries under a home health plan of care under the home health prospective payment system (HH PPS). These types of claims must be billed under the cost reimbursement system on form

HCFA-1450 (UB-92), with form locator 4 (FL 4), Type of bill, completed with first digit 3, second digit 2 or 3, and a varying third digit represented as X.

UPINs and 15-minute increments have been required on Medicare home health claims since October 1999, and that has not changed under the HH PPS. Likewise, existing laws affecting claims payment, such as specifying a payment floor and Medicare secondary payer payment procedures, are still valid for Medicare claims and have not been changed. HH PPS are to use the paper and electronic form HCFA-1450 (UB-92) for requests for anticipated payments (RAPs) and claims. Related existing transaction formats, such as the 835 electronic and paper remittances, should still be used.

A 60-day episode makes up the unit of payment under the HH PPS. Each of these episodes will be paid in two payments. The first episode is to be billed at the beginning of the episode on an RAP and another one should be billed at the end of the episode. Claims must provide line items that list the individual services provided.

Like inpatient diagnosis-related groups, home health now has home health resource groups (HHRGs) that are represented by HCFA health insurance prospective payment system (HIPPS) coding on claims. HHRGs are the basis of payment for each sixty-day episode. The HHRG is produced through grouper software when the results of comprehensive assessments of the beneficiary, created with the Outcome and Assessment Information Set (OASIS) data set, are input or grouped in this software. Should there be a significant change in the patient's health status during the middle of the sixty-day episode, the HHRGs can be changed. This is referred to as a significant change in condition adjustment.

Episodes can be broken up and given partial episode payments if beneficiaries choose to transfer among HHAs or if a patient is discharged and then readmitted during the same sixty-day episode. Payments are case-mix and wage adjusted using pricer software at the regional home health intermediary. If the number of visits falls to four or below, there are reducing adjustments made in payment called low-utilization payment adjustments (LUPAs). There are downward adjustments in HHRGs if the number of therapy services delivered during the sixty-day episode does not meet the anticipated therapy threshold.

In addition to episode payments, there are also cost outliers built into the HH PPS. To qualify for an outlier payment, the amount of the episode must exceed the outlier threshold.

$$\text{Outlier threshold} = \text{Case-mix-adjusted and wage-adjusted episode amount} + \text{Wage-adjusted fixed dollar loss amount}$$

The fixed dollar loss amount is 113 percent of the sixty-day national standardized amount, which is $2,115.30.

The primary HHA under consolidated billing must identify itself to HCFA and its claims processing agents through submission of RAPs and claims. The primary HHA can bill for home health services under "home health benefit other than durable medical equipment." If there are multiple agencies providing services simultaneously, they must take payment under arrangement with the primary HHA.

The following are guidelines for billing on the UB-92 for home health claims.

- The episode should be billed with the new revenue code 0023 with new HIPPS code on the HCPCS field of the same line.

- Services/visits should be billed with revenue codes 42x, 43x, 55x, 56x, and 57x with Gxxxx HCPCS codes for incremental reporting. Revenue codes 58x and 59x are no longer permitted under HH PPS billing.

141

- For the type of bill, use 32x bill type only. For HH PPS, HHA submitted RAP Type of bill must be 322. Usage of 328 may be cancelled.

- Services/visits should be billed on type of bill 32x only if plan of care.

- The outlier appears on the remittance only for HH PPS claims via the pricer. The outlier is determined by the pricer and should not be billed by HHAs.

- In regard to the payment basis, the PPS episode rate is impacted by four issues:

  —Full 60-day episode with or without significant change in condition adjustment

  —Less than full episode with partial episode payment adjustment

  —LUPA paid on a per-visit basis

  —Therapy threshold adjustment

- When LUPAs are billed on 32x, the visits are paid on an adjusted national standardized per-visit rate. For 34x, the visit will be paid as part of the outpatient PPS.

Under a prospective payment system, payment is made before services are delivered, or payment levels are determined prior to the completion of care. HH PPS considers a patient's clinical condition and functional ability, as well as service demands, in determining case mix for home healthcare. Assessments of the patient as well as the HCPCS service codes provided all affect reimbursement under HH PPS.

Diagnosis-related groups link case-mix to inpatient hospital payment. The current diagnosis-related group definitions manual describes a diagnosis-related group as "a manageable, clinically coherent set of patient classes that relate a hospital's case mix to the resource demands and associated costs experienced by the hospital" (HCFA 2000b). The HH PPS is built on this model, using HHRGs instead of diagnosis-related groups.

The HH PPS total case-mix-adjusted episode payment is based on elements of the OASIS data set, including therapy hours or visits provided over the course of the 60-day episode. The number of therapy hours or visits is projected at the start of the episode, and this information is entered into OASIS and should be confirmed by the hour or visit information submitted on the claim for the episode. With the HH PPS, a minimum of one service must be delivered before billing can occur. Once initial coding is complete and the claim contains at least one billable service, RAPs or claims are submitted to regional home health intermediaries (RHHIs).

In the HH PPS, the grouper links patient assessment results with the payment. In 1999, Medicare required HHAs to begin performing assessments on potential patients and to reassess the patients while they were under the care of an HHA. OASIS is used to assess patients. Grouper software calculates and assigns the appropriate HHRG for payment of the sixty-day HHA episode. The assignment is based on the results of an OASIS submission for a beneficiary that is input or grouped in this software. The grouper produces HHRGs as HIPPS coding. The grouper will also produce a claims-OASIS matching key, which links the HIPPS code to a particular OASIS submission. Under the HH PPS, both the HIPPS code and the claims-OASIS matching key will be entered on RAP claims. If an OASIS assessment is rejected upon transmission and is then corrected, resulting in a different HIPPS code, the RAP and/or claim for the episode must also be canceled and rebilled using the corrected HIPPS code.

Coding of Services and Diagnoses

Under the HH PPS, a case-mix-adjusted payment for a sixty-day episode will be made using one of 80 HHRGs. Although HHRGs differ from diagnosis-related groups in that they utilize the OASIS assessment tool to determine the HHRGs, both require ICD-9-CM assignment. However, there are differences in the ICD-9-CM codes required for HH PPS claims.

The principal diagnosis code is required in form locator 67 for home health claims coding. The HHA must enter the ICD-9-CM code for the principal diagnosis and include fourth- and fifth-digit specificity when warranted. The ICD-9-CM principal diagnosis code reported must match the primary diagnosis code reported on the OASIS form.

As on DRG claims, form locators 68 through 75 of the UB-92 require other diagnosis codes or secondary ICD-9-CM diagnosis code assignments. These secondary diagnoses are required if they coexisted at the time of the establishment of the plan of care. They must also match the additional diagnoses reported on the OASIS form under other diagnoses. The additional ICD-9-CM diagnoses are all conditions that coexisted at the time the plan of care was established. The additional diagnoses should be assigned in order to best reflect the seriousness of the patient's condition and to justify the services provided. Surgical and V codes, which are not acceptable in M0230 or M0240 on the OASIS or as the principal or first secondary diagnosis on the form HCFA-485, may be reported as additional diagnoses on the UB-92 for home health billing.

The following types of ICD-9-CM codes are not required on home health claims:

- Admitting diagnosis

- E codes, such as injury and place of occurrence

- Principal procedure code

- Secondary or additional procedures

Form 485 requires a procedure code in locator 12 if the surgical procedure performed is related to the plan of care. HCPCS codes are also required in form locator 44 for the billing of home health services. Like outpatient hospital billing, the HCPCS must correlate by line item with the revenue center and date of service as well as the units of service. Units of service should not be reported for line items designated with the 0023 revenue code.

The following are examples of common treatments and therapies provided to home health patients and the HCPCS codes that should be assigned. Note that for each HCPCS code, the service units represent the number of fifteen-minute increments that constituted the visit.

- Physical therapy involves therapeutic exercises, massage, use of heat and cold, and other techniques for diagnosis and rehabilitation of patients who have orthopedic, neuromuscular, or other disabilities. Use HCPCS code G0151, Services of a physical therapist under a home health plan of care, each fifteen minutes.

- Occupational therapy includes therapeutic activities and exercises, training in psychosocial skills, training in the usage of orthopedic devices, and cognitive retraining, provided by a qualified occupational therapy practitioner in order to improve, sustain, or restore an individual's level of function in performance of activities of daily living and work. Use HCPCS code G0152, Services of an occupational therapist under a home health plan of care, each fifteen minutes.

143

- Speech therapy involves services provided to persons with impaired functional communications skills. Use HCPCS code G0153, Services of a speech and language pathologist under a home health plan of care, each fifteen minutes.

- Skilled nursing involves nursing services that must be provided under the direct supervision of a licensed nurse to assure the safety of the patient and to achieve medical goals. Use HCPCS code G0154, Services of a skilled nurse under a home health plan of care, each fifteen minutes.

- Medical social services involve services such as counseling, interviewing, and assisting with social situation problems that patients may encounter. Use HCPCS code G0155, Services of a clinical social worker under a home health plan of care, each fifteen minutes.

- Home health aide involves charges for HHA personnel that are primarily responsible for the personal care of the patient. Use HCPCS code G0156, Services of a home health aide under a home health plan of care, each fifteen minutes.

An HHA claim would commonly contain a combination of the above types of services with the HCPCS code listed multiple times for different dates of service. For example, the UB-92 might have five line items listing code G0151 for five physical therapy visits, eight line items billed with G0155 for eight home health aide encounters, and three line items listing G0154 for three skilled nursing visits. On each of these line items the units listed should reflect how many fifteen-minute increments composed the visit.

Durable medical equipment, such as hospital beds, walkers, and commode chairs, should be billed with the HCPCS alphanumeric codes that begin with E. Examples of durable medical equipment items seen on HHA claims include:

E0114	Crutches
E0180	Alternating pressure pad
E0296	Hospital bed, total electric
E0435	Portable liquid oxygen system
E1050	Wheelchair

Supplies are billed under 270 revenue codes and do not require HCPCS code assignments. When the only reason for an HHA visit is to administer an influenza, pneumonia, or hepatitis B vaccine, Medicare will not pay additionally for a skilled nursing visit. The vaccine and administration code should be assigned and is covered under the vaccine benefit. Charges should only be billed for the supplies being used and the cost of the injection. The vaccine should be billed with revenue code 636, along with the HCPCS code for the vaccine, and revenue code 771, along with the appropriate HCPCS code for the administration. The HCPCS codes for the administration of the vaccines are:

G0008	Influenza virus vaccine
G0009	Pneumococcal polysaccharide vaccine (PPV)
G0010	Hepatitis B vaccine

HCPCS codes assigned to the vaccines include:

90657	Influenza virus vaccine, split virus, 6–35 months dosage, for intramuscular or jet injection use

90658	Influenza virus vaccine, split virus, 3 years and above dosage, for intramuscular or jet injection use
90659	Influenza virus vaccine, whole virus, for intramuscular or jet injection use
90732	Pneumococcal polysaccharide vaccine, 23-valent, adult dosage, for subcutaneous or intramuscular use
90744	Hepatitis B vaccine, pediatric or pediatric/adolescent dosage, for intramuscular use
90745	Hepatitis B vaccine, adolescent/high-risk infant dosage, for intramuscular use
90746	Hepatitis B vaccine, adult dosage, for intramuscular use
90747	Hepatitis B vaccine, dialysis or immunosuppressed patient dosage, for intramuscular use
90748	Hepatitis B and Hemophilus influenza b vaccine (HepB-Hib), for intramuscular use

A diagnosis code for each vaccine should also be reported for visits that entail vaccine administration only. The ICD-9-CM codes are:

V04.8	Influenza virus vaccine
V03.82	Pneumococcal polysaccharide vaccine (PPV)
V05.3	Hepatitis B vaccine

Health Insurance Prospective Payment System Codes

As with HCPCS codes, form locator 44 is also the location that the new HIPPS codes are to be assigned for HH PPS billing. A HIPPS code is required and listed with a new revenue code, 0023. HHAs must report the HIPPS code that was also reported on the RAP. On those claims that have a significant change in condition, the HHAs must report on each additional 0023 line the HIPPS codes produced by the grouper based on each additional OASIS assessment. If the change in the HIPPS code has no payment impact, then it does not have to be reported because it is the same HHRG.

On Medicare claims, HHRGs are represented as HIPPS codes. HIPPS codes allow the HHRG code to be carried more efficiently and include additional data on how the HHRG was derived. The 80 HHRGs of the HH PPS are represented by 640 HIPPS codes, with a set of eight codes available for each HHRG. Only one of the eight codes, with a final digit 1, indicates a complete data set. The eight codes of a particular HHRG all have the same case-mix weight assigned to them. Thus, the eight codes for that HHRG are priced identically by the pricer. HIPPS codes are only valid on claim lines with the new revenue code 0023.

Up to six HIPPS codes may be assigned for any sixty-day episode, and two for any line item. This represents the basis of payment for episodes other than those receiving a low-utilization payment adjustment. Each 0023 revenue code line should have the date of the first service provided on the HIPPS code line item. HIPPS codes represent specific patient characteristics (case mix) by which Medicare payments are determined. HIPPS codes are distinct five-position, alphanumeric codes. The first character is a fixed letter H, to designate home health, and does not correspond to any part of HHRG coding. The second, third, and fourth positions of the HIPPS code are a one-to-one crosswalk to three elements of the HHRG coding system. The second through fourth positions of the HH PPS HIPPS code will only allow alphabetical characters.

The fifth position of the HIPPS code indicates those elements of the code that were output from the grouper based on complete OASIS data. This position does not correspond to HHRGs since these codes do not differentiate payment groups depending on derived information. The fifth position is made up of numeric characters only. Codes output with a fifth-position value other than 1 are produced from incomplete OASIS assessments and are not likely to be accepted by state OASIS repositories. An example of a fully computed code for the minimum level in all three domains would be HAEJ1. See appendix T for a full listing of HHRGs and HIPPS.

Documentation Requirements

Documentation requirements for home health records include the following:

- Assessment

- Physician orders, initial and subsequent (usually documentation of a physician's verbal orders)

- Plan of care

- Documentation of the service visits

Request for Anticipated Payment

A RAP is not a claim and is not subject to the requirement that the physician signs the plan of care before the HHA bills for the initial percentage payment. If the signed plan of care is not available, the request for anticipated payment of the initial percentage payment is based on one of the following:

- A physician's verbal order that is recorded in the plan of care and includes a description of the patient's condition and the provided services

- An attestation signed and dated by the nurse or qualified therapist responsible for furnishing or supervising the plan of care that is copied into the plan of care, then immediately submitted to the physician

- A referral prescribing detailed orders for the services to be provided that is signed and dated by the physician

HCFA automatically cancels RAPs and recoup payments if the final claim is not submitted within sixty days of the end of the episode or sixty days from the issuance of the anticipated payment, whichever is greater. The final percentage payment claim is subject to physician signature requirements. Any changes in the plan must be signed and dated by a physician before each episode for services is submitted for the final percentage payment. Agencies submit a RAP with a UB-92 claim form. However, a RAP is not a claim. A RAP is subject to the same civil penalties as claims. Agencies can submit their request for anticipated payment after making the first skilled home health visit.

The HIPPS codes used to pay claims under HH PPS may be changed in the course of processing in two ways. Claims that fail to meet the threshold of 10 therapy visits required for payment of certain HIPPS codes may be automatically downcoded by the HH PPS pricer software. Claims that medical review verification procedures determine to have inaccurate HIPPS codes may be downcoded or upcoded as appropriate by medical review staff. In order to distinguish these two cases for providers, HCFA has instructed regional intermediaries to apply the following remark codes on the remittance advice (HCFA 2001):

N69   PPS code changed by claims processing system. Insufficient visits or therapies.

N72   PPS code changed by medical reviewers. Not supported by clinical records.

Intermediaries also look for information on the plan of care to validate the patient's qualification for Medicare coverage. For example, locator 18, Functional Limitations and Activities Permitted, is the most important locator to support homebound determination.

Compliance

The Office of Inspector General (OIG) issued a special fraud alert in January 1999, in order to promote voluntary compliance in the healthcare industry and assist providers in their compliance efforts. The alert addressed potential problem areas with regard to physician certification in providing medical equipment, supplies, and home health services. In addition, it addressed the following:

- The importance of physician certification for Medicare

- How improper physician certifications foster fraud

- Potential consequences for knowingly signing a false or misleading certification, or signing with reckless disregard for the truth

Excerpts from the January 1999 special fraud alert related to home health services are found in appendix U.

> **Example 1:** An 82-year-old woman, status post CVA four days ago, with late effects of left hemiplegia and dysphagia, has been assessed and certified by the physician for skilled nursing visits four times a week and physical therapy three times a week. The patient has osteoarthritis of her knees and CAD. She is also malnourished with a PEG tube put into place prior to discharge from her CVA-related inpatient stay. Durable medical equipment was ordered for a bedside commode. Patient assessment revealed clinical to be low, functional as moderate, and the service level as low. Coding and billing for one week's visits would be as follows:

ICD-9-CM Diagnosis Codes

438.20	438.12	414.00
436	263.9	715.96

HCPCS Codes

E0163	DME: bedside commode (listed once per month with one unit of service assigned)
G0151	Listed on three line items for three dates of service per week (and units assigned per 15-minute increment of service provided)
G0154	Listed on four line items for four dates of service per week (and units assigned per 15-minute increment of service provided)

> **Example 2:** A 74-year-old male with Alzheimer's dementia, decubiti formation of left heel, hypertension, and fecal and urinary incontinence was certified for five visits weekly for personal care from a home health aide and for two visits weekly from a skilled nurse. The patient required wound care, baths, and other personnel care services. In addition to supplies, an alternating pressure pad was provided to the patient for prevention of further decubitus ulcer formation. Coding and billing for one week's visits would be as follows:

ICD-9-CM Diagnosis Codes

331.0	707.0	788.30
294.11	787.6	401.9

HCPCS Codes

E0180   DME: alternating pressure pad (listed once per month with one unit of service assigned)

G0156   Listed on five line items for five dates of service per week (and units assigned per 15-minute increment of service provided)

G0154   Listed on two line items for two dates of service per week (and units assigned per 15-minute increment of service provided)

Summary

Much of home health billing for Medicare beneficiaries remains the same under the HH PPS as it was under the prior payment system. Medicaid, health maintenance organizations, third-party carriers, and commercial insurance companies have different billing requirements. HIPAA regulations will standardize claim transaction data requirements for providers that electronically bill payers. Meanwhile, home care agencies must work closely with each payer group to define claim requirements and determine the clinical record documents needed to support claims.

References and Bibliography

Health Care Financing Administration. 1998. Implementing OASIS to improve patient outcomes. In *Outcome and Assessment Information Set User's Manual.* Washington, D.C.: Government Printing Office.

Health Care Financing Administration. 2000a. Rules and Regulations. *Federal Register* 65(128).

Health Care Financing Administration. 2000b. *Medicare Home Health Agency Manual,* Transmittal 296. Washington, D.C.: Government Printing Office.

Health Care Financing Administration. 2001. *Program Memorandum Intermediaries/Carriers,* Transmittal AB-01-48. Washington, D.C.: Government Printing Office.

United Government Services Training. 2000. *Medicare Program Prospective Payment System for Home Health Agencies.*

Appendix A

National Association for Home Care Uniform Data Set for Home Care and Hospice

The uniform data set (UDS) is intended to meet the common data needs of multiple users and will not necessarily meet the total data needs of any one organization. It also does not limit additional data collection by an organization to meet its specific information needs. The UDS addresses data documentation and collection at the organizational level and at the individual patient level. Appendix A shows the listing of all data elements with their definitions and categories. This data set will be used for future data collection efforts conducted by the National Association for Home Care (NAHC). Other entities involved in home care and hospice are encouraged to use these definitions when constructing surveys and questionnaires. In 1997, the information resources and quality assurance committee added the outcome and assessment information set (OASIS) to the uniform data set (UDS). As of this writing NAHC has not added OASIS B1 to the UDS.

Source: National Association for Home Care. 1998 (March). *Uniform Data Set for Home Care and Hospice.* Available at www.nahc.org/NAHC/Research/unidata.html.

Uniform Data Set for Home Care & Hospice

March 1998

Introduction

In 1993 the National Association for Home Care Board of Directors charged the Information Resources and Quality Assurance Committee with the task of developing standardized definitions for home care and hospice data elements through a consensus conference process. The Board recognized this as a necessary first step toward achieving standardized, comparable home care and hospice data. The consensus conference was held in December 1993.

The following data set is the result of that conference and periodic revisions based on recommendations made to the Information Resources and Quality Assurance Committee.

Consensus conference participants agreed that the purpose in defining a data set is to facilitate data collection that will be comparable across agencies, geographic regions, and time. Some of the reasons for collecting data include:

1. Describing home care and hospice services, including the patients/clients and providers

2. Analyzing home care and hospice utilization and costs

3. Analyzing the effectiveness and quality of home and hospice care

4. Analyzing the business and financial aspects of home care and hospice

The framework adopted to guide development of the data set was based on the Department of Health and Human Services' concept of a uniform minimum data set. A uniform minimum data set for home care and hospice is a minimum set of items of information with uniform definitions and categories, concerning the specific dimension of home care and hospice services, that meets the essential information needs of multiple data users in the health care system.

The uniform data set (UDS) is intended to meet the common data needs of multiple users and will not necessarily meet the total data needs of any one organization. It also does not limit additional data collection by an organization to meet its specific information needs.

Criteria agreed upon for selecting data items and definitions included:

1. Demonstrated utility for multiple users

2. Relevance to national as well as local, state, or regional needs

3. Reasonable ease, accuracy, and economy in collection

4. "Need to know," not just "nice to know," information

5. Ability to be defined and measured

6. Use of the most common existing language, whenever possible

---

Source: National Association for Home Care. 1998 (March). *Uniform Data Set for Home Care and Hospice.* Available at www.nahc.org/NAHC/Research/unidata.html.

7. Uniformity with other applicable data sets

8. Ability to be coded for computer processing

The conference participants also affirmed that establishing a minimum data set is only the first step in achieving uniform data. Home care agencies, hospices, and data collectors must be encouraged to adopt it and a process must be established to refine the data set as users identify needed revisions. Home care and hospice providers are encouraged to make recommendations to the Committee using the format indicated at the end of this document.

The data set is organized into two major categories of organizational- and individual-level data elements. On an organizational level, the data set includes items that describe the organization, its services, and its aggregate utilization, financial, and personnel data. On the individual level, items include demographic, clinical, service, and utilization data for patients/clients.

In 1997 the Information Resources and Quality Assurance Committee added the OASIS data set to the UDS. The committee recognizes that the demonstration on using OASIS for outcome-based quality improvement is still ongoing and therefore has not yet incorporated the outcome measures into the UDS. For now, the OASIS items are included as standardized definitions to describe home care patients.

This data set will be used as the basis for future data collection efforts by the National Association for Home Care. Other entities involved in home care and hospice data are also encouraged to use these definitions when constructing surveys and questionnaires.

Uniform Data Set for Home Care and Hospice

List of Categories and Items

The data elements are numbered consecutively. The terms that are not considered data elements but required standard definitions are numbered separately and preceded by T.

ORGANIZATIONAL LEVEL DATA

Organization/Services

T1 Home Care Organization
1. Type of Home Care Programs
2. Ownership of Home Care Organization
3. Control of the Home Care Organization
4. Controlling Organization
5. Profit Status
6. Number of Branches
7. Services
8. Programs
9. Certification
10. Licensure
11. Accreditation
12. Service Area

Utilization

13. Unduplicated Patient/Client Census
14. Duplicated Patient/Client Census
15. Number of Non-Admissions

Financial

16. Gross Revenue
17. Net Revenue
18. Other Revenue
19. Bad Debt Expense
20. Charity Care
21. Total Payroll Costs
22. Contractor Expense
23. Benefits and Payroll Tax Expense
24. Total Personnel Expense

Source: National Association for Home Care. 1998 (March). *Uniform Data Set for Home Care and Hospice.* Available at www.nahc.org/NAHC/Research/unidata.html.

ORGANIZATIONAL LEVEL DATA (continued)

Financial (continued)

25. Total Expense
26. Annual Capital Expenditures
27. Gross Accounts Receivable
28. Net Accounts Receivable
29. Days Sales Outstanding
30. Operating Income
31. Cost per Unit of Service
32. Charge

Personnel

T2 Work Force Status
T3 Pay Status
33. Number of Employees
34. Number of Independent Contractors

35. Number of Subcontracted Workers
36. Number of Volunteers
37. Number of FTE Employees
38. Number of FTE Independent Contractors
39. Number of FTE Subcontracted Workers
40. Number of FTE Volunteers
T4 Clinical Personnel
T5 Clinical Support Personnel
T6 Administrative Personnel
T7 Administrative Support Personnel
41. Total Number of FTEs by Personnel Category
42. Productivity

INDIVIDUAL LEVEL PATIENT/CLIENT DATA

T8 Patient/Client

Demographic Items

43. Personal Identification
44. Date of Birth
45. Race
46. Ethnicity
47. Sex
48. Location of Residence
49. Type of Residence
50. Living Arrangements
51. Caregiver Availability
52. Caregiver
53. Preadmission Location

Clinical Items

54. Medical Diagnoses
55. Surgical Procedures
56. Functional Status
57. Patient/Client Problem
58. Patient/Client Classification

59. Intervention
60. Outcome
61. Discharge Status

Service/Utilization Items

62. Provider Identification
63. Admission Date
64. Discharge Date
T9 Episode of Care
T10 Length of Stay
65. Discharge Reason
66. Discharge Disposition
67. Expected Payer
T11 Unit of Service-Visit
T12 Unit of Service-Hour
T13 Care Coordination
68. Units of Service per Discipline
69. Number of Days per Level of Hospice Care

OASIS Data Set

Source: National Association for Home Care. 1998 (March). *Uniform Data Set for Home Care and Hospice.* Available at www.nahc.org/NAHC/Research/unidata.html.

Organizational Level Data

Organization/Services

This section identifies the organizational level data elements that describe and categorize various types of home care organizations and services.

T1

Term: Home Care Organization

Definition: Broadly defined as the operational unit that provides one or more of the home care programs listed below to individuals in their residence. Staffing agencies or Durable Medical Equipment (DME) companies are not included.

Comment: The data set is for home care services rather than equipment or staffing registries.

1

Data Element Name: Type of Home Care Programs

Definition: Major classification of home care programs:
  Home health care: professional services provided in the place of residence on either a part-time, intermittent, hourly, or shift basis
  Hospice: organized program of interdisciplinary services for terminally ill patients and their families to provide palliative medical care and supportive social, emotional, and spiritual services in the place of residence
  Support care: supportive services related to assistance with Instrumental Activities of Daily Living (IADL) provided on a part-time, intermittent, shift, or hourly basis in the place of residence
  Personal care: personal care related to assistance with Activities of Daily Living (ADL) provided on a part-time, intermittent, hourly, or shift basis in the place of residence
  Home infusion therapy: provision of both pharmaceuticals and skilled nursing services in the place of residence

Comment: Home care organizations may provide one or more home care programs.

2

Data Element Name: Ownership of Home Care Organization

Definition: The type of ownership of the home care organization:
  Voluntary: governed by a community-based, voluntary board of directors
  Private: non-profit or proprietary; privately owned and controlled by an individual, partnership, or corporation
  Government (public, official): operated by a government entity (state, city, county, federal)
  Combination Government/Voluntary: combination of government and voluntary control within one organization
  Publicly held company: Company that issues stocks that are traded on a stock exchange.

Comment: The title Visiting Nurse Association/Service no longer exclusively designates a voluntary organization.

Source: National Association for Home Care. 1998 (March). *Uniform Data Set for Home Care and Hospice.* Available at www.nahc.org/NAHC/Research/unidata.html.

3

Data Element Name: Control of the Home Care Organization

Definition: Relationship of the home care organization to the controlling organization:

Sole corporation: independently incorporated and controlled; not a division, department, or subsidiary of a larger organization

Chain affiliate: freestanding health care facility that is either owned, controlled, or operated under lease or contract (franchise) by an organization consisting of two or more freestanding health care facilities organized within or across state lines that is under the ownership, or through any other device, control and direction of a common party

Wholly owned or subsidiary corporation: organization owned by another corporation such as a hospital or health system

Hospital-based: organized as a department/division of a hospital

Nursing facility-based: organized as a department/division of a nursing facility

Rehab-based: organized as a department/division of a rehab facility

HMO-based: organized as a department/division of an HMO

Health Department-based: organized as a department/division of a public health department

Comment: Organizations owned by a hospital but not organized as a department are not hospital-based.

4

Data Element Name: Controlling Organization

Definition: The entity that owns and controls a home care organization:

No separate controlling organization
Hospital
National company
Nursing home
Other institution
Health department
Health plan
Health system
Other

5

Data Element Name: Profit Status

Definition: Disposition of excess revenue over expenses:

Not-for-profit: excess revenue retained by the corporation; exempt from Federal income taxation under section 501 of the Internal Revenue Code of 1954

Proprietary (for profit): excess revenue distributed to owners or shareholders or held as retained earnings, subject to federal taxation

Source: National Association for Home Care. 1998 (March). *Uniform Data Set for Home Care and Hospice.* Available at www.nahc.org/NAHC/Research/unidata.html.

6

Data Element Name: Number of Branches

Definition: Total number of locations providing services to patients/clients under the control of the home care organization.

7

Data Element Name: Services

Definition: Care provided by or under the direction of specific disciplines offered by the home care organization:

Nursing (RN, LPN, LVN)
Home Care Aide (3 levels: environmental, personal care, medically directed services)
Physical therapy
Occupational therapy
Speech-language pathology
Social service
Respiratory therapy
Dietitian service
Pastoral care
Volunteer
Physician care
Dental care
Pharmacy
Other
Expressive therapy (art, music)

8

Data Element Name: Programs

Definition: Organization of single or multiple services for a designated population with specific care needs:

AIDS
Cardiopulmonary
Case management
Diabetic
Enterostomal therapy
Geriatrics
Hospice
Infusion therapy
Maternal/Child
Oncology
Pediatric
Psychiatric/Mental health
Rehab
Respite care
Other

Source: National Association for Home Care. 1998 (March). *Uniform Data Set for Home Care and Hospice.* Available at www.nahc.org/NAHC/Research/unidata.html.

9

Data Element Name: Certification

Definition: Required approval to provide services reimbursed by Medicare and/or Medicaid: (1) home health agency Medicare certification, (2) hospice Medicare certification, (3) home health agency Medicaid certification, (4) hospice Medicaid certification.

10

Data Element Name: Licensure

Definition: Required approval granted by a state to operate a home care organization: (1) home care agency licensure, (2) hospice licensure, (3) other licensure, (4) not required.

11

Data Element Name: Accreditation

Definition: Voluntary process of obtaining approval by demonstrating compliance with non-regulatory standards: (1) Community Health Accreditation Program (CHAP), (2) Joint Commission on Accreditation of Healthcare Organizations (JCAHO), (3) National HomeCaring Council, (4) other.

12

Data Element Name: Service Area

Definition: Geographic areas served by all branches of the home care organization by zip codes including partial zip code areas.

Utilization

13

Data Element Name: Unduplicated Patient/Client Census

Definition: Number of individuals receiving service from an organization during a given period of time counted only once, regardless of the number of services, frequency of admission, or payer source.

14

Data Element Name: Duplicated Patient/Client Census

Definition: The total number of admissions during a given period of time regardless of the number of individuals involved.

Comment: For example, the same individual admitted more than once during a reporting period would be counted each time admitted.

Source: National Association for Home Care. 1998 (March). *Uniform Data Set for Home Care and Hospice.* Available at www.nahc.org/NAHC/Research/unidata.html.

15

Data Element Name: Number of Non-Admissions

Definition: Total number of patient/client referrals during a given period of time for which the organization intended to provide service based on a request for service but patient/client not admitted to the organization for the following reasons: (1) moved/unable to locate, (2) refused services, (3) deceased, (4) admitted to hospital, (5) admitted to nursing home, (6) patient/client being seen by another home care organization, (7) patient/client does not meet organization admission criteria, (8) other.

Financial

This section identifies organizational level data elements for recording financial aspects of home care services.

16

Data Element Name: Gross Revenue

Definition: All billable charges for services and products at the full billable rate (prior to taking discounts or allowances).

Comment: Charity care should NOT be included in gross revenue calculations.

17

Data Element Name: Net Revenue

Definition: Gross revenue less all discounts or allowances (expected amount due from payer).

18

Data Element Name: Other Revenue

Definition: Nonservice and nonproduct related revenue.

Comment: For example, this may include interest, donations, charitable contributions, community support.

19

Data Element Name: Bad Debt Expense

Definition: The expense for the estimated amount of net revenue that is uncollectible.

Comment: Charity care is NOT considered a bad debt expense.

20

Data Element Name: Charity Care (Indigent Care)

Definition: Total charge of services and products based on full billable rate provided for clients identified on admission as a charity case, or after admission based on client's inability to pay.

Comments: Charity care should NOT be included in gross and net revenue calculations. Charity care is NOT considered a bad debt expense.

Source: National Association for Home Care. 1998 (March). *Uniform Data Set for Home Care and Hospice.* Available at www.nahc.org/NAHC/Research/unidata.html.

21

Data Element Name: Total Payroll Costs

Definition: Salary and wages paid to all employees.

22

Data Element Name: Contractor Expense

Definition: Personnel costs associated with contractors and/or subcontractors providing patient/client services or substituting for job functions normally performed by an employee of the organization.

23

Data Element Name: Benefits and Payroll Tax Expense

Definition: The employer's portion of all benefits and payroll taxes

Comment: Typically, this includes benefits to the individual, not the employer and organization (e.g., insurance, health care, etc.).

24

Data Element Name: Total Personnel Expense

Definition: The sum of total payroll costs, benefits and payroll tax expense, and contractor expense.

25

Data Element Name: Total Expense

Definition: The sum of all expenses.

26

Data Element Name: Annual Capital Expenditures

Definition: Expenditures for items to be depreciated with a minimum threshold of $500 and a service life of three years or more, including capitalized leases.

27

Data Element Name: Gross Accounts Receivable

Definition: The amount of gross charges for which payment has not yet been received.

28

Data Element Name: Net Accounts Receivable

Definition: Amount of net revenue for which payment has not been received minus an allowance for bad debt.

Source: National Association for Home Care. 1998 (March). *Uniform Data Set for Home Care and Hospice.* Available at www.nahc.org/NAHC/Research/unidata.html.

29

Data Element Name: Days Sales Outstanding

Definition: Net accounts receivable divided by (annual net revenue divided by 365) = NAR/(ANR/365)

30

Data Element Name: Operating Income

Definition: Net revenue less total expenses excluding income taxes.

31

Data Element Name: Cost Per Unit of Service

Definition: Total expense for a service divided by total number of units of service provided.

32

Data Element Name: Charge

Definition: The published full billable rate by unit of service or product.

Personnel

This section identifies organizational level data elements used to describe the home care work force.

T2

Term: Work Force Status

Definition: Working relationship with an organization:
> *Employee:* individual under the supervision and control of the organization
> *Independent contractor:* individual that meets the Internal Revenue Service criteria and for whom a W-2 form is not submitted
> *Subcontracted worker:* individual providing services to an organization through a contractual relationship with another organization (subcontractor)
> *Volunteer:* uncompensated individual directly under supervision and control of the organization

T3

Term: Pay Status

Definition: Method of payment to the work force:
> *Salary:* Fixed base compensation paid regularly
> *Hourly:* Compensation paid by the number of hours worked
> *Per-Visit:* Compensation paid based on the number of visits made
> *Other:* Per case, capitation, per fixed interval negotiated amount, and commission

Source: National Association for Home Care. 1998 (March). *Uniform Data Set for Home Care and Hospice.* Available at www.nahc.org/NAHC/Research/unidata.html.

33

Data Element Name: Number of Employees

Definition: Total number of employees working for the organization regardless of number of hours worked.

34

Data Element Name: Number of Independent Contractors

Definition: Total number of independent contractors working for the organization.

35

Data Element Name: Number of Subcontracted Workers

Definition: Total number of individuals providing service to the organization through a contractual relationship with another organization (subcontractor).

Comment: The number of subcontracted workers may be too difficult to track but FTEs can be calculated based on hours or visits paid.

36

Data Element Name: Number of Volunteers

Definition: Total number of volunteers working for the organization.

37

Data Element Name: Number of FTE Employees (full-time equivalent)

Definition: The sum of annual paid hours for all employees divided by 2080 hours.

Comments: This sets the standard for reporting FTEs. It will not interfere with individual agency procedures. For per-visit employees, divide their number of visits by the average number of visits made by a full-time employee.

38

Data Element Name: Number of FTE Independent Contractors

Definition: The sum of annual paid hours for all independent contractors divided by 2080 hours.

Comment: For per-visit contractors, divide their number of visits by the average number of visits made by a full-time employee.

39

Data Element Name: Number of FTE Subcontracted Workers

Definition: The sum of annual paid hours for all subcontracted workers divided by 2080 hours.

Comment: For per-visit subcontracted workers, divide their number of visits by the average number of visits made by a full-time employee.

Source: National Association for Home Care. 1998 (March). *Uniform Data Set for Home Care and Hospice.* Available at www.nahc.org/NAHC/Research/unidata.html.

40

Data Element Name: Number of FTE Volunteers

Definition: The sum of annual worked hours by all volunteers divided by 2080 hours.

T4

Term: Clinical Personnel

Definition: Those workers performing job functions having direct face-to-face patient/client contact:

RN: Registered nurse
Advanced Practice Registered Nurse: RN with Master's level education or special certification or Nurse Practitioner
LPN/LVN: Licensed practical/vocational nurse
Home Care Aide: I: environmental; II: personal care; III: medically directed services
PT: Physical therapist
PTA: Physical therapy assistant
OT: Occupational therapist
COTA: Certified occupational therapy assistant
SLP: Speech-language pathologist
MSW: Master's prepared social worker
BSW: Bachelor's prepared social worker
RT: Respiratory therapist
RD: Registered dietitian
Chaplain/Pastoral Care Worker
Physician
Bereavement counselor
Expressive therapist: (Art therapist, Music therapist)
Pharmacist

Comment: The source of the Home Care Aide I, II, III designations is the Home Care Aide Association of America's position statement "National Uniformity for Paraprofessional Title, Qualifications, and Supervision" (March, 1993).

T5

Term: Clinical Support Personnel

Definition: Those workers performing job functions providing direct support to the clinical personnel (e.g., QA, records, supplies, intake, education, clerical, clinical supervision).

T6

Term: Administrative Personnel

Definition: Those workers performing job functions having administrative responsibility for, and providing direction to, the organization (e.g., executives, chief officers, directors).

Source: National Association for Home Care. 1998 (March). *Uniform Data Set for Home Care and Hospice.* Available at www.nahc.org/NAHC/Research/unidata.html.

T7

Term: Administrative Support Personnel

Definition: Those workers performing job functions providing support to the administrative personnel or the entire organization (e.g., facilities services, clerical, reception, accounting, information systems, human resources, middle management/supervision).

41

Data Element Name: Total Number of FTEs by Personnel Category

Definition: The total number of FTEs for all workers for each personnel category: clinical, clinical support, administrative, and administrative support.

42

Data Element Name: Productivity

Definition: The average number of visits (or patient contact hours) for hourly or salaried workers per 8-hour day per discipline. [Total number of visits made (or hours of service) during a given period of time by hourly and salaried workers] divided by (paid hours minus vacation/holiday/sick days) multiplied by (8).

$$= (Total\ visits\ (T11)\ per\ discipline\ /\ Paid\ hours\ -\ (vac,\ hol,\ sick)\ per\ discipline)\ \times\ 8$$
$$= (Direct\ contact\ hours\ per\ discipline\ /\ Paid\ hours\ -\ (vac,\ hol,\ sick)\ per\ discipline)\ \times\ 8$$

Comment: Vacation, holiday and sick days are deducted to eliminate differences based on different benefit packages. Productivity for per-visit employees cannot be calculated without accurate time records.

Individual Level Patient/Client Data

This section includes those individual level data items that should be recorded in the home care record and can be abstracted for data collection.

T8

Term: Patient/Client

Definition: Individual receiving home care services.

Demographic Items

43

Data Element Name: Personal Identification

Definition: The unique number assigned to each patient/client that distinguishes the patient/client from all others.

Comments: Use of the same unique personal identifier as adopted with national health care reform is recommended. This number must only be used in accordance with confidentiality laws/privacy acts.

Source: National Association for Home Care. 1998 (March). *Uniform Data Set for Home Care and Hospice.* Available at www.nahc.org/NAHC/Research/unidata.html.

44

Data Element Name: Date of Birth

Definition: Month, day, year of birth, recorded MM/DD/YYYY.

45

Data Element Name: Race

Definition: As identified by the patient/client: (1) White, (2) Black, (3) American Indian or Alaskan Native, (4) Asian or Pacific Islander, (5) other, and (6) not identified.

Comment: This is in conformance with the United States Census Bureau categorization.

46

Data Element Name: Ethnicity

Definition: As identified by the patient/client: (1) Hispanic origin, (2) Non-Hispanic origin, (3) not identified.

Comment: This is in conformance with the United States Census Bureau categorization.

47

Data Element Name: Sex

Definition: Gender, as defined by male or female.

48

Data Element Name: Location of Residence

Definition: Zip code of dwelling where patient/client usually receives home care services.

49

Data Element Name: Type of Residence

Definition: Type of residence categorized as: (1) residence that does not provide formal support, (2) residential facility with staff that does provide formal support, (3) SNF (skilled nursing facility), (4) no permanent residence.

50

Data Element Name: Living Arrangements

Definition: Presence of others in the residence indicated by: (1) lives alone, (2) lives with others.

51

Data Element Name: Caregiver Availability

Definition: Availability of caregiver who accepts responsibility for patient's/client's well-being as defined by the following categories: (1) none needed, (2) needed/partially available, (3) needed/fully available, (4) needed/not available.

Source: National Association for Home Care. 1998 (March). *Uniform Data Set for Home Care and Hospice.* Available at www.nahc.org/NAHC/Research/unidata.html.

52

Data Element Name: Caregiver

Definition: The classification of the person(s) who accept(s) responsibility for the patient's/client's well being: (1) self, (2) relative, (3) friend/neighbor, (4) privately employed caregiver, (5) facility/residence staff, (6) legal representative, (7) other.

53

Data Element Name: Preadmission Location

Definition: The location of the patient/client in any of the following sites during the five days prior to admission to the home care organization: (1) home, (2) acute inpatient hospital, (3) skilled nursing facility, (4) rehabilitation facility, (5) assisted living facility, (6) board and care residence, (7) outpatient surgery center, (8) other.

Comment: The number of days prior to admission needs to be examined further.

Clinical Items

54

Data Element Name: Medical Diagnosis

Definition: Any medical diagnoses that affect the care provided by the home care organization as defined by ICD-CM codes:

Principal: the diagnosis most responsible for the admission of the patient/client for home care service

Other: all other diagnoses that affect the care provided by the home care organization

Not applicable: if the home care services are not related to health care needs (e.g., homemaker)

55

Data Element Name: Surgical Procedures

Definition: Any surgical procedure that affects the care provided by the home care organization as defined by ICD-CM or CPT codes.

56

Data Element Name: Functional Status

Definition: Description of the individual's ability to perform activities of daily living and instrumental activities of daily living.

Comment: Need to decide on what measures to use. Some suggested sources are: Katz, Uniform Needs Assessment, Long-Term Health Care Data Set, Nursing Home Resident Assessment Data Set, Outcome Assessment Item Set (OASIS), Functional Independence Measure (FIM), Karnofsky Performance Scale.

Source: National Association for Home Care. 1998 (March). *Uniform Data Set for Home Care and Hospice.* Available at www.nahc.org/NAHC/Research/unidata.html.

57

Data Element Name: Patient/Client Problem

Definition: Clinical judgement made by professional health care personnel about a human response to an actual or potential health problem.

Comment: Possible approaches are: Omaha system, Home Health Care Classification (HHCC), North America Nursing Diagnosis Association (NANDA).

58

Data Element Name: Patient/Client Classification

Definition: Indicator of intensity of services.

Comments: Standard system not yet identified. Consider use of other indicators, such as stability on admission, number of meds, etc.

59

Data Element Name: Intervention

Definition: An action intended to benefit the patient/client in one of four categories: assess/evaluate, care, teach, and manage.

Comment: Possible approaches are: Medicare treatment codes, Omaha system, HHCC, Nursing Intervention Classification (NIC), care requirement categories from Uniform Needs Assessment.

60

Data Element Name: Outcome

Definition: A change in patient health status between two or more time points.

Comment: Health status encompasses physiologic, functional, cognitive, emotional, palliative and behavioral health. Outcomes may also address psychosocial factors related to the patient/family unit.

61

Data Element Name: Discharge Status

Definition: Change in overall condition of patient/client at time of discharge from the organization: recovered, stabilized, deteriorated, died (in home, hospital, or other setting).

Service/Utilization Items

62

Data Element Name: Provider Identification

Definition: The unique number assigned to each provider organization.

Comment: The ID number should be the same as the one assigned under national health care reform.

Source: National Association for Home Care. 1998 (March). *Uniform Data Set for Home Care and Hospice.* Available at www.nahc.org/NAHC/Research/unidata.html.

63

Data Element Name: Admission Date

Definition: Date the patient/client is accepted for service per episode by the home care organization.

Comment: The referral date or first billable visit may or may not coincide with the admission date.

64

Data Element Name: Discharge Date

Definition: Date when the home care organization is no longer responsible for patient/client services per episode.

Comment: For reporting purposes, patients are considered discharged if admitted to hospital greater than 48 hours. However, organizations may continue their own policies regarding paperwork when home care services are resumed after a hospitalization. This does not apply to hospice patients where the hospice is responsible for both inpatient and home care services.

T9

Term: Episode of Care

Definition: A discrete period of time starting with the admission date and ending with the discharge date during which home care is provided to the patient/client.

T10

Term: Length of Stay

Definition: Total continuous days of service from admission to discharge including both the admission and discharge days.

Comment: This can be calculated from admission and discharge dates so it does not need to be a separate data element.

65

Data Element Name: Discharge Reason

Definition: The primary reason for discontinuing services:
Patient/client no longer needs service
Admitted to institution
Death
Moved from service area
Unable to locate patient/client
Patient/client requests discharge or revocation of hospice election
Physician requests discharge
Patient/client unwilling to participate in treatment plan
Unsafe for staff

Source: National Association for Home Care. 1998 (March). *Uniform Data Set for Home Care and Hospice.* Available at www.nahc.org/NAHC/Research/unidata.html.

Unsafe for patient/client
Organization unable to provide level/mix of services needed
Does not meet reimbursement criteria and patient fails to elect private pay
Other
Not applicable

66

Data Element Name: Discharge Disposition

Definition: Primary source of care after discharge from organization: (1) self, (2) family, (3) acute inpatient hospital, (4) skilled nursing facility, (5) residence that provides formal support, (6) hospice/other hospice, (7) home care/other home care organization (except hospice), (8) other, (9) not applicable.

67

Data Element Name: Expected Payer

Definition: Payer expected to be responsible for paying for services. Payers are defined as:
> *Primary:* the person or entity that has the first responsibility for paying for services rendered
>
> *Secondary:* additional parties responsible for paying a portion or all of the remaining charges
>
> *Common payers include:*
> Medicare
> Medicaid
> Private Insurance: any insurance system funded by employer and/or individuals including fee-for-service and managed care plans
> Title III: Older Americans Act
> Title XX: Social Service Block Grant
> Other government funded programs: CHAMPUS, VA, IHS
> Workers' compensation
> County/state/local: nonfederal government funding
> Self-pay (private pay): patient/client or other private party pays for services out-of-pocket (full fee or sliding scale)
> Charity (indigent care): specific funds designated to pay for care of patients that meet established eligibility criteria, e.g., United Way, etc.
> Other

T11

Term: Unit of Service-Visit

Definition: Direct face-to-face contact with a patient/client for the purpose of delivering service measured in visits regardless of length of time of visit.

T12

Term: Unit of Service-Hour

Definition: Direct face-to-face contact with a patient/client for the purpose of delivering service measured in hours (in quarter hour increments).

Source: National Association for Home Care. 1998 (March). *Uniform Data Set for Home Care and Hospice.* Available at www.nahc.org/NAHC/Research/unidata.html.

T13

Term: Care Coordination

Definition: Contact with patient/client, family, significant other, and any number of providers of service other than by direct patient contact in order to coordinate the plan of care. Contacts are measured in time by quarter hour increments.

Comment: Some examples include contact with: physician, equipment company, lab, payer, and conferences.

68

Data Element Name: Units of Service per Discipline

Definition: Total number of units of service (visits or hours) per discipline from admission to discharge.

69

Data Element Name: Number of Days per Level of Hospice Care

Definition: Level of hospice care measured in days. There are four levels of care: (1) routine home care, (2) continuous home care, (3) inpatient respite care, (4) general inpatient care.

Source: National Association for Home Care. 1998 (March). *Uniform Data Set for Home Care and Hospice.* Available at www.nahc.org/NAHC/Research/unidata.html.

Medicare's OASIS: Standardized Outcome and Assessment Information Set for Home Health Care

OASIS-B

Peter W. Shaughnessy, PhD; Kathryn S. Crisler, MS, RN; Robert E. Schlenker, PhD

Distributed by the National Association for Home Care
March 1997

Source: National Association for Home Care. 1998 (March). *Uniform Data Set for Home Care and Hospice.* Available at www.nahc.org/NAHC/Research/unidata.html.

Medicare's OASIS: Standardized Outcome And Assessment Information Set For Home Health Care—OASIS-B, March 1997

Peter W. Shaughnessy, Ph.D.; Kathryn S. Crisler, MS, RN; Robert E. Schlenker, Ph.D.

University of Colorado

The Outcome and ASsessment Information Set (OASIS) that HCFA is proposing for purposes of outcome-based quality improvement under Medicare (as part of the new *Conditions of Participation*)[1] has undergone several years of development and refinement. The first version was published in August 1995 as OASIS-A. This publication contains the second, refined version, namely OASIS-B. In addition to reviewing the purpose and evolution of the OASIS to date, this prologue provides information on operational issues such as whether the OASIS should be expected to increase or decrease time required for visits and documentation.

Purpose, History, and Improvements

The data items that constitute the OASIS were developed largely for purposes of measuring patient outcomes in home health care. Nearly all of the items also are useful for assessing the care needs of patients, but no pretense is made that the OASIS constitutes a comprehensive assessment instrument. Since the vast majority of OASIS items are similar to those currently used by most home health agencies at start of care (often in less precise form), it can be useful for home care agencies and others to replace their current versions of these items with the actual OASIS items. Experience in demonstration programs has shown that this not only facilitates gaining experience with OASIS, but it also enables home care providers to conduct more precise assessments of patient conditions for these items.

The OASIS has its genesis in a five-year national research program to develop outcome measures for home care (funded by HCFA and the Robert Wood Johnson Foundation). One of the important products from this program was a 73-item data set required to measure outcomes, first published in a 1994 report written by the Center for Health Services and Policy Research (the Research Center) at the University of Colorado. This was expanded to a 79-item data set as a result of recommendations from a HCFA-convened task force of home care experts which reviewed the data set from the perspective of items judged essential for assessment. The Research Center revised and rearranged the 79-items into a data set termed OASIS-A in 1995.

The OASIS-A items that had been developed and tested in the national research program (along with those added by the expert panel) were then used operationally in two demonstration programs (summarized below) in late 1995 and 1996. This experience suggested selected

Source: National Association for Home Care. 1998 (March). *Uniform Data Set for Home Care and Hospice.* Available at www.nahc.org/NAHC/Research/unidata.html.

refinements, resulting in OASIS-B, which contains 79 items. Although a few items were dropped, a few were added, and wording changes were made to clarify items, the substance of OASIS-B is virtually the same as OASIS-A. This publication contains OASIS-B, including the 79 core items preceded by 10 routine identifiers (termed clinical record items) that have proved useful in tracking, managing, and organizing data collection and processing. We had many requests for such identifiers after the release of OASIS-A in August 1995 and therefore include them here for agency use. As the Medicare program moves forward with OASIS, it is clear such identifiers (also used for billing, care planning, etc., under Medicare) would naturally accompany the core OASIS items and be of value for agency-specific applications of OASIS.

Thus, OASIS-B is largely the result of applying and testing OASIS-A in 1996 in (1) the national demonstration of outcome-based quality improvement (OBQI) that HCFA is sponsoring and the University of Colorado Research Center is administering, and (2) an analogous OBQI demonstration in New York State that the Department of Health is sponsoring and the University of Colorado Research Center is administering. The experience of the 50 national demonstration agencies and the 22 New York State demonstration agencies in using the OASIS for purposes of collecting outcome data, as well as selected experiences of other agencies throughout the country which have elected to use the OASIS data set, were taken into consideration in the modest set of revisions that resulted in OASIS-B. Reliability testing, programmatic applications, and provider suggestions to improve OASIS will continue with a view toward improving the data set. Nonetheless, OASIS is now regarded as a stable data set that can be used in the context of patient assessment and outcome monitoring. At the same time we recognize that as home care practices, patient conditions, and policies change, it will be necessary to occasionally update and refine the data set. (As other revisions are released, the suffixes "C," "D," etc., will be used.)

Deliberations took place on whether it would be wise for the Research Center to release OASIS-A in August 1995, since it would be followed within an 18-month period of time by OASIS-B, and perhaps subsequently by OASIS-C (at a minimum). In keeping with its philosophy of establishing a partnership with the home health industry announced under its Home Health Initiative in 1994, HCFA staff determined it appropriate to provide the industry with each of these versions of the OASIS as they become available.[2] This is not only in keeping with a philosophy of open communication and sharing, but also should (1) be of value to home health providers in preparing for the expected Medicare approach to data collection required for purposes of monitoring outcomes, (2) assist providers in collecting more precise data for purposes of assessment, (3) allow providers to begin to fit the OASIS data items into the unique, often more comprehensive data set tailored to their agency's assessment approach—depending on the types of cases admitted and approaches to assessment used by each agency, and (4) assist the industry and Medicare in continuing to use an important data set before HCFA finalizes and implements new Conditions of Participation, thereby facilitating refinement of the OASIS on a prospective basis.

It is our intent at the Research Center to provide the home care industry with regular updates on OBQI demonstrations, operational issues related to OBQI that are important to both individual agencies and Medicare, strengths and weaknesses associated with using the OASIS for various purposes, and other issues pertinent to smoothly and effectively implementing the OASIS data set in order to measure outcomes. We have used and will continue to use several different forums for these communications. Information related to operational features of the OASIS is summarized in subsequent paragraphs.

Source: National Association for Home Care. 1998 (March). *Uniform Data Set for Home Care and Hospice.* Available at www.nahc.org/NAHC/Research/unidata.html.

Operational Issues

With respect to understanding and using OASIS data items, several points are important to take into consideration. If an agency wishes to incorporate OASIS items into its assessment protocols, the items should be kept intact rather than modified. This almost always requires revising existing items in agency forms. We make this suggestion both because OASIS items are likely to be required by Medicare in their exact form and because uniformity of items is imperative for across-agency comparisons and benchmarking. The OASIS items have been arranged in a clinically meaningful sequence to facilitate incorporating them into current instruments, although it is not necessary to retain this sequence. We have written a set of guidelines, termed OASIS Basics, which is available from our Research Center (until another means of publishing this monograph is determined) for agencies to use in the process of implementing the OASIS.[3] Each item in the data set includes a unique identifier (which consists of five characters [one letter and four numbers]). While these identifiers are not required for assessment and care planning, they assist in data entry for computerization and subsequent report preparation. We therefore recommend that they be retained.

Since the OASIS is used for measuring outcomes defined as change in health status between two or more time points, most data items are obtained at start of care and follow-up time points (i.e., every 60 days and discharge). Selected items are unique to either start of care or follow-up times. These are indicated as such on the OASIS. All OASIS items are intended to be completed through routine patient assessment approaches and collection of patient subjective and objective data. The items should not be used in the form of a patient interview for collecting data.

The first impression of the OASIS may be that it is a lengthy data set. However, its length cannot be attributed to new items that agencies presently do not use at assessment. Rather, it is due to the greater precision that characterizes many of the items. This precision helps for purposes of measuring outcomes and improving the accuracy of assessing health status. Considerable experience with agencies suggests that once staff are familiar with the OASIS and OASIS items are integrated into (not added onto) the clinical record, assessment takes at most five or ten minutes longer, usually less. If, after staff have acclimated to the OASIS, it requires more time than this, we have found it highly likely that either the OASIS was not properly implemented and integrated, previous initial assessments were not comprehensive, or individual care providers might benefit from additional orientation to conducting assessment in the home.

We have very recently conducted a time survey among OASIS users who have properly integrated OASIS items into their assessment process and record keeping approach. Owing to the timing of the release of the draft Conditions in the Federal Register, it was not possible to incorporate the results of this new study in that release on March 10, 1997. The study involved a matched control design. A survey was undertaken to determine whether use of the OASIS in and of itself requires additional data collection time. This is a challenging issue to address precisely because many agencies implement changes concurrently with integrating OASIS into their clinical records. Multiple changes therefore precluded a pre-OASIS, post-OASIS design. Consequently, a study-control comparative approach was employed, with telephone survey data collected from nurses in branches using OASIS and from nurses in branches not using OASIS—in the same agencies. All respondents were "blinded" as to the purpose of the survey, and 58 providers from 11 participating agencies were interviewed. The providers had been using the OASIS for approximately eight months. Each provider (i.e., each OASIS user and

---

Source: National Association for Home Care. 1998 (March). *Uniform Data Set for Home Care and Hospice.* Available at www.nahc.org/NAHC/Research/unidata.html.

each non-OASIS user) was asked to provide the time spent in the patient's home and time spent documenting outside the home for the start-of-care visit and the discharge visit, on average and for their most recent visit of each type.

The basic finding was that the OASIS does not increase the total visit and documentation time. The pattern of results proved similar for average and most-recent-visit times. Findings for the average time are summarized here. At start of care, no statistically significant differences were found, with OASIS users spending an average of eight additional minutes in the home, but 15 minutes less in documentation (the precision of the OASIS items often reduces documentation time). Total visit and documentation time for OASIS users at start of care was 154 minutes, compared with 161 minutes for non-OASIS users. There were no statistically significant differences at time of discharge, with both groups averaging the same amount of time in the home and OASIS users averaging one minute less in documentation outside the home. Total visit and documentation time at discharge was 67 minutes for OASIS users and 68 minutes for non-OASIS users.

Several software developers either have software available or are developing software that incorporates the OASIS into their electronic clinical record systems.[4] In addition, stand-alone OASIS-specific software, not part of a more comprehensive electronic clinical record system, is under development for agencies that do not have or are not presently interested in a more comprehensive electronic clinical record system. This stand-alone software will enable an agency to computerize or enter OASIS data that have been recorded by clinicians using forms that integrate the exact OASIS items into the agency's assessment instrument. Regardless of whether an agency uses a comprehensive electronic clinical record system (e.g., possibly with laptops) or stand-alone software to specifically computerize OASIS items, it is important that the exact OASIS items are directly incorporated into the clinical record. Agencies should be certain that their software (1) can be efficiently updated with occasional changes that might occur in OASIS, and (2) provides the capability to extract OASIS items for purposes of transmission to a central source for outcome comparisons and benchmarking, as well as other agency internal applications that will naturally be of interest once OASIS data are computerized.

We have attempted to be as responsive as our resources permit to questions and issues raised by software vendors. It is apparent that a number of vendors are moving in the right direction, and we encourage agencies to be diligent in making certain that OASIS items are incorporated verbatim or in some form equivalent to how they appear in the OASIS. The items should be integrated into and not added onto the end of the assessment. Care providers should not have the option to carry the same OASIS data from start of care to follow up in describing or assessing patient health status (this often results in inaccurate follow-up data because providers are tempted to minimize their time by carrying forward the data from the initial time point instead of properly reassessing and recording the information at follow up). This carry-forward approach should not be used in either paper or electronic documentation approaches.

We have had considerable input from care providers in response to the OASIS. A few points are highlighted here. Some providers have suggested that more detail should accompany selected data items. For example, some physical therapists have noted that selected scales exist that provide more detail than the functional scales in the OASIS. In reviewing the many approaches to measuring health status in our research program, we found it necessary to strike a balance among competing objectives such as (1) minimizing the burden of data collection, (2) increasing the specificity of health status scales, (3) maximizing consistency among different individuals collecting the same information, and (4) rendering the data items as discipline-neutral as possible (i.e., individuals from one discipline should be able to provide information with

Source: National Association for Home Care. 1998 (March). *Uniform Data Set for Home Care and Hospice.* Available at www.nahc.org/NAHC/Research/unidata.html.

the same accuracy and precision as those from another discipline). The data items in OASIS-B are the result of blending these competing priorities in an effort to produce a data set that is precise yet practical, and for the most part, reliable yet not overly burdensome.

Care providers have indicated that it may take four to six visits for a provider to become familiar and comfortable with using the OASIS, in much the same manner it takes to familiarize new staff with current forms or current staff with a change in assessment forms. We have also received a large number of comments on the utility of the increased precision of patient assessment that results from the OASIS. For example, care planning can be more specific, more precise documentation of patient condition facilitates communication with physicians, and the increased precision can be advantageous in justifying approaches to and quantities of service provision to managed care organizations.

We wish to repeat that the OASIS was not developed as a comprehensive assessment instrument. It was developed primarily for purposes of measuring outcomes for adult home care patients. Agencies will find it necessary to supplement the OASIS in order to comprehensively assess health status and care needs of patients (for example, the OASIS does not include vital signs, nor was it developed with pediatric patients in mind). The purpose in disseminating OASIS-B at the present time is to assist home care agencies and other providers in acclimating to these types of data items and to benefit from our collective experiences as we move toward a standardized data set under Medicare and other purchasers of home care services.

It is also important to note that the purpose of measuring patient outcomes through the OASIS is to assist home care agencies with quality improvement activities. In 1995, we authored a book published by the National Association for Home Care, *Outcome-Based Quality Improvement: A Manual for Home Care Agencies on How to Use Outcomes.*[5] This publication provides guidance to agencies on measuring and reporting outcomes, and using them to improve quality.

---

[1]See the *Federal Register,* 1997, Vol. 62 (46):11035-11064

[2]Until such time that the OASIS is required under Conditions of Participation, HCFA is not imposing the OASIS on any agency. An agency's decision to use OASIS is entirely voluntary.

Use or nonuse of OASIS will not be a factor in determining compliance or noncompliance with the Medicare home health agency Conditions of Participation in effect at the time of this publication. Likewise, the research Center's release of the OASIS-B does not constitute HCFA's endorsement of the data set. Only the publication of an effective rule that includes the use of a specific data set will serve as HCFA's requirement.

[3]For additional information on *OASIS Basics,* call or write the Center for Health Services and Policy Research, 1355 S. Colorado Boulevard #306, Denver, CO 80222, (303) 756-8350, fax: (303) 759-8196.

[4]The OASIS data items have been copyrighted by the Center for Health Policy Research (now termed the Center for Health Services and Policy Research) and are in the public domain. They cannot be further copyrighted for exclusive use by a particular agent or organization.

[5]For additional information on *Outcome-Based Quality Improvement,* call or write the National Association for Home Care, 228 7th St. SE, Washington, DC 20003, (202) 547-7424, fax: (202) 547-3540.

Source: National Association for Home Care. 1998 (March). *Uniform Data Set for Home Care and Hospice.* Available at www.nahc.org/NAHC/Research/unidata.html.

Medicare Home Health Care Quality Assurance and Improvement Demonstration Outcome and Assessment Information Set (OASIS-B)

> **This data set should not be reviewed or used without first reading the accompanying narrative prologue that explains the purpose of the OASIS and its past and planned evolution.**
>
> **OASIS Items to be Used at Specific Time Points**
>
> Start of Care (or Resumption of Care Following Inpatient Facility Stay): 1–69
>
> Follow-Up: 1, 4, 9–11, 13, 16–26, 29–71
>
> Discharge (not to inpatient facility): 1, 4, 9–11, 13, 16–26, 29–74, 78–79
>
> Transfer to Inpatient Facility (with or without agency discharge): 1, 70–72, 75–79
>
> Death at Home: 1, 79 Note: For items 51–67, please note special instructions at the beginning of the section.

Clinical Record Items

a. (M0010) Agency ID: ____ ____ ____ ____

____ ____ ____ ____

b. (M0020) Patient ID Number: _____

c. (M0030) Start of Care Date:
____ ____ / ____ ____ / ____ ____ ____ ____

c. (M0030) Start of Care Date:
____ ____ / ____ ____ / ____ ____ ____ ____

d. (M0040) Patient's Last Name:

__ __ __ __ __ __ __ __ __ __

__ __ __

e. (M0050) Patient State of Residence: ____ ____

f. (M0060) Patient Zip Code: ____ ____

____ ____ ____

g. (M0063) Medicare Number: (including suffix if any)

— — — — — — — — — — —

☐ NA – No Medicare

h. (M0066) Birth Date:
____ ____ / ____ ____ / ____ ____ ____ ____

h. (M0066) Birth Date:
____ ____ / ____ ____ / ____ ____ ____ ____

i. (M0080) Discipline of Person Completing Assessment:

| ☐ 1–RN | ☐ 2–LPN | ☐ 3–PT |
| ☐ 4–SLP/ST | ☐ 5–OT | ☐ 6–MSW |

j. (M0090) Date Assessment Information Recorded:
____ ____ / ____ ____ / ____ ____ ____ ____
month / day / year

Demographics and Patient History

1. **(M0100) This Assessment is Currently Being Completed for the Following Reason:**
   - ☐ 1 – Start of care
   - ☐ 2 – Resumption of care (after inpatient stay)
   - ☐ 3 – Discharge from agency—not to an inpatient facility **[Go to M0150]**
   - ☐ 4 – Transferred to an inpatient facility—discharged from agency **[Go to M0830]**
   - ☐ 5 – Transferred to an inpatient facility—not discharged from agency **[Go to M0830]**
   - ☐ 6 – Died at home **[Go to M0906]**
   - ☐ 7 – Recertification reassessment (follow-up) **[Go to M0150]**
   - ☐ 8 – Other follow-up **[Go to M0150]**

Source: National Association for Home Care. 1998 (March). *Uniform Data Set for Home Care and Hospice.* Available at www.nahc.org/NAHC/Research/unidata.html.

2. **(M0130) Gender:**

   ☐ 1 – Male
   ☐ 2 – Female

3. **(M0140) Race/Ethnicity (as identified by patient):**

   ☐ 1 – White, non-Hispanic
   ☐ 2 – Black, African-American
   ☐ 3 – Hispanic
   ☐ 4 – Asian, Pacific Islander
   ☐ 5 – American Indian, Eskimo, Aleut
   ☐ 6 – Other (r) UK – Unknown

4. **(M0150) Current Payment Sources for Home Care: (Mark all that apply.)**

   ☐ 0 – None; no charge for current services
   ☐ 1 – Medicare (traditional fee-for-service)
   ☐ 2 – Medicare (HMO/managed care)
   ☐ 3 – Medicaid (traditional fee-for-service)
   ☐ 4 – Medicaid (HMO/managed care)
   ☐ 5 – Workers' compensation
   ☐ 6 – Title programs (e.g., Title III, V, or XX)
   ☐ 7 – Other government (e.g., CHAMPUS, VA, etc.)
   ☐ 8 – Private insurance
   ☐ 9 – Private HMO/managed care
   ☐ 10 – Self-pay
   ☐ 11 – Other (specify)
   ☐ UK – Unknown

5. **(M0160) Financial Factors** limiting the ability of the patient/family to meet basic health needs:
   (Mark all that apply.)

   ☐ 0 – None
   ☐ 1 – Unable to afford medicine or medical supplies
   ☐ 2 – Unable to afford medical expenses that are not covered by insurance/Medicare (e.g., copayments)
   ☐ 3 – Unable to afford rent/utility bills
   ☐ 4 – Unable to afford food
   ☐ 5 – Other (specify)

6. **(M0170)** From which of the following **Inpatient Facilities** was the patient discharged during the past 14 days? **(Mark all that apply.)**

   ☐ 1 – Hospital
   ☐ 2 – Rehabilitation facility
   ☐ 3 – Nursing home
   ☐ 4 – Other (specify)_____
   ☐ NA – Patient was not discharged from an inpatient facility **[If NA, go to M0200]**

7. **(M0180) Inpatient Discharge Date (most recent):**

   ___ ___ / ___ ___ / ___ ___ ___ ___
   month / day / year
   ☐ UK – Unknown

8. **(M0190) Inpatient Diagnoses** and three-digit ICD code categories <u>for only those conditions treated during an inpatient facility stay within the last 14 days</u> (no surgical or V-codes):

Inpatient Facility Diagnosis	ICD
a.	(___ ___ ___)
b.	(___ ___ ___)

Source: National Association for Home Care. 1998 (March). *Uniform Data Set for Home Care and Hospice.* Available at www.nahc.org/NAHC/Research/unidata.html.

9. **(M0200) Medical or Treatment Regimen Change Within Past 14 Days:** Has this patient experienced a change in medical or treatment regimen (e.g., medication, treatment, or service change due to new or additional diagnosis, etc.) within the last 14 days?

    ☐   0 – No **[If No, go to M0220]**
    ☐   1 – Yes

10. **(M0210)** List the patient's **Medical Diagnoses** and three-digit ICD code categories <u>for those conditions requiring changed medical or treatment regimen</u> (no surgical or V-codes):

Changed Medical Regimen Diagnosis	ICD
a.	(___ ___ ___)
b.	(___ ___ ___)
c.	(___ ___ ___)
d.	(___ ___ ___)

11. **(M0220) Conditions Prior to Medical or Treatment Regimen Change or Inpatient Stay Within Past 14 Days:** If this patient experienced an inpatient facility discharge or change in medical or treatment regimen within the past 14 days, indicate any conditions which existed <u>prior to</u> the inpatient stay or change in medical or treatment regimen. **(Mark all that apply.)**

    ☐   1 – Urinary incontinence
    ☐   2 – Indwelling/suprapubic catheter
    ☐   3 – Intractable pain
    ☐   4 – Impaired decision-making
    ☐   5 – Disruptive or socially inappropriate behavior
    ☐   6 – Memory loss to the extent that supervision required
    ☐   7 – None of the above
    ☐   NA – No inpatient facility discharge and no change in medical or treatment regimen in past 14 days
    ☐   UK – Unknown

12. **(M0230/M0240) Diagnoses and Severity Index:** List each medical diagnosis or problem for which the patient is receiving home care and ICD code category (no surgical or V-codes) and rate them using the following severity index. (Choose one value that represents the most severe rating appropriate for each diagnosis.)

0 – Asymptomatic, no treatment needed at this time
1 – Symptoms well controlled with current therapy
2 – Symptoms controlled with difficulty, affecting daily functioning; patient needs ongoing monitoring
3 – Symptoms poorly controlled, patient needs frequent adjustment intreatment and dose monitoring
4 – Symptoms poorly controlled, history of rehospitalizations

Primary Diagnosis	ICD	Severity Rating				
a.	(___ ___ ___)	☐ 0	☐ 1	☐ 2	☐ 3	☐ 4

Other Diagnoses	ICD	Severity Rating				
b.	(___ ___ ___)	☐ 0	☐ 1	☐ 2	☐ 3	☐ 4
c.	(___ ___ ___)	☐ 0	☐ 1	☐ 2	☐ 3	☐ 4
d.	(___ ___ ___)	☐ 0	☐ 1	☐ 2	☐ 3	☐ 4
e.	(___ ___ ___)	☐ 0	☐ 1	☐ 2	☐ 3	☐ 4
f.	(___ ___ ___)	☐ 0	☐ 1	☐ 2	☐ 3	☐ 4

13. **(M0250) Therapies** the patient receives <u>at home</u>: **(Mark all that apply.)**

    ☐   1 – Intravenous or infusion therapy (excludes TPN)
    ☐   2 – Parenteral nutrition (TPN or lipids)
    ☐   3 – Enteral nutrition (nasogastric, gastrostomy, jejunostomy, or any other artificial entry into the alimentary canal)
    ☐   4 – None of the above

Source: National Association for Home Care. 1998 (March). *Uniform Data Set for Home Care and Hospice.* Available at www.nahc.org/NAHC/Research/unidata.html.

14. **(M0260) Overall Prognosis:** BEST description of patient's overall prognosis for <u>recovery from this episode of illness</u>.

    ☐ 0 – Poor: little or no recovery is expected and/or further decline is imminent
    ☐ 1 – Good/Fair: partial to full recovery is expected
    ☐ UK –   Unknown

15. **(M0270) Rehabilitative Prognosis:** BEST description of patient's prognosis for <u>functional status</u>.

    ☐ 0 – Guarded: minimal improvement in functional status is expected; decline is possible
    ☐ 1 – Good: marked improvement in functional status is expected
    ☐ UK –   Unknown

16. **(M0280) Life Expectancy:** (Physician documentation is not required.)

    ☐ 0 – Life expectancy is greater than 6 months
    ☐ 1 – Life expectancy is 6 months or fewer

17. **(M0290) High Risk Factors** characterizing this patient: **(Mark all that apply.)**

    ☐ 1 – Heavy smoking
    ☐ 2 – Obesity
    ☐ 3 – Alcohol dependency
    ☐ 4 – Drug dependency
    ☐ 5 – None of the above
    ☐ UK –   Unknown

Living Arrangements

18. **(M0300) Current Residence:**

    ☐ 1 – Patient's owned or rented residence (house, apartment, or mobile home owned or rented by patient/couple/significant other)
    ☐ 2 – Family member's residence
    ☐ 3 – Boarding home or rented room
    ☐ 4 – Board and care or assisted living facility
    ☐ 5 – Other (specify) _____

19. **(M0310) Structural Barriers** in the patient's environment limiting independent mobility: **(Mark all that apply.)**

    ☐ 0 – None
    ☐ 1 – Stairs inside home which must be used by the patient (e.g., to get to toileting, sleeping, eating areas)
    ☐ 2 – Stairs inside home which are used optionally (e.g., to get to laundry facilities)
    ☐ 3 – Stairs leading from inside house to outside
    ☐ 4 – Narrow or obstructed doorways

20. **(M0320) Safety Hazards** found in the patient's current place of residence: **(Mark all that apply.)**

    ☐ 0 – None
    ☐ 1 – Inadequate floor, roof, or windows
    ☐ 2 – Inadequate lighting
    ☐ 3 – Unsafe gas/electric appliance
    ☐ 4 – Inadequate heating
    ☐ 5 – Inadequate cooling
    ☐ 6 – Lack of fire safety devices
    ☐ 7 – Unsafe floor coverings
    ☐ 8 – Inadequate stair railings
    ☐ 9 – Improperly stored hazardous materials
    ☐ 10 – Lead-based paint
    ☐ 11 – Other (specify) _____

Source: National Association for Home Care. 1998 (March). *Uniform Data Set for Home Care and Hospice.* Available at www.nahc.org/NAHC/Research/unidata.html.

21. **(M0330) Sanitation Hazards** found in the patient's current place of residence: **(Mark all that apply.)**

☐ 0 – None
☐ 1 – No running water
☐ 2 – Contaminated water
☐ 3 – No toileting facilities
☐ 4 – Outdoor toileting facilities only
☐ 5 – Inadequate sewage disposal
☐ 6 – Inadequate/improper food storage
☐ 7 – No food refrigeration
☐ 8 – No cooking facilities
☐ 9 – Insects/rodents present
☐ 10 – No scheduled trash pickup
☐ 11 – Cluttered/soiled living area
☐ 12 – Other (specify) _____

22. **(M0340) Patient Lives With: (Mark all that apply.)**

☐ 1 – Lives alone
☐ 2 – With spouse or significant other
☐ 3 – With other family member
☐ 4 – With a friend
☐ 5 – With paid help (other than home care agency staff)
☐ 6 – With other than above

Supportive Assistance

23. **(M0350) Assisting Person(s) Other than Home Care Agency Staff: (Mark all that apply.)**

☐ 1 – Relatives, friends, or neighbors living outside the home
☐ 2 – Person residing in the home (EXCLUDING paid help)
☐ 3 – Paid help
☐ 4 – None of the above **[If None of the above, go to M0390]**
☐ UK – Unknown **[If Unknown, go to M0390]**

24. **(M0360) Primary Caregiver** taking lead responsibility for providing or managing the patient's care, providing the most frequent assistance, etc. (other than home care agency staff):

☐ 0 – No one person **[If No one person, go to M0390]**
☐ 1 – Spouse or significant other
☐ 2 – Daughter or son
☐ 3 – Other family member
☐ 4 – Friend or neighbor or community or church member
☐ 5 – Paid help
☐ UK – Unknown [If Unknown, go to M0390]

25. **(M0370) How Often** does the patient receive assistance from the primary caregiver?

☐ 1 – Several times during day and night
☐ 2 – Several times during day
☐ 3 – Once daily
☐ 4 – Three or more times per week
☐ 5 – One to two times per week
☐ 6 – Less often than weekly
☐ UK – Unknown

26. **(M0380) Type of Primary Caregiver Assistance: (Mark all that apply.)**

☐ 1 – ADL assistance (e.g., bathing, dressing, toileting, bowel/bladder, eating/feeding)
☐ 2 – IADL assistance (e.g., meds, meals, housekeeping, laundry, telephone, shopping, finances)
☐ 3 – Environmental support (housing, home maintenance)
☐ 4 – Psychosocial support (socialization, companionship, recreation)
☐ 5 – Advocates or facilitates patient's participation in appropriate medical care
☐ 6 – Financial agent, power of attorney, or conservator of finance
☐ 7 – Health care agent, conservator of person, or medical power of attorney
☐ UK – Unknown

Source: National Association for Home Care. 1998 (March). *Uniform Data Set for Home Care and Hospice.* Available at www.nahc.org/NAHC/Research/unidata.html.

Sensory Status

27. **(M0390) Vision** with corrective lenses if the patient usually wears them:

☐ 0 – Normal vision: sees adequately in most situations; can see medication labels, newsprint.

☐ 1 – Partially impaired: cannot see medication labels or newsprint, but can see obstacles in path, and the surrounding layout; can count fingers at arm's length.

☐ 2 – Severely impaired: cannot locate objects without hearing or touching them or patient nonresponsive.

28. **(M0400) Hearing and Ability to Understand Spoken Language** in patient's own language (with hearing aids if the patient usually uses them):

☐ 0 – No observable impairment. Able to hear and understand complex or detailed instructions and extended or abstract conversation.

☐ 1 – With minimal difficulty, able to hear and understand most multi-step instructions and ordinary conversation. May need occasional repetition, extra time, or louder voice.

☐ 2 – Has moderate difficulty hearing and understanding simple, one-step instructions and brief conversation; needs frequent prompting or assistance.

☐ 3 – Has severe difficulty hearing and understanding simple greetings and short comments. Requires multiple repetitions, restatements, demonstrations, additional time.

☐ 4 – Unable to hear and understand familiar words or common expressions consistently, or patient nonresponsive.

29. **(M0410) Speech and Oral (Verbal) Expression of Language** (in patient's own language):

☐ 0 – Expresses complex ideas, feelings, and needs clearly, completely, and easily in all situations with no observable impairment.

☐ 1 – Minimal difficulty in expressing ideas and needs (may take extra time; makes occasional errors in word choice, grammar or speech intelligibility; needs minimal prompting or assistance).

☐ 2 – Expresses simple ideas or needs with moderate difficulty (needs prompting or assistance, errors in word choice, organization or speech intelligibility). Speaks in phrases or short sentences.

☐ 3 – Has severe difficulty expressing basic ideas or needs and requires maximal assistance or guessing by listener. Speech limited to single words or short phrases.

☐ 4 – Unable to express basic needs even with maximal prompting or assistance but is not comatose or unresponsive (e.g., speech is nonsensical or unintelligible).

☐ 5 – Patient nonresponsive or unable to speak.

30. **(M0420) Frequency of Pain** interfering with patient's activity or movement:

☐ 0 – Patient has no pain or pain does not interfere with activity or movement

☐ 1 – Less often than daily

☐ 2 – Daily, but not constantly

☐ 3 – All of the time

31. **(M0430) Intractable Pain:** Is the patient experiencing pain that is not easily relieved, occurs at least daily, and affects the patient's sleep, appetite, physical or emotional energy, concentration, personal relationships, emotions, or ability or desire to perform physical activity?

☐ 0 – No

☐ 1 – Yes

Integumentary Status

32. **(M0440)** Does this patient have a **Skin Lesion** or an **Open Wound**? This excludes "OSTOMIES."

☐ 0 – No **[If No, go to M0490]**

☐ 1 – Yes

33. **(M0445)** Does this patient have a **Pressure Ulcer**?

☐ 0 – No **[If No, go to M0468]**

☐ 1 – Yes

Source: National Association for Home Care. 1998 (March). *Uniform Data Set for Home Care and Hospice.* Available at www.nahc.org/NAHC/Research/unidata.html.

33a. **(M0450) Current Number of Pressure Ulcers at Each Stage:** (Circle one response for each stage.)

Pressure Ulcer Stages	Number of Pressure Ulcers				
a) Stage 1: Nonblanchable erythema of intact skin; the heralding of skin ulceration. In darker-pigmented skin, warmth, edema, hardness, or discolored skin may be indicators.	0	1	2	3	4 OR MORE
b) Stage 2: Partial thickness skin loss involving epidermis and/or dermis. The ulcer is superficial and presents clinically as an abrasion, blister, or shallow crater.	0	1	2	3	4 OR MORE
c) Stage 3: Full-thickness skin loss involving damage or necrosis of subcutaneous tissue which may extend down to, but not through, underlying fascia. The ulcer presents clinically as a deep crater with or without undermining of adjacent tissue.	0	1	2	3	4 OR MORE
d) Stage 4: Full-thickness skin loss with extensive destruction, tissue necrosis, or damage to muscle, bone, or supporting structures (e.g., tendon, joint capsule, etc.)	0	1	2	3	4 OR MORE

e) In addition to the above, is there at least one pressure ulcer that cannot be observed due to the presence of eschar or a nonremovable dressing, including casts?
- ☐ 0 – No
- ☐ 1 – Yes

33b. **(M0460) Stage of Most Problematic (Observable) Pressure Ulcer:**
- ☐ 1 – Stage 1
- ☐ 2 – Stage 2
- ☐ 3 – Stage 3
- ☐ 4 – Stage 4
- ☐ NA – No observable pressure ulcer

33c. **(M0464) Status of Most Problematic (Observable) Pressure Ulcer:**
- ☐ 1 – Fully granulating
- ☐ 2 – Early/partial granulation
- ☐ 3 – Not healing
- ☐ NA – No observable pressure ulcer

34. (M0468) Does this patient have a **Stasis Ulcer**?
- ☐ 0 – No **[If No, go to M0482]**
- ☐ 1 – Yes

34a. **(M0470) Current Number of Observable Stasis Ulcer(s):**
- ☐ 0 – Zero
- ☐ 1 – One
- ☐ 2 – Two
- ☐ 3 – Three
- ☐ 4 – Four or more

34b. **(M0474)** Does this patient have at least one **Stasis Ulcer that Cannot be Observed** due to the presence of a nonremovable dressing?
- ☐ 0 – No
- ☐ 1 – Yes

34c. **(M0476) Status of Most Problematic (Observable) Stasis Ulcer:**
- ☐ 1 – Fully granulating
- ☐ 2 – Early/partial granulation
- ☐ 3 – Not healing
- ☐ NA – No observable stasis ulcer

Source: National Association for Home Care. 1998 (March). *Uniform Data Set for Home Care and Hospice.* Available at www.nahc.org/NAHC/Research/unidata.html.

35.   **(M0482)** Does this patient have a **Surgical Wound**?

    □ 0 – No **[If No, go to M0490]**
    □ 1 – Yes

    35a. **(M0484) Current Number of (Observable) Surgical Wounds:** (If a wound is partially closed but has more than one opening, consider each opening as a separate wound.)

        □ 0 – Zero
        □ 1 – One
        □ 2 – Two
        □ 3 – Three
        □ 4 – Four or more

    35b. **(M0486)** Does this patient have at least one **Surgical Wound that Cannot be Observed** due to the presence of a nonremovable dressing?

        □ 0 – No
        □ 1 – Yes

    35c. **(M0488) Status of Most Problematic (Observable) Surgical Wound:**

        □ 1 – Fully granulating
        □ 2 – Early/partial granulation
        □ 3 – Not healing
        □ NA – No observable surgical wound

Respiratory Status

36.   **(M0490)** When is the patient dyspneic or noticeably **Short of Breath**?

    □ 0 – Never, patient is not short of breath
    □ 1 – When walking more than 20 feet, climbing stairs
    □ 2 – With moderate exertion (e.g., while dressing, using commode or bedpan, walking distances less than 20 feet)
    □ 3 – With minimal exertion (e.g., while eating, talking, or performing other ADLs) or with agitation
    □ 4 – At rest (during day or night)

37.   **(M0500) Respiratory Treatments** utilized at home: **(Mark all that apply.)**

    □ 1 – Oxygen (intermittent or continuous)
    □ 2 – Ventilator (continually or at night)
    □ 3 – Continuous positive airway pressure
    □ 4 – None of the above

Elimination Status

38.   **(M0510)** Has this patient been treated for a **Urinary Tract Infection** in the past 14 days?

    □ 0 – No
    □ 1 – Yes
    □ NA – Patient on prophylactic treatment
    □ UK – Unknown

39.   **(M0520) Urinary Incontinence or Urinary Catheter Presence:**

    □ 0 – No incontinence or catheter (includes anuria or ostomy for urinary drainage) **[If No, go to M0540]**
    □ 1 – Patient is incontinent
    □ 2 – Patient requires a urinary catheter (i.e., external, indwelling, intermittent, suprapubic) **[Go to M0540]**

40.   **(M0530)** When does **Urinary Incontinence** occur?

    □ 0 – Timed-voiding defers incontinence
    □ 1 – During the night only
    □ 2 – During the day and night

Source: National Association for Home Care. 1998 (March). *Uniform Data Set for Home Care and Hospice.* Available at www.nahc.org/NAHC/Research/unidata.html.

41. **(M0540) Bowel Incontinence Frequency:**

 ☐ 0 – Very rarely or never has bowel incontinence
 ☐ 1 – Less than once weekly
 ☐ 2 – One to three times weekly
 ☐ 3 – Four to six times weekly
 ☐ 4 – On a daily basis
 ☐ 5 – More often than once daily
 ☐ NA – Patient has ostomy for bowel elimination
 ☐ UK – Unknown

42. **(M0550) Ostomy for Bowel Elimination:** Does this patient have an ostomy for bowel elimination that (within the last 14 days): a) was related to an inpatient facility stay, or b) necessitated a change in medical or treatment regimen?

 ☐ 0 – Patient does not have an ostomy for bowel elimination.
 ☐ 1 – Patient's ostomy was not related to an inpatient stay and did not necessitate change in medical or treatment regimen.
 ☐ 2 – The ostomy was related to an inpatient stay or did necessitate change in medical or treatment regimen.

Neuro/Emotional/Behavioral Status

43. **(M0560) Cognitive Functioning:** (Patient's current level of alertness, orientation, comprehension, concentration, and immediate memory for simple commands.)

 ☐ 0 – Alert/oriented, able to focus and shift attention, comprehends and recalls task directions independently.
 ☐ 1 – Requires prompting (cuing, repetition, reminders) only under stressful or unfamiliar conditions.
 ☐ 2 – Requires assistance and some direction in specific situations (e.g., on all tasks involving shifting of attention), or consistently requires low stimulus environment due to distractibility.
 ☐ 3 – Requires considerable assistance in routine situations. Is not alert and oriented or is unable to shift attention and recall directions more than half the time.
 ☐ 4 – Totally dependent due to disturbances such as constant disorientation, coma, persistent vegetative state, or delirium.

44. **(M0570) When Confused (Reported or Observed):**

 ☐ 0 – Never
 ☐ 1 – In new or complex situations only
 ☐ 2 – On awakening or at night only
 ☐ 3 – During the day and evening, but not constantly
 ☐ 4 – Constantly
 ☐ NA – Patient nonresponsive

45. **(M0580) When Anxious (Reported or Observed):**

 ☐ 0 – None of the time
 ☐ 1 – Less often than daily
 ☐ 2 – Daily, but not constantly
 ☐ 3 – All of the time
 ☐ NA – Patient nonresponsive

46. **(M0590) Depressive Feelings Reported or Observed in Patient: (Mark all that apply.)**

 ☐ 1 – Depressed mood (e.g., feeling sad, tearful)
 ☐ 2 – Sense of failure or self reproach
 ☐ 3 – Hopelessness
 ☐ 4 – Recurrent thoughts of death
 ☐ 5 – Thoughts of suicide
 ☐ 6 – None of the above feelings observed or reported

47. **(M0600) Patient Behaviors (Reported or Observed): (Mark all that apply.)**

 ☐ 1 – Indecisiveness, lack of concentration
 ☐ 2 – Diminished interest in most activities
 ☐ 3 – Sleep disturbances
 ☐ 4 – Recent change in appetite or weight
 ☐ 5 – Agitation
 ☐ 6 – A suicide attempt
 ☐ 7 – None of the above behaviors observed or reported

Source: National Association for Home Care. 1998 (March). *Uniform Data Set for Home Care and Hospice.* Available at www.nahc.org/NAHC/Research/unidata.html.

48. **(M0610) Behaviors Demonstrated at Least Once a Week (Reported or Observed): (Mark all that apply.)**

- ☐ 1 – Memory deficit: failure to recognize familiar persons/places, inability to recall events of past 24 hours, significant memory loss so that supervision is required
- ☐ 2 – Impaired decision-making: failure to perform usual ADLs or IADLs, inability to appropriately stop activities, jeopardizes safety through actions
- ☐ 3 – Verbal disruption: yelling, threatening, excessive profanity, sexual references, etc.
- ☐ 4 – Physical aggression: aggressive or combative to self and others (e.g., hits self, throws objects, punches, dangerous maneuvers with wheelchair or other objects)
- ☐ 5 – Disruptive, infantile, or socially inappropriate behavior (excludes verbal actions)
- ☐ 6 – Delusional, hallucinatory, or paranoid behavior
- ☐ 7 – None of the above behaviors demonstrated

49. **(M0620) Frequency of Behavior Problems (Reported or Observed)** (e.g., wandering episodes, self abuse, verbal disruption, physical aggression, etc.):

- ☐ 0 – Never
- ☐ 1 – Less than once a month
- ☐ 2 – Once a month
- ☐ 3 – Several times each month
- ☐ 4 – Several times a week
- ☐ 5 – At least daily

50. **(M0630)** Is this patient receiving **Psychiatric Nursing Services** at home provided by a qualified psychiatric nurse?

- ☐ 0 – No
- ☐ 1 – Yes

ADL/IADLs

For Questions 51–67, complete the "current" column for all patients. For these same items, complete the "prior" column at start of care or resumption of care; mark the level that corresponds to the patient's condition 14 days prior to start of care. In all cases, record what the patient is able to do.

51. **(M0640) Grooming:** Ability to tend to personal hygiene needs (i.e., washing face and hands, hair care, shaving or makeup, teeth or denture care, fingernail care).

Prior	Current	
☐	☐	0 – Able to groom self unaided, with or without the use of assistive devices or adapted methods.
☐	☐	1 – Grooming utensils must be placed within reach before able to complete grooming activities.
☐	☐	2 – Someone must assist the patient to groom self.
☐	☐	3 – Patient depends entirely upon someone else for grooming needs.
☐		UK – Unknown

Source: National Association for Home Care. 1998 (March). *Uniform Data Set for Home Care and Hospice.* Available at www.nahc.org/NAHC/Research/unidata.html.

52. **(M0650) Ability to Dress Upper Body** (with or without dressing aids) including undergarments, pullovers, front-opening shirts and blouses, managing zippers, buttons, and snaps:

Prior	Current	
☐	☐	0 – Able to get clothes out of closets and drawers, put them on and remove them from the upper body without assistance.
☐	☐	1 – Able to dress upper body without assistance if clothing is laid out or handed to the patient.
☐	☐	2 – Someone must help the patient put on upper body clothing.
☐	☐	3 – Patient depends entirely upon another person to dress the upper body.
☐		UK – Unknown

53. **(M0660) Ability to Dress Lower Body** (with or without dressing aids) including undergarments, slacks, socks or nylons, shoes:

Prior	Current	
☐	☐	0 – Able to obtain, put on, and remove clothing and shoes without assistance.
☐	☐	1 – Able to dress lower body without assistance if clothing and shoes are are laid out or handed to the patient.
☐	☐	2 – Someone must help the patient put on undergarments, slacks, socks or nylons, and shoes.
☐	☐	3 – Patient depends entirely upon another person to dress lower body.
☐		UK – Unknown

54. **(M0670) Bathing:** Ability to wash entire body. **Excludes grooming (washing face and hands only).**

Prior	Current	
☐	☐	0 – Able to bathe self in shower or tub independently.
☐	☐	1 – With the use of devices, is able to bathe self in shower or tub independently.
☐	☐	2 – Able to bathe in shower or tub with the assistance of another person: (a) for intermittent supervision or encouragement or reminders, OR (b) to get in and out of the shower or tub, OR (c) for washing difficult to reach areas.
☐	☐	3 – Participates in bathing self in shower or tub, but requires presence of another person throughout the bath for assistance or supervision.
☐	☐	4 – Unable to use the shower or tub and is bathed in bed or bedside chair.
☐	☐	5 – Unable to effectively participate in bathing and is totally bathed by another person.
☐		UK – Unknown

Source: National Association for Home Care. 1998 (March). *Uniform Data Set for Home Care and Hospice.* Available at www.nahc.org/NAHC/Research/unidata.html.

55. **(M0680) Toileting:** Ability to get to and from the toilet or bedside commode.

Prior	Current	
☐	☐	0 – Able to get to and from the toilet independently with or without a device.
☐	☐	1 – When reminded, assisted, or supervised by another person, able to get to and from the toilet.
☐	☐	2 – Unable to get to and from the toilet but is able to use a bedside commode (with or without assistance).
☐	☐	3 – Unable to get to and from the toilet or bedside commode but is able to use a bedpan/urinal independently.
☐	☐	4 – Is totally dependent in toileting.
☐		UK – Unknown

56. **(M0690) Transferring:** Ability to move from bed to chair, on and off toilet or commode, into and out of tub or shower, and ability to turn and position self in bed if patient is bedfast.

Prior	Current	
☐	☐	0 – Able to independently transfer.
☐	☐	1 – Transfers with minimal human assistance or with use of an assistive device.
☐	☐	2 – Unable to transfer self but is able to bear weight and pivot during the transfer process.
☐	☐	3 – Unable to transfer self and is unable to bear weight or pivot when transferred by another person.
☐	☐	4 – Bedfast, unable to transfer but is able to turn and position self in bed.
☐	☐	5 – Bedfast, unable to transfer and is unable to turn and position self.
☐		UK – Unknown

57. **(M0700) Ambulation/Locomotion:** Ability to SAFELY walk, once in a standing position, or use a wheelchair, once in a seated position, on a variety of surfaces.

Prior	Current	
☐	☐	0 – Able to independently walk on even and uneven surfaces and climb stairs with or without railings (i.e., needs no human assistance or assistive device.
☐	☐	1 – Requires use of a device (e.g., cane, walker) to walk alone or requires human supervision or assistance to negotiate stairs or steps or uneven surfaces.
☐	☐	2 – Able to walk only with the supervision or assistance of another person at all times.
☐	☐	3 – Chairfast, unable to ambulate but is able to wheel self independently.
☐	☐	4 – Chairfast, unable to ambulate and is unable to wheel self.
☐	☐	5 – Bedfast, unable to ambulate or be up in a chair.
☐		UK – Unknown

Source: National Association for Home Care. 1998 (March). *Uniform Data Set for Home Care and Hospice.* Available at www.nahc.org/NAHC/Research/unidata.html.

58. **(M0710) Feeding or Eating:** Ability to feed self meals and snacks. **Note: This refers only to the process of <u>eating</u>, <u>chewing</u>, and <u>swallowing</u>, <u>not preparing</u> the food to be eaten.**

Prior	Current	
☐	☐	0 – Able to independently feed self.
☐	☐	1 – Able to feed self independently but requires: (a) meal set-up; OR (b) intermittent assistance or supervision from another person; OR (c) a liquid, pureed or ground meat diet.
☐	☐	2 – Unable to feed self and must be assisted or supervised throughout the meal/snack.
☐	☐	3 – Able to take in nutrients orally and receives supplemental nutrients only through a nasogastric tube or gastrostomy.
☐	☐	4 – Unable to take in nutrients orally and is fed nutrients through a nasogastric tube or gastrostomy.
☐	☐	5 – Unable to take in nutrients orally or by tube feeding.
☐		UK – Unknown

59. **(0720) Planning and Preparing Light Meals** (e.g., cereal, sandwich) or reheat delivered meals:

Prior	Current	
☐	☐	0 – (a) Able to independently plan and prepare all light meals for self or reheat delivered meals; OR (b) Is physically, cognitively, and mentally able to prepare light meals on a regular basis but has not routinely performed light meal preparation in the past (i.e., prior to this home care admission).
☐	☐	1 – Unable to prepare light meals on a regular basis due to physical, cognitive, or mental limitations
☐	☐	2 – Unable to prepare any light meals or reheat any delivered meals.
☐		UK – Unknown

60. **(M0730) Transportation:** Physical and mental ability to safely use a car, taxi, or public transportation (bus, train, subway).

Prior	Current	
☐	☐	0 – Able to independently drive a regular or adapted car; OR uses a regular or handicap-accessible public bus.
☐	☐	1 – Able to ride in a car only when driven by another person; OR able to use a bus or handicap van only when assisted or accompanied by another person.
☐	☐	2 – Unable to ride in a car, taxi, bus, or van, and requires transportation by ambulance.
☐		UK – Unknown

Source: National Association for Home Care. 1998 (March). *Uniform Data Set for Home Care and Hospice.* Available at www.nahc.org/NAHC/Research/unidata.html.

61. **(M0740) Laundry:** Ability to do own laundry — to carry laundry to and from washing machine, to use washer and dryer, to wash small items by hand.

Prior	Current	
☐	☐	0 – (a) Able to independently take care of all laundry tasks; OR (b) Physically, cognitively, and mentally able to do laundry and access facilities, but has not routinely performed laundry tasks in the past (i.e., prior to this home care admission).
☐	☐	1 – Able to do only light laundry, such as minor hand wash or light washer loads. Due to physical, cognitive, or mental limitations, needs assistance with heavy laundry such as carrying large loads of laundry.
☐	☐	2 – Unable to do any laundry due to physical limitation or needs continual supervision and assistance due to cognitive or mental limitation.
☐		UK – Unknown

62. **(M0750) Housekeeping:** Ability to safely and effectively perform light housekeeping and heavier cleaning tasks.

Prior	Current	
☐	☐	0 – (a) Able to independently perform all housekeeping tasks; OR (b) Physically, cognitively, and mentally able to perform all housekeeping tasks but has not routinely participated in housekeeping tasks in the past (i.e., prior to this home care admission).
☐	☐	1 – Able to perform only light housekeeping (e.g., dusting, wiping kitchen counters) tasks independently.
☐	☐	2 – Able to perform housekeeping tasks with intermittent assistance or supervision from another person.
☐	☐	3 – Unable to consistently perform any housekeeping tasks unless assisted by another person throughout the process.
☐	☐	4 – Unable to effectively participate in any housekeeping tasks.
☐		UK – Unknown

63. **(M0760) Shopping:** Ability to plan for, select, and purchase items in a store and to carry them home or arrange delivery.

Prior	Current	
☐	☐	0 – (a) Able to plan for shopping needs and independently perform shopping tasks, including carrying packages; OR (b) Physically, cognitively, and mentally able to take care of shopping, but has not done shopping in the past (i.e., prior to this home care admission).
☐	☐	1 – Able to go shopping, but needs some assistance: (a) By self is able to do only light shopping and carry small packages, but needs someone to do occasional major shopping; OR (b) Unable to go shopping alone, but can go with someone to assist.
☐	☐	2 – Unable to go shopping, but is able to identify items needed, place orders, and arrange home delivery.
☐	☐	3 – Needs someone to do all shopping and errands.
☐		UK – Unknown

Source: National Association for Home Care. 1998 (March). *Uniform Data Set for Home Care and Hospice.* Available at www.nahc.org/NAHC/Research/unidata.html.

64.   **(M0770)4 Ability to Use Telephone:** Ability to answer the phone, dial numbers, and effectively use the telephone to communicate.

Prior	Current	
☐	☐	0 – Able to dial numbers and answer calls appropriately and as desired.
☐	☐	1 – Able to use a specially adapted telephone (i.e., large numbers on the dial, teletype phone for the deaf) and call essential numbers.
☐	☐	2 – Able to answer the telephone and carry on a normal conversation but has difficulty with placing calls.
☐	☐	3 – Able to answer the telephone only some of the time or is able to carry on only a limited conversation.
☐	☐	4 – Unable to answer the telephone at all but can listen if assisted with equipment.
☐	☐	5 – Totally unable to use the telephone.
☐		NA – Patient does not have a telephone.
☐		UK – Unknown

Medications

65.   **(M0780) Management of Oral Medications:** Patient's ability to prepare and take all prescribed oral medications reliably and safely, including administration of the correct dosage at the appropriate times/intervals. **Excludes injectable and IV medications. (NOTE: This refers to ability, not compliance or willingness.)**

Prior	Current	
☐	☐	0 – Able to independently take the correct oral medication(s) and proper dosage(s) at the correct times.
☐	☐	1 – Able to take medication(s) at the correct times if: (a) individual dosages are prepared in advance by another person; OR (b) given daily reminders; OR (c) someone develops a drug diary or chart.
☐	☐	2 – Unable to take medication unless administered by someone else.
☐		NA – No oral medications prescribed.
☐		UK – Unknown

66.   **(M0790) Management of Inhalant/Mist Medications:** Patient's ability to prepare and take all prescribed inhalant/mist medications (nebulizers, metered dose devices) reliably and safely, including administration of the correct dosage at the appropriate times/intervals. Excludes all other forms of medication (oral tablets, injectable and IV medications).

Prior	Current	
☐	☐	0 – Able to independently take the correct medication and proper dosage at the correct times.
☐	☐	1 – Able to take medication at the correct times if: (a) individual dosages are prepared in advance by another person, OR (b) given daily reminders.
☐	☐	2 – Unable to take medication unless administered by someone else.
☐		NA – No inhalant/mist medications prescribed.
☐		UK – Unknown

Source: National Association for Home Care. 1998 (March). *Uniform Data Set for Home Care and Hospice.* Available at www.nahc.org/NAHC/Research/unidata.html.

67. **(M0800) Management of Injectable Medications:** <u>Patient's ability</u> to prepare and take all prescribed injectable medications reliably and safely, including administration of correct dosage at the appropriate times/intervals. <u>**Excludes**</u> **IV medications.**

Prior	Current	
☐	☐	0 – Able to independently take the correct medication and proper dosage at the correct times.
☐	☐	1 – Able to take injectable medication at the correct times if: (a) individual syringes are prepared in advance by another person, OR (b) given daily reminders.
☐	☐	2 – Unable to take injectable medications unless administered by someone else.
☐		NA – No injectable medications prescribed.
☐		UK – Unknown

Equipment Management

68. **(M0810) Patient Management of Equipment (includes <u>ONLY</u> oxygen, IV/infusion therapy, enteral/parenteral nutrition equipment or supplies):** <u>Patient's ability</u> to set up, monitor and change equipment reliably and safely, add appropriate fluids or medication, clean/store/dispose of equipment or supplies using proper technique. **(NOTE: This refers to ability, not compliance or willingness.)**

    ☐ 0 – Patient manages all tasks related to equipment completely independently.
    ☐ 1 – If someone else sets up equipment (i.e., fills portable oxygen tank, provides patient with prepared solutions), patient is able to manage all other aspects of equipment.
    ☐ 2 – Patient requires considerable assistance from another person to manage equipment, but independently completes portions of the task.
    ☐ 3 – Patient is only able to monitor equipment (e.g., liter flow, fluid in bag) and must call someone else to manage the equipment.
    ☐ 4 – Patient is completely dependent on someone else to manage all equipment.
    ☐ NA – No equipment of this type used in care [**If NA, go to M0830**]

69. **(M0820) Caregiver Management of Equipment (includes <u>ONLY</u> oxygen, IV/infusion equipment, enteral/parenteral nutrition, ventilator therapy equipment or supplies):** <u>Caregiver's ability</u> to set up, monitor, and change equipment reliably and safely, add appropriate fluids or medication, clean/store/dispose of equipment or supplies using proper technique. **(NOTE: This refers to ability, not compliance or willingness.)**

    ☐ 0 – Caregiver manages all tasks related to equipment completely independently.
    ☐ 1 – If someone else sets up equipment, caregiver is able to manage all other aspects.
    ☐ 2 – Caregiver requires considerable assistance from another person to manage equipment, but independently completes significant portions of task.
    ☐ 3 – Caregiver is only able to complete small portions of task (e.g., administer nebulizer treatment, clean/store/dispose of equipment or supplies).
    ☐ 4 – Caregiver is completely dependent on someone else to manage all equipment.
    ☐ NA – No caregiver
    ☐ UK – Unknown

Emergent Care

70. **(M0830) Emergent Care:** Since the last time OASIS data were collected, has the patient utilized any of the following services for emergent care (other than home care agency services)? **(Mark all that apply.)**

    ☐ 0 – No emergent care services [**If No emergent care and patient discharged, go to M0855**]
    ☐ 1 – Hospital emergency room (includes 23-hour holding)
    ☐ 2 – Doctor's office emergency visit/house call
    ☐ 3 – Outpatient department/clinic emergency (includes urgicenter sites)
    ☐ UK – Unknown

Source: National Association for Home Care. 1998 (March). *Uniform Data Set for Home Care and Hospice.* Available at www.nahc.org/NAHC/Research/unidata.html.

71. **(M0840) Emergent Care Reason:** For what reason(s) did the patient/family seek emergent care? **(Mark all that apply.)**

☐ 1 – Improper medication administration, medication side effects, toxicity, anaphylaxis
☐ 2 – Nausea, dehydration, malnutrition, constipation, impaction
☐ 3 – Injury caused by fall or accident at home
☐ 4 – Respiratory problems (e.g., shortness of breath, respiratory infection, tracheobronchial obstruction)
☐ 5 – Wound infection, deteriorating wound status, new lesion/ulcer
☐ 6 – Cardiac problems (e.g., fluid overload, exacerbation of CHF, chest pain)
☐ 7 – Hypo/Hyperglycemia, diabetes out of control
☐ 8 – GI bleeding, obstruction
☐ 9 – Other than above reasons
☐ UK – Reason unknown

Data Items Collected at Inpatient Facility Admission or Agency Discharge Only

72. **(M0855)** To which **Inpatient Facility** has the patient been admitted?

☐ 1 – Hospital **[Go to M0890]**
☐ 2 – Rehabilitation facility **[Go to M0903]**
☐ 3 – Nursing home **[Go to M0900]**
☐ 4 – Hospice **[Go to M0903]**
☐ NA – No inpatient facility admission

73. **(M0870) Discharge Disposition:** Where is the patient after discharge from your agency? **(Choose only one answer.)**

☐ 1 – Patient remained in the community (not in hospital, nursing home, or rehab facility)
☐ 2 – Patient transferred to a noninstitutional hospice **[Go to M0903]**
☐ 3 – Unknown because patient moved to a geographic location not served by this agency **[Go to M0903]**
☐ UK – Other unknown **[Go to M0903]**

74. **(M0880)** After discharge, does the patient receive health, personal, or support **Services or Assistance? (Mark all that apply.)**

☐ 1 – No assistance or services received
☐ 2 – Yes, assistance or services provided by family or friends
☐ 3 – Yes, assistance or services provided by other community resources (e.g., meals-on-wheels, home health services, homemaker assistance, transportation assistance, assisted living, board and care)

| Go to M0903 |

75. **(M0890)** If the patient was admitted to an acute care Hospital, for what **Reason** was he/she admitted?

☐ 1 – Hospitalization for emergent (unscheduled) care
☐ 2 – Hospitalization for urgent (scheduled within 24 hours of admission) care
☐ 3 – Hospitalization for elective (scheduled more than 24 hours before admission) care
☐ UK – Unknown

76. **(M0895) Reason for Hospitalization: (Mark all that apply.)**

☐ 1 – Improper medication administration, medication side effects, toxicity, anaphylaxis
☐ 2 – Injury caused by fall or accident at home
☐ 3 – Respiratory problems (SOB, infection, obstruction)
☐ 4 – Wound or tube site infection, deteriorating wound status, new lesion/ulcer
☐ 5 – Hypo/Hyperglycemia, diabetes out of control
☐ 6 – GI bleeding, obstruction
☐ 7 – Exacerbation of CHF, fluid overload, heart failure
☐ 8 – Myocardial infarction, stroke
☐ 9 – Chemotherapy
☐ 10 – Scheduled surgical procedure
☐ 11 – Urinary tract infection
☐ 12 – IV catheter-related infection
☐ 13 – Deep vein thrombosis, pulmonary embolus
☐ 14 – Uncontrolled pain
☐ 15 – Psychotic episode
☐ 16 – Other than above reasons

| Go to M0903 |

Source: National Association for Home Care. 1998 (March). *Uniform Data Set for Home Care and Hospice.* Available at www.nahc.org/NAHC/Research/unidata.html.

77. (M0900) For what **Reason(s)** was the patient **Admitted** to a **Nursing Home**? (**Mark all that apply.**)

☐ 1 – Therapy services
☐ 2 – Respite care
☐ 3 – Hospice care
☐ 4 – Permanent placement
☐ 5 – Unsafe for care at home
☐ 6 – Other
☐ UK – Unknown

78. (M0903) **Date of Last (Most Recent) Home Visit:**

___ ___ / ___ ___ / ___ ___ ___ ___
   month   /   day   /   year

79. (M0906) **Discharge/Transfer/Death Date:** Enter the date of the discharge, transfer, or death (at home) of the patient.

___ ___ / ___ ___ / ___ ___ ___ ___
   month   /   day   /   year

☐ UK – Unknown

Change Recommendations

Recommendations for changes to the draft data set should be submitted in writing in the following format to the Information Resources Committee c/o NAHC. Attention: Data Set, 228 Seventh St. SE, Washington, DC 20003-4306.

1. Indicate the type of recommendation: change____   addition____   deletion____

2. Data Element Name:

3. Definition:

4. Explain the reason(s) for the recommendation. For **changes**, indicate why the current data element name/definition is not sufficient and how the change adds clarity. For **additions**, indicate why the data element is essential to multiple users and has relevance to national as well as local, state, or regional needs. For **deletions**, indicate why the data element is not essential or too difficult to collect.

Name_____ Phone _____

Date_____

Organization_____ NAHC ID _____

Address _____

Source: National Association for Home Care. 1998 (March). *Uniform Data Set for Home Care and Hospice.* Available at www.nahc.org/NAHC/Research/unidata.html.

Appendix B

Home Care Bill of Rights

HCFA requires that home health organizations explain and give a copy of the bill of rights to each patient in the course of the admission process. This patient's bill of rights meets federal Medicare requirements but may not meet state requirements. Home health organizations should develop an addendum, if needed, to meet additional state requirements.

AHIMA thanks the National Association for Home Care for its generous contribution to this book.

BILL OF RIGHTS

Home care clients have a right to be notified in writing of their rights and obligations before treatment begins and to exercise those rights. The client's family or guardian may exercise the client's rights when the client has been judged incompetent. Home care providers have an obligation to protect and promote the rights of their clients, including the following rights:

Clients and Providers Have a Right to Dignity and Respect

Home care clients and their formal caregivers have a right to not be discriminated against based on race, color, religion, national origin, age, sex, or handicap. Furthermore, clients and caregivers have a right to mutual respect and dignity, including respect for property. Caregivers are prohibited from accepting personal gifts and borrowing from clients.

Clients have the right:

- to have relationships with home care providers that are based on honesty and ethical standards of conduct;
- to be informed of the procedure they can follow to lodge complaints with the home care provider about the care

that is, or fails to be, furnished and about a lack of respect for property. (To lodge complaints with us call _____);
- to know about the disposition of such complaints;
- to voice their grievances without fear of discrimination or reprisal for having done so; and
- to be advised of the telephone number and hours of operation of the state's home care "hot line," which receives questions and complaints about local home care agencies, including complaints about implementation of advance directive requirements.

The hours are _____ and the number is _____.

Decisionmaking

Clients have the right:

- to be notified in advance about the care that is to be furnished, the types (disciplines) of the caregivers who will furnish the care, and the frequency of the visits that are proposed to be furnished;
- to be advised of any change in the plan of care before the change is made;
- to participate in the planning of the care and in planning changes in the care, and to be advised that they have the right to do so;
- to be informed in writing of rights under state law to make decisions concerning medical care, including the right to accept or refuse treatment and the right to formulate advance directives;

- to be informed in writing of policies and procedures for implementing advance directives, including any limitations if the provider cannot implement an advance directive on the basis of conscience;
- to have health care providers comply with advance directives in accordance with state law requirements;
- to receive care without condition on, or discrimination based on, the execution of advance directives; and
- to refuse services without fear of reprisal or discrimination.

The home care provider or the client's physician may be forced to refer the client to another source of care if the client's refusal to comply with the plan of care threatens to compromise the provider's commitment to quality care.

Privacy

Clients have the right:

- to confidentiality of the medical record as well as information about their health, social, and financial circumstances and about what takes place in the home; and

- to expect the home care provider to release information only as required by law or authorized by the client and to be informed of procedures for disclosure.

Reprinted with permission from the National Association for Home Care.

Financial Information

Clients have the right:

- to be informed of the extent to which payment may be expected from Medicare, Medicaid, or any other payor known to the home care provider;
- to be informed of the charges that will not be covered by Medicare;
- to be informed of the charges for which the client may be liable;
- to receive this information, orally and in writing, before care is initiated and within 30 calendar days of the date the home care provider becomes aware of any changes; and
- to have access, upon request, to all bills for service the client has received regardless of whether the bills are paid out-of-pocket or by another party.

Quality of Care

Clients have the right:

- to receive care of the highest quality;
- in general, to be admitted by a home care provider only if it has the resources needed to provide the care safely and at the required level of intensity, as determined by a professional assessment; a provider with less than optimal resources may nevertheless admit the client if a more appropriate provider is not available, but only after fully informing the client of the provider's limitations and the lack of suitable alternative arrangements; and
- to be told what to do in the case of an emergency.

The home care provider shall assure that:

- all medically related home care is provided in accordance with physician's orders and that a plan of care specifics the services and their frequency and duration; and
- all medically related personal care is provided by an appropriately trained home care aide who is supervised by a nurse or other qualified home care professional.

Client Responsibility

Clients have the responsibility:

- to notify the provider of changes in their condition (e.g., hospitalization, changes in the plan of care, symptoms to be reported);
- to follow the plan of care;
- to notify the provider if the visit schedule needs to be changed;
- to inform providers of the existence of any changes made to advance directives;
- to advise the provider of any problems or dissatisfaction with the services provided;
- to provide a safe environment for care to be provided; and
- to carry out mutually agreed responsibilities.

Additional Agency Information

To satisfy the Medicare certification requirement, the Health Care Financing Administration requires that agencies:

1. Give a copy of the Bill of Rights to each patient in the course of the admission process.
2. Explain the Bill of Rights to the patient and document that this has been done.

Agencies may have clients sign a copy of the patients *Bill of Rights* to acknowledge receipt. This patients *Bill of Rights* meets Federal Medicare requirements but may not meet state requirements. Agencies should develop an addendum if needed to meet additional state requirements.

Reprinted with permission from the National Association for Home Care.

Appendix C

Statement of Patient Privacy Rights—Medicare and Medicaid

Home health agencies must incorporate into their admission process for Medicare and Medicaid patients both pages of the statement of patient privacy rights.

Home Health Agency
Outcome and Assessment Information Set (OASIS)
STATEMENT OF PATIENT PRIVACY RIGHTS

As a home health patient, you have the privacy rights listed below.

- **You have the right to know why we need to ask you questions.**
  We are required by law to collect health information to make sure:
  1) you get quality health care, and
  2) payment for Medicare and Medicaid patients is correct.

- **You have the right to have your personal health care information kept confidential.**
  You may be asked to tell us information about yourself so that we will know which home health services will be best for you.
  We keep anything we learn about you confidential.
  This means, only those who are legally authorized to know, or who have a medical need to know, will see your personal health information.

- **You have the right to refuse to answer questions.**
  We may need your help in collecting your health information.
  If you choose not to answer, we will fill in the information as best we can.
  You do not have to answer every question to get services.

- **You have the right to look at your personal health information.**
  - We know how important it is that the information we collect about you is correct. If you think we made a mistake, ask us to correct it.
  - If you are not satisfied with our response, you can ask the Health Care Financing Administration, the federal Medicare and Medicaid agency, to correct your information.

> You can ask the Health Care Financing Administration
> to see, review, copy, or correct
> your personal health information which that Federal agency maintains in its
> HHA OASIS System of Records. See the back of this Notice for CONTACT INFORMATION.
> If you want a more detailed description of your privacy rights, see the back of this Notice:
> **PRIVACY ACT STATEMENT - HEALTH CARE RECORDS.**

This is a Medicare & Medicaid Approved Notice.

Source: Health Care Financing Administration. 1999 (June 18). Notices. *Federal Register* 64(117):32989–90.

PRIVACY ACT STATEMENT - HEALTH CARE RECORDS

THIS STATEMENT GIVES YOU ADVICE REQUIRED BY LAW (the Privacy Act of 1974).
THIS STATEMENT IS NOT A CONSENT FORM. IT WILL NOT BE USED TO RELEASE OR TO USE YOUR HEALTH CARE INFORMATION.

I. AUTHORITY FOR COLLECTION OF YOUR INFORMATION, INCLUDING YOUR SOCIAL SECURITY NUMBER, AND WHETHER OR NOT YOU ARE REQUIRED TO PROVIDE INFORMATION FOR THIS ASSESSMENT.
Sections 1102(a), 1154, 1861(o), 1861(z), 1863, 1864, 1865, 1866, 1871, 1891(b) of the Social Security Act.

Medicare and Medicaid participating home health agencies must do a complete assessment that accurately reflects your current health and includes information that can be used to show your progress toward your health goals. The home health agency must use the "Outcome and Assessment Information Set" (OASIS) when evaluating your health. To do this, the agency must get information from every patient. This information is used by the Health Care Financing Administration (HCFA, the federal Medicare & Medicaid agency) to be sure that the home health agency meets quality standards and gives appropriate health care to its patients. You have the right to refuse to provide information for the assessment to the home health agency. If your information is included in an assessment, it is protected under the federal Privacy Act of 1974 and the "Home Health Agency Outcome and Assessment Information Set" (HHA OASIS) System of Records. You have the right to see, copy, review, and request correction of your information in the HHA OASIS System of Records.

II. PRINCIPAL PURPOSES FOR WHICH YOUR INFORMATION IS INTENDED TO BE USED

The information collected will be entered into the Home Health Agency Outcome and Assessment Information Set (HHA OASIS) System No. 09-70-9002. Your health care information in the HHA OASIS System of Records will be used for the following purposes:
- support litigation involving the Health Care Financing Administration;
- support regulatory, reimbursement, and policy functions performed within the Health Care Financing Administration or by a contractor or consultant;
- study the effectiveness and quality of care provided by those home health agencies;
- survey and certification of Medicare and Medicaid home health agencies;
- provide for development, validation, and refinement of a Medicare prospective payment system;
- enable regulators to provide home health agencies with data for their internal quality improvement activities;
- support research, evaluation, or epidemiological projects related to the prevention of disease or disability, or the restoration or maintenance of health,
  and for health care payment related projects; and
- support constituent requests made to a Congressional representative.

III. ROUTINE USES

These "routine uses" specify the circumstances when the Health Care Financing Administration may release your information from the HHA OASIS System of Records without your consent. Each prospective recipient must agree in writing to ensure the continuing confidentiality and security of your information. Disclosures of the information may be to:
1. the federal Department of Justice for litigation involving the Health Care Financing Administration;
2. contractors or consultants working for the Health Care Financing Administration to assist in the performance of a service related to this system of records and who need to access these records to perform the activity;
3. an agency of a State government for purposes of determining, evaluating, and/or assessing cost, effectiveness, and/or quality of health care services provided in the State; for developing and operating Medicaid reimbursement systems; or for the administration of Federal/State home health agency programs within the State;
4. another Federal or State agency to contribute to the accuracy of the Health Care Financing Administration's health insurance operations (payment, treatment and coverage) and/or to support State agencies in the evaluations and monitoring of care provided by HHAs;
5. Peer Review Organizations, to perform Title XI or Title XVIII functions relating to assessing and improving home health agency quality of care;
6. an individual or organization for a research, evaluation, or epidemiological project related to the prevention of disease or disability, the restoration or maintenance of health, or payment related projects;
7. a congressional office in response to a constituent inquiry made at the written request of the constituent about whom the record is maintained.

IV. EFFECT ON YOU, IF YOU DO NOT PROVIDE INFORMATION

The home health agency needs the information contained in the Outcome and Assessment Information Set in order to give you quality care. It is important that the information be correct. Incorrect information could result in payment errors. Incorrect information also could make it hard to be sure that the agency is giving you quality services. If you choose not to provide information, there is no federal requirement for the home health agency to refuse you services.

NOTE: This statement may be included in the admission packet for all new home health agency admissions. Home health agencies may request you or your representative to sign this statement to document that this statement was given to you. Your signature is NOT required. If you or your representative sign the statement, the signature merely indicates that you received this statement. You or your representative must be supplied with a copy of this statement.

CONTACT INFORMATION
If you want to ask the Health Care Financing Administration to see, review, copy, or correct your personal health information which that Federal agency maintains in its HHA OASIS System of Records:

Call 1-800-638-6833, toll free, for assistance in contacting the HHA OASIS System Manager.
TTY for the hearing and speech impaired: 1-800-820-1202.

Source: Health Care Financing Administration. 1999 (June 18). Notices. *Federal Register* 64(117):32989–90.

Appendix D

Notice about Privacy—
Non-Medicare/Medicaid

Home health agencies must incorporate the notice about privacy into their admission process.

Home Health Agency
Outcome and Assessment Information Set (OASIS)

NOTICE ABOUT PRIVACY
For Patients Who Do Not Have Medicare or Medicaid Coverage

- **As a home health patient, there are a few things that you need to know about our collection of your personal health care information.**

    - Federal and State governments oversee home health care to be sure that we furnish quality home health care services, and that you, in particular, get quality home health care services.

    - We need to ask you questions because we are required by law to collect health information to make sure that you get quality health care services.

    - We will make your information anonymous. That way, the Health Care Financing Administration, the federal agency that oversees this home health agency, cannot know that the information is about you.

- **We keep anything we learn about you confidential.**

This is a Medicare & Medicaid Approved Notice.

[FR Doc. 99–15529 Filed 6–16–99; 9:00 am]
BILLING CODE 4120–03–C

Source: Health Care Financing Administration. 1999 (June 18). Notices. *Federal Register* 64(117):32989–90.

Appendix E

Comprehensive Assessment Forms

Included among these comprehensive assessment forms are the start of care assessment, follow-up assessment, transfer to inpatient facility, discharge assessment, and death at home. Specific time points have been identified for completing the comprehensive assessment. The home care episode may not proceed smoothly from start of care to discharge. Agency staff must know and monitor when the comprehensive assessment and data collection are required.

The following forms can be accessed at www.hcfa.gov/medicaid/oasis/oasisdat.htm.

START OF CARE ASSESSMENT

(Also used for Resumption of Care Following Inpatient Stay)

(Page 1 of 13)

Client's Name: _____

Client Record No. _____

The *Outcome and Assessment Information Set (OASIS)* is the intellectual property of The Center for Health Services and Policy Research. Copyright ©2000 Used with Permission.

A. DEMOGRAPHIC/GENERAL INFORMATION

1. **(M0010) Agency Medicare Provider Number:**

    __ __ __ __ __ __ __ __

2. **(M0012) Agency Medicaid Provider Number:**

    __ __ __ __ __ __ __ __ __ __ __ __ __ __ __

Branch Identification (Optional, for Agency Use)

3. **(M0014) Branch State:** __ __

4. **(M0016) Branch ID Number:** __ __ __ __ __ __ __ __ __ __

    (Agency-assigned)

5. **(M0020) Patient ID Number:** __ __ __ __ __ __ __ __ __ __ __ __ __ __ __ __

6. **(M0030) Start of Care Date:**

    __ __ - __ __ - __ __ __ __
    m m   d d   y y y y

7. **(M0032) Resumption of Care Date:**

    __ __ - __ __ - __ __ __ __   ☐ NA - Not Applicable
    m m   d d   y y y y

8. **(M0040) Patient Name:**

    _____ _____ _____ _____
    (First)   (MI)   (Last)   (Suffix)

9. **Patient Address:**

    Street, Route, Apt. Number - not P.O. Box

10. **Patient Phone:**

    (___) ___ - _____

    City _____   (M0050) State _____   (M0060) Zip Code _____

11. **(M0063) Medicare Number:**

    __ __ __ __ __ __ __ __ __ __ __   ☐ NA - No Medicare
    (including suffix if any)

12. **(M0064) Social Security Number:**

    __ __ __ - __ __ - __ __ __ __   ☐ UK - Unknown or Not Available

13. **(M0065) Medicaid Number:**

    __ __ __ __ __ __ __ __ __ __ __ __   ☐ NA - No Medicaid

14. **(M0066) Birth Date:**

    __ __ - __ __ - __ __ __ __
    m m   d d   y y y y

15. **(M0069) Gender:**   ☐ 1 - Male   ☐ 2 - Female

16. **(M0072) Primary Referring Physician ID:**   __ __ __ __ __ __ (UPIN#)   ☐ UK - Unknown or Not Available

    Name _____   Phone (__ __) __ __ __ - __ __ __ __

    Address _____   FAX (__ __) __ __ __ - __ __ __ __

17. **(M0080) Discipline of Person Completing Assessment:**

    ☐ 1 - RN   ☐ 3 - SLP/ST
    ☐ 2 - PT   ☐ 4 - OT

18. **(M0090) Date Assessment Completed:**

    __ __ - __ __ - __ __ __ __
    m m   d d   y y y y

19. **(M0100) This Assessment is Currently Being Completed for the Following Reason:**

    Start/Resumption of Care
    ☐ 1 - Start of care—further visits planned
    ☐ 2 - Start of care—no further visits planned
    ☐ 3 - Resumption of care (after inpatient stay)

    Follow-Up
    4 - Recertification (follow-up) reassessment
    5 - Other follow-up

    Transfer to an Inpatient Facility
    6 - Transferred to an inpatient facility—patient not discharged from agency
    7 - Transferred to an inpatient facility—patient discharged from agency

    Discharge from Agency — Not to an Inpatient Facility
    8 - Death at home
    9 - Discharge from agency
    10 - Discharge from agency—no visits completed after start/resumption of care assessment

20. **Marital Status:**   ☐ Not Married   ☐ Married   ☐ Widowed   ☐ Divorced   ☐ Separated   ☐ Unknown

21. **(M0140) Race/Ethnicity (as identified by patient): (Mark all that apply.)**
    ☐ 1 - American Indian or Alaska Native   ☐ 3 - Black or African-American   ☐ 5 - Native Hawaiian or Pacific Islander   ☐ UK - Unknown
    ☐ 2 - Asian   ☐ 4 - Hispanic or Latino   ☐ 6 - White

22. **Emergency Contact (Relationship):**

23. **Emergency Contact Address:**

24. **Emergency Contact Telephone No.:**   (___) ___ - _____

25. **(M0150) Current Payment Sources for Home Care: (Mark all that apply.)**
    ☐ 0 - None; no charge for current services
    ☐ 1 - Medicare (traditional fee-for-service)
    ☐ 2 - Medicare (HMO/managed care)
    ☐ 3 - Medicaid (traditional fee-for-service)
    ☐ 4 - Medicaid (HMO/managed care)
    ☐ 5 - Workers' compensation
    ☐ 6 - Title programs (e.g., Title III, V or XX)
    ☐ 7 - Other government (e.g., CHAMPUS, VA, etc.)
    ☐ 8 - Private insurance
    ☐ 9 - Private HMO/managed care
    ☐ 10 - Self-pay
    ☐ 11 - Other (specify) _____
    ☐ UK - Unknown

26. **(M0160) Financial Factors** limiting the ability of the patient/family to meet basic health needs: **(Mark all that apply.)**
    ☐ 0 - None
    ☐ 1 - Unable to afford medicine or medical supplies
    ☐ 2 - Unable to afford medical expenses that are not covered by insurance/Medicare (e.g., copayments)
    ☐ 3 - Unable to afford rent/utility bills
    ☐ 4 - Unable to afford food
    ☐ 5 - Other (specify) _____

OASIS-B1 SOC (08/2000)

Outcome and Assessment Information Set (OASIS) is the intellectual property of The Center for Health Services and Policy Research © 2000.

START OF CARE ASSESSMENT
(Also used for Resumption of Care Following Inpatient Stay)
(Page 2 of 13)

| Client's Name: |
| Client Record No. |

27. **(M0175)** From which of the following **Inpatient Facilities** was the patient discharged <u>during the past 14 days</u>? **(Mark all that apply.)**
   - ☐ 1 - Hospital
   - ☐ 2 - Rehabilitation facility
   - ☐ 3 - Skilled nursing facility
   - ☐ 4 - Other nursing home
   - ☐ 5 - Other (specify) _____
   - ☐ NA - Patient was not discharged from an inpatient facility
     [If NA, go to #30 - Medical or Treatment Regimen Change]

28. **(M0180) Inpatient Discharge Date** (most recent):

   __ __ - __ __ - __ __ __ __
   m m   d d   y y y y

   ☐ UK - Unknown

29. **(M0190) Inpatient Diagnoses** and ICD code categories (three digits required; five digits optional) <u>for only those conditions treated during an inpatient facility stay within the last 14 days</u> (no surgical or V-codes):

Inpatient Facility Diagnosis	ICD
a. _____	(__ __ __ . __ __)
b. _____	(__ __ __ . __ __)

30. **(M0200) Medical or Treatment Regimen Change Within Past 14 Days:** Has this patient experienced a change in medical or treatment regimen (e.g., medication, treatment, or service change due to new or additional diagnosis, etc.) within the last 14 days?
   - ☐ 0 - No **[If No, go to #32 - Conditions Prior]**
   - ☐ 1 - Yes

31. **(M0210)** List the patient's **Medical Diagnoses** and ICD code categories (three digits required; five digits optional) <u>for those conditions requiring changed medical or treatment regimen</u> (no surgical or V-codes):

Changed Medical Regimen Diagnosis	ICD
a. _____	(__ __ __ . __ __)
b. _____	(__ __ __ . __ __)
c. _____	(__ __ __ . __ __)
d. _____	(__ __ __ . __ __)

32. **(M0220) Conditions Prior to Medical or Treatment Regimen Change or Inpatient Stay Within Past 14 Days:** If this patient experienced an inpatient facility discharge or change in medical or treatment regimen within the past 14 days, indicate any conditions which existed <u>prior to</u> the inpatient stay or change in medical or treatment regimen. **(Mark all that apply.)**
   - ☐ 1 - Urinary incontinence
   - ☐ 2 - Indwelling/suprapubic catheter
   - ☐ 3 - Intractable pain
   - ☐ 4 - Impaired decision-making
   - ☐ 5 - Disruptive or socially inappropriate behavior
   - ☐ 6 - Memory loss to the extent that supervision required
   - ☐ 7 - None of the above
   - ☐ NA - No inpatient facility discharge <u>and</u> no change in medical or treatment regimen in past 14 days
   - ☐ UK - Unknown

B. CURRENT ILLNESS

1. **(M0230/M0240) Diagnoses and Severity Index:** List each medical diagnosis or problem for which the patient is receiving home care and ICD code category (three digits required; five digits optional - no surgical or V-codes) and rate them using the following severity index. (Choose one value that represents the most severe rating appropriate for each diagnosis.)

   0 - Asymptomatic, no treatment needed at this time
   1 - Symptoms well controlled with current therapy
   2 - Symptoms controlled with difficulty, affecting daily functioning; patient needs ongoing monitoring
   3 - Symptoms poorly controlled, patient needs frequent adjustment in treatment and dose monitoring
   4 - Symptoms poorly controlled, history of rehospitalizations

(M0230) Primary Diagnosis	ICD	Severity Rating				
a. _____	(__ __ __ . __ __)	☐ 0	☐ 1	☐ 2	☐ 3	☐ 4

(M0240) Other Diagnoses	ICD	Severity Rating				
b. _____	(__ __ __ . __ __)	☐ 0	☐ 1	☐ 2	☐ 3	☐ 4
c. _____	(__ __ __ . __ __)	☐ 0	☐ 1	☐ 2	☐ 3	☐ 4
d. _____	(__ __ __ . __ __)	☐ 0	☐ 1	☐ 2	☐ 3	☐ 4
e. _____	(__ __ __ . __ __)	☐ 0	☐ 1	☐ 2	☐ 3	☐ 4
f. _____	(__ __ __ . __ __)	☐ 0	☐ 1	☐ 2	☐ 3	☐ 4

2. **Patient/Family Knowledge and Coping Level Regarding Present Illness:**

   Patient:

   Family:

C. SIGNIFICANT PAST HEALTH HISTORY:

OASIS-B1 SOC (08/2000)

START OF CARE ASSESSMENT
(Also used for Resumption of Care Following Inpatient Stay)
(Page 3 of 13)

| Client's Name: |
| Client Record No. |

D. (M0250) THERAPIES the patient receives <u>at home</u>: **(Mark all that apply.)**

- ☐ 1 - Intravenous or infusion therapy (excludes TPN)
- ☐ 2 - Parenteral nutrition (TPN or lipids)
- ☐ 3 - Enteral nutrition (nasogastric, gastrostomy, jejunostomy, or any other artificial entry into the alimentary canal)
- ☐ 4 - None of the above

E. PROGNOSIS

1. **(M0260) Overall Prognosis:** BEST description of patient's overall prognosis for <u>recovery from this episode of illness</u>.
   - ☐ 0 - Poor: little or no recovery is expected and/or further decline is imminent
   - ☐ 1 - Good/Fair: partial to full recovery is expected
   - ☐ UK - Unknown

2. **(M0270) Rehabilitative Prognosis:** BEST description of patient's prognosis for <u>functional status</u>.
   - ☐ 0 - Guarded: minimal improvement in functional status is expected; decline is possible
   - ☐ 1 - Good: marked improvement in functional status is expected
   - ☐ UK - Unknown

3. **(M0280) Life Expectancy:** (Physician documentation is not required.)
   - ☐ 0 - Life expectancy is greater than 6 months
   - ☐ 1 - Life expectancy is 6 months or fewer

F. ALLERGIES: (Environmental, drugs, food, etc.)

G. IMMUNIZATION/SCREENING TESTS

1. **Immunizations:**   Flu   Yes ___ No ___ Date _____   Pneumonia   Yes ___ No ___ Date _____
   Tetanus   Yes ___ No ___ Date _____   Other: _____   Date _____

2. **Screening:**   Cholesterol level   Yes ___ No ___ Date _____   Colon cancer screen   Yes ___ No ___ Date _____
   Mammogram   Yes ___ No ___ Date _____   Prostate cancer screen   Yes ___ No ___ Date _____

3. **Self-Exam Frequency:**   Breast self-exam frequency _____   Testicular self-exam frequency _____

H. (M0290) HIGH RISK FACTORS characterizing this patient: **(Mark all that apply.)**

- ☐ 1 - Heavy smoking
- ☐ 2 - Obesity
- ☐ 3 - Alcohol dependency
- ☐ 4 - Drug dependency
- ☐ 5 - None of the above
- ☐ UK - Unknown

I. LIVING ARRANGEMENTS

1. **(M0300) Current Residence:**
   - ☐ 1 - Patient's owned or rented residence (house, apartment, or mobile home owned or rented by patient/couple/significant other)
   - ☐ 2 - Family member's residence
   - ☐ 3 - Boarding home or rented room
   - ☐ 4 - Board and care or assisted living facility
   - ☐ 5 - Other (specify) _____

2. **(M0310) Structural Barriers** in the patient's environment limiting independent mobility: **(Mark all that apply.)**
   - ☐ 0 - None
   - ☐ 1 - Stairs inside home which <u>must</u> be used by the patient (e.g., to get to toileting, sleeping, eating areas)
   - ☐ 2 - Stairs inside home which are used optionally (e.g., to get to laundry facilities)
   - ☐ 3 - Stairs leading from inside house to outside
   - ☐ 4 - Narrow or obstructed doorways

3. **(M0320) Safety Hazards** found in the patient's current place of residence: **(Mark all that apply.)**
   - ☐ 0 - None
   - ☐ 1 - Inadequate floor, roof, or windows
   - ☐ 2 - Inadequate lighting
   - ☐ 3 - Unsafe gas/electric appliance
   - ☐ 4 - Inadequate heating
   - ☐ 5 - Inadequate cooling
   - ☐ 6 - Lack of fire safety devices
   - ☐ 7 - Unsafe floor coverings
   - ☐ 8 - Inadequate stair railings
   - ☐ 9 - Improperly stored hazardous materials
   - ☐ 10 - Lead-based paint
   - ☐ 11 - Other (specify) _____

OASIS-B1 SOC (08/2000)

START OF CARE ASSESSMENT (Also used for Resumption of Care Following Inpatient Stay) (Page 4 of 13)	Client's Name:
	Client Record No.

4. **(M0330) Sanitation Hazards** found in the patient's current place of residence: **(Mark all that apply.)**
   - ☐ 0 - None
   - ☐ 1 - No running water
   - ☐ 2 - Contaminated water
   - ☐ 3 - No toileting facilities
   - ☐ 4 - Outdoor toileting facilities only
   - ☐ 5 - Inadequate sewage disposal
   - ☐ 6 - Inadequate/improper food storage
   - ☐ 7 - No food refrigeration
   - ☐ 8 - No cooking facilities
   - ☐ 9 - Insects/rodents present
   - ☐ 10 - No scheduled trash pickup
   - ☐ 11 - Cluttered/soiled living area
   - ☐ 12 - Other (specify) _____

5. **(M0340) Patient Lives With: (Mark all that apply.)**
   - ☐ 1 - Lives alone
   - ☐ 2 - With spouse or significant other
   - ☐ 3 - With other family member
   - ☐ 4 - With a friend
   - ☐ 5 - With paid help (other than home care agency staff)
   - ☐ 6 - With other than above

   COMMENTS:

J. OTHERS LIVING IN HOUSEHOLD:

Name	Age	Sex	Relationship	Able & willing to assist?	Name	Age	Sex	Relationship	Able & willing to assist?

K. SUPPORTIVE ASSISTANCE

1. **Names of Persons/Organizations Providing Assistance:**

2. **(M0350) Assisting Person(s) Other than Home Care Agency Staff: (Mark all that apply.)**
   - ☐ 1 - Relatives, friends, or neighbors living outside the home
   - ☐ 2 - Person residing in the home (EXCLUDING paid help)
   - ☐ 3 - Paid help
   - ☐ 4 - None of the above **[If None of the above, go to Section L - Review of Systems/Physical Assessment]**
   - ☐ UK - Unknown **[If Unknown, go to Section L - Review of Systems/Physical Assessment]**

3. **(M0360) Primary Caregiver** taking <u>lead</u> responsibility for providing or managing the patient's care, providing the most frequent assistance, etc. (other than home care agency staff):
   - ☐ 0 - No one person **[If No one person, go to Section L - Review of Systems/Physical Assessment]**
   - ☐ 1 - Spouse or significant other
   - ☐ 2 - Daughter or son
   - ☐ 3 - Other family member
   - ☐ 4 - Friend or neighbor or community or church member
   - ☐ 5 - Paid help
   - ☐ UK - Unknown **[If Unknown, go to Section L - Review of Systems/Physical Assessment]**

4. **(M0370) How Often** does the patient receive assistance from the primary caregiver?
   - ☐ 1 - Several times during day and night
   - ☐ 2 - Several times during day
   - ☐ 3 - Once daily
   - ☐ 4 - Three or more times per week
   - ☐ 5 - One to two times per week
   - ☐ 6 - Less often than weekly
   - ☐ UK - Unknown

5. **(M0380) Type of Primary Caregiver Assistance: (Mark all that apply.)**
   - ☐ 1 - ADL assistance (e.g., bathing, dressing, toileting, bowel/bladder, eating/feeding)
   - ☐ 2 - IADL assistance (e.g., meds, meals, housekeeping, laundry, telephone, shopping, finances)
   - ☐ 3 - Environmental support (housing, home maintenance)
   - ☐ 4 - Psychosocial support (socialization, companionship, recreation)
   - ☐ 5 - Advocates or facilitates patient's participation in appropriate medical care
   - ☐ 6 - Financial agent, power of attorney, or conservator of finance
   - ☐ 7 - Health care agent, conservator of person, or medical power of attorney
   - ☐ UK - Unknown

Comments regarding assistance available to patient:

OASIS-B1 SOC (08/2000)

START OF CARE ASSESSMENT	Client's Name:
(Also used for Resumption of Care Following Inpatient Stay)	Client Record No.
(Page 5 of 13)	

L. REVIEW OF SYSTEMS/PHYSICAL ASSESSMENT

(Mark S for subjective, O for objectively assessed problem. If no problem present or if not assessed, mark NA.)

1. **HEAD:** _____ Dizziness   _____ Headache (describe location, duration) _____

2. **EYES:** _____ Glasses   _____ Blurred/double vision   _____ Glaucoma
             _____ Cataracts   _____ PERRL   _____ Other (specify) _____

   (M0390) Vision with corrective lenses if the patient usually wears them:
   - ☐ 0 - Normal vision: sees adequately in most situations; can see medication labels, newsprint.
   - ☐ 1 - Partially impaired: cannot see medication labels or newsprint, but <u>can</u> see obstacles in path, and the surrounding layout; can count fingers at arm's length.
   - ☐ 2 - Severely impaired: cannot locate objects without hearing or touching them <u>or</u> patient nonresponsive.

3. **EARS:** _____ Hearing Aid   _____ Tinnitus   _____ Other (specify) _____

   (M0400) Hearing and Ability to Understand Spoken Language in patient's own language (with hearing aids if the patient usually uses them):
   - ☐ 0 - No observable impairment. Able to hear and understand complex or detailed instructions and extended or abstract conversation.
   - ☐ 1 - With minimal difficulty, able to hear and understand most multi-step instructions and ordinary conversation. May need occasional repetition, extra time, or louder voice.
   - ☐ 2 - Has moderate difficulty hearing and understanding simple, one-step instructions and brief conversation; needs frequent prompting or assistance.
   - ☐ 3 - Has severe difficulty hearing and understanding simple greetings and short comments. Requires multiple repetitions, restatements, demonstrations, additional time.
   - ☐ 4 - <u>Unable</u> to hear and understand familiar words or common expressions consistently, <u>or</u> patient nonresponsive.

4. **ORAL:** _____ Gum problems   _____ Chewing problems   _____ Dentures   _____ Other (specify) _____

   (M0410) Speech and Oral (Verbal) Expression of Language (in patient's own language):
   - ☐ 0 - Expresses complex ideas, feelings, and needs clearly, completely, and easily in all situations with no observable impairment.
   - ☐ 1 - Minimal difficulty in expressing ideas and needs (may take extra time; makes occasional errors in word choice, grammar or speech intelligibility; needs minimal prompting or assistance).
   - ☐ 2 - Expresses simple ideas or needs with moderate difficulty (needs prompting or assistance, errors in word choice, organization or speech intelligibility). Speaks in phrases or short sentences.
   - ☐ 3 - Has severe difficulty expressing basic ideas or needs and requires maximal assistance or guessing by listener. Speech limited to single words or short phrases.
   - ☐ 4 - <u>Unable</u> to express basic needs even with maximal prompting or assistance but is not comatose or unresponsive (e.g., speech is nonsensical or unintelligible).
   - ☐ 5 - Patient nonresponsive or unable to speak.

5. **NOSE AND SINUS:**   _____ Epistaxis   _____ Other (specify) _____

6. **NECK AND THROAT:**   _____ Hoarseness   _____ Difficulty swallowing   _____ Other (specify) _____

7. **MUSCULOSKELETAL, NEUROLOGICAL:**

_____ Hx arthritis	_____ Joint pain	_____ Syncope	_____ Paralysis (describe) _____
_____ Gout	_____ Weakness	_____ Seizure	_____ Amputation (where) _____
_____ Stiffness	_____ Leg cramps	_____ Tenderness	_____ Tremor
_____ Swollen joints	_____ Numbness	_____ Deformities	_____ Aphasia/inarticulate speech
_____ Unequal grasp	_____ Temp changes	_____ Comatose	_____ Other (specify) _____

Coordination, gait, balance (describe):

COMMENTS: (Prostheses, appliances)

Patient's Perceived Pain Level: _____ (Scale 1-10)

(M0420) Frequency of Pain interfering with patient's activity or movement:
- ☐ 0 - Patient has no pain or pain does not interfere with activity or movement
- ☐ 1 - Less often than daily
- ☐ 2 - Daily, but not constantly
- ☐ 3 - All of the time

Comments on pain management:

(M0430) Intractable Pain: Is the patient experiencing pain that is <u>not easily relieved</u>, occurs at least daily, and affects the patient's sleep, appetite, physical or emotional energy, concentration, personal relationships, emotions, or ability or desire to perform physical activity?
- ☐ 0 - No
- ☐ 1 - Yes

OASIS-B1 SOC (08/2000)

START OF CARE ASSESSMENT	Client's Name:
(Also used for Resumption of Care Following Inpatient Stay) (Page 6 of 13)	Client Record No.

8. **INTEGUMENT:**

a. ____ Hair changes (where) _____ ____ Pruritus ____ Other (specify) _____

b. Skin condition (Record type # on body area. Indicate size to right of numbered category.)

	Type	Size
1.	Lesions	
2.	Bruises	
3.	Masses	
4.	Scars	
5.	Stasis Ulcers	
6.	Pressure Ulcers	
7.	Incisions	
8.	Other (specify) _____	

c. **(M0440)** Does this patient have a **Skin Lesion** or an **Open Wound**? This excludes "OSTOMIES."
- ☐ 0 - No [If No, go to *Section 9 - Cardiorespiratory*]
- ☐ 1 - Yes

d. **(M0445)** Does this patient have a **Pressure Ulcer**?
- ☐ 0 - No [If No, go to *#8.e - Stasis Ulcer*]
- ☐ 1 - Yes

(M0450) Current Number of Pressure Ulcers at Each Stage: (Circle one response for each stage.)

	Pressure Ulcer Stages	Number of Pressure Ulcers				
a)	Stage 1: Nonblanchable erythema of intact skin; the heralding of skin ulceration. In darker-pigmented skin, warmth, edema, hardness, or discolored skin may be indicators.	0	1	2	3	4 or more
b)	Stage 2: Partial thickness skin loss involving epidermis and/or dermis. The ulcer is superficial and presents clinically as an abrasion, blister, or shallow crater.	0	1	2	3	4 or more
c)	Stage 3: Full-thickness skin loss involving damage or necrosis of subcutaneous tissue which may extend down to, but not through, underlying fascia. The ulcer presents clinically as a deep crater with or without undermining of adjacent tissue.	0	1	2	3	4 or more
d)	Stage 4: Full-thickness skin loss with extensive destruction, tissue necrosis, or damage to muscle, bone, or supporting structures (e.g., tendon, joint capsule, etc.).	0	1	2	3	4 or more
e)	In addition to the above, is there at least one pressure ulcer that cannot be observed due to the presence of eschar or a nonremovable dressing, including casts? ☐ 0 - No ☐ 1 - Yes					

(M0460) Stage of Most Problematic (Observable) Pressure Ulcer:
- ☐ 1 - Stage 1
- ☐ 2 - Stage 2
- ☐ 3 - Stage 3
- ☐ 4 - Stage 4
- ☐ NA - No observable pressure ulcer

(M0464) Status of Most Problematic (Observable) Pressure Ulcer:
- ☐ 1 - Fully granulating
- ☐ 2 - Early/partial granulation
- ☐ 3 - Not healing
- ☐ NA - No observable pressure ulcer

OASIS-B1 SOC (08/2000)

START OF CARE ASSESSMENT
(Also used for Resumption of Care Following Inpatient Stay)
(Page 7 of 13)

Client's Name:

Client Record No.

e. **(M0468)** Does this patient have a **Stasis Ulcer?**
☐ 0 - No **[If No, go to #8.f - *Surgical Wound*]**
☐ 1 - Yes

    (M0470) Current Number of Observable Stasis Ulcer(s):
☐   0 - Zero
☐   1 - One
☐   2 - Two
☐   3 - Three
☐   4 - Four or more

    (M0474) Does this patient have at least one **Stasis Ulcer that Cannot be Observed** due to the presence of a nonremovable dressing?
☐   0 - No
☐   1 - Yes

    (M0476) Status of Most Problematic (Observable) Stasis Ulcer:
☐   1 - Fully granulating
☐   2 - Early/partial granulation
☐   3 - Not healing
☐ NA - No observable stasis ulcer

f. **(M0482)** Does this patient have a **Surgical Wound?**
☐ 0 - No **[If No, go to *Section 9 - Cardiorespiratory*]**
☐ 1 - Yes

    (M0484) Current Number of (Observable) Surgical Wounds: (If a wound is partially closed but has more than one opening, consider each opening as a separate wound.)
☐   0 - Zero
☐   1 - One
☐   2 - Two
☐   3 - Three
☐   4 - Four or more

    (M0486) Does this patient have at least one **Surgical Wound that Cannot be Observed** due to the presence of a nonremovable dressing?
☐   0 - No
☐   1 - Yes

    (M0488) Status of Most Problematic (Observable) Surgical Wound:
☐   1 - Fully granulating
☐   2 - Early/partial granulation
☐   3 - Not healing
☐ NA - No observable surgical wound

COMMENTS: (Wound/lesion history, treatments, etc.)

9. **CARDIORESPIRATORY:**   Temperature _____   Respirations _____

    BLOOD PRESSURE: Lying _____   Sitting _____   Standing _____

    PULSE: Apical rate _____   Radial rate _____   Rhythm _____   Quality _____

    CARDIOVASCULAR:

____Palpitations   ____Dyspnea on exertion   ____BP problems   ____Murmurs

____Claudication   ____Paroxysmal nocturnal dyspnea   ____Chest pain   ____Edema

____Fatigues easily   ____Orthopnea (# of pillows _____)   ____Cardiac problems (specify) _____   ____Cyanosis

____Pacemaker _____   ____Other (specify) _____   ____Varicosities
        (Date of last battery change)

    COMMENTS:

    RESPIRATORY:

History of: _____ Asthma   _____ Bronchitis   _____ Pneumonia   _____ Other (specify) _____

        _____ TB   _____ Pleurisy   _____ Emphysema

    Present Condition:

_____ Cough (describe) _____   _____ Sputum (character and amount) _____

_____ Breath sounds (describe) _____   _____ Other (specify) _____

(M0490) When is the patient dyspneic or noticeably **Short of Breath?**
☐   0 - Never, patient is not short of breath
☐   1 - When walking more than 20 feet, climbing stairs
☐   2 - With moderate exertion (e.g., while dressing, using commode or bedpan, walking distances less than 20 feet)
☐   3 - With minimal exertion (e.g., while eating, talking, or performing other ADLs) or with agitation
☐   4 - At rest (during day or night)

COMMENTS:

(M0500) Respiratory Treatments utilized at home: **(Mark all that apply.)**
☐   1 - Oxygen (intermittent or continuous)
☐   2 - Ventilator (continually or at night)
☐   3 - Continuous positive airway pressure
☐   4 - None of the above

OASIS-B1 SOC (08/2000)

START OF CARE ASSESSMENT (Also used for Resumption of Care Following Inpatient Stay) (Page 8 of 13)	Client's Name: Client Record No.

10. GENITOURINARY TRACT:

____ Frequency	____ Nocturia	____ Dysmenorrhea	____ Gravida/Para
____ Pain	____ Urgency	____ Lesions	____ Date last PAP test
____ Hematuria	____ Prostate disorder	____ Hx hysterectomy	____ Contraception
____ Vaginal discharge/bleeding	____ Other (specify)_____		

(M0510) Has this patient been treated for a **Urinary Tract Infection** in the past 14 days?
☐ 0 - No
☐ 1 - Yes
☐ NA - Patient on prophylactic treatment
☐ UK - Unknown

(M0530) When does **Urinary Incontinence** occur?
☐ 0 - Timed-voiding defers incontinence
☐ 1 - During the night only
☐ 2 - During the day and night

(M0520) Urinary Incontinence or Urinary Catheter Presence:
☐ 0 - No incontinence or catheter (includes anuria or ostomy for urinary drainage) **[If No, go to Section 11 - Gastrointestinal Tract]**
☐ 1 - Patient is incontinent
☐ 2 - Patient requires a urinary catheter (i.e., external, indwelling, intermittent, suprapubic) **[Go to Section 11 - Gastrointestinal Tract]**

COMMENTS: (e.g., appliances and care, bladder programs, catheter type, frequency of irrigation and change)

11. GASTROINTESTINAL TRACT:

____ Indigestion	____ Pain	____ Rectal bleeding	____ Jaundice
____ Nausea, vomiting	____ Hernias (where) _____	____ Hemorrhoids	____ Tenderness
____ Ulcers	____ Diarrhea/constipation	____ Gallbladder problems	____ Other (specify) _____

(M0540) Bowel Incontinence Frequency:
☐ 0 - Very rarely or never has bowel incontinence
☐ 1 - Less than once weekly
☐ 2 - One to three times weekly
☐ 3 - Four to six times weekly
☐ 4 - On a daily basis
☐ 5 - More often than once daily
☐ NA - Patient has ostomy for bowel elimination
☐ UK - Unknown

(M0550) Ostomy for Bowel Elimination: Does this patient have an ostomy for bowel elimination that (within the last 14 days):
a) was related to an inpatient facility stay, or b) necessitated a change in medical or treatment regimen?
☐ 0 - Patient does not have an ostomy for bowel elimination.
☐ 1 - Patient's ostomy was not related to an inpatient stay and did not necessitate change in medical or treatment regimen.
☐ 2 - The ostomy was related to an inpatient stay or did necessitate change in medical or treatment regimen.

COMMENTS: (bowel function, stool color, bowel program, GI series, abd. girth)

12. NUTRITIONAL STATUS:

____ Weight loss/gain last 3 mos. (Give amount _____)   ____ Over/under weight   ____ Change in appetite   Diet _____

____ Other (specify) _____   Meals prepared by _____

COMMENTS:

13. BREASTS: (For both male and female)

____ Lumps   ____ Tenderness   ____ Discharge   ____ Pain   ____ Other (specify) _____

COMMENTS:

OASIS-B1 SOC (08/2000)

START OF CARE ASSESSMENT	Client's Name:
(Also used for Resumption of Care Following Inpatient Stay) (Page 9 of 13)	Client Record No.

14. **NEURO/EMOTIONAL/BEHAVIORAL STATUS:**

_____ Hx of previous psych. illness   _____ Other (specify) _____

(M0560) Cognitive Functioning: (Patient's current level of alertness, orientation, comprehension, concentration, and immediate memory for simple commands.)
- ☐ 0 - Alert/oriented, able to focus and shift attention, comprehends and recalls task directions independently.
- ☐ 1 - Requires prompting (cueing, repetition, reminders) only under stressful or unfamiliar conditions.
- ☐ 2 - Requires assistance and some direction in specific situations (e.g., on all tasks involving shifting of attention), or consistently requires low stimulus environment due to distractibility.
- ☐ 3 - Requires considerable assistance in routine situations. Is not alert and oriented or is unable to shift attention and recall directions more than half the time.
- ☐ 4 - Totally dependent due to disturbances such as constant disorientation, coma, persistent vegetative state, or delirium.

(M0570) When Confused (Reported or Observed):
- ☐ 0 - Never
- ☐ 1 - In new or complex situations only
- ☐ 2 - On awakening or at night only
- ☐ 3 - During the day and evening, but not constantly
- ☐ 4 - Constantly
- ☐ NA - Patient nonresponsive

(M0580) When Anxious (Reported or Observed):
- ☐ 0 - None of the time
- ☐ 1 - Less often than daily
- ☐ 2 - Daily, but not constantly
- ☐ 3 - All of the time
- ☐ NA - Patient nonresponsive

(M0590) Depressive Feelings Reported or Observed in Patient: (Mark all that apply.)
- ☐ 1 - Depressed mood (e.g., feeling sad, tearful)
- ☐ 2 - Sense of failure or self reproach
- ☐ 3 - Hopelessness
- ☐ 4 - Recurrent thoughts of death
- ☐ 5 - Thoughts of suicide
- ☐ 6 - None of the above feelings observed or reported

(M0600) Patient Behaviors (Reported or Observed): (Mark all that apply.)
- ☐ 1 - Indecisiveness, lack of concentration
- ☐ 2 - Diminished interest in most activities
- ☐ 3 - Sleep disturbances
- ☐ 4 - Recent change in appetite or weight
- ☐ 5 - Agitation
- ☐ 6 - A suicide attempt
- ☐ 7 - None of the above behaviors observed or reported

(M0610) Behaviors Demonstrated at Least Once a Week (Reported or Observed): (Mark all that apply.)
- ☐ 1 - Memory deficit: failure to recognize familiar persons/places, inability to recall events of past 24 hours, significant memory loss so that supervision is required
- ☐ 2 - Impaired decision-making: failure to perform usual ADLs or IADLs, inability to appropriately stop activities, jeopardizes safety through actions
- ☐ 3 - Verbal disruption: yelling, threatening, excessive profanity, sexual references, etc.
- ☐ 4 - Physical aggression: aggressive or combative to self and others (e.g., hits self, throws objects, punches, dangerous maneuvers with wheelchair or other objects)
- ☐ 5 - Disruptive, infantile, or socially inappropriate behavior (excludes verbal actions)
- ☐ 6 - Delusional, hallucinatory, or paranoid behavior
- ☐ 7 - None of the above behaviors demonstrated

(M0620) Frequency of Behavior Problems (Reported or Observed) (e.g., wandering episodes, self abuse, verbal disruption, physical aggression, etc.):
- ☐ 0 - Never
- ☐ 1 - Less than once a month
- ☐ 2 - Once a month
- ☐ 3 - Several times each month
- ☐ 4 - Several times a week
- ☐ 5 - At least daily

(M0630) Is this patient receiving Psychiatric Nursing Services at home provided by a qualified psychiatric nurse?
- ☐ 0 - No
- ☐ 1 - Yes

COMMENTS:

15. **ENDOCRINE AND HEMATOPOIETIC:**

_____ Diabetes   _____ Polyuria   _____ Polydipsia   _____ Thyroid problem   _____ Excessive bleeding or bruising

Fractionals: Usual results _____   _____ Intolerance to heat and cold

Frequency checked _____   _____ Other (specify) _____

COMMENTS:

M. LIFE SYSTEM PROFILE: For M0640-M0800, complete the "Current" column for all patients. For these same items, complete the "Prior" column only at start of care and at resumption of care; mark the level that corresponds to the patient's condition 14 days prior to start of care date (M0030) or resumption of care date (M0032). In all cases, record what the patient is *able to do.*

1. **(M0640) Grooming:** Ability to tend to personal hygiene needs (i.e., washing face and hands, hair care, shaving or make up, teeth or denture care, fingernail care).

Prior Current
- ☐ ☐ 0 - Able to groom self unaided, with or without the use of assistive devices or adapted methods.
- ☐ ☐ 1 - Grooming utensils must be placed within reach before able to complete grooming activities.
- ☐ ☐ 2 - Someone must assist the patient to groom self.
- ☐ ☐ 3 - Patient depends entirely upon someone else for grooming needs.
- ☐   UK - Unknown

OASIS-B1 SOC (08/2000)

START OF CARE ASSESSMENT	Client's Name:
(Also used for Resumption of Care Following Inpatient Stay) (Page 10 of 13)	Client Record No.

2. **(M0650) Ability to Dress Upper Body** (with or without dressing aids) including undergarments, pullovers, front-opening shirts and blouses, managing zippers, buttons, and snaps:

Prior Current
- ☐ ☐ 0 - Able to get clothes out of closets and drawers, put them on and remove them from the upper body without assistance.
- ☐ ☐ 1 - Able to dress upper body without assistance if clothing is laid out or handed to the patient.
- ☐ ☐ 2 - Someone must help the patient put on upper body clothing.
- ☐ ☐ 3 - Patient depends entirely upon another person to dress the upper body.
- ☐ UK - Unknown

3. **(M0660) Ability to Dress Lower Body** (with or without dressing aids) including undergarments, slacks, socks or nylons, shoes:

Prior Current
- ☐ ☐ 0 - Able to obtain, put on, and remove clothing and shoes without assistance.
- ☐ ☐ 1 - Able to dress lower body without assistance if clothing and shoes are laid out or handed to the patient.
- ☐ ☐ 2 - Someone must help the patient put on undergarments, slacks, socks or nylons, and shoes.
- ☐ ☐ 3 - Patient depends entirely upon another person to dress lower body.
- ☐ UK - Unknown

4. **(M0670) Bathing:** Ability to wash entire body. **Excludes grooming (washing face and hands only).**

Prior Current
- ☐ ☐ 0 - Able to bathe self in shower or tub independently.
- ☐ ☐ 1 - With the use of devices, is able to bathe self in shower or tub independently.
- ☐ ☐ 2 - Able to bathe in shower or tub with the assistance of another person:
  (a) for intermittent supervision or encouragement or reminders, OR
  (b) to get in and out of the shower or tub, OR
  (c) for washing difficult to reach areas.
- ☐ ☐ 3 - Participates in bathing self in shower or tub, but requires presence of another person throughout the bath for assistance or supervision.
- ☐ ☐ 4 - Unable to use the shower or tub and is bathed in bed or bedside chair.
- ☐ ☐ 5 - Unable to effectively participate in bathing and is totally bathed by another person.
- ☐ UK - Unknown

5. **(M0680) Toileting:** Ability to get to and from the toilet or bedside commode.

Prior Current
- ☐ ☐ 0 - Able to get to and from the toilet independently with or without a device.
- ☐ ☐ 1 - When reminded, assisted, or supervised by another person, able to get to and from the toilet.
- ☐ ☐ 2 - Unable to get to and from the toilet but is able to use a bedside commode (with or without assistance).
- ☐ ☐ 3 - Unable to get to and from the toilet or bedside commode but is able to use a bedpan/urinal independently.
- ☐ ☐ 4 - Is totally dependent in toileting.
- ☐ UK - Unknown

6. **(M0690) Transferring:** Ability to move from bed to chair, on and off toilet or commode, into and out of tub or shower, and ability to turn and position self in bed if patient is bedfast.

Prior Current
- ☐ ☐ 0 - Able to independently transfer.
- ☐ ☐ 1 - Transfers with minimal human assistance or with use of an assistive device.
- ☐ ☐ 2 - Unable to transfer self but is able to bear weight and pivot during the transfer process.
- ☐ ☐ 3 - Unable to transfer self and is unable to bear weight or pivot when transferred by another person.
- ☐ ☐ 4 - Bedfast, unable to transfer but is able to turn and position self in bed.
- ☐ ☐ 5 - Bedfast, unable to transfer and is unable to turn and position self.
- ☐ UK - Unknown

7. **(M0700) Ambulation/Locomotion:** Ability to SAFELY walk, once in a standing position, or use a wheelchair, once in a seated position, on a variety of surfaces.

Prior Current
- ☐ ☐ 0 - Able to independently walk on even and uneven surfaces and climb stairs with or without railings (i.e., needs no human assistance or assistive device).
- ☐ ☐ 1 - Requires use of a device (e.g., cane, walker) to walk alone or requires human supervision or assistance to negotiate stairs or steps or uneven surfaces.
- ☐ ☐ 2 - Able to walk only with the supervision or assistance of another person at all times.
- ☐ ☐ 3 - Chairfast, unable to ambulate but is able to wheel self independently.
- ☐ ☐ 4 - Chairfast, unable to ambulate and is unable to wheel self.
- ☐ ☐ 5 - Bedfast, unable to ambulate or be up in a chair.
- ☐ UK - Unknown

OASIS-B1 SOC (08/2000)

Outcome and Assessment Information Set (OASIS) is the intellectual property of The Center for Health Services and Policy Research © 2000.

START OF CARE ASSESSMENT
(Also used for Resumption of Care Following Inpatient Stay)
(Page 11 of 13)

Client's Name:

Client Record No.

8. **(M0710) Feeding or Eating:** Ability to feed self meals and snacks. **Note: This refers only to the process of <u>eating</u>, <u>chewing</u>, and <u>swallowing</u>, not preparing the food to be eaten.**

Prior Current
- ☐ ☐ 0 - Able to independently feed self.
- ☐ ☐ 1 - Able to feed self independently but requires:
  - (a) meal set-up; <u>OR</u>
  - (b) intermittent assistance or supervision from another person; <u>OR</u>
  - (c) a liquid, pureed or ground meat diet.
- ☐ ☐ 2 - <u>Unable</u> to feed self and must be assisted or supervised throughout the meal/snack.
- ☐ ☐ 3 - Able to take in nutrients orally <u>and</u> receives supplemental nutrients through a nasogastric tube or gastrostomy.
- ☐ ☐ 4 - <u>Unable</u> to take in nutrients orally and is fed nutrients through a nasogastric tube or gastrostomy.
- ☐ ☐ 5 - Unable to take in nutrients orally or by tube feeding.
- ☐   UK - Unknown

9. **(M0720) Planning and Preparing Light Meals** (e.g., cereal, sandwich) or reheat delivered meals:

Prior Current
- ☐ ☐ 0 - (a) Able to independently plan and prepare all light meals for self or reheat delivered meals; <u>OR</u>
  - (b) Is physically, cognitively, and mentally able to prepare light meals on a regular basis but has not routinely performed light meal preparation in the past (i.e., prior to this home care admission).
- ☐ ☐ 1 - <u>Unable</u> to prepare light meals on a regular basis due to physical, cognitive, or mental limitations.
- ☐ ☐ 2 - Unable to prepare any light meals or reheat any delivered meals.
- ☐   UK - Unknown

10. **(M0730) Transportation:** Physical and mental ability to <u>safely</u> use a car, taxi, or public transportation (bus, train, subway).

Prior Current
- ☐ ☐ 0 - Able to independently drive a regular or adapted car; <u>OR</u> uses a regular or handicap-accessible public bus.
- ☐ ☐ 1 - Able to ride in a car only when driven by another person; <u>OR</u> able to use a bus or handicap van only when assisted or accompanied by another person.
- ☐ ☐ 2 - <u>Unable</u> to ride in a car, taxi, bus, or van, and requires transportation by ambulance.
- ☐   UK - Unknown

11. **(M0740) Laundry:** Ability to do own laundry – to carry laundry to and from washing machine, to use washer and dryer, to wash small items by hand.

Prior Current
- ☐ ☐ 0 - (a) Able to independently take care of all laundry tasks; <u>OR</u>
  - (b) Physically, cognitively, and mentally able to do laundry and access facilities, <u>but</u> has not routinely performed laundry tasks in the past (i.e., prior to this home care admission).
- ☐ ☐ 1 - Able to do only light laundry, such as minor hand wash or light washer loads. Due to physical, cognitive, or mental limitations, needs assistance with heavy laundry such as carrying large loads of laundry.
- ☐ ☐ 2 - <u>Unable</u> to do any laundry due to physical limitation or needs continual supervision and assistance due to cognitive or mental limitation.
- ☐   UK - Unknown

12. **(M0750) Housekeeping:** Ability to safely and effectively perform light housekeeping and heavier cleaning tasks.

Prior Current
- ☐ ☐ 0 - (a) Able to independently perform all housekeeping tasks; <u>OR</u>
  - (b) Physically, cognitively, and mentally able to perform <u>all</u> housekeeping tasks but has not routinely participated in housekeeping tasks in the past (i.e., prior to this home care admission).
- ☐ ☐ 1 - Able to perform only <u>light</u> housekeeping (e.g., dusting, wiping kitchen counters) tasks independently.
- ☐ ☐ 2 - Able to perform housekeeping tasks with intermittent assistance or supervision from another person.
- ☐ ☐ 3 - <u>Unable</u> to consistently perform any housekeeping tasks unless assisted by another person throughout the process.
- ☐ ☐ 4 - Unable to effectively participate in any housekeeping tasks.
- ☐   UK - Unknown

13. **(M0760) Shopping:** Ability to plan for, select, and purchase items in a store and to carry them home or arrange delivery.

Prior Current
- ☐ ☐ 0 - (a) Able to plan for shopping needs and independently perform shopping tasks, including carrying packages; <u>OR</u>
  - (b) Physically, cognitively, and mentally able to take care of shopping, but has not done shopping in the past (i.e., prior to this home care admission).
- ☐ ☐ 1 - Able to go shopping, but needs some assistance:
  - (a) By self is able to do only light shopping and carry small packages, but needs someone to do occasional major shopping; <u>OR</u>
  - (b) <u>Unable</u> to go shopping alone, but can go with someone to assist.
- ☐ ☐ 2 - <u>Unable</u> to go shopping, but is able to identify items needed, place orders, and arrange home delivery.
- ☐ ☐ 3 - Needs someone to do all shopping and errands.
- ☐   UK - Unknown

OASIS-B1 SOC (08/2000)

Outcome and Assessment Information Set (OASIS) is the intellectual property of The Center for Health Services and Policy Research © 2000.

START OF CARE ASSESSMENT	Client's Name:
(Also used for Resumption of Care Following Inpatient Stay) (Page 12 of 13)	Client Record No.

14. **(M0770) Ability to Use Telephone:** Ability to answer the phone, dial numbers, and <u>effectively</u> use the telephone to communicate.

Prior Current
- ☐ ☐ 0 - Able to dial numbers and answer calls appropriately and as desired.
- ☐ ☐ 1 - Able to use a specially adapted telephone (i.e., large numbers on the dial, teletype phone for the deaf) and call essential numbers.
- ☐ ☐ 2 - Able to answer the telephone and carry on a normal conversation but has difficulty with placing calls.
- ☐ ☐ 3 - Able to answer the telephone only some of the time or is able to carry on only a limited conversation.
- ☐ ☐ 4 - <u>Unable</u> to answer the telephone at all but can listen if assisted with equipment.
- ☐ ☐ 5 - Totally unable to use the telephone.
- ☐ ☐ NA - Patient does not have a telephone.
- ☐ UK - Unknown

15. **(M0780) Management of Oral Medications:** <u>Patient's ability</u> to prepare and take <u>all</u> prescribed oral medications reliably and safely, including administration of the correct dosage at the appropriate times/intervals. **<u>Excludes</u> injectable and IV medications. (NOTE: This refers to ability, not compliance or willingness.)**

Prior Current
- ☐ ☐ 0 - Able to independently take the correct oral medication(s) and proper dosage(s) at the correct times.
- ☐ ☐ 1 - Able to take medication(s) at the correct times if:
  - (a) individual dosages are prepared in advance by another person; <u>OR</u>
  - (b) given daily reminders; <u>OR</u>
  - (c) someone develops a drug diary or chart.
- ☐ ☐ 2 - <u>Unable</u> to take medication unless administered by someone else.
- ☐ ☐ NA - No oral medications prescribed.
- ☐ UK - Unknown

16. **(M0790) Management of Inhalant/Mist Medications:** <u>Patient's ability</u> to prepare and take <u>all</u> prescribed inhalant/mist medications (nebulizers, metered dose devices) reliably and safely, including administration of the correct dosage at the appropriate times/intervals. **<u>Excludes</u> all other forms of medication (oral tablets, injectable and IV medications).**

Prior Current
- ☐ ☐ 0 - Able to independently take the correct medication and proper dosage at the correct times.
- ☐ ☐ 1 - Able to take medication at the correct times if:
  - (a) individual dosages are prepared in advance by another person, <u>OR</u>
  - (b) given daily reminders.
- ☐ ☐ 2 - <u>Unable</u> to take medication unless administered by someone else.
- ☐ ☐ NA - No inhalant/mist medications prescribed.
- ☐ UK - Unknown

17. **(M0800) Management of Injectable Medications:** <u>Patient's ability</u> to prepare and take <u>all</u> prescribed injectable medications reliably and safely, including administration of correct dosage at the appropriate times/intervals. **<u>Excludes</u> IV medications.**

Prior Current
- ☐ ☐ 0 - Able to independently take the correct medication and proper dosage at the correct times.
- ☐ ☐ 1 - Able to take injectable medication at correct times if:
  - (a) individual syringes are prepared in advance by another person, <u>OR</u>
  - (b) given daily reminders.
- ☐ ☐ 2 - <u>Unable</u> to take injectable medications unless administered by someone else.
- ☐ ☐ NA - No injectable medications prescribed.
- ☐ UK - Unknown

18. **(M0810) Patient Management of Equipment (includes <u>ONLY</u> oxygen, IV/infusion therapy, enteral/parenteral nutrition equipment or supplies):** <u>Patient's ability</u> to set up, monitor and change equipment reliably and safely, add appropriate fluids or medication, clean/store/dispose of equipment or supplies using proper technique. **(NOTE: This refers to ability, not compliance or willingness.)**
- ☐ 0 - Patient manages all tasks related to equipment completely independently.
- ☐ 1 - If someone else sets up equipment (i.e., fills portable oxygen tank, provides patient with prepared solutions), patient is able to manage all other aspects of equipment.
- ☐ 2 - Patient requires considerable assistance from another person to manage equipment, but independently completes portions of the task.
- ☐ 3 - Patient is only able to monitor equipment (e.g., liter flow, fluid in bag) and must call someone else to manage the equipment.
- ☐ 4 - Patient is completely dependent on someone else to manage all equipment.
- ☐ NA - No equipment of this type used in care **[If NA, go to *Section N - Therapy Need*]**

19. **(M0820) Caregiver Management of Equipment (includes <u>ONLY</u> oxygen, IV/infusion equipment, enteral/parenteral nutrition, ventilator therapy equipment or supplies):** <u>Caregiver's ability</u> to set up, monitor and change equipment reliably and safely, add appropriate fluids or medication, clean/store/dispose of equipment or supplies using proper technique. **(NOTE: This refers to ability, not compliance or willingness.)**
- ☐ 0 - Caregiver manages all tasks related to equipment completely independently.
- ☐ 1 - If someone else sets up equipment, caregiver is able to manage all other aspects.
- ☐ 2 - Caregiver requires considerable assistance from another person to manage equipment, but independently completes significant portions of task.
- ☐ 3 - Caregiver is only able to complete small portions of task (e.g., administer nebulizer treatment, clean/store/dispose of equipment or supplies).
- ☐ 4 - Caregiver is completely dependent on someone else to manage all equipment.
- ☐ NA - No caregiver
- ☐ UK - Unknown

OASIS-B1 SOC (08/2000)

START OF CARE ASSESSMENT
(Also used for Resumption of Care Following Inpatient Stay)
(Page 13 of 13)

Client's Name:

Client Record No.

N. THERAPY NEED

1. **(M0825) Therapy Need:** Does the care plan of the Medicare payment period for which this assessment will define a case mix group indicate a need for therapy (physical, occupational, or speech therapy) that meets the threshold for a Medicare high-therapy case mix group?
   - ☐ 0 - No
   - ☐ 1 - Yes
   - ☐ NA - Not applicable

O. EQUIPMENT AND SUPPLIES:

1. Equipment Needs: (check appropriate box)

	Has	Needs
a. Oxygen/Respiratory Equip.		
b. Wheelchair		
c. Hospital Bed		
d. Other (specify)		

2. Supplies Needed and Comments Regarding Equipment Needs:

3. Financial Problems/Needs:

P. SAFETY MEASURES RECOMMENDED TO PROTECT PATIENT FROM INJURY:

Q. EMERGENCY PLANS:

R. CONCLUSIONS/IMPRESSIONS AND SKILLED INTERVENTIONS PERFORMED THIS VISIT:

Date of Assessment: _____   Signature of Assessor: _____

OASIS-B1 SOC (08/2000)

FOLLOW-UP ASSESSMENT
(Page 1 of 10)

Client's Name:

Client Record No.

The *Outcome and Assessment Information Set (OASIS)* is the intellectual property of The Center for Health Services and Policy Research. Copyright ©2000 Used with Permission.

A. DEMOGRAPHIC/GENERAL INFORMATION

1. **(M0010) Agency Medicare Provider Number:**

   _ _ _ _ _ _

2. **(M0012) Agency Medicaid Provider Number:**

   _ _ _ _ _ _ _ _ _ _ _ _

Branch Identification (Optional, for Agency Use)

3. **(M0014) Branch State:** _ _

4. **(M0016) Branch ID Number:** _ _ _ _ _ _ _ _ _
   (Agency-assigned)

5. **(M0020) Patient ID Number:** _ _ _ _ _ _ _ _ _ _ _ _ _ _ _ _ _

6. **(M0030) Start of Care Date:**

   _ _ - _ _ - _ _ _ _
   m m   d d   y y y y

7. **(M0032) Resumption of Care Date:**

   _ _ - _ _ - _ _ _ _   ☐ NA - Not Applicable
   m m   d d   y y y y

8. **(M0040) Patient Name:**

   _____ ____ _____ _____
   (First)   (MI)   (Last)   (Suffix)

9. **Patient Address:**

   _____
   Street, Route, Apt. Number - not P.O. Box

10. **Patient Phone:**

    ( ) _ - _____

    City _____ (M0050) State   (M0060) Zip Code

11. **(M0063) Medicare Number:**

    _ _ _ _ _ _ _ _ _ _   ☐ NA - No Medicare
    (including suffix if any)

12. **(M0064) Social Security Number:**

    _ _ _ _ _ _ _ _ _   ☐ UK - Unknown or
                              Not Available

13. **(M0065) Medicaid Number:**

    _ _ _ _ _ _ _ _ _ _ _ _   ☐ NA - No Medicaid

14. **(M0066) Birth Date:**

    _ _ - _ _ - _ _ _ _
    m m   d d   y y y y

15. **(M0069) Gender:**   ☐ 1 - Male   ☐ 2 - Female

16. **(M0072) Primary Referring Physician ID:**   _ _ _ _ _ _ _ _ _ (UPIN#)   ☐ UK - Unknown or Not Available

    Name_____   Phone (_ _ _) _ _ _ _ _ _ _

    Address_____   FAX   (_ _ _) _ _ _ _ _ _ _

17. **(M0080) Discipline of Person Completing Assessment:**

    ☐ 1 - RN   ☐ 3 - SLP/ST
    ☐ 2 - PT   ☐ 4 - OT

18. **(M0090) Date Assessment Completed:**

    _ _ - _ _ - _ _ _ _
    m m   d d   y y y y

19. **(M0100) This Assessment is Currently Being Completed for the Following Reason:**

    Start/Resumption of Care
    1 - Start of care—further visits planned
    2 - Start of care—no further visits planned
    3 - Resumption of care (after inpatient stay)

    Follow-Up
    ☐ 4 - Recertification (follow-up) reassessment [Go to *M0150*]
    ☐ 5 - Other follow-up [Go to *M0150*]

    Transfer to an Inpatient Facility
    6 - Transferred to an inpatient facility—patient not discharged from agency
    7 - Transferred to an inpatient facility—patient discharged from agency
    Discharge from Agency — Not to an Inpatient Facility
    8 - Death at home
    9 - Discharge from agency
    10 - Discharge from agency—no visits completed after start/resumption of care assessment

20. **(M0150) Current Payment Sources for Home Care: (Mark all that apply.)**

    ☐ 0 - None; no charge for current services
    ☐ 1 - Medicare (traditional fee-for-service)
    ☐ 2 - Medicare (HMO/managed care)
    ☐ 3 - Medicaid (traditional fee-for-service)
    ☐ 4 - Medicaid (HMO/managed care)
    ☐ 5 - Workers' compensation
    ☐ 6 - Title programs (e.g., Title III, V or XX)
    ☐ 7 - Other government (e.g., CHAMPUS, VA, etc.)
    ☐ 8 - Private insurance
    ☐ 9 - Private HMO/managed care
    ☐ 10 - Self-pay
    ☐ 11 - Other (specify) _____

21. **(M0175)** From which of the following **Inpatient Facilities** was the patient discharged <u>during the past 14 days</u>? **(Mark all that apply.)**

    ☐ 1 - Hospital
    ☐ 2 - Rehabilitation facility
    ☐ 3 - Skilled nursing facility
    ☐ 4 - Other nursing home
    ☐ 5 - Other (specify) _____
    ☐ NA - Patient was not discharged from an inpatient facility
       [If NA, go to *M0200*]

22. **(M0200) Medical or Treatment Regimen Change Within Past 14 Days:** Has this patient experienced a change in medical or treatment regimen (e.g., medication, treatment, or service change due to new or additional diagnosis, etc.) within the last 14 days?

    ☐ 0 - No **[If No, go to #24 - *Conditions Prior to Medical or Treatment Regimen Change or Inpatient Stay Within the Last 14 Days*]**
    ☐ 1 - Yes

OASIS-B1 FU (08/2000)

FOLLOW-UP ASSESSMENT
(Page 2 of 10)

Client's Name:

Client Record No.

---

23. **(M0210)** List the patient's **Medical Diagnoses** and ICD code categories (three digits required; five digits optional) <u>for those conditions requiring changed medical or treatment regimen</u> (no surgical or V-codes):

Changed Medical Regimen Diagnosis	ICD
a. _____	(_ _ _ . _ _)
b. _____	(_ _ _ . _ _)
c. _____	(_ _ _ . _ _)
d. _____	(_ _ _ . _ _)

24. **(M0220) Conditions Prior to Medical or Treatment Regimen Change or Inpatient Stay Within Past 14 Days:** If this patient experienced an inpatient facility discharge or change in medical or treatment regimen within the past 14 days, indicate any conditions which existed <u>prior to</u> the inpatient stay or change in medical or treatment regimen. **(Mark all that apply.)**
   - ☐ 1 - Urinary incontinence
   - ☐ 2 - Indwelling/suprapubic catheter
   - ☐ 3 - Intractable pain
   - ☐ 4 - Impaired decision-making
   - ☐ 5 - Disruptive or socially inappropriate behavior
   - ☐ 6 - Memory loss to the extent that supervision required
   - ☐ 7 - None of the above
   - ☐ NA - No inpatient facility discharge and no change in medical or treatment regimen in past 14 days
   - ☐ UK - Unknown

25. **(M0230/M0240) Diagnoses and Severity Index:** List each medical diagnosis or problem for which the patient is receiving home care and ICD code category (three digits required; five digits optional - no surgical or V-codes) and rate it using the following severity index. (Choose one value that represents the most severe rating appropriate for each diagnosis.)

   0 - Asymptomatic, no treatment needed at this time
   1 - Symptoms well controlled with current therapy
   2 - Symptoms controlled with difficulty, affecting daily functioning; patient needs ongoing monitoring
   3 - Symptoms poorly controlled, patient needs frequent adjustment in treatment and dose monitoring
   4 - Symptoms poorly controlled, history of rehospitalizations

(M0230) Primary Diagnosis	ICD	Severity Rating
a. _____	(_ _ _ . _ _)	☐ 0 ☐ 1 ☐ 2 ☐ 3 ☐ 4

(M0240) Other Diagnoses	ICD	Severity Rating
b. _____	(_ _ _ . _ _)	☐ 0 ☐ 1 ☐ 2 ☐ 3 ☐ 4
c. _____	(_ _ _ . _ _)	☐ 0 ☐ 1 ☐ 2 ☐ 3 ☐ 4
d. _____	(_ _ _ . _ _)	☐ 0 ☐ 1 ☐ 2 ☐ 3 ☐ 4
e. _____	(_ _ _ . _ _)	☐ 0 ☐ 1 ☐ 2 ☐ 3 ☐ 4
f. _____	(_ _ _ . _ _)	☐ 0 ☐ 1 ☐ 2 ☐ 3 ☐ 4

B. **(M0250) THERAPIES** the patient receives <u>at home</u>: **(Mark all that apply.)**
   - ☐ 1 - Intravenous or infusion therapy (excludes TPN)
   - ☐ 2 - Parenteral nutrition (TPN or lipids)
   - ☐ 3 - Enteral nutrition (nasogastric, gastrostomy, jejunostomy, or any other artificial entry into the alimentary canal)
   - ☐ 4 - None of the above

C. PROGNOSIS

(M0280) Life Expectancy: (Physician documentation is not required.)
   - ☐ 0 - Life expectancy is greater than 6 months
   - ☐ 1 - Life expectancy is 6 months or fewer

D. **(M0290) HIGH RISK FACTORS** characterizing this patient: **(Mark all that apply.)**
   - ☐ 1 - Heavy smoking
   - ☐ 2 - Obesity
   - ☐ 3 - Alcohol dependency
   - ☐ 4 - Drug dependency
   - ☐ 5 - None of the above

E. LIVING ARRANGEMENTS

1. **(M0300) Current Residence:**
   - ☐ 1 - Patient's owned or rented residence (house, apartment, or mobile home owned or rented by patient/couple/significant other)
   - ☐ 2 - Family member's residence
   - ☐ 3 - Boarding home or rented room
   - ☐ 4 - Board and care or assisted living facility
   - ☐ 5 - Other (specify) _____

2. **(M0310) Structural Barriers** in the patient's environment limiting independent mobility: **(Mark all that apply.)**
   - ☐ 0 - None
   - ☐ 1 - Stairs inside home which <u>must</u> be used by the patient (e.g., to get to toileting, sleeping, eating areas)
   - ☐ 2 - Stairs inside home which are used optionally (e.g., to get to laundry facilities)
   - ☐ 3 - Stairs leading from inside house to outside
   - ☐ 4 - Narrow or obstructed doorways

OASIS-B1 FU (08/2000)

FOLLOW-UP ASSESSMENT (Page 3 of 10)	Client's Name: Client Record No.

3. **(M0320) Safety Hazards** found in the patient's current place of residence: **(Mark all that apply.)**
- ☐ 0 - None
- ☐ 1 - Inadequate floor, roof, or windows
- ☐ 2 - Inadequate lighting
- ☐ 3 - Unsafe gas/electric appliance
- ☐ 4 - Inadequate heating
- ☐ 5 - Inadequate cooling
- ☐ 6 - Lack of fire safety devices
- ☐ 7 - Unsafe floor coverings
- ☐ 8 - Inadequate stair railings
- ☐ 9 - Improperly stored hazardous materials
- ☐ 10 - Lead-based paint
- ☐ 11 - Other (specify) _____

4. **(M0330) Sanitation Hazards** found in the patient's current place of residence: **(Mark all that apply.)**
- ☐ 0 - None
- ☐ 1 - No running water
- ☐ 2 - Contaminated water
- ☐ 3 - No toileting facilities
- ☐ 4 - Outdoor toileting facilities only
- ☐ 5 - Inadequate sewage disposal
- ☐ 6 - Inadequate/improper food storage
- ☐ 7 - No food refrigeration
- ☐ 8 - No cooking facilities
- ☐ 9 - Insects/rodents present
- ☐ 10 - No scheduled trash pickup
- ☐ 11 - Cluttered/soiled living area
- ☐ 12 - Other (specify) _____

5. **(M0340) Patient Lives With: (Mark all that apply.)**
- ☐ 1 - Lives alone
- ☐ 2 - With spouse or significant other
- ☐ 3 - With other family member
- ☐ 4 - With a friend
- ☐ 5 - With paid help (other than home care agency staff)
- ☐ 6 - With other than above

COMMENTS:

F. SUPPORTIVE ASSISTANCE

1. **Names of Persons/Organizations Providing Assistance:**

2. **(M0350) Assisting Person(s) Other than Home Care Agency Staff: (Mark all that apply.)**
- ☐ 1 - Relatives, friends, or neighbors living outside the home
- ☐ 2 - Person residing in the home (EXCLUDING paid help)
- ☐ 3 - Paid help
- ☐ 4 - None of the above **[If None of the above, go to Section G - Review of Systems/Physical Assessment]**

3. **(M0360) Primary Caregiver** taking <u>lead</u> responsibility for providing or managing the patient's care, providing the most frequent assistance, etc. (other than home care agency staff):
- ☐ 0 - No one person **[If No one person, go to Section G - Review of Systems/Physical Assessment]**
- ☐ 1 - Spouse or significant other
- ☐ 2 - Daughter or son
- ☐ 3 - Other family member
- ☐ 4 - Friend or neighbor or community or church member
- ☐ 5 - Paid help

4. **(M0370) How Often** does the patient receive assistance from the primary caregiver?
- ☐ 1 - Several times during day and night
- ☐ 2 - Several times during day
- ☐ 3 - Once daily
- ☐ 4 - Three or more times per week
- ☐ 5 - One to two times per week
- ☐ 6 - Less often than weekly

5. **(M0380) Type of Primary Caregiver Assistance: (Mark all that apply.)**
- ☐ 1 - ADL assistance (e.g., bathing, dressing, toileting, bowel/bladder, eating/feeding)
- ☐ 2 - IADL assistance (e.g., meds, meals, housekeeping, laundry, telephone, shopping, finances)
- ☐ 3 - Environmental support (housing, home maintenance)
- ☐ 4 - Psychosocial support (socialization, companionship, recreation)
- ☐ 5 - Advocates or facilitates patient's participation in appropriate medical care
- ☐ 6 - Financial agent, power of attorney, or conservator of finance
- ☐ 7 - Health care agent, conservator of person, or medical power of attorney

G. REVIEW OF SYSTEMS/PHYSICAL ASSESSMENT

1. <u>**EYES**</u>:

(M0390) Vision with corrective lenses if the patient usually wears them:
- ☐ 0 - Normal vision: sees adequately in most situations; can see medication labels, newsprint.
- ☐ 1 - Partially impaired: cannot see medication labels or newsprint, but <u>can</u> see obstacles in path, and the surrounding layout; can count fingers at arm's length.
- ☐ 2 - Severely impaired: cannot locate objects without hearing or touching them <u>or</u> patient nonresponsive.

OASIS-B1 FU (08/2000)

FOLLOW-UP ASSESSMENT
(Page 4 of 10)

Client's Name:

Client Record No.

---

2. <u>ORAL</u>:

(M0410) Speech and Oral (Verbal) Expression of Language (in patient's own language):
- ☐ 0 - Expresses complex ideas, feelings, and needs clearly, completely, and easily in all situations with no observable impairment.
- ☐ 1 - Minimal difficulty in expressing ideas and needs (may take extra time; makes occasional errors in word choice, grammar or speech intelligibility; needs minimal prompting or assistance).
- ☐ 2 - Expresses simple ideas or needs with moderate difficulty (needs prompting or assistance, errors in word choice, organization or speech intelligibility). Speaks in phrases or short sentences.
- ☐ 3 - Has severe difficulty expressing basic ideas or needs and requires maximal assistance or guessing by listener. Speech limited to single words or short phrases.
- ☐ 4 - <u>Unable</u> to express basic needs even with maximal prompting or assistance but is not comatose or unresponsive (e.g., speech is nonsensical or unintelligible).
- ☐ 5 - Patient nonresponsive or unable to speak.

3. <u>NEUROLOGICAL</u>:

(M0420) Frequency of Pain interfering with patient's activity or movement:
- ☐ 0 - Patient has no pain or pain does not interfere with activity or movement
- ☐ 1 - Less often than daily
- ☐ 2 - Daily, but not constantly
- ☐ 3 - All of the time

Comments on pain management:

(M0430) Intractable Pain: Is the patient experiencing pain that is <u>not easily relieved</u>, occurs at least daily, and affects the patient's sleep, appetite, physical or emotional energy, concentration, personal relationships, emotions, or ability or desire to perform physical activity?
- ☐ 0 - No
- ☐ 1 - Yes

4. <u>INTEGUMENT</u>:

a. Skin condition (Record type # on body area. Indicate size to right of numbered category.)

<u>Type</u>	<u>Size</u>
1. Lesions	
2. Bruises	
3. Masses	
4. Scars	
5. Stasis Ulcers	
6. Pressure Ulcers	
7. Incisions	
8. Other (specify) _____	

b. **(M0440)** Does this patient have a **Skin Lesion** or an **Open Wound**? This excludes "OSTOMIES."
- ☐ 0 - No [If No, go to *Section 5 - Cardiorespiratory*]
- ☐ 1 - Yes

OASIS-B1 FU (08/2000)

FOLLOW-UP ASSESSMENT
(Page 5 of 10)

Client's Name:

Client Record No.

c. **(M0445)** Does this patient have a **Pressure Ulcer?**
- ☐ 0 - No [**If No, go to #4.d - Stasis Ulcer**]
- ☐ 1 - Yes

(M0450) Current Number of Pressure Ulcers at Each Stage: (Circle one response for each stage.)

Pressure Ulcer Stages		Number of Pressure Ulcers				
a)	Stage 1: Nonblanchable erythema of intact skin; the heralding of skin ulceration. In darker-pigmented skin, warmth, edema, hardness, or discolored skin may be indicators.	0	1	2	3	4 or more
b)	Stage 2: Partial thickness skin loss involving epidermis and/or dermis. The ulcer is superficial and presents clinically as an abrasion, blister, or shallow crater.	0	1	2	3	4 or more
c)	Stage 3: Full-thickness skin loss involving damage or necrosis of subcutaneous tissue which may extend down to, but not through, underlying fascia. The ulcer presents clinically as a deep crater with or without undermining of adjacent tissue.	0	1	2	3	4 or more
d)	Stage 4: Full-thickness skin loss with extensive destruction, tissue necrosis, or damage to muscle, bone, or supporting structures (e.g., tendon, joint capsule, etc.).	0	1	2	3	4 or more
e)	In addition to the above, is there at least one pressure ulcer that cannot be observed due to the presence of eschar or a nonremovable dressing, including casts? ☐ 0 - No ☐ 1 - Yes					

(M0460) Stage of Most Problematic (Observable) Pressure Ulcer:
- ☐ 1 - Stage 1
- ☐ 2 - Stage 2
- ☐ 3 - Stage 3
- ☐ 4 - Stage 4
- ☐ NA - No observable pressure ulcer

(M0464) Status of Most Problematic (Observable) Pressure Ulcer:
- ☐ 1 - Fully granulating
- ☐ 2 - Early/partial granulation
- ☐ 3 - Not healing
- ☐ NA - No observable pressure ulcer

d. **(M0468)** Does this patient have a **Stasis Ulcer?**
- ☐ 0 - No [**If No, go to #4.e - Surgical Wound**]
- ☐ 1 - Yes

(M0470) Current Number of Observable Stasis Ulcer(s):
- ☐ 0 - Zero
- ☐ 1 - One
- ☐ 2 - Two
- ☐ 3 - Three
- ☐ 4 - Four or more

(M0474) Does this patient have at least one **Stasis Ulcer that Cannot be Observed** due to the presence of a nonremovable dressing?
- ☐ 0 - No
- ☐ 1 - Yes

(M0476) Status of Most Problematic (Observable) Stasis Ulcer:
- ☐ 1 - Fully granulating
- ☐ 2 - Early/partial granulation
- ☐ 3 - Not healing
- ☐ NA - No observable stasis ulcer

e. **(M0482)** Does this patient have a **Surgical Wound?**
- ☐ 0 - No [**If No, go to Section 5- Cardiorespiratory**]
- ☐ 1 - Yes

(M0484) Current Number of (Observable) Surgical Wounds: (If a wound is partially closed but has more than one opening, consider each opening as a separate wound.)
- ☐ 0 - Zero
- ☐ 1 - One
- ☐ 2 - Two
- ☐ 3 - Three
- ☐ 4 - Four or more

(M0486) Does this patient have at least one **Surgical Wound that Cannot be Observed** due to the presence of a nonremovable dressing?
- ☐ 0 - No
- ☐ 1 - Yes

(M0488) Status of Most Problematic (Observable) Surgical Wound:
- ☐ 1 - Fully granulating
- ☐ 2 - Early/partial granulation
- ☐ 3 - Not healing
- ☐ NA - No observable surgical wound

COMMENTS: (Wound/lesion history, treatments, etc.)

OASIS-B1 FU (08/2000)

FOLLOW-UP ASSESSMENT (Page 6 of 10)	Client's Name: Client Record No.

5. **CARDIORESPIRATORY:**   Temperature _____   Respirations _____

   BLOOD PRESSURE: Lying _____   Sitting _____   Standing _____

   PULSE: Apical rate _____   Radial rate _____   Rhythm _____   Quality _____

(M0490) When is the patient dyspneic or noticeably **Short of Breath?**
- ☐ 0 - Never, patient is not short of breath
- ☐ 1 - When walking more than 20 feet, climbing stairs
- ☐ 2 - With moderate exertion (e.g., while dressing, using commode or bedpan, walking distances less than 20 feet)
- ☐ 3 - With minimal exertion (e.g., while eating, talking, or performing other ADLs) or with agitation
- ☐ 4 - At rest (during day or night)

COMMENTS:

(M0500) Respiratory Treatments utilized at home: **(Mark all that apply.)**
- ☐ 1 - Oxygen (intermittent or continuous)
- ☐ 2 - Ventilator (continually or at night)
- ☐ 3 - Continuous positive airway pressure
- ☐ 4 - None of the above

6. **GENITOURINARY TRACT:**

(M0510) Has this patient been treated for a **Urinary Tract Infection** in the past 14 days?
- ☐ 0 - No
- ☐ 1 - Yes
- ☐ NA - Patient on prophylactic treatment

(M0520) Urinary Incontinence or Urinary Catheter Presence:
- ☐ 0 - No incontinence or catheter (includes anuria or ostomy for urinary drainage) **[If No, go to Section 7 - Gastrointestinal Tract]**
- ☐ 1 - Patient is incontinent
- ☐ 2 - Patient requires a urinary catheter (i.e., external, indwelling, intermittent, suprapubic) **[Go to Section 7 - Gastrointestinal Tract]**

(M0530) When does **Urinary Incontinence** occur?
- ☐ 0 - Timed-voiding defers incontinence
- ☐ 1 - During the night only
- ☐ 2 - During the day and night

7. **GASTROINTESTINAL TRACT:**

(M0540) Bowel Incontinence Frequency:
- ☐ 0 - Very rarely or never has bowel incontinence
- ☐ 1 - Less than once weekly
- ☐ 2 - One to three times weekly
- ☐ 3 - Four to six times weekly
- ☐ 4 - On a daily basis
- ☐ 5 - More often than once daily
- ☐ NA - Patient has ostomy for bowel elimination

(M0550) Ostomy for Bowel Elimination: Does this patient have an ostomy for bowel elimination that (within the last 14 days): a) was related to an inpatient facility stay, <u>or</u> b) necessitated a change in medical or treatment regimen?
- ☐ 0 - Patient does <u>not</u> have an ostomy for bowel elimination.
- ☐ 1 - Patient's ostomy was <u>not</u> related to an inpatient stay and did <u>not</u> necessitate change in medical or treatment regimen.
- ☐ 2 - The ostomy <u>was</u> related to an inpatient stay or <u>did</u> necessitate change in medical or treatment regimen.

8. **NEURO/EMOTIONAL/BEHAVIORAL STATUS:**

(M0560) Cognitive Functioning: (Patient's current level of alertness, orientation, comprehension, concentration, and immediate memory for simple commands.)
- ☐ 0 - Alert/oriented, able to focus and shift attention, comprehends and recalls task directions independently.
- ☐ 1 - Requires prompting (cueing, repetition, reminders) only under stressful or unfamiliar conditions.
- ☐ 2 - Requires assistance and some direction in specific situations (e.g., on all tasks involving shifting of attention), or consistently requires low stimulus environment due to distractibility.
- ☐ 3 - Requires considerable assistance in routine situations. Is not alert and oriented or is unable to shift attention and recall directions more than half the time.
- ☐ 4 - Totally dependent due to disturbances such as constant disorientation, coma, persistent vegetative state, or delirium.

(M0570) When Confused (Reported or Observed):
- ☐ 0 - Never
- ☐ 1 - In new or complex situations only
- ☐ 2 - On awakening or at night only
- ☐ 3 - During the day and evening, but not constantly
- ☐ 4 - Constantly
- ☐ NA - Patient nonresponsive

(M0580) When Anxious (Reported or Observed):
- ☐ 0 - None of the time
- ☐ 1 - Less often than daily
- ☐ 2 - Daily, but not constantly
- ☐ 3 - All of the time
- ☐ NA - Patient nonresponsive

OASIS-B1 FU (08/2000)

FOLLOW-UP ASSESSMENT (Page 7 of 10)	Client's Name:
	Client Record No.

(M0590) Depressive Feelings Reported or Observed In Patient: (Mark all that apply.)
- ☐ 1 - Depressed mood (e.g., feeling sad, tearful)
- ☐ 2 - Sense of failure or self reproach
- ☐ 3 - Hopelessness
- ☐ 4 - Recurrent thoughts of death
- ☐ 5 - Thoughts of suicide
- ☐ 6 - None of the above feelings observed or reported

(M0600) Patient Behaviors (Reported or Observed): (Mark all that apply.)
- ☐ 1 - Indecisiveness, lack of concentration
- ☐ 2 - Diminished interest in most activities
- ☐ 3 - Sleep disturbances
- ☐ 4 - Recent change in appetite or weight
- ☐ 5 - Agitation
- ☐ 6 - A suicide attempt
- ☐ 7 - None of the above behaviors observed or reported

(M0610) Behaviors Demonstrated at Least Once a Week (Reported or Observed): (Mark all that apply.)
- ☐ 1 - Memory deficit: failure to recognize familiar persons/places, inability to recall events of past 24 hours, significant memory loss so that supervision is required
- ☐ 2 - Impaired decision-making: failure to perform usual ADLs or IADLs, inability to appropriately stop activities, jeopardizes safety through actions
- ☐ 3 - Verbal disruption: yelling, threatening, excessive profanity, sexual references, etc.
- ☐ 4 - Physical aggression: aggressive or combative to self and others (e.g., hits self, throws objects, punches, dangerous maneuvers with wheelchair or other objects)
- ☐ 5 - Disruptive, infantile, or socially inappropriate behavior (excludes verbal actions)
- ☐ 6 - Delusional, hallucinatory, or paranoid behavior
- ☐ 7 - None of the above behaviors demonstrated

COMMENTS:

(M0620) Frequency of Behavior Problems (Reported or Observed) (e.g., wandering episodes, self abuse, verbal disruption, physical aggression, etc.):
- ☐ 0 - Never
- ☐ 1 - Less than once a month
- ☐ 2 - Once a month
- ☐ 3 - Several times each month
- ☐ 4 - Several times a week
- ☐ 5 - At least daily

(M0630) Is this patient receiving **Psychiatric Nursing Services** at home provided by a qualified psychiatric nurse?
- ☐ 0 - No
- ☐ 1 - Yes

9. **OTHER UPDATED ASSESSMENTS:**

H. LIFE SYSTEM PROFILE: For M0640-M0800, record what the patient currently is *able to do*.

1. **(M0640) Grooming:** Ability to tend to personal hygiene needs (i.e., washing face and hands, hair care, shaving or make up, teeth or denture care, fingernail care).
   - ☐ 0 - Able to groom self unaided, with or without the use of assistive devices or adapted methods.
   - ☐ 1 - Grooming utensils must be placed within reach before able to complete grooming activities.
   - ☐ 2 - Someone must assist the patient to groom self.
   - ☐ 3 - Patient depends entirely upon someone else for grooming needs.

2. **(M0650) Ability to Dress Upper Body** (with or without dressing aids) including undergarments, pullovers, front-opening shirts and blouses, managing zippers, buttons, and snaps:
   - ☐ 0 - Able to get clothes out of closets and drawers, put them on and remove them from the upper body without assistance.
   - ☐ 1 - Able to dress upper body without assistance if clothing is laid out or handed to the patient.
   - ☐ 2 - Someone must help the patient put on upper body clothing.
   - ☐ 3 - Patient depends entirely upon another person to dress the upper body.

OASIS-B1 FU (08/2000)

FOLLOW-UP ASSESSMENT
(Page 8 of 10)

Client's Name:

Client Record No.

3. **(M0660) Ability to Dress Lower Body** (with or without dressing aids) including undergarments, slacks, socks or nylons, shoes:
   - ☐ 0 - Able to obtain, put on, and remove clothing and shoes without assistance.
   - ☐ 1 - Able to dress lower body without assistance if clothing and shoes are laid out or handed to the patient.
   - ☐ 2 - Someone must help the patient put on undergarments, slacks, socks or nylons, and shoes.
   - ☐ 3 - Patient depends entirely upon another person to dress lower body.

4. **(M0670) Bathing:** Ability to wash entire body. **Excludes grooming (washing face and hands only).**
   - ☐ 0 - Able to bathe self in shower or tub independently.
   - ☐ 1 - With the use of devices, is able to bathe self in shower or tub independently.
   - ☐ 2 - Able to bathe in shower or tub with the assistance of another person:
     (a) for intermittent supervision or encouragement or reminders, OR
     (b) to get in and out of the shower or tub, OR
     (c) for washing difficult to reach areas.
   - ☐ 3 - Participates in bathing self in shower or tub, but requires presence of another person throughout the bath for assistance or supervision.
   - ☐ 4 - Unable to use the shower or tub and is bathed in bed or bedside chair.
   - ☐ 5 - Unable to effectively participate in bathing and is totally bathed by another person.

5. **(M0680) Toileting:** Ability to get to and from the toilet or bedside commode.
   - ☐ 0 - Able to get to and from the toilet independently with or without a device.
   - ☐ 1 - When reminded, assisted, or supervised by another person, able to get to and from the toilet.
   - ☐ 2 - Unable to get to and from the toilet but is able to use a bedside commode (with or without assistance).
   - ☐ 3 - Unable to get to and from the toilet or bedside commode but is able to use a bedpan/urinal independently.
   - ☐ 4 - Is totally dependent in toileting.

6. **(M0690) Transferring:** Ability to move from bed to chair, on and off toilet or commode, into and out of tub or shower, and ability to turn and position self in bed if patient is bedfast.
   - ☐ 0 - Able to independently transfer.
   - ☐ 1 - Transfers with minimal human assistance or with use of an assistive device.
   - ☐ 2 - Unable to transfer self but is able to bear weight and pivot during the transfer process.
   - ☐ 3 - Unable to transfer self and is unable to bear weight or pivot when transferred by another person.
   - ☐ 4 - Bedfast, unable to transfer but is able to turn and position self in bed.
   - ☐ 5 - Bedfast, unable to transfer and is unable to turn and position self.

7. **(M0700) Ambulation/Locomotion:** Ability to SAFELY walk, once in a standing position, or use a wheelchair, once in a seated position, on a variety of surfaces.
   - ☐ 0 - Able to independently walk on even and uneven surfaces and climb stairs with or without railings (i.e., needs no human assistance or assistive device).
   - ☐ 1 - Requires use of a device (e.g., cane, walker) to walk alone or requires human supervision or assistance to negotiate stairs or steps or uneven surfaces.
   - ☐ 2 - Able to walk only with the supervision or assistance of another person at all times.
   - ☐ 3 - Chairfast, unable to ambulate but is able to wheel self independently.
   - ☐ 4 - Chairfast, unable to ambulate and is unable to wheel self.
   - ☐ 5 - Bedfast, unable to ambulate or be up in a chair.

8. **(M0710) Feeding or Eating:** Ability to feed self meals and snacks. **Note: This refers only to the process of eating, chewing, and swallowing, not preparing the food to be eaten.**
   - ☐ 0 - Able to independently feed self.
   - ☐ 1 - Able to feed self independently but requires:
     (a) meal set-up; OR
     (b) intermittent assistance or supervision from another person; OR
     (c) a liquid, pureed or ground meat diet.
   - ☐ 2 - Unable to feed self and must be assisted or supervised throughout the meal/snack.
   - ☐ 3 - Able to take in nutrients orally and receives supplemental nutrients through a nasogastric tube or gastrostomy.
   - ☐ 4 - Unable to take in nutrients orally and is fed nutrients through a nasogastric tube or gastrostomy.
   - ☐ 5 - Unable to take in nutrients orally or by tube feeding.

9. **(M0720) Planning and Preparing Light Meals** (e.g., cereal, sandwich) or reheat delivered meals:
   - ☐ 0 - (a) Able to independently plan and prepare all light meals for self or reheat delivered meals; OR
     (b) Is physically, cognitively, and mentally able to prepare light meals on a regular basis but has not routinely performed light meal preparation in the past (i.e., prior to this home care admission).
   - ☐ 1 - Unable to prepare light meals on a regular basis due to physical, cognitive, or mental limitations.
   - ☐ 2 - Unable to prepare any light meals or reheat any delivered meals.

10. **(M0730) Transportation:** Physical and mental ability to safely use a car, taxi, or public transportation (bus, train, subway).
    - ☐ 0 - Able to independently drive a regular or adapted car; OR uses a regular or handicap-accessible public bus.
    - ☐ 1 - Able to ride in a car only when driven by another person; OR able to use a bus or handicap van only when assisted or accompanied by another person.
    - ☐ 2 - Unable to ride in a car, taxi, bus, or van, and requires transportation by ambulance.

OASIS-B1 FU (08/2000)

FOLLOW-UP ASSESSMENT (Page 9 of 10)	Client's Name:
	Client Record No.

11. **(M0740) Laundry:** Ability to do own laundry – to carry laundry to and from washing machine, to use washer and dryer, to wash small items by hand.
- ☐ 0 - (a) Able to independently take care of all laundry tasks; <u>OR</u>
  (b) Physically, cognitively, and mentally able to do laundry and access facilities, <u>but</u> has not routinely performed laundry tasks in the past (i.e., prior to this home care admission).
- ☐ 1 - Able to do only light laundry, such as minor hand wash or light washer loads. Due to physical, cognitive, or mental limitations, needs assistance with heavy laundry such as carrying large loads of laundry.
- ☐ 2 - <u>Unable</u> to do any laundry due to physical limitation or needs continual supervision and assistance due to cognitive or mental limitation.

12. **(M0750) Housekeeping:** Ability to safely and effectively perform light housekeeping and heavier cleaning tasks.
- ☐ 0 - (a) Able to independently perform all housekeeping tasks; <u>OR</u>
  (b) Physically, cognitively, and mentally able to perform <u>all</u> housekeeping tasks but has not routinely participated in housekeeping tasks in the past (i.e., prior to this home care admission).
- ☐ 1 - Able to perform only <u>light</u> housekeeping (e.g., dusting, wiping kitchen counters) tasks independently.
- ☐ 2 - Able to perform housekeeping tasks with intermittent assistance or supervision from another person.
- ☐ 3 - <u>Unable</u> to consistently perform any housekeeping tasks unless assisted by another person throughout the process.
- ☐ 4 - Unable to effectively participate in any housekeeping tasks.

13. **(M0760) Shopping:** Ability to plan for, select, and purchase items in a store and to carry them home or arrange delivery.
- ☐ 0 - (a) Able to plan for shopping needs and independently perform shopping tasks, including carrying packages; <u>OR</u>
  (b) Physically, cognitively, and mentally able to take care of shopping, but has not done shopping in the past (i.e., prior to this home care admission).
- ☐ 1 - Able to go shopping, but needs some assistance:
  (a) By self is able to do only light shopping and carry small packages, but needs someone to do occasional major shopping; <u>OR</u>
  (b) <u>Unable</u> to go shopping alone, but can go with someone to assist.
- ☐ 2 - <u>Unable</u> to go shopping, but is able to identify items needed, place orders, and arrange home delivery.
- ☐ 3 - Needs someone to do all shopping and errands.

14. **(M0770) Ability to Use Telephone:** Ability to answer the phone, dial numbers, and <u>effectively</u> use the telephone to communicate.
- ☐ 0 - Able to dial numbers and answer calls appropriately and as desired.
- ☐ 1 - Able to use a specially adapted telephone (i.e., large numbers on the dial, teletype phone for the deaf) and call essential numbers.
- ☐ 2 - Able to answer the telephone and carry on a normal conversation but has difficulty with placing calls.
- ☐ 3 - Able to answer the telephone only some of the time or is able to carry on only a limited conversation.
- ☐ 4 - <u>Unable</u> to answer the telephone at all but can listen if assisted with equipment.
- ☐ 5 - Totally unable to use the telephone.
- ☐ NA - Patient does not have a telephone.

15. **(M0780) Management of Oral Medications:** <u>Patient's ability</u> to prepare and take <u>all</u> prescribed oral medications reliably and safely, including administration of the correct dosage at the appropriate times/intervals. <u>Excludes injectable and IV medications.</u> **(NOTE: This refers to ability, not compliance or willingness.)**
- ☐ 0 - Able to independently take the correct oral medication(s) and proper dosage(s) at the correct times.
- ☐ 1 - Able to take medication(s) at the correct times if:
  (a) individual dosages are prepared in advance by another person; <u>OR</u>
  (b) given daily reminders; <u>OR</u>
  (c) someone develops a drug diary or chart.
- ☐ 2 - <u>Unable</u> to take medication unless administered by someone else.
- ☐ NA - No oral medications prescribed.

16. **(M0790) Management of Inhalant/Mist Medications:** <u>Patient's ability</u> to prepare and take <u>all</u> prescribed inhalant/mist medications (nebulizers, metered dose devices) reliably and safely, including administration of the correct dosage at the appropriate times/intervals. <u>Excludes</u> **all other forms of medication (oral tablets, injectable and IV medications).**
- ☐ 0 - Able to independently take the correct medication and proper dosage at the correct times.
- ☐ 1 - Able to take medication at the correct times if:
  (a) individual dosages are prepared in advance by another person, <u>OR</u>
  (b) given daily reminders.
- ☐ 2 - <u>Unable</u> to take medication unless administered by someone else.
- ☐ NA - No inhalant/mist medications prescribed.

17. **(M0800) Management of Injectable Medications:** <u>Patient's ability</u> to prepare and take <u>all</u> prescribed injectable medications reliably and safely, including administration of correct dosage at the appropriate times/intervals. <u>Excludes</u> **IV medications.**
- ☐ 0 - Able to independently take the correct medication and proper dosage at the correct times.
- ☐ 1 - Able to take injectable medication at correct times if:
  (a) individual syringes are prepared in advance by another person, <u>OR</u>
  (b) given daily reminders.
- ☐ 2 - <u>Unable</u> to take injectable medications unless administered by someone else.
- ☐ NA - No injectable medications prescribed.

OASIS-B1 FU (08/2000)

FOLLOW-UP ASSESSMENT (Page 10 of 10)	Client's Name: Client Record No.

18. **(M0810) Patient Management of Equipment (includes <u>ONLY</u> oxygen, IV/infusion therapy, enteral/parenteral nutrition equipment or supplies):** <u>Patient's ability</u> to set up, monitor and change equipment reliably and safely, add appropriate fluids or medication, clean/store/dispose of equipment or supplies using proper technique. **(NOTE: This refers to ability, not compliance or willingness.)**
- ☐ 0 - Patient manages all tasks related to equipment completely independently.
- ☐ 1 - If someone else sets up equipment (i.e., fills portable oxygen tank, provides patient with prepared solutions), patient is able to manage all other aspects of equipment.
- ☐ 2 - Patient requires considerable assistance from another person to manage equipment, but independently completes portions of the task.
- ☐ 3 - Patient is only able to monitor equipment (e.g., liter flow, fluid in bag) and must call someone else to manage the equipment.
- ☐ 4 - Patient is completely dependent on someone else to manage all equipment.
- ☐ NA - No equipment of this type used in care **[If NA, go to *Section I - Therapy Need*]**

19. **(M0820) Caregiver Management of Equipment (includes <u>ONLY</u> oxygen, IV/infusion equipment, enteral/parenteral nutrition, ventilator therapy equipment or supplies):** <u>Caregiver's ability</u> to set up, monitor and change equipment reliably and safely, add appropriate fluids or medication, clean/store/dispose of equipment or supplies using proper technique. **(NOTE: This refers to ability, not compliance or willingness.)**
- ☐ 0 - Caregiver manages all tasks related to equipment completely independently.
- ☐ 1 - If someone else sets up equipment, caregiver is able to manage all other aspects.
- ☐ 2 - Caregiver requires considerable assistance from another person to manage equipment, but independently completes significant portions of task.
- ☐ 3 - Caregiver is only able to complete small portions of task (e.g., administer nebulizer treatment, clean/store/dispose of equipment or supplies).
- ☐ 4 - Caregiver is completely dependent on someone else to manage all equipment.
- ☐ NA - No caregiver

I. THERAPY NEED

1. **(M0825) Therapy Need:** Does the care plan of the Medicare payment period for which this assessment will define a case mix group indicate a need for therapy (physical, occupational, or speech therapy) that meets the threshold for a Medicare high-therapy case mix group?
- ☐ 0 - No
- ☐ 1 - Yes
- ☐ NA - Not applicable

J. EMERGENT CARE

1. **(M0830) Emergent Care:** Since the last time OASIS data were collected, has the patient utilized any of the following services for emergent care (other than home care agency services)? **(Mark all that apply.)**
- ☐ 0 - No emergent care services **[If no emergent care, go to *Section K - Conclusions*]**
- ☐ 1 - Hospital emergency room (includes 23-hour holding)
- ☐ 2 - Doctor's office emergency visit/house call
- ☐ 3 - Outpatient department/clinic emergency (includes urgicenter sites)
- ☐ UK - Unknown **[If UK, go to *Section K - Conclusions*]**

2. **(M0840) Emergent Care Reason:** For what reason(s) did the patient/family seek emergent care? **(Mark all that apply.)**
- ☐ 1 - Improper medication administration, medication side effects, toxicity, anaphylaxis
- ☐ 2 - Nausea, dehydration, malnutrition, constipation, impaction
- ☐ 3 - Injury caused by fall or accident at home
- ☐ 4 - Respiratory problems (e.g., shortness of breath, respiratory infection, tracheobronchial obstruction)
- ☐ 5 - Wound infection, deteriorating wound status, new lesion/ulcer
- ☐ 6 - Cardiac problems (e.g., fluid overload, exacerbation of CHF, chest pain)
- ☐ 7 - Hypo/Hyperglycemia, diabetes out of control
- ☐ 8 - GI bleeding, obstruction
- ☐ 9 - Other than above reasons
- ☐ UK - Reason unknown

K. CONCLUSIONS:

Date of Assessment: _____   Signature of Assessor: _____

OASIS-B1 FU (08/2000)

Outcome and Assessment Information Set (OASIS) is the intellectual property of The Center for Health Services and Policy Research © 2000.

TRANSFER TO INPATIENT FACILITY (Page 1 of 2)	Client's Name: Client Record No.

The *Outcome and Assessment Information Set (OASIS)* is the intellectual property of The Center for Health Services and Policy Research. Copyright ©2000 Used with Permission.

A. DEMOGRAPHIC/GENERAL INFORMATION

1. **(M0010) Agency Medicare Provider Number:**

2. **(M0012) Agency Medicaid Provider Number:**

Branch Identification (Optional, for Agency Use)

3. **(M0014) Branch State:** __ __

4. **(M0016) Branch ID Number:** __ __ __ __ __ __ __ __ __ __
(Agency-assigned)

5. **(M0020) Patient ID Number:** __ __ __ __ __ __ __ __ __ __ __ __ __ __

6. **(M0030) Start of Care Date:**
__ __ - __ __ - __ __ __ __
m m   d d   y y y y

7. **(M0032) Resumption of Care Date:**
__ __ - __ __ - __ __ __ __   □ NA - Not Applicable
m m   d d   y y y y

8. **(M0040) Patient Name:**
(First)   (MI)   (Last)   (Suffix)

9. **Patient Address:**
Street, Route, Apt. Number - not P.O. Box

10. **Patient Phone:**
( ) ___ - ___

City   (M0050) State   (M0060) Zip Code

11. **(M0063) Medicare Number:**
__ __ __ __ __ __ __ __ __   □ NA - No Medicare
(including suffix if any)

12. **(M0064) Social Security Number:**
__ __ __ __ __ __ __ __ __   □ UK - Unknown or Not Available

13. **(M0065) Medicaid Number:**
__ __ __ __ __ __ __ __ __ __ __ __   □ NA - No Medicaid

14. **(M0066) Birth Date:**
__ __ - __ __ - __ __ __ __
m m   d d   y y y y

15. **(M0069) Gender:**   □ 1 - Male   □ 2 - Female

16. **(M0072) Primary Referring Physician ID:** __ __ __ __ __ __ __ __ __ (UPIN#)   □ UK - Unknown or Not Available

17. **(M0080) Discipline of Person Completing Assessment:**
□ 1 - RN   □ 3 - SLP/ST
□ 2 - PT   □ 4 - OT

18. **(M0090) Date Assessment Completed:**
__ __ - __ __ - __ __ __ __
m m   d d   y y y y

19. **(M0100) This Assessment is Currently Being Completed for the Following Reason:**

Start/Resumption of Care
1 - Start of care—further visits planned
2 - Start of care—no further visits planned
3 - Resumption of care (after inpatient stay)

Follow-Up
4 - Recertification (follow-up) reassessment
5 - Other follow-up

Transfer to an Inpatient Facility
□ 6 - Transferred to an inpatient facility—patient not discharged from agency [Go to *M0150*]
□ 7 - Transferred to an inpatient facility—patient discharged from agency [Go to *M0150*]

Discharge from Agency — Not to an Inpatient Facility
8 - Death at home
9 - Discharge from agency
10 - Discharge from agency—no visits completed after start/resumption of care assessment

20. **(M0150) Current Payment Sources for Home Care:** (Mark all that apply.)
□ 0 - None; no charge for current services
□ 1 - Medicare (traditional fee-for-service)
□ 2 - Medicare (HMO/managed care)
□ 3 - Medicaid (traditional fee-for-service)
□ 4 - Medicaid (HMO/managed care)
□ 5 - Workers' compensation
□ 6 - Title programs (e.g., Title III, V or XX)
□ 7 - Other government (e.g., CHAMPUS, VA, etc.)
□ 8 - Private insurance
□ 9 - Private HMO/managed care
□ 10 - Self-pay
□ 11 - Other (specify) _____

OASIS-B1 XFR (08/2000)

TRANSFER TO INPATIENT FACILITY
(Page 2 of 2)

Client's Name:

Client Record No.

B. EMERGENT CARE

1. **(M0830) Emergent Care:** Since the last time OASIS data were collected, has the patient utilized any of the following services for emergent care (other than home care agency services)? **(Mark all that apply.)**
   - ☐ 0 - No emergent care services **[If no emergent care, go to Section C #1 - Inpatient Facility]**
   - ☐ 1 - Hospital emergency room (includes 23-hour holding)
   - ☐ 2 - Doctor's office emergency visit/house call
   - ☐ 3 - Outpatient department/clinic emergency (includes urgicenter sites)
   - ☐ UK - Unknown **[If UK, go to Section C #1 - Inpatient Facility]**

2. **(M0840) Emergent Care Reason:** For what reason(s) did the patient/family seek emergent care? **(Mark all that apply.)**
   - ☐ 1 - Improper medication administration, medication side effects, toxicity, anaphylaxis
   - ☐ 2 - Nausea, dehydration, malnutrition, constipation, impaction
   - ☐ 3 - Injury caused by fall or accident at home
   - ☐ 4 - Respiratory problems (e.g., shortness of breath, respiratory infection, tracheobronchial obstruction)
   - ☐ 5 - Wound infection, deteriorating wound status, new lesion/ulcer
   - ☐ 6 - Cardiac problems (e.g., fluid overload, exacerbation of CHF, chest pain
   - ☐ 7 - Hypo/Hyperglycemia, diabetes out of control
   - ☐ 8 - GI bleeding, obstruction
   - ☐ 9 - Other than above reasons
   - ☐ UK - Reason unknown

C. INPATIENT FACILITY ADMISSION OR DISCHARGE FROM HOME CARE

1. **(M0855)** To which **Inpatient Facility** has the patient been admitted?
   - ☐ 1 - Hospital **[Go to #2 - Hospital Reason]**
   - ☐ 2 - Rehabilitation facility **[Go to #5 - Most Recent Home Visit Date]**
   - ☐ 3 - Nursing home **[Go to #4 - Reason Admitted Nursing Home]**
   - ☐ 4 - Hospice **[Go to #5 - Most Recent Home Visit Date]**

2. **(M0890)** If the patient was admitted to an acute care **Hospital,** for what **Reason** was he/she admitted?
   - ☐ 1 - Hospitalization for emergent (unscheduled) care
   - ☐ 2 - Hospitalization for urgent (scheduled within 24 hours of admission) care
   - ☐ 3 - Hospitalization for elective (scheduled more than 24 hours before admission) care
   - ☐ UK - Unknown

3. **(M0895) Reason for Hospitalization: (Mark all that apply.)**
   - ☐ 1 - Improper medication administration, medication side effects, toxicity, anaphylaxis
   - ☐ 2 - Injury caused by fall or accident at home
   - ☐ 3 - Respiratory problems (SOB, infection, obstruction)
   - ☐ 4 - Wound or tube site infection, deteriorating wound status, new lesion/ulcer
   - ☐ 5 - Hypo/Hyperglycemia, diabetes out of control
   - ☐ 6 - GI bleeding, obstruction
   - ☐ 7 - Exacerbation of CHF, fluid overload, heart failure
   - ☐ 8 - Myocardial infarction, stroke
   - ☐ 9 - Chemotherapy
   - ☐ 10 - Scheduled surgical procedure
   - ☐ 11 - Urinary tract infection
   - ☐ 12 - IV catheter-related infection
   - ☐ 13 - Deep vein thrombosis, pulmonary embolus
   - ☐ 14 - Uncontrolled pain
   - ☐ 15 - Psychotic episode
   - ☐ 16 - Other than above reasons

   Go to #5 - Most Recent Home Visit Date

4. **(M0900)** For what **Reason(s)** was the patient **Admitted** to a **Nursing Home? (Mark all that apply.)**
   - ☐ 1 - Therapy services
   - ☐ 2 - Respite care
   - ☐ 3 - Hospice care
   - ☐ 4 - Permanent placement
   - ☐ 5 - Unsafe for care at home
   - ☐ 6 - Other
   - ☐ UK - Unknown

5. **(M0903) Date of Last (Most Recent) Home Visit:**

   __ __ - __ __ - __ __ __ __
   m m   d d   y y y y

6. **(M0906) Discharge/Transfer/Death Date:** Enter the date of the discharge, transfer, or death (at home) of the patient.

   __ __ - __ __ - __ __ __ __
   m m   d d   y y y y

7. Was the patient **Discharged** from the **Agency?**
   - ☐ No **[If No, STOP here]**
   - ☐ Yes **[If Yes, go to Section D]**

D. SUMMARY OF CARE PROVIDED DURING HOME CARE EPISODE

1. Identified Problem | Interventions | Current Status

2. Overall Status at Discharge:

Copy of Summary to   ☐ Referral Source   ☐ Attending Physician

Date of Assessment: _____   Signature of Assessor: _____

OASIS-B1 XFR (08/2000)

Outcome and Assessment Information Set (OASIS) is the intellectual property of The Center for Health Services and Policy Research © 2000.

DISCHARGE ASSESSMENT	Client's Name:
(Page 1 of 11)	Client Record No.

The *Outcome and Assessment Information Set (OASIS)* is the intellectual property of The Center for Health Services and Policy Research. Copyright ©2000 Used with Permission.

A. DEMOGRAPHIC/GENERAL INFORMATION

1. **(M0010) Agency Medicare Provider Number:**

2. **(M0012) Agency Medicaid Provider Number:**

Branch Identification (Optional, for Agency Use)

3. **(M0014) Branch State:** __ __

4. **(M0016) Branch ID Number:** __ __ __ __ __ __ __ __ __ __
(Agency-assigned)

5. **(M0020) Patient ID Number:** __ __ __ __ __ __ __ __ __ __ __ __ __ __ __ __

6. **(M0030) Start of Care Date:**

m m d d y y y y

7. **(M0032) Resumption of Care Date:**

m m d d y y y y ☐ NA - Not Applicable

8. **(M0040) Patient Name:**

(First) (MI) (Last) (Suffix)

9. **Patient Address:**

Street, Route, Apt. Number - not P.O. Box

10. **Patient Phone:**
(   ) ____ - _____

City **(M0050) State** **(M0060) Zip Code**

11. **(M0063) Medicare Number:**

__ __ __ __ __ __ __ __ __ ☐ NA - No Medicare
(including suffix if any)

12. **(M0064) Social Security Number:**

__ __ __ __ __ __ __ __ __ ☐ UK - Unknown or Not Available

13. **(M0065) Medicaid Number:**

__ __ __ __ __ __ __ __ __ __ __ ☐ NA - No Medicaid

14. **(M0066) Birth Date:**

m m d d y y y y

15. **(M0069) Gender:** ☐ 1 - Male ☐ 2 - Female

16. **(M0072) Primary Referring Physician ID:** __ __ __ __ __ __ __ __ (UPIN#) ☐ UK - Unknown or Not Available

17. **(M0080) Discipline of Person Completing Assessment:**
☐ 1 - RN ☐ 3 - SLP/ST
☐ 2 - PT ☐ 4 - OT

18. **(M0090) Date Assessment Completed:**

m m d d y y y y

19. **(M0100) This Assessment is Currently Being Completed for the Following Reason:**

Start/Resumption of Care
1 - Start of care—further visits planned
2 - Start of care—no further visits planned
3 - Resumption of care (after inpatient stay)

Follow-Up
4 - Recertification (follow-up) reassessment
5 - Other follow-up

Transfer to an Inpatient Facility
☐ 6 - Transferred to an inpatient facility—patient not discharged from agency [Go to *M0150*]
☐ 7 - Transferred to an inpatient facility—patient discharged from agency [Go to *M0150*]
Discharge from Agency — Not to an Inpatient Facility
☐ 8 - Death at home [Go to *M0150*]
☐ 9 - Discharge from agency [Go to *M0150*]
☐ 10 - Discharge from agency—no visits completed after start/resumption of care assessment [Go to *M0150*]

20. **(M0150) Current Payment Sources for Home Care:** (Mark all that apply.)
☐ 0 - None; no charge for current services
☐ 1 - Medicare (traditional fee-for-service)
☐ 2 - Medicare (HMO/managed care)
☐ 3 - Medicaid (traditional fee-for-service)
☐ 4 - Medicaid (HMO/managed care)
☐ 5 - Workers' compensation
☐ 6 - Title programs (e.g., Title III, V or XX)
☐ 7 - Other government (e.g., CHAMPUS, VA, etc.)
☐ 8 - Private insurance
☐ 9 - Private HMO/managed care
☐ 10 - Self-pay
☐ 11 - Other (specify) _____

If reason for assessment (RFA) for M0100 is 6 or 7, go to *M0830*.
If RFA for M0100 is 8 or 10, go to *M0906*.
If RFA for M0100 is 9, go to *M0200*.

21. **(M0200) Medical or Treatment Regimen Change Within Past 14 Days:** Has this patient experienced a change in medical or treatment regimen (e.g., medication, treatment, or service change due to new or additional diagnosis, etc.) within the last 14 days?
☐ 0 - No [If No, go to *Section B - Therapies*]
☐ 1 - Yes

22. **(M0210)** List the patient's **Medical Diagnoses** and ICD code categories (three digits required; five digits optional) for those conditions requiring changed medical or treatment regimen (no surgical or V-codes):

Changed Medical Regimen Diagnosis   ICD
a. _____   (__ __ __ . __ __)
b. _____   (__ __ __ . __ __)
c. _____   (__ __ __ . __ __)
d. _____   (__ __ __ . __ __)

OASIS-B1 DC (08/2000)

DISCHARGE ASSESSMENT
(Page 2 of 11)

Client's Name:

Client Record No.

23. **(M0220) Conditions Prior to Medical or Treatment Regimen Change Within Past 14 Days:** If this patient experienced a change in medical or treatment regimen within the past 14 days, indicate any conditions which existed prior to the change in medical or treatment regimen.
(Mark all that apply.)
- ☐ 1 - Urinary incontinence
- ☐ 2 - Indwelling/suprapubic catheter
- ☐ 3 - Intractable pain
- ☐ 4 - Impaired decision-making
- ☐ 5 - Disruptive or socially inappropriate behavior
- ☐ 6 - Memory loss to the extent that supervision required
- ☐ 7 - None of the above

B. **(M0250) THERAPIES** the patient receives at home: **(Mark all that apply.)**

- ☐ 1 - Intravenous or infusion therapy (excludes TPN)
- ☐ 2 - Parenteral nutrition (TPN or lipids)
- ☐ 3 - Enteral nutrition (nasogastric, gastrostomy, jejunostomy, or any other artificial entry into the alimentary canal)
- ☐ 4 - None of the above

C. PROGNOSIS

(M0280) Life Expectancy: (Physician documentation is not required.)
- ☐ 0 - Life expectancy is greater than 6 months
- ☐ 1 - Life expectancy is 6 months or fewer

D. **(M0290) HIGH RISK FACTORS** characterizing this patient: **(Mark all that apply.)**

- ☐ 1 - Heavy smoking
- ☐ 2 - Obesity
- ☐ 3 - Alcohol dependency
- ☐ 4 - Drug dependency
- ☐ 5 - None of the above

E. LIVING ARRANGEMENTS

1. **(M0300) Current Residence:**
   - ☐ 1 - Patient's owned or rented residence (house, apartment, or mobile home owned or rented by patient/couple/significant other)
   - ☐ 2 - Family member's residence
   - ☐ 3 - Boarding home or rented room
   - ☐ 4 - Board and care or assisted living facility
   - ☐ 5 - Other (specify) _____

2. **(M0310) Structural Barriers** in the patient's environment limiting independent mobility: **(Mark all that apply.)**
   - ☐ 0 - None
   - ☐ 1 - Stairs inside home which must be used by the patient (e.g., to get to toileting, sleeping, eating areas)
   - ☐ 2 - Stairs inside home which are used optionally (e.g., to get to laundry facilities)
   - ☐ 3 - Stairs leading from inside house to outside
   - ☐ 4 - Narrow or obstructed doorways

3. **(M0320) Safety Hazards** found in the patient's current place of residence: **(Mark all that apply.)**
   - ☐ 0 - None
   - ☐ 1 - Inadequate floor, roof, or windows
   - ☐ 2 - Inadequate lighting
   - ☐ 3 - Unsafe gas/electric appliance
   - ☐ 4 - Inadequate heating
   - ☐ 5 - Inadequate cooling
   - ☐ 6 - Lack of fire safety devices
   - ☐ 7 - Unsafe floor coverings
   - ☐ 8 - Inadequate stair railings
   - ☐ 9 - Improperly stored hazardous materials
   - ☐ 10 - Lead-based paint
   - ☐ 11 - Other (specify) _____

4. **(M0330) Sanitation Hazards** found in the patient's current place of residence: **(Mark all that apply.)**
   - ☐ 0 - None
   - ☐ 1 - No running water
   - ☐ 2 - Contaminated water
   - ☐ 3 - No toileting facilities
   - ☐ 4 - Outdoor toileting facilities only
   - ☐ 5 - Inadequate sewage disposal
   - ☐ 6 - Inadequate/improper food storage
   - ☐ 7 - No food refrigeration
   - ☐ 8 - No cooking facilities
   - ☐ 9 - Insects/rodents present
   - ☐ 10 - No scheduled trash pickup
   - ☐ 11 - Cluttered/soiled living area
   - ☐ 12 - Other (specify) _____

5. **(M0340) Patient Lives With: (Mark all that apply.)**
   - ☐ 1 - Lives alone
   - ☐ 2 - With spouse or significant other
   - ☐ 3 - With other family member
   - ☐ 4 - With a friend
   - ☐ 5 - With paid help (other than home care agency staff)
   - ☐ 6 - With other than above

COMMENTS:

OASIS-B1 DC (08/2000)

DISCHARGE ASSESSMENT (Page 3 of 11)	Client's Name: Client Record No.

F. SUPPORTIVE ASSISTANCE

1. Names of Persons/Organizations Providing Assistance:

2. (M0350) Assisting Person(s) Other than Home Care Agency Staff: (Mark all that apply.)
- ☐ 1 - Relatives, friends, or neighbors living outside the home
- ☐ 2 - Person residing in the home (EXCLUDING paid help)
- ☐ 3 - Paid help
- ☐ 4 - None of the above [**If None of the above, go to** *Section G - Review of Systems/Physical Assessment*]

3. (M0360) Primary Caregiver taking <u>lead</u> responsibility for providing or managing the patient's care, providing the most frequent assistance, etc. (other than home care agency staff):
- ☐ 0 - No one person [**If No one person, go to** *Section G - Review of Systems/Physical Assessment*]
- ☐ 1 - Spouse or significant other
- ☐ 2 - Daughter or son
- ☐ 3 - Other family member
- ☐ 4 - Friend or neighbor or community or church member
- ☐ 5 - Paid help

4. (M0370) How Often does the patient receive assistance from the primary caregiver?
- ☐ 1 - Several times during day and night
- ☐ 2 - Several times during day
- ☐ 3 - Once daily
- ☐ 4 - Three or more times per week
- ☐ 5 - One to two times per week
- ☐ 6 - Less often than weekly

5. (M0380) Type of Primary Caregiver Assistance: (Mark all that apply.)
- ☐ 1 - ADL assistance (e.g., bathing, dressing, toileting, bowel/bladder, eating/feeding)
- ☐ 2 - IADL assistance (e.g., meds, meals, housekeeping, laundry, telephone, shopping, finances)
- ☐ 3 - Environmental support (housing, home maintenance)
- ☐ 4 - Psychosocial support (socialization, companionship, recreation)
- ☐ 5 - Advocates or facilitates patient's participation in appropriate medical care
- ☐ 6 - Financial agent, power of attorney, or conservator of finance
- ☐ 7 - Health care agent, conservator of person, or medical power of attorney

G. REVIEW OF SYSTEMS/PHYSICAL ASSESSMENT

1. <u>ORAL</u>:

(M0410) Speech and Oral (Verbal) Expression of Language (in patient's own language):
- ☐ 0 - Expresses complex ideas, feelings, and needs clearly, completely, and easily in all situations with no observable impairment.
- ☐ 1 - Minimal difficulty in expressing ideas and needs (may take extra time; makes occasional errors in word choice, grammar or speech intelligibility; needs minimal prompting or assistance).
- ☐ 2 - Expresses simple ideas or needs with moderate difficulty (needs prompting or assistance, errors in word choice, organization or speech intelligibility). Speaks in phrases or short sentences.
- ☐ 3 - Has severe difficulty expressing basic ideas or needs and requires maximal assistance or guessing by listener. Speech limited to single words or short phrases.
- ☐ 4 - <u>Unable</u> to express basic needs even with maximal prompting or assistance but is not comatose or unresponsive (e.g., speech is nonsensical or unintelligible).
- ☐ 5 - Patient nonresponsive or unable to speak.

2. <u>NEUROLOGICAL</u>:

(M0420) Frequency of Pain interfering with patient's activity or movement:
- ☐ 0 - Patient has no pain or pain does not interfere with activity or movement
- ☐ 1 - Less often than daily
- ☐ 2 - Daily, but not constantly
- ☐ 3 - All of the time

Comments on pain management:

(M0430) Intractable Pain: Is the patient experiencing pain that is <u>not easily relieved</u>, occurs at least daily, and affects the patient's sleep, appetite, physical or emotional energy, concentration, personal relationships, emotions, or ability or desire to perform physical activity?
- ☐ 0 - No
- ☐ 1 - Yes

OASIS-B1 DC (08/2000)

DISCHARGE ASSESSMENT (Page 4 of 11)	Client's Name: Client Record No.

3. **INTEGUMENT**:

a. Skin condition (Record type # on body area. Indicate size to right of numbered category.)

	Type	Size
1.	Lesions	
2.	Bruises	
3.	Masses	
4.	Scars	
5.	Stasis Ulcers	
6.	Pressure Ulcers	
7.	Incisions	
8.	Other (specify) _____	

b. **(M0440)** Does this patient have a **Skin Lesion** or an **Open Wound**? This excludes "OSTOMIES."
   - ☐ 0 - No [If No, go to *Section 4 - Cardiorespiratory*]
   - ☐ 1 - Yes

c. **(M0445)** Does this patient have a **Pressure Ulcer**?
   - ☐ 0 - No [If No, go to #3.*d - Stasis Ulcer*]
   - ☐ 1 - Yes

(M0450) Current Number of Pressure Ulcers at Each Stage: (Circle one response for each stage.)

	Pressure Ulcer Stages	Number of Pressure Ulcers				
a)	Stage 1: Nonblanchable erythema of intact skin; the heralding of skin ulceration. In darker-pigmented skin, warmth, edema, hardness, or discolored skin may be indicators.	0	1	2	3	4 or more
b)	Stage 2: Partial thickness skin loss involving epidermis and/or dermis. The ulcer is superficial and presents clinically as an abrasion, blister, or shallow crater.	0	1	2	3	4 or more
c)	Stage 3: Full-thickness skin loss involving damage or necrosis of subcutaneous tissue which may extend down to, but not through, underlying fascia. The ulcer presents clinically as a deep crater with or without undermining of adjacent tissue.	0	1	2	3	4 or more
d)	Stage 4: Full-thickness skin loss with extensive destruction, tissue necrosis, or damage to muscle, bone, or supporting structures (e.g., tendon, joint capsule, etc.).	0	1	2	3	4 or more
e)	In addition to the above, is there at least one pressure ulcer that cannot be observed due to the presence of eschar or a nonremovable dressing, including casts? ☐ 0 - No ☐ 1 - Yes					

(M0460) Stage of Most Problematic (Observable)
Pressure Ulcer:
- ☐ 1 - Stage 1
- ☐ 2 - Stage 2
- ☐ 3 - Stage 3
- ☐ 4 - Stage 4
- ☐ NA - No observable pressure ulcer

(M0464) Status of Most Problematic (Observable)
Pressure Ulcer:
- ☐ 1 - Fully granulating
- ☐ 2 - Early/partial granulation
- ☐ 3 - Not healing
- ☐ NA - No observable pressure ulcer

OASIS-B1 DC (08/2000)

DISCHARGE ASSESSMENT (Page 5 of 11)	Client's Name:
	Client Record No.

d. **(M0468)** Does this patient have a **Stasis Ulcer?**
- ☐ 0 - No [If No, go to #3.e - *Surgical Wound*]
- ☐ 1 - Yes

   (M0470) Current Number of Observable Stasis Ulcer(s):
   - ☐ 0 - Zero
   - ☐ 1 - One
   - ☐ 2 - Two
   - ☐ 3 - Three
   - ☐ 4 - Four or more

   (M0474) Does this patient have at least one **Stasis Ulcer that Cannot be Observed** due to the presence of a nonremovable dressing?
   - ☐ 0 - No
   - ☐ 1 - Yes

   (M0476) Status of Most Problematic (Observable) Stasis Ulcer:
   - ☐ 1 - Fully granulating
   - ☐ 2 - Early/partial granulation
   - ☐ 3 - Not healing
   - ☐ NA - No observable stasis ulcer

COMMENTS: (Wound/lesion history, treatments, etc.)

e. **(M0482)** Does this patient have a **Surgical Wound?**
- ☐ 0 - No [If No, go to *Section 4 - Cardiorespiratory*]
- ☐ 1 - Yes

   (M0484) Current Number of (Observable) Surgical Wounds: (If a wound is partially closed but has <u>more</u> than one opening, consider each opening as a separate wound.)
   - ☐ 0 - Zero
   - ☐ 1 - One
   - ☐ 2 - Two
   - ☐ 3 - Three
   - ☐ 4 - Four or more

   (M0486) Does this patient have at least one **Surgical Wound that Cannot be Observed** due to the presence of a nonremovable dressing?
   - ☐ 0 - No
   - ☐ 1 - Yes

   (M0488) Status of Most Problematic (Observable) Surgical Wound:
   - ☐ 1 - Fully granulating
   - ☐ 2 - Early/partial granulation
   - ☐ 3 - Not healing
   - ☐ NA - No observable surgical wound

4. **CARDIORESPIRATORY:**

Temperature _____ Respirations _____

BLOOD PRESSURE: Lying _____ Sitting _____ Standing _____

PULSE: Apical rate _____ Radial rate _____ Rhythm _____ Quality _____

(M0490) When is the patient dyspneic or noticeably **Short of Breath?**
- ☐ 0 - Never, patient is not short of breath
- ☐ 1 - When walking more than 20 feet, climbing stairs
- ☐ 2 - With moderate exertion (e.g., while dressing, using commode or bedpan, walking distances less than 20 feet)
- ☐ 3 - With minimal exertion (e.g., while eating, talking, or performing other ADLs) or with agitation
- ☐ 4 - At rest (during day or night)

COMMENTS:

(M0500) Respiratory Treatments utilized at home: **(Mark all that apply.)**
- ☐ 1 - Oxygen (intermittent or continuous)
- ☐ 2 - Ventilator (continually or at night)
- ☐ 3 - Continuous positive airway pressure
- ☐ 4 - None of the above

5. **GENITOURINARY TRACT:**

(M0510) Has this patient been treated for a **Urinary Tract Infection** in the past 14 days?
- ☐ 0 - No
- ☐ 1 - Yes
- ☐ NA - Patient on prophylactic treatment

(M0520) Urinary Incontinence or Urinary Catheter Presence:
- ☐ 0 - No incontinence or catheter (includes anuria or ostomy for urinary drainage) [If No, go to *Section 6 - Gastrointestinal Tract*]
- ☐ 1 - Patient is incontinent
- ☐ 2 - Patient requires a urinary catheter (i.e., external, indwelling, intermittent, suprapubic) [Go to *Section 6 - Gastrointestinal Tract*]

(M0530) When does **Urinary Incontinence** occur?
- ☐ 0 - Timed-voiding defers incontinence
- ☐ 1 - During the night only
- ☐ 2 - During the day and night

OASIS-B1 DC (08/2000)

DISCHARGE ASSESSMENT
(Page 6 of 11)

Client's Name:

Client Record No.

6. **GASTROINTESTINAL TRACT:**

(M0540) Bowel Incontinence Frequency:
- ☐ 0 - Very rarely or never has bowel incontinence
- ☐ 1 - Less than once weekly
- ☐ 2 - One to three times weekly
- ☐ 3 - Four to six times weekly
- ☐ 4 - On a daily basis
- ☐ 5 - More often than once daily
- ☐ NA - Patient has ostomy for bowel elimination

(M0550) Ostomy for Bowel Elimination: Does this patient have an ostomy for bowel elimination that (within the last 14 days) necessitated a change in medical or treatment regimen?
- ☐ 0 - Patient does <u>not</u> have an ostomy for bowel elimination.
- ☐ 1 - Patient's ostomy did <u>not</u> necessitate change in medical or treatment regimen.
- ☐ 2 - The ostomy <u>did</u> necessitate change in medical or treatment regimen.

7. **NEURO/EMOTIONAL/BEHAVIORAL STATUS:**

(M0560) Cognitive Functioning: (Patient's current level of alertness, orientation, comprehension, concentration, and immediate memory for simple commands.)
- ☐ 0 - Alert/oriented, able to focus and shift attention, comprehends and recalls task directions independently.
- ☐ 1 - Requires prompting (cueing, repetition, reminders) only under stressful or unfamiliar conditions.
- ☐ 2 - Requires assistance and some direction in specific situations (e.g., on all tasks involving shifting of attention), or consistently requires low stimulus environment due to distractibility.
- ☐ 3 - Requires considerable assistance in routine situations. Is not alert and oriented or is unable to shift attention and recall directions more than half the time.
- ☐ 4 - Totally dependent due to disturbances such as constant disorientation, coma, persistent vegetative state, or delirium.

(M0570) When Confused (Reported or Observed):
- ☐ 0 - Never
- ☐ 1 - In new or complex situations only
- ☐ 2 - On awakening or at night only
- ☐ 3 - During the day and evening, but not constantly
- ☐ 4 - Constantly
- ☐ NA - Patient nonresponsive

(M0580) When Anxious (Reported or Observed):
- ☐ 0 - None of the time
- ☐ 1 - Less often than daily
- ☐ 2 - Daily, but not constantly
- ☐ 3 - All of the time
- ☐ NA - Patient nonresponsive

(M0590) Depressive Feelings Reported or Observed in Patient: (Mark all that apply.)
- ☐ 1 - Depressed mood (e.g., feeling sad, tearful)
- ☐ 2 - Sense of failure or self reproach
- ☐ 3 - Hopelessness
- ☐ 4 - Recurrent thoughts of death
- ☐ 5 - Thoughts of suicide
- ☐ 6 - None of the above feelings observed or reported

COMMENTS:

(M0600) Patient Behaviors (Reported or Observed): (Mark all that apply.)
- ☐ 1 - Indecisiveness, lack of concentration
- ☐ 2 - Diminished interest in most activities
- ☐ 3 - Sleep disturbances
- ☐ 4 - Recent change in appetite or weight
- ☐ 5 - Agitation
- ☐ 6 - A suicide attempt
- ☐ 7 - None of the above behaviors observed or reported

(M0610) Behaviors Demonstrated <u>at Least Once a Week</u> (Reported or Observed): (Mark all that apply.)
- ☐ 1 - Memory deficit: failure to recognize familiar persons/places, inability to recall events of past 24 hours, significant memory loss so that supervision is required
- ☐ 2 - Impaired decision-making: failure to perform usual ADLs or IADLs, inability to appropriately stop activities, jeopardizes safety through actions
- ☐ 3 - Verbal disruption: yelling, threatening, excessive profanity, sexual references, etc.
- ☐ 4 - Physical aggression: aggressive or combative to self and others (e.g., hits self, throws objects, punches, dangerous maneuvers with wheelchair or other objects)
- ☐ 5 - Disruptive, infantile, or socially inappropriate behavior (excludes verbal actions)
- ☐ 6 - Delusional, hallucinatory, or paranoid behavior
- ☐ 7 - None of the above behaviors demonstrated

(M0620) Frequency of Behavior Problems (Reported or Observed) (e.g., wandering episodes, self abuse, verbal disruption, physical aggression, etc.):
- ☐ 0 - Never
- ☐ 1 - Less than once a month
- ☐ 2 - Once a month
- ☐ 3 - Several times each month
- ☐ 4 - Several times a week
- ☐ 5 - At least daily

(M0630) Is this patient receiving Psychiatric Nursing Services at home provided by a qualified psychiatric nurse?
- ☐ 0 - No
- ☐ 1 - Yes

8. **OTHER UPDATED ASSESSMENTS:**

OASIS-B1 DC (08/2000)

Outcome and Assessment Information Set (OASIS) is the intellectual property of The Center for Health Services and Policy Research © 2000.

| DISCHARGE ASSESSMENT (Page 7 of 11) | Client's Name: |
| | Client Record No. |

H. LIFE SYSTEM PROFILE: For M0640-M0800, record what the patient currently **is** *able to do.*

1. **(M0640) Grooming:** Ability to tend to personal hygiene needs (i.e., washing face and hands, hair care, shaving or make up, teeth or denture care, fingernail care).
   - ☐ 0 - Able to groom self unaided, with or without the use of assistive devices or adapted methods.
   - ☐ 1 - Grooming utensils must be placed within reach before able to complete grooming activities.
   - ☐ 2 - Someone must assist the patient to groom self.
   - ☐ 3 - Patient depends entirely upon someone else for grooming needs.

2. **(M0650) Ability to Dress Upper Body** (with or without dressing aids) including undergarments, pullovers, front-opening shirts and blouses, managing zippers, buttons, and snaps:
   - ☐ 0 - Able to get clothes out of closets and drawers, put them on and remove them from the upper body without assistance.
   - ☐ 1 - Able to dress upper body without assistance if clothing is laid out or handed to the patient.
   - ☐ 2 - Someone must help the patient put on upper body clothing.
   - ☐ 3 - Patient depends entirely upon another person to dress the upper body.

3. **(M0660) Ability to Dress Lower Body** (with or without dressing aids) including undergarments, slacks, socks or nylons, shoes:
   - ☐ 0 - Able to obtain, put on, and remove clothing and shoes without assistance.
   - ☐ 1 - Able to dress lower body without assistance if clothing and shoes are laid out or handed to the patient.
   - ☐ 2 - Someone must help the patient put on undergarments, slacks, socks or nylons, and shoes.
   - ☐ 3 - Patient depends entirely upon another person to dress lower body.

4. **(M0670) Bathing:** Ability to wash entire body. **Excludes** grooming (washing face and hands only).
   - ☐ 0 - Able to bathe self in shower or tub independently.
   - ☐ 1 - With the use of devices, is able to bathe self in shower or tub independently.
   - ☐ 2 - Able to bathe in shower or tub with the assistance of another person:
     - (a) for intermittent supervision or encouragement or reminders, OR
     - (b) to get in and out of the shower or tub, OR
     - (c) for washing difficult to reach areas.
   - ☐ 3 - Participates in bathing self in shower or tub, **but** requires presence of another person throughout the bath for assistance or supervision.
   - ☐ 4 - Unable to use the shower or tub and is bathed in bed or bedside chair.
   - ☐ 5 - Unable to effectively participate in bathing and is totally bathed by another person.

5. **(M0680) Toileting:** Ability to get to and from the toilet or bedside commode.
   - ☐ 0 - Able to get to and from the toilet independently with or without a device.
   - ☐ 1 - When reminded, assisted, or supervised by another person, able to get to and from the toilet.
   - ☐ 2 - Unable to get to and from the toilet but is able to use a bedside commode (with or without assistance).
   - ☐ 3 - Unable to get to and from the toilet or bedside commode but is able to use a bedpan/urinal independently.
   - ☐ 4 - Is totally dependent in toileting.

6. **(M0690) Transferring:** Ability to move from bed to chair, on and off toilet or commode, into and out of tub or shower, and ability to turn and position self in bed if patient is bedfast.
   - ☐ 0 - Able to independently transfer.
   - ☐ 1 - Transfers with minimal human assistance or with use of an assistive device.
   - ☐ 2 - Unable to transfer self but is able to bear weight and pivot during the transfer process.
   - ☐ 3 - Unable to transfer self and is unable to bear weight or pivot when transferred by another person.
   - ☐ 4 - Bedfast, unable to transfer but is able to turn and position self in bed.
   - ☐ 5 - Bedfast, unable to transfer and is unable to turn and position self.

7. **(M0700) Ambulation/Locomotion:** Ability to SAFELY walk, once in a standing position, or use a wheelchair, once in a seated position, on a variety of surfaces.
   - ☐ 0 - Able to independently walk on even and uneven surfaces and climb stairs with or without railings (i.e., needs no human assistance or assistive device).
   - ☐ 1 - Requires use of a device (e.g., cane, walker) to walk alone or requires human supervision or assistance to negotiate stairs or steps or uneven surfaces.
   - ☐ 2 - Able to walk only with the supervision or assistance of another person at all times.
   - ☐ 3 - Chairfast, unable to ambulate but is able to wheel self independently.
   - ☐ 4 - Chairfast, unable to ambulate and is unable to wheel self.
   - ☐ 5 - Bedfast, unable to ambulate or be up in a chair.

8. **(M0710) Feeding or Eating:** Ability to feed self meals and snacks. **Note: This refers only to the process of eating, chewing, and swallowing, not preparing the food to be eaten.**
   - ☐ 0 - Able to independently feed self.
   - ☐ 1 - Able to feed self independently but requires:
     - (a) meal set-up; OR
     - (b) intermittent assistance or supervision from another person; OR
     - (c) a liquid, pureed or ground meat diet.
   - ☐ 2 - Unable to feed self and must be assisted or supervised throughout the meal/snack.
   - ☐ 3 - Able to take in nutrients orally and receives supplemental nutrients through a nasogastric tube or gastrostomy.
   - ☐ 4 - Unable to take in nutrients orally and is fed nutrients through a nasogastric tube or gastrostomy.
   - ☐ 5 - Unable to take in nutrients orally or by tube feeding.

OASIS-B1 DC (08/2000)

Outcome and Assessment Information Set (OASIS) is the intellectual property of The Center for Health Services and Policy Research © 2000.

DISCHARGE ASSESSMENT (Page 8 of 11)	Client's Name:
	Client Record No.

9. **(M0720) Planning and Preparing Light Meals** (e.g., cereal, sandwich) or reheat delivered meals:
   - ☐ 0 - (a) Able to independently plan and prepare all light meals for self or reheat delivered meals; OR
     - (b) Is physically, cognitively, and mentally able to prepare light meals on a regular basis but has not routinely performed light meal preparation in the past (i.e., prior to this home care admission).
   - ☐ 1 - Unable to prepare light meals on a regular basis due to physical, cognitive, or mental limitations.
   - ☐ 2 - Unable to prepare any light meals or reheat any delivered meals.

10. **(M0730) Transportation:** Physical and mental ability to safely use a car, taxi, or public transportation (bus, train, subway).
    - ☐ 0 - Able to independently drive a regular or adapted car; OR uses a regular or handicap-accessible public bus.
    - ☐ 1 - Able to ride in a car only when driven by another person; OR able to use a bus or handicap van only when assisted or accompanied by another person.
    - ☐ 2 - Unable to ride in a car, taxi, bus, or van, and requires transportation by ambulance.

11. **(M0740) Laundry:** Ability to do own laundry -- to carry laundry to and from washing machine, to use washer and dryer, to wash small items by hand.
    - ☐ 0 - (a) Able to independently take care of all laundry tasks; OR
      - (b) Physically, cognitively, and mentally able to do laundry and access facilities, but has not routinely performed laundry tasks in the past (i.e., prior to this home care admission).
    - ☐ 1 - Able to do only light laundry, such as minor hand wash or light washer loads. Due to physical, cognitive, or mental limitations, needs assistance with heavy laundry such as carrying large loads of laundry.
    - ☐ 2 - Unable to do any laundry due to physical limitation or needs continual supervision and assistance due to cognitive or mental limitation.

12. **(M0750) Housekeeping:** Ability to safely and effectively perform light housekeeping and heavier cleaning tasks.
    - ☐ 0 - (a) Able to independently perform all housekeeping tasks; OR
      - (b) Physically, cognitively, and mentally able to perform all housekeeping tasks but has not routinely participated in housekeeping tasks in the past (i.e., prior to this home care admission).
    - ☐ 1 - Able to perform only light housekeeping (e.g., dusting, wiping kitchen counters) tasks independently.
    - ☐ 2 - Able to perform housekeeping tasks with intermittent assistance or supervision from another person.
    - ☐ 3 - Unable to consistently perform any housekeeping tasks unless assisted by another person throughout the process.
    - ☐ 4 - Unable to effectively participate in any housekeeping tasks.

13. **(M0760) Shopping:** Ability to plan for, select, and purchase items in a store and to carry them home or arrange delivery.
    - ☐ 0 - (a) Able to plan for shopping needs and independently perform shopping tasks, including carrying packages; OR
      - (b) Physically, cognitively, and mentally able to take care of shopping, but has not done shopping in the past (i.e., prior to this home care admission).
    - ☐ 1 - Able to go shopping, but needs some assistance:
      - (a) By self is able to do only light shopping and carry small packages, but needs someone to do occasional major shopping; OR
      - (b) Unable to go shopping alone, but can go with someone to assist.
    - ☐ 2 - Unable to go shopping, but is able to identify items needed, place orders, and arrange home delivery.
    - ☐ 3 - Needs someone to do all shopping and errands.

14. **(M0770) Ability to Use Telephone:** Ability to answer the phone, dial numbers, and effectively use the telephone to communicate.
    - ☐ 0 - Able to dial numbers and answer calls appropriately and as desired.
    - ☐ 1 - Able to use a specially adapted telephone (i.e., large numbers on the dial, teletype phone for the deaf) and call essential numbers.
    - ☐ 2 - Able to answer the telephone and carry on a normal conversation but has difficulty with placing calls.
    - ☐ 3 - Able to answer the telephone only some of the time or is able to carry on only a limited conversation.
    - ☐ 4 - Unable to answer the telephone at all but can listen if assisted with equipment.
    - ☐ 5 - Totally unable to use the telephone.
    - ☐ NA - Patient does not have a telephone.

15. **(M0780) Management of Oral Medications:** Patient's ability to prepare and take all prescribed oral medications reliably and safely, including administration of the correct dosage at the appropriate times/intervals. **Excludes injectable and IV medications. (NOTE: This refers to ability, not compliance or willingness.)**
    - ☐ 0 - Able to independently take the correct oral medication(s) and proper dosage(s) at the correct times.
    - ☐ 1 - Able to take medication(s) at the correct times if:
      - (a) individual dosages are prepared in advance by another person; OR
      - (b) given daily reminders; OR
      - (c) someone develops a drug diary or chart.
    - ☐ 2 - Unable to take medication unless administered by someone else.
    - ☐ NA - No oral medications prescribed.

16. **(M0790) Management of Inhalant/Mist Medications:** Patient's ability to prepare and take all prescribed inhalant/mist medications (nebulizers, metered dose devices) reliably and safely, including administration of the correct dosage at the appropriate times/intervals. **Excludes all other forms of medication (oral tablets, injectable and IV medications).**
    - ☐ 0 - Able to independently take the correct medication and proper dosage at the correct times.
    - ☐ 1 - Able to take medication at the correct times if:
      - (a) individual dosages are prepared in advance by another person, OR
      - (b) given daily reminders.
    - ☐ 2 - Unable to take medication unless administered by someone else.
    - ☐ NA - No inhalant/mist medications prescribed.

OASIS-B1 DC (08/2000)

DISCHARGE ASSESSMENT (Page 9 of 11)	Client's Name: Client Record No.

17. **(M0800) Management of Injectable Medications:** <u>Patient's ability</u> to prepare and take <u>all</u> prescribed injectable medications reliably and safely, including administration of correct dosage at the appropriate times/intervals. **Excludes IV medications.**
  - ☐ 0 - Able to independently take the correct medication and proper dosage at the correct times.
  - ☐ 1 - Able to take injectable medication at correct times if:
    - (a) individual syringes are prepared in advance by another person, <u>OR</u>
    - (b) given daily reminders.
  - ☐ 2 - <u>Unable</u> to take injectable medications unless administered by someone else.
  - ☐ NA - No injectable medications prescribed.

18. **(M0810) Patient Management of Equipment (includes <u>ONLY</u> oxygen, IV/infusion therapy, enteral/parenteral nutrition equipment or supplies):** <u>Patient's ability</u> to set up, monitor and change equipment reliably and safely, add appropriate fluids or medication, clean/store/dispose of equipment or supplies using proper technique. **(NOTE: This refers to ability, not compliance or willingness.)**
  - ☐ 0 - Patient manages all tasks related to equipment completely independently.
  - ☐ 1 - If someone else sets up equipment (i.e., fills portable oxygen tank, provides patient with prepared solutions), patient is able to manage all other aspects of equipment.
  - ☐ 2 - Patient requires considerable assistance from another person to manage equipment, but independently completes portions of the task.
  - ☐ 3 - Patient is only able to monitor equipment (e.g., liter flow, fluid in bag) and must call someone else to manage the equipment.
  - ☐ 4 - Patient is completely dependent on someone else to manage all equipment.
  - ☐ NA - No equipment of this type used in care **[If NA, go to Section I - Emergent Care]**

19. **(M0820) Caregiver Management of Equipment (includes <u>ONLY</u> oxygen, IV/infusion equipment, enteral/parenteral nutrition, ventilator therapy equipment or supplies):** <u>Caregiver's ability</u> to set up, monitor and change equipment reliably and safely, add appropriate fluids or medication, clean/store/dispose of equipment or supplies using proper technique. **(NOTE: This refers to ability, not compliance or willingness.)**
  - ☐ 0 - Caregiver manages all tasks related to equipment completely independently.
  - ☐ 1 - If someone else sets up equipment, caregiver is able to manage all other aspects.
  - ☐ 2 - Caregiver requires considerable assistance from another person to manage equipment, but independently completes significant portions of task.
  - ☐ 3 - Caregiver is only able to complete small portions of task (e.g., administer nebulizer treatment, clean/store/dispose of equipment or supplies).
  - ☐ 4 - Caregiver is completely dependent on someone else to manage all equipment.
  - ☐ NA - No caregiver

I.   EMERGENT CARE

1. **(M0830) Emergent Care:** Since the last time OASIS data were collected, has the patient utilized any of the following services for emergent care (other than home care agency services)? **(Mark all that apply.)**
  - ☐ 0 - No emergent care services **[If no emergent care, go to Section J - Inpatient Facility Admission or Discharge]**
  - ☐ 1 - Hospital emergency room (includes 23-hour holding)
  - ☐ 2 - Doctor's office emergency visit/house call
  - ☐ 3 - Outpatient department/clinic emergency (includes urgicenter sites)
  - ☐ UK - Unknown **[If UK, go to Section J - Inpatient Facility Admission or Discharge]**

2. **(M0840) Emergent Care Reason:** For what reason(s) did the patient/family seek emergent care? **(Mark all that apply.)**
  - ☐ 1 - Improper medication administration, medication side effects, toxicity, anaphylaxis
  - ☐ 2 - Nausea, dehydration, malnutrition, constipation, impaction
  - ☐ 3 - Injury caused by fall or accident at home
  - ☐ 4 - Respiratory problems (e.g., shortness of breath, respiratory infection, tracheobronchial obstruction)
  - ☐ 5 - Wound infection, deteriorating wound status, new lesion/ulcer
  - ☐ 6 - Cardiac problems (e.g., fluid overload, exacerbation of CHF, chest pain)
  - ☐ 7 - Hypo/Hyperglycemia, diabetes out of control
  - ☐ 8 - GI bleeding, obstruction
  - ☐ 9 - Other than above reasons
  - ☐ UK - Reason unknown

OASIS-B1 DC (08/2000)

Outcome and Assessment Information Set (OASIS) is the intellectual property of The Center for Health Services and Policy Research © 2000.

DISCHARGE ASSESSMENT (Page 10 of 11)	Client's Name:
	Client Record No.

J. INPATIENT FACILITY ADMISSION OR DISCHARGE FROM HOME CARE

1. **(M0855)** To which **Inpatient Facility** has the patient been admitted? **(Choose only one answer.)**

☐ 1 - Hospital   ☐ 2 - Rehabilitation facility   ☐ 3 - Nursing home   ☐ 4 - Hospice   ☐ **NA** - No inpatient facility admission

2. **(M0890)** If the patient was admitted to an acute care **Hospital**, for what **Reason** was he/she admitted?

☐ 1 - Hospitalization for emergent (unscheduled) care
☐ 2 - Hospitalization for urgent (scheduled within 24 hours of admission) care
☐ 3 - Hospitalization for elective (scheduled more than 24 hours before admission) care
☐ UK - Unknown

(M0895) Reason for Hospitalization: (Mark all that apply.)
☐ 1 - Improper medication administration, medication side effects, toxicity, anaphylaxis
☐ 2 - Injury caused by fall or accident at home
☐ 3 - Respiratory problems (SOB, infection, obstruction)
☐ 4 - Wound or tube site infection, deteriorating wound status, new lesion/ulcer
☐ 5 - Hypo/Hyperglycemia, diabetes out of control
☐ 6 - GI bleeding, obstruction
☐ 7 - Exacerbation of CHF, fluid overload, heart failure
☐ 8 - Myocardial infarction, stroke
☐ 9 - Chemotherapy
☐ 10 - Scheduled surgical procedure
☐ 11 - Urinary tract infection
☐ 12 - IV catheter-related infection
☐ 13 - Deep vein thrombosis, pulmonary embolus
☐ 14 - Uncontrolled pain
☐ 15 - Psychotic episode
☐ 16 - Other than above reasons

[Go to #5 - Most Recent Home Visit Date]

[Go to #5 - Most Recent Home Visit Date]

3. **(M0900)** For what **Reason(s)** was the patient **Admitted to a Nursing Home?** (Mark all that apply.)
☐ 1 - Therapy services
☐ 2 - Respite care
☐ 3 - Hospice care
☐ 4 - Permanent placement
☐ 5 - Unsafe for care at home
☐ 6 - Other
☐ UK - Unknown

[Go to #5 - Most Recent Home Visit Date]

[Go to #5 - Most Recent Home Visit Date]

4. **(M0870) Discharge Disposition:** Where is the patient after discharge from your agency? **(Choose only one answer.)**
☐ 1 - Patient remained in the community (not in hospital, nursing home, or rehab facility) **[Go to next question - Services or Assistance]**
☐ 2 - Patient transferred to a noninstitutional hospice **[Go to #5 - Most Recent Home Visit Date]**
☐ 3 - Unknown because patient moved to a geographic location not served by this agency **[Go to #5 - Most Recent Home Visit Date]**
☐ UK - Other unknown **[Go to #5 - Most Recent Home Visit Date]**

(M0880) After discharge, does the patient receive health, personal, or support **Services or Assistance?** (Mark all that apply.)
☐ 1 - No assistance or services received
☐ 2 - Yes, assistance or services provided by family or friends
☐ 3 - Yes, assistance or services provided by other community resources (e.g., meals-on-wheels, home health services, homemaker assistance, transportation assistance, assisted living, board and care)

[Go to #5 - Most Recent Home Visit Date]

5. **(M0903) Date of Last (Most Recent) Home Visit:**

_ _ - _ _ - _ _ _ _
m m   d d   y y y y

6. **(M0906) Discharge/Transfer/Death Date:** Enter the date of the discharge, transfer, or death (at home) of the patient.

_ _ - _ _ - _ _ _ _
m m   d d   y y y y

OASIS-B1 DC (08/2000)

Outcome and Assessment Information Set (OASIS) is the intellectual property of The Center for Health Services and Policy Research © 2000.

DISCHARGE ASSESSMENT	Client's Name:
(Page 11 of 11)	Client Record No.

K. SUMMARY OF CARE PROVIDED DURING HOME CARE EPISODE

1.

Identified Problem	Interventions	Current Status

2. Overall Status at Discharge:

Date of Assessment: _____   Signature of Assessor: _____

OASIS-B1 DC (08/2000)

DEATH AT HOME (Page 1 of 1)	Client's Name:
	Client Record No.

The *Outcome and Assessment Information Set (OASIS)* is the intellectual property of The Center for Health Services and Policy Research. Copyright ©2000 Used with Permission.

A. DEMOGRAPHIC/GENERAL INFORMATION

1. (M0010) Agency Medicare Provider Number: — — — — —	2. (M0012) Agency Medicaid Provider Number: — — — — — — — — — — — —

Branch Identification (Optional, for Agency Use)

3. (M0014) Branch State: __ __	4. (M0016) Branch ID Number: __ __ __ __ __ __ __ __ __ __ (Agency-assigned)

5. (M0020) Patient ID Number: __ __ __ __ __ __ __ __ __ __ __ __ __ __ __ __ __

6. (M0030) Start of Care Date: — — - — — - — — — — m m d d y y y y	7. (M0032) Resumption of Care Date: — — - — — - — — — — ☐ NA - Not Applicable m m d d y y y y

8. (M0040) Patient Name: (First) (MI) (Last) (Suffix)	9. Patient Address: Street, Route, Apt. Number - not P.O. Box

10. Patient Phone: ( ) ____ - _____	City (M0050) State (M0060) Zip Code

11. (M0063) Medicare Number: — — — — — — — — — — ☐ NA - No Medicare (including suffix if any)	12. (M0064) Social Security Number: — — — — — — — — — ☐ UK - Unknown or Not Available

13. (M0065) Medicaid Number: — — — — — — — — — — — — — — — ☐ NA - No Medicaid	14. (M0066) Birth Date: — — - — — - — — — — m m d d y y y y

15. (M0069) Gender: ☐ 1 - Male ☐ 2 - Female	

16. (M0072) Primary Referring Physician ID: — — — — — — — — — (UPIN#)   ☐ UK - Unknown or Not Available

17. (M0080) Discipline of Person Completing Assessment: ☐ 1 - RN ☐ 3 - SLP/ST ☐ 2 - PT ☐ 4 - OT	18. (M0090) Date Assessment Completed: — — - — — - — — — — m m d d y y y y

19. **(M0100) This Assessment is Currently Being Completed for the Following Reason:**

Start/Resumption of Care	Follow-Up	Transfer to an Inpatient Facility
1 - Start of care—further visits planned	4 - Recertification (follow-up) reassessment	6 - Transferred to an inpatient facility—patient not discharged from agency
2 - Start of care—no further visits planned	5 - Other follow-up	7 - Transferred to an inpatient facility—patient discharged from agency
3 - Resumption of care (after inpatient stay)		**Discharge from Agency — Not to an Inpatient Facility** ☐ 8 - Death at home [Go to *M0150*] 9 - Discharge from agency 10 - Discharge from agency—no visits completed after start/resumption of care assessment

20. (M0150) Current Payment Sources for Home Care: (Mark all that apply.) ☐ 0 - None; no charge for current services ☐ 1 - Medicare (traditional fee-for-service) ☐ 2 - Medicare (HMO/managed care) ☐ 3 - Medicaid (traditional fee-for-service) ☐ 4 - Medicaid (HMO/managed care) ☐ 5 - Workers' compensation ☐ 6 - Title programs (e.g., Title III, V or XX) ☐ 7 - Other government (e.g., CHAMPUS, VA, etc.) ☐ 8 - Private insurance ☐ 9 - Private HMO/managed care ☐ 10 - Self-pay ☐ 11 - Other (specify) _____	21. (M0906) Discharge/Transfer/Death Date: Enter the date of the discharge, transfer, or death (at home) of the patient. — — - — — - — — — — m m d d y y y y

B. SUMMARY OF CARE PROVIDED DURING HOME CARE EPISODE:

Date of Assessment: _____   Signature of Assessor: _____

OASIS-B1 DH (08/2000)

Outcome and Assessment Information Set (OASIS) is the intellectual property of The Center for Health Services and Policy Research © 2000.

Outcome and Assessment Information Set (OASIS-B1)

START OF CARE VERSION
(also used for Resumption of Care Following Inpatient Stay)

Items to be Used at this Time Point --- M0010-M0825

CLINICAL RECORD ITEMS

(M0010) Agency Medicare Provider Number: __ __ __ __ __ __

(M0012) Agency Medicaid Provider Number: __ __ __ __ __ __ __ __ __ __ __ __ __ __

Branch Identification (Optional, for Agency Use)

(M0014) Branch State: __ __

(M0016) Branch ID Number: __ __ __ __ __ __ __ __ __ __
                                              (Agency-assigned)

(M0020) Patient ID Number: __

(M0030) Start of Care Date: __ __ / __ __ / __ __ __ __
                                     month day   year

(M0032) Resumption of Care Date: __ __ / __ __ / __ __ __ __   ☐ NA – Not Applicable
                                          month day   year

(M0040) Patient Name:

__ __ __ __ __ __ __ __ __ __ __ __ __ __ __ __ __ __ __ __ __ __ __ __ __ __   __ __ __
(First)   (MI) (Last)   (Suffix)

(M0050) Patient State of Residence: __ __

(M0060) Patient Zip Code: __ __ __ __ __ __ __ __ __

(M0063) Medicare Number: __ __ __ __ __ __ __ __ __ __ __ __   ☐ NA – No Medicare
                                  (including suffix)

(M0064) Social Security Number: __ __ __ - __ __ - __ __ __ __   ☐ UK – Unknown or Not Available

(M0065) Medicaid Number: __ __ __ __ __ __ __ __ __ __ __ __ __   ☐ NA – No Medicaid

(M0066) Birth Date: __ __ / __ __ / __ __ __ __
                            month day   year

(M0069) Gender:

    ☐ 1 - Male
    ☐ 2 - Female

(M0072) Primary Referring Physician ID:

    __ __ __ __ __ __ __ __ __ __   ☐ UK – Unknown or Not Available

(M0080) **Discipline of Person Completing Assessment:**

         1-RN   2-PT   3-SLP/ST   4-OT

(M0090) **Date Assessment Completed:**   __ __ / __ __ / __ __ __ __
                                       month day   year

(M0100) **This Assessment is Currently Being Completed for the Following Reason:**

    Start/Resumption of Care
      1 – Start of care—further visits planned
      2 – Start of care—no further visits planned
      3 – Resumption of care (after inpatient stay)
    Follow-Up
      4 – Recertification (follow-up) reassessment [Go to *M0150*]
      5 – Other follow-up [Go to *M0150*]
    Transfer to an Inpatient Facility
      6 – Transferred to an inpatient facility—patient not discharged from agency [Go to *M0150*]
      7 – Transferred to an inpatient facility—patient discharged from agency [Go to *M0150*]
    Discharge from Agency — Not to an Inpatient Facility
      8 – Death at home [Go to *M0150*]
      9 – Discharge from agency [Go to *M0150*]
      10 – Discharge from agency—no visits completed after start/resumption of care assessment [Go to *M0150*]

DEMOGRAPHICS AND PATIENT HISTORY

(M0140) **Race/Ethnicity** (as identified by patient): **(Mark all that apply.)**

    1 - American Indian or Alaska Native
    2 - Asian
    3 - Black or African-American
    4 - Hispanic or Latino
    5 - Native Hawaiian or Pacific Islander
    6 - White
  UK - Unknown

(M0150) **Current Payment Sources for Home Care: (Mark all that apply.)**

    0 - None; no charge for current services
    1 - Medicare (traditional fee-for-service)
    2 - Medicare (HMO/managed care)
    3 - Medicaid (traditional fee-for-service)
    4 - Medicaid (HMO/managed care)
    5 - Workers' compensation
    6 - Title programs (e.g., Title III, V, or XX)
    7 - Other government (e.g., CHAMPUS, VA, etc.)
    8 - Private insurance
    9 - Private HMO/managed care
  10 - Self-pay
  11 - Other (specify) _____
  UK - Unknown

(M0160) Financial Factors limiting the ability of the patient/family to meet basic health needs: **(Mark all that apply.)**

- ☐ 0 - None
- ☐ 1 - Unable to afford medicine or medical supplies
- ☐ 2 - Unable to afford medical expenses that are not covered by insurance/Medicare (e.g., copayments)
- ☐ 3 - Unable to afford rent/utility bills
- ☐ 4 - Unable to afford food
- ☐ 5 - Other (specify) _____

(M0175) From which of the following **Inpatient Facilities** was the patient discharged <u>during the past 14 days</u>? **(Mark all that apply.)**

- ☐ 1 - Hospital
- ☐ 2 - Rehabilitation facility
- ☐ 3 - Skilled nursing facility
- ☐ 4 - Other nursing home
- ☐ 5 - Other (specify) _____
- ☐ NA - Patient was not discharged from an inpatient facility **[If NA, go to *M0200*]**

(M0180) Inpatient Discharge Date (most recent):

   __ __ / __ __ / __ __ __ __
   month   day   year

- ☐ UK - Unknown

(M0190) Inpatient Diagnoses and ICD code categories (three digits required; five digits optional) <u>for only those conditions treated during an inpatient facility stay within the last 14 days</u> (no surgical or V-codes):

<u>Inpatient Facility Diagnosis</u>	<u>ICD</u>
a. _____	(__ __ __ . __ __)
b. _____	(__ __ __ . __ __)

(M0200) Medical or Treatment Regimen Change Within Past 14 Days: Has this patient experienced a change in medical or treatment regimen (e.g., medication, treatment, or service change due to new or additional diagnosis, etc.) within the last 14 days?

- ☐ 0 - No **[If No, go to *M0220*]**
- ☐ 1 - Yes

(M0210) List the patient's **Medical Diagnoses** and ICD code categories (three digits required; five digits optional) <u>for those conditions requiring changed medical or treatment regimen</u> (no surgical or V-codes):

<u>Changed Medical Regimen Diagnosis</u>	<u>ICD</u>
a. _____	(__ __ __ . __ __)
b. _____	(__ __ __ . __ __)
c. _____	(__ __ __ . __ __)
d. _____	(__ __ __ . __ __)

(M0220) **Conditions Prior to Medical or Treatment Regimen Change or Inpatient Stay Within Past 14 Days**: If this patient experienced an inpatient facility discharge or change in medical or treatment regimen within the past 14 days, indicate any conditions which existed <u>prior to</u> the inpatient stay or change in medical or treatment regimen. **(Mark all that apply.)**

- ☐ 1 - Urinary incontinence
- ☐ 2 - Indwelling/suprapubic catheter
- ☐ 3 - Intractable pain
- ☐ 4 - Impaired decision-making
- ☐ 5 - Disruptive or socially inappropriate behavior
- ☐ 6 - Memory loss to the extent that supervision required
- ☐ 7 - None of the above
- ☐ NA - No inpatient facility discharge <u>and</u> no change in medical or treatment regimen in past 14 days
- ☐ UK - Unknown

(M0230/M0240) **Diagnoses and Severity Index**: List each medical diagnosis or problem for which the patient is receiving home care and ICD code category (three digits required; five digits optional – no surgical or V-codes) and rate them using the following severity index. (Choose one value that represents the most severe rating appropriate for each diagnosis.)

- 0 - Asymptomatic, no treatment needed at this time
- 1 - Symptoms well controlled with current therapy
- 2 - Symptoms controlled with difficulty, affecting daily functioning; patient needs ongoing monitoring
- 3 - Symptoms poorly controlled, patient needs frequent adjustment in treatment and dose monitoring
- 4 - Symptoms poorly controlled, history of rehospitalizations

(M0230) Primary Diagnosis	ICD	Severity Rating
a. _____	(_ _ _ . _ _)	☐ 0 ☐ 1 ☐ 2 ☐ 3 ☐ 4

(M0240) Other Diagnoses	ICD	Severity Rating
b. _____	(_ _ _ . _ _)	☐ 0 ☐ 1 ☐ 2 ☐ 3 ☐ 4
c. _____	(_ _ _ . _ _)	☐ 0 ☐ 1 ☐ 2 ☐ 3 ☐ 4
d. _____	(_ _ _ . _ _)	☐ 0 ☐ 1 ☐ 2 ☐ 3 ☐ 4
e. _____	(_ _ _ . _ _)	☐ 0 ☐ 1 ☐ 2 ☐ 3 ☐ 4
f. _____	(_ _ _ . _ _)	☐ 0 ☐ 1 ☐ 2 ☐ 3 ☐ 4

(M0250) **Therapies** the patient receives <u>at home</u>: **(Mark all that apply.)**

- ☐ 1 - Intravenous or infusion therapy (excludes TPN)
- ☐ 2 - Parenteral nutrition (TPN or lipids)
- ☐ 3 - Enteral nutrition (nasogastric, gastrostomy, jejunostomy, or any other artificial entry into the alimentary canal)
- ☐ 4 - None of the above

(M0260) **Overall Prognosis:** BEST description of patient's overall prognosis for <u>recovery from this episode of illness</u>.

- ☐ 0 - Poor: little or no recovery is expected and/or further decline is imminent
- ☐ 1 - Good/Fair: partial to full recovery is expected
- ☐ UK - Unknown

(M0270) **Rehabilitative Prognosis:** BEST description of patient's prognosis for <u>functional status</u>.

- ☐ 0 - Guarded: minimal improvement in functional status is expected; decline is possible
- ☐ 1 - Good: marked improvement in functional status is expected
- ☐ UK - Unknown

(M0280) **Life Expectancy:** (Physician documentation is not required.)

☐ 0 - Life expectancy is greater than 6 months
☐ 1 - Life expectancy is 6 months or fewer

(M0290) **High Risk Factors** characterizing this patient: **(Mark all that apply.)**

☐ 1 - Heavy smoking
☐ 2 - Obesity
☐ 3 - Alcohol dependency
☐ 4 - Drug dependency
☐ 5 - None of the above
☐ UK - Unknown

LIVING ARRANGEMENTS

(M0300) **Current Residence:**

☐ 1 - Patient's owned or rented residence (house, apartment, or mobile home owned or rented by patient/couple/significant other)
☐ 2 - Family member's residence
☐ 3 - Boarding home or rented room
☐ 4 - Board and care or assisted living facility
☐ 5 - Other (specify) _____

(M0310) **Structural Barriers** in the patient's environment limiting independent mobility: **(Mark all that apply.)**

☐ 0 - None
☐ 1 - Stairs inside home which <u>must</u> be used by the patient (e.g., to get to toileting, sleeping, eating areas)
☐ 2 - Stairs inside home which are used optionally (e.g., to get to laundry facilities)
☐ 3 - Stairs leading from inside house to outside
☐ 4 - Narrow or obstructed doorways

(M0320) **Safety Hazards** found in the patient's current place of residence: **(Mark all that apply.)**

☐ 0 - None
☐ 1 - Inadequate floor, roof, or windows
☐ 2 - Inadequate lighting
☐ 3 - Unsafe gas/electric appliance
☐ 4 - Inadequate heating
☐ 5 - Inadequate cooling
☐ 6 - Lack of fire safety devices
☐ 7 - Unsafe floor coverings
☐ 8 - Inadequate stair railings
☐ 9 - Improperly stored hazardous materials
☐ 10 - Lead-based paint
☐ 11 - Other (specify) _____

(M0330) Sanitation Hazards found in the patient's current place of residence: **(Mark all that apply.)**

- ☐ 0 - None
- ☐ 1 - No running water
- ☐ 2 - Contaminated water
- ☐ 3 - No toileting facilities
- ☐ 4 - Outdoor toileting facilities only
- ☐ 5 - Inadequate sewage disposal
- ☐ 6 - Inadequate/improper food storage
- ☐ 7 - No food refrigeration
- ☐ 8 - No cooking facilities
- ☐ 9 - Insects/rodents present
- ☐ 10 - No scheduled trash pickup
- ☐ 11 - Cluttered/soiled living area
- ☐ 12 - Other (specify) _____

(M0340) Patient Lives With: (Mark all that apply.)

- ☐ 1 - Lives alone
- ☐ 2 - With spouse or significant other
- ☐ 3 - With other family member
- ☐ 4 - With a friend
- ☐ 5 - With paid help (other than home care agency staff)
- ☐ 6 - With other than above

SUPPORTIVE ASSISTANCE

(M0350) Assisting Person(s) Other than Home Care Agency Staff: (Mark all that apply.)

- ☐ 1 - Relatives, friends, or neighbors living outside the home
- ☐ 2 - Person residing in the home (EXCLUDING paid help)
- ☐ 3 - Paid help
- ☐ 4 - None of the above **[If None of the above, go to *M0390*]**
- ☐ UK - Unknown **[If Unknown, go to *M0390*]**

(M0360) Primary Caregiver taking <u>lead</u> responsibility for providing or managing the patient's care, providing the most frequent assistance, etc. (other than home care agency staff):

- ☐ 0 - No one person **[If No one person, go to *M0390*]**
- ☐ 1 - Spouse or significant other
- ☐ 2 - Daughter or son
- ☐ 3 - Other family member
- ☐ 4 - Friend or neighbor or community or church member
- ☐ 5 - Paid help
- ☐ UK - Unknown **[If Unknown, go to *M0390*]**

(M0370) How Often does the patient receive assistance from the primary caregiver?

- ☐ 1 - Several times during day and night
- ☐ 2 - Several times during day
- ☐ 3 - Once daily
- ☐ 4 - Three or more times per week
- ☐ 5 - One to two times per week
- ☐ 6 - Less often than weekly
- ☐ UK - Unknown

(M0380) Type of Primary Caregiver Assistance: (Mark all that apply.)

- ☐ 1 - ADL assistance (e.g., bathing, dressing, toileting, bowel/bladder, eating/feeding)
- ☐ 2 - IADL assistance (e.g., meds, meals, housekeeping, laundry, telephone, shopping, finances)
- ☐ 3 - Environmental support (housing, home maintenance)
- ☐ 4 - Psychosocial support (socialization, companionship, recreation)
- ☐ 5 - Advocates or facilitates patient's participation in appropriate medical care
- ☐ 6 - Financial agent, power of attorney, or conservator of finance
- ☐ 7 - Health care agent, conservator of person, or medical power of attorney
- ☐ UK - Unknown

SENSORY STATUS

(M0390) Vision with corrective lenses if the patient usually wears them:

- ☐ 0 - Normal vision: sees adequately in most situations; can see medication labels, newsprint.
- ☐ 1 - Partially impaired: cannot see medication labels or newsprint, but <u>can</u> see obstacles in path, and the surrounding layout; can count fingers at arm's length.
- ☐ 2 - Severely impaired: cannot locate objects without hearing or touching them <u>or</u> patient nonresponsive.

(M0400) Hearing and Ability to Understand Spoken Language in patient's own language (with hearing aids if the patient usually uses them):

- ☐ 0 - No observable impairment. Able to hear and understand complex or detailed instructions and extended or abstract conversation.
- ☐ 1 - With minimal difficulty, able to hear and understand most multi-step instructions and ordinary conversation. May need occasional repetition, extra time, or louder voice.
- ☐ 2 - Has moderate difficulty hearing and understanding simple, one-step instructions and brief conversation; needs frequent prompting or assistance.
- ☐ 3 - Has severe difficulty hearing and understanding simple greetings and short comments. Requires multiple repetitions, restatements, demonstrations, additional time.
- ☐ 4 - <u>Unable</u> to hear and understand familiar words or common expressions consistently, <u>or</u> patient nonresponsive.

(M0410) Speech and Oral (Verbal) Expression of Language (in patient's own language):

- ☐ 0 - Expresses complex ideas, feelings, and needs clearly, completely, and easily in all situations with no observable impairment.
- ☐ 1 - Minimal difficulty in expressing ideas and needs (may take extra time; makes occasional errors in word choice, grammar or speech intelligibility; needs minimal prompting or assistance).
- ☐ 2 - Expresses simple ideas or needs with moderate difficulty (needs prompting or assistance, errors in word choice, organization or speech intelligibility). Speaks in phrases or short sentences.
- ☐ 3 - Has severe difficulty expressing basic ideas or needs and requires maximal assistance or guessing by listener. Speech limited to single words or short phrases.
- ☐ 4 - <u>Unable</u> to express basic needs even with maximal prompting or assistance but is not comatose or unresponsive (e.g., speech is nonsensical or unintelligible).
- ☐ 5 - Patient nonresponsive or unable to speak.

(M0420) Frequency of Pain interfering with patient's activity or movement:

- ☐ 0 - Patient has no pain or pain does not interfere with activity or movement
- ☐ 1 - Less often than daily
- ☐ 2 - Daily, but not constantly
- ☐ 3 - All of the time

(M0430) Intractable Pain: Is the patient experiencing pain that is <u>not easily relieved</u>, occurs at least daily, and affects the patient's sleep, appetite, physical or emotional energy, concentration, personal relationships, emotions, or ability or desire to perform physical activity?

☐ 0 - No
☐ 1 - Yes

INTEGUMENTARY STATUS

(M0440) Does this patient have a **Skin Lesion** or an **Open Wound?** This excludes "OSTOMIES."

☐ 0 - No [If No, go to *M0490*]
☐ 1 - Yes

(M0445) Does this patient have a **Pressure Ulcer?**

☐ 0 - No [If No, go to *M0468*]
☐ 1 - Yes

(M0450) Current Number of Pressure Ulcers at Each Stage: (Circle one response for each stage.)

	Pressure Ulcer Stages	Number of Pressure Ulcers				
a)	Stage 1: Nonblanchable erythema of intact skin; the heralding of skin ulceration. In darker-pigmented skin, warmth, edema, hardness, or discolored skin may be indicators.	0	1	2	3	4 or more
b)	Stage 2: Partial thickness skin loss involving epidermis and/or dermis. The ulcer is superficial and presents clinically as an abrasion, blister, or shallow crater.	0	1	2	3	4 or more
c)	Stage 3: Full-thickness skin loss involving damage or necrosis of subcutaneous tissue which may extend down to, but not through, underlying fascia. The ulcer presents clinically as a deep crater with or without undermining of adjacent tissue.	0	1	2	3	4 or more
d)	Stage 4: Full-thickness skin loss with extensive destruction, tissue necrosis, or damage to muscle, bone, or supporting structures (e.g., tendon, joint capsule, etc.)	0	1	2	3	4 or more
e)	In addition to the above, is there at least one pressure ulcer that cannot be observed due to the presence of eschar or a nonremovable dressing, including casts? ☐ 0 - No ☐ 1 - Yes					

(M0460) Stage of Most Problematic (Observable) Pressure Ulcer:

☐ 1 - Stage 1
☐ 2 - Stage 2
☐ 3 - Stage 3
☐ 4 - Stage 4
☐ NA - No observable pressure ulcer

(M0464) Status of Most Problematic (Observable) Pressure Ulcer:

☐ 1 - Fully granulating
☐ 2 - Early/partial granulation
☐ 3 - Not healing
☐ NA - No observable pressure ulcer

© 2000, Center for Health Services and Policy Research, Denver, CO
OASIS-B1 SOC (8/2000)
8

Outcome and Assessment Information Set (OASIS) is the intellectual property of The Center for Health Services and Policy Research © 2000.

(M0468) Does this patient have a **Stasis Ulcer?**

    ☐ 0 - No **[If No, go to *M0482*]**
    ☐ 1 - Yes

    (M0470) **Current Number of Observable Stasis Ulcer(s):**

        ☐ 0 - Zero
        ☐ 1 - One
        ☐ 2 - Two
        ☐ 3 - Three
        ☐ 4 - Four or more

    (M0474) Does this patient have at least one **Stasis Ulcer that Cannot be Observed** due to the presence of a nonremovable dressing?

        ☐ 0 - No
        ☐ 1 - Yes

    (M0476) **Status of Most Problematic (Observable) Stasis Ulcer:**

        ☐ 1 - Fully granulating
        ☐ 2 - Early/partial granulation
        ☐ 3 - Not healing
        ☐ NA - No observable stasis ulcer

(M0482) Does this patient have a **Surgical Wound?**

    ☐ 0 - No **[If No, go to *M0490*]**
    ☐ 1 - Yes

    (M0484) **Current Number of (Observable) Surgical Wounds:** (If a wound is partially closed but has <u>more</u> than one opening, consider each opening as a separate wound.)

        ☐ 0 - Zero
        ☐ 1 - One
        ☐ 2 - Two
        ☐ 3 - Three
        ☐ 4 - Four or more

    (M0486) Does this patient have at least one **Surgical Wound that Cannot be Observed** due to the presence of a nonremovable dressing?

        ☐ 0 - No
        ☐ 1 - Yes

    (M0488) **Status of Most Problematic (Observable) Surgical Wound:**

        ☐ 1 - Fully granulating
        ☐ 2 - Early/partial granulation
        ☐ 3 - Not healing
        ☐ NA - No observable surgical wound

RESPIRATORY STATUS

(M0490) When is the patient dyspneic or noticeably **Short of Breath**?

☐   0 -   Never, patient is not short of breath
☐   1 -   When walking more than 20 feet, climbing stairs
☐   2 -   With moderate exertion (e.g., while dressing, using commode or bedpan, walking distances less than 20 feet)
☐   3 -   With minimal exertion (e.g., while eating, talking, or performing other ADLs) or with agitation
☐   4 -   At rest (during day or night)

(M0500) **Respiratory Treatments** utilized at home: **(Mark all that apply.)**

☐   1 -   Oxygen (intermittent or continuous)
☐   2 -   Ventilator (continually or at night)
☐   3 -   Continuous positive airway pressure
☐   4 -   None of the above

ELIMINATION STATUS

(M0510) Has this patient been treated for a **Urinary Tract Infection** in the past 14 days?

☐   0 -   No
☐   1 -   Yes
☐   NA -   Patient on prophylactic treatment
☐   UK -   Unknown

(M0520) Urinary Incontinence or Urinary Catheter Presence:

☐   0 -   No incontinence or catheter (includes anuria or ostomy for urinary drainage) **[If No, go to M0540]**
☐   1 -   Patient is incontinent
☐   2 -   Patient requires a urinary catheter (i.e., external, indwelling, intermittent, suprapubic) **[Go to M0540]**

(M0530) When does **Urinary Incontinence** occur?

☐   0 -   Timed-voiding defers incontinence
☐   1 -   During the night only
☐   2 -   During the day and night

(M0540) Bowel Incontinence Frequency:

☐   0 -   Very rarely or never has bowel incontinence
☐   1 -   Less than once weekly
☐   2 -   One to three times weekly
☐   3 -   Four to six times weekly
☐   4 -   On a daily basis
☐   5 -   More often than once daily
☐   NA -   Patient has ostomy for bowel elimination
☐   UK -   Unknown

(M0550) Ostomy for Bowel Elimination: Does this patient have an ostomy for bowel elimination that (within the last 14 days): a) was related to an inpatient facility stay, or b) necessitated a change in medical or treatment regimen?

- ☐ 0 - Patient does not have an ostomy for bowel elimination.
- ☐ 1 - Patient's ostomy was not related to an inpatient stay and did not necessitate change in medical or treatment regimen.
- ☐ 2 - The ostomy was related to an inpatient stay or did necessitate change in medical or treatment regimen.

NEURO/EMOTIONAL/BEHAVIORAL STATUS

(M0560) Cognitive Functioning: (Patient's current level of alertness, orientation, comprehension, concentration, and immediate memory for simple commands.)

- ☐ 0 - Alert/oriented, able to focus and shift attention, comprehends and recalls task directions independently.
- ☐ 1 - Requires prompting (cuing, repetition, reminders) only under stressful or unfamiliar conditions.
- ☐ 2 - Requires assistance and some direction in specific situations (e.g., on all tasks involving shifting of attention), or consistently requires low stimulus environment due to distractibility.
- ☐ 3 - Requires considerable assistance in routine situations. Is not alert and oriented or is unable to shift attention and recall directions more than half the time.
- ☐ 4 - Totally dependent due to disturbances such as constant disorientation, coma, persistent vegetative state, or delirium.

(M0570) When Confused (Reported or Observed):

- ☐ 0 - Never
- ☐ 1 - In new or complex situations only
- ☐ 2 - On awakening or at night only
- ☐ 3 - During the day and evening, but not constantly
- ☐ 4 - Constantly
- ☐ NA - Patient nonresponsive

(M0580) When Anxious (Reported or Observed):

- ☐ 0 - None of the time
- ☐ 1 - Less often than daily
- ☐ 2 - Daily, but not constantly
- ☐ 3 - All of the time
- ☐ NA - Patient nonresponsive

(M0590) Depressive Feelings Reported or Observed in Patient: (Mark all that apply.)

- ☐ 1 - Depressed mood (e.g., feeling sad, tearful)
- ☐ 2 - Sense of failure or self reproach
- ☐ 3 - Hopelessness
- ☐ 4 - Recurrent thoughts of death
- ☐ 5 - Thoughts of suicide
- ☐ 6 - None of the above feelings observed or reported

(M0600) Patient Behaviors (Reported or Observed): (Mark all that apply.)

    1 - Indecisiveness, lack of concentration
    2 - Diminished interest in most activities
    3 - Sleep disturbances
    4 - Recent change in appetite or weight
    5 - Agitation
    6 - A suicide attempt
    7 - None of the above behaviors observed or reported

(M0610) Behaviors Demonstrated <u>at Least Once a Week</u> (Reported or Observed): (Mark all that apply.)

    1 - Memory deficit: failure to recognize familiar persons/places, inability to recall events of past 24 hours, significant memory loss so that supervision is required
    2 - Impaired decision-making: failure to perform usual ADLs or IADLs, inability to appropriately stop activities, jeopardizes safety through actions
    3 - Verbal disruption: yelling, threatening, excessive profanity, sexual references, etc.
    4 - Physical aggression: aggressive or combative to self and others (e.g., hits self, throws objects, punches, dangerous maneuvers with wheelchair or other objects)
    5 - Disruptive, infantile, or socially inappropriate behavior (**excludes** verbal actions)
    6 - Delusional, hallucinatory, or paranoid behavior
    7 - None of the above behaviors demonstrated

(M0620) Frequency of Behavior Problems (Reported or Observed) (e.g., wandering episodes, self abuse, verbal disruption, physical aggression, etc.):

    0 - Never
    1 - Less than once a month
    2 - Once a month
    3 - Several times each month
    4 - Several times a week
    5 - At least daily

(M0630) Is this patient receiving **Psychiatric Nursing Services** at home provided by a qualified psychiatric nurse?

    0 - No
    1 - Yes

ADL/IADLs

> For M0640-M0800, complete the "Current" column for all patients. For these same items, complete the "Prior" column only at start of care and at resumption of care; mark the level that corresponds to the patient's condition 14 days prior to start of care date (M0030) or resumption of care date (M0032). In all cases, record what the patient is *able to do.*

(M0640) Grooming: Ability to tend to personal hygiene needs (i.e., washing face and hands, hair care, shaving or make up, teeth or denture care, fingernail care).

Prior   Current

    0 - Able to groom self unaided, with or without the use of assistive devices or adapted methods.
    1 - Grooming utensils must be placed within reach before able to complete grooming activities.
    2 - Someone must assist the patient to groom self.
    3 - Patient depends entirely upon someone else for grooming needs.
    UK - Unknown

(M0650) Ability to Dress Upper Body (with or without dressing aids) including undergarments, pullovers, front-opening shirts and blouses, managing zippers, buttons, and snaps:

Prior Current

☐   ☐   0 -   Able to get clothes out of closets and drawers, put them on and remove them from the upper body without assistance.

☐   ☐   1 -   Able to dress upper body without assistance if clothing is laid out or handed to the patient.

☐   ☐   2 -   Someone must help the patient put on upper body clothing.

☐   ☐   3 -   Patient depends entirely upon another person to dress the upper body.

☐   UK -   Unknown

(M0660) Ability to Dress Lower Body (with or without dressing aids) including undergarments, slacks, socks or nylons, shoes:

Prior Current

☐   ☐   0 -   Able to obtain, put on, and remove clothing and shoes without assistance.

☐   ☐   1 -   Able to dress lower body without assistance if clothing and shoes are laid out or handed to the patient.

☐   ☐   2 -   Someone must help the patient put on undergarments, slacks, socks or nylons, and shoes.

☐   ☐   3 -   Patient depends entirely upon another person to dress lower body.

☐   UK -   Unknown

(M0670) Bathing: Ability to wash entire body. **Excludes grooming (washing face and hands only).**

Prior Current

☐   ☐   0 -   Able to bathe self in shower or tub independently.

☐   ☐   1 -   With the use of devices, is able to bathe self in shower or tub independently.

☐   ☐   2 -   Able to bathe in shower or tub with the assistance of another person:
(a) for intermittent supervision or encouragement or reminders, OR
(b) to get in and out of the shower or tub, OR
(c) for washing difficult to reach areas.

☐   ☐   3 -   Participates in bathing self in shower or tub, but requires presence of another person throughout the bath for assistance or supervision.

☐   ☐   4 -   Unable to use the shower or tub and is bathed in bed or bedside chair.

☐   ☐   5 -   Unable to effectively participate in bathing and is totally bathed by another person.

☐   UK -   Unknown

(M0680) Toileting: Ability to get to and from the toilet or bedside commode.

Prior Current

☐   ☐   0 -   Able to get to and from the toilet independently with or without a device.

☐   ☐   1 -   When reminded, assisted, or supervised by another person, able to get to and from the toilet.

☐   ☐   2 -   Unable to get to and from the toilet but is able to use a bedside commode (with or without assistance).

☐   ☐   3 -   Unable to get to and from the toilet or bedside commode but is able to use a bedpan/urinal independently.

☐   ☐   4 -   Is totally dependent in toileting.

☐   UK -   Unknown

(M0690) Transferring: Ability to move from bed to chair, on and off toilet or commode, into and out of tub or shower, and ability to turn and position self in bed if patient is bedfast.

Prior Current

☐   ☐   0 -   Able to independently transfer.

☐   ☐   1 -   Transfers with minimal human assistance or with use of an assistive device.

☐   ☐   2 -   Unable to transfer self but is able to bear weight and pivot during the transfer process.

☐   ☐   3 -   Unable to transfer self and is unable to bear weight or pivot when transferred by another person.

☐   ☐   4 -   Bedfast, unable to transfer but is able to turn and position self in bed.

☐   ☐   5 -   Bedfast, unable to transfer and is unable to turn and position self.

☐   UK -   Unknown

© 2000, Center for Health Services and Policy Research, Denver, CO
OASIS-B1 SOC (8/2000)
13

(M0700) Ambulation/Locomotion: Ability to <u>SAFELY</u> walk, once in a standing position, or use a wheelchair, once in a seated position, on a variety of surfaces.

<u>Prior</u> <u>Current</u>

☐ ☐ 0 - Able to independently walk on even and uneven surfaces and climb stairs with or without railings (i.e., needs no human assistance or assistive device).

☐ ☐ 1 - Requires use of a device (e.g., cane, walker) to walk alone <u>or</u> requires human supervision or assistance to negotiate stairs or steps or uneven surfaces.

☐ ☐ 2 - Able to walk only with the supervision or assistance of another person at all times.

☐ ☐ 3 - Chairfast, <u>unable</u> to ambulate but is able to wheel self independently.

☐ ☐ 4 - Chairfast, unable to ambulate and is <u>unable</u> to wheel self.

☐ ☐ 5 - Bedfast, unable to ambulate or be up in a chair.

☐   UK - Unknown

(M0710) Feeding or Eating: Ability to feed self meals and snacks. **Note: This refers only to the process of <u>eating, chewing,</u> and <u>swallowing, not preparing</u> the food to be eaten.**

<u>Prior</u> <u>Current</u>

☐ ☐ 0 - Able to independently feed self.

☐ ☐ 1 - Able to feed self independently but requires:
(a) meal set-up; <u>OR</u>
(b) intermittent assistance or supervision from another person; <u>OR</u>
(c) a liquid, pureed or ground meat diet.

☐ ☐ 2 - <u>Unable</u> to feed self and must be assisted or supervised throughout the meal/snack.

☐ ☐ 3 - Able to take in nutrients orally <u>and</u> receives supplemental nutrients through a nasogastric tube or gastrostomy.

☐ ☐ 4 - <u>Unable</u> to take in nutrients orally and is fed nutrients through a nasogastric tube or gastrostomy.

☐ ☐ 5 - Unable to take in nutrients orally or by tube feeding.

☐   UK - Unknown

(M0720) Planning and Preparing Light Meals (e.g., cereal, sandwich) or reheat delivered meals:

<u>Prior</u> <u>Current</u>

☐ ☐ 0 - (a) Able to independently plan and prepare all light meals for self or reheat delivered meals; <u>OR</u>
(b) Is physically, cognitively, and mentally able to prepare light meals on a regular basis but has not routinely performed light meal preparation in the past (i.e., prior to this home care admission).

☐ ☐ 1 - <u>Unable</u> to prepare light meals on a regular basis due to physical, cognitive, or mental limitations.

☐ ☐ 2 - Unable to prepare any light meals or reheat any delivered meals.

☐   UK - Unknown

(M0730) Transportation: Physical and mental ability to <u>safely</u> use a car, taxi, or public transportation (bus, train, subway).

<u>Prior</u> <u>Current</u>

☐ ☐ 0 - Able to independently drive a regular or adapted car; <u>OR</u> uses a regular or handicap-accessible public bus.

☐ ☐ 1 - Able to ride in a car only when driven by another person; <u>OR</u> able to use a bus or handicap van only when assisted or accompanied by another person.

☐ ☐ 2 - <u>Unable</u> to ride in a car, taxi, bus, or van, and requires transportation by ambulance.

☐   UK - Unknown

(M0740) Laundry: Ability to do own laundry -- to carry laundry to and from washing machine, to use washer and dryer, to wash small items by hand.

Prior Current

☐ ☐ 0 - (a) Able to independently take care of all laundry tasks; OR
(b) Physically, cognitively, and mentally able to do laundry and access facilities, but has not routinely performed laundry tasks in the past (i.e., prior to this home care admission).

☐ ☐ 1 - Able to do only light laundry, such as minor hand wash or light washer loads. Due to physical, cognitive, or mental limitations, needs assistance with heavy laundry such as carrying large loads of laundry.

☐ ☐ 2 - Unable to do any laundry due to physical limitation or needs continual supervision and assistance due to cognitive or mental limitation.

☐ UK - Unknown

(M0750) Housekeeping: Ability to safely and effectively perform light housekeeping and heavier cleaning tasks.

Prior Current

☐ ☐ 0 - (a) Able to independently perform all housekeeping tasks; OR
(b) Physically, cognitively, and mentally able to perform all housekeeping tasks but has not routinely participated in housekeeping tasks in the past (i.e., prior to this home care admission).

☐ ☐ 1 - Able to perform only light housekeeping (e.g., dusting, wiping kitchen counters) tasks independently.

☐ ☐ 2 - Able to perform housekeeping tasks with intermittent assistance or supervision from another person.

☐ ☐ 3 - Unable to consistently perform any housekeeping tasks unless assisted by another person throughout the process.

☐ ☐ 4 - Unable to effectively participate in any housekeeping tasks.

☐ UK - Unknown

(M0760) Shopping: Ability to plan for, select, and purchase items in a store and to carry them home or arrange delivery.

Prior Current

☐ ☐ 0 - (a) Able to plan for shopping needs and independently perform shopping tasks, including carrying packages; OR
(b) Physically, cognitively, and mentally able to take care of shopping, but has not done shopping in the past (i.e., prior to this home care admission).

☐ ☐ 1 - Able to go shopping, but needs some assistance:
(a) By self is able to do only light shopping and carry small packages, but needs someone to do occasional major shopping; OR
(b) Unable to go shopping alone, but can go with someone to assist.

☐ ☐ 2 - Unable to go shopping, but is able to identify items needed, place orders, and arrange home delivery.

☐ ☐ 3 - Needs someone to do all shopping and errands.

☐ UK - Unknown

(M0770) Ability to Use Telephone: Ability to answer the phone, dial numbers, and <u>effectively</u> use the telephone to communicate.

Prior Current

☐ ☐ 0 - Able to dial numbers and answer calls appropriately and as desired.

☐ ☐ 1 - Able to use a specially adapted telephone (i.e., large numbers on the dial, teletype phone for the deaf) and call essential numbers.

☐ ☐ 2 - Able to answer the telephone and carry on à normal conversation but has difficulty with placing calls.

☐ ☐ 3 - Able to answer the telephone only some of the time or is able to carry on only a limited conversation.

☐ ☐ 4 - <u>Unable</u> to answer the telephone at all but can listen if assisted with equipment.

☐ ☐ 5 - Totally unable to use the telephone.

☐ ☐ NA - Patient does not have a telephone.

☐   UK - Unknown

MEDICATIONS

(M0780) Management of Oral Medications: <u>Patient's ability</u> to prepare and take <u>all</u> prescribed oral medications reliably and safely, including administration of the correct dosage at the appropriate times/intervals. <u>**Excludes**</u> **injectable and IV medications. (NOTE: This refers to ability, not compliance or willingness.)**

Prior Current

☐ ☐ 0 - Able to independently take the correct oral medication(s) and proper dosage(s) at the correct times.

☐ ☐ 1 - Able to take medication(s) at the correct times if:
   (a) individual dosages are prepared in advance by another person; <u>OR</u>
   (b) given daily reminders; <u>OR</u>
   (c) someone develops a drug diary or chart.

☐ ☐ 2 - <u>Unable</u> to take medication unless administered by someone else.

☐ ☐ NA - No oral medications prescribed.

☐   UK - Unknown

(M0790) Management of Inhalant/Mist Medications: <u>Patient's ability</u> to prepare and take <u>all</u> prescribed inhalant/mist medications (nebulizers, metered dose devices) reliably and safely, including administration of the correct dosage at the appropriate times/intervals. <u>**Excludes**</u> **all other forms of medication (oral tablets, injectable and IV medications).**

Prior Current

☐ ☐ 0 - Able to independently take the correct medication and proper dosage at the correct times.

☐ ☐ 1 - Able to take medication at the correct times if:
   (a) individual dosages are prepared in advance by another person, <u>OR</u>
   (b) given daily reminders.

☐ ☐ 2 - <u>Unable</u> to take medication unless administered by someone else.

☐ ☐ NA - No inhalant/mist medications prescribed.

☐   UK - Unknown

(M0800) **Management of Injectable Medications:** <u>Patient's ability</u> to prepare and take <u>all</u> prescribed injectable medications reliably and safely, including administration of correct dosage at the appropriate times/intervals. **<u>Excludes</u> IV medications.**

Prior   Current

☐   ☐   0 -   Able to independently take the correct medication and proper dosage at the correct times.

☐   ☐   1 -   Able to take injectable medication at correct times if:
> (a) individual syringes are prepared in advance by another person, <u>OR</u>
> (b) given daily reminders.

☐   ☐   2 -   <u>Unable</u> to take injectable medications unless administered by someone else.

☐   ☐   NA -   No injectable medications prescribed.

☐   UK -   Unknown

EQUIPMENT MANAGEMENT

(M0810) **Patient Management of Equipment (Includes <u>ONLY</u> oxygen, IV/infusion therapy, enteral/parenteral nutrition equipment or supplies):** <u>Patient's ability</u> to set up, monitor and change equipment reliably and safely, add appropriate fluids or medication, clean/store/dispose of equipment or supplies using proper technique. **(NOTE: This refers to ability, not compliance or willingness.)**

☐   0 -   Patient manages all tasks related to equipment completely independently.

☐   1 -   If someone else sets up equipment (i.e., fills portable oxygen tank, provides patient with prepared solutions), patient is able to manage all other aspects of equipment.

☐   2 -   Patient requires considerable assistance from another person to manage equipment, but independently completes portions of the task.

☐   3 -   Patient is only able to monitor equipment (e.g., liter flow, fluid in bag) and must call someone else to manage the equipment.

☐   4 -   Patient is completely dependent on someone else to manage all equipment.

☐   NA -   No equipment of this type used in care **[If NA, go to *M0825*]**

(M0820) **Caregiver Management of Equipment (includes <u>ONLY</u> oxygen, IV/infusion equipment, enteral/parenteral nutrition, ventilator therapy equipment or supplies):** <u>Caregiver's ability</u> to set up, monitor, and change equipment reliably and safely, add appropriate fluids or medication, clean/store/dispose of equipment or supplies using proper technique. **(NOTE: This refers to ability, not compliance or willingness.)**

☐   0 -   Caregiver manages all tasks related to equipment completely independently.

☐   1 -   If someone else sets up equipment, caregiver is able to manage all other aspects.

☐   2 -   Caregiver requires considerable assistance from another person to manage equipment, but independently completes significant portions of task.

☐   3 -   Caregiver is only able to complete small portions of task (e.g., administer nebulizer treatment, clean/store/dispose of equipment or supplies).

☐   4 -   Caregiver is completely dependent on someone else to manage all equipment.

☐   NA -   No caregiver

☐   UK -   Unknown

THERAPY NEED

(M0825) **Therapy Need:** Does the care plan of the Medicare payment period for which this assessment will define a case mix group indicate a need for therapy (physical, occupational, or speech therapy) that meets the threshold for a Medicare high-therapy case mix group?

☐   0 -   No

☐   1 -   Yes

☐   NA -   Not applicable

Outcome and Assessment Information Set (OASIS-B1)

DISCHARGE VERSION

(also used for Transfer to an Inpatient Facility or Patient Death at Home)

Items to be Used at Specific Time Points

Transfer to an Inpatient Facility ———————————————— M0010-M0100, M0150, M0830-M0855, M0890-M0906

    Transferred to an inpatient facility—patient not discharged from an agency
    Transferred to an inpatient facility—patient discharged from agency

Discharge from Agency — Not to an Inpatient Facility

    Death at home ———————————————————— M0010-M0100, M0150, M0906
    Discharge from agency ————————————————— M0010-M0100, M0150, M0200-M0220, M0250,
                                           M0280-M0380, M0410-M0820, M0830-M0880,
                                           M0903-M0906

    Discharge from agency—no visits completed
      after start/resumption of care assessment ——————— M0010-M0100, M0150, M0906

CLINICAL RECORD ITEMS

(M0010) Agency Medicare Provider Number: __ __ __ __ __ __

(M0012) Agency Medicaid Provider Number: __ __ __ __ __ __ __ __ __ __ __ __ __ __

> **Branch Identification** (Optional, for Agency Use)
>
> **(M0014) Branch State:** __ __
>
> **(M0016) Branch ID Number:** __ __ __ __ __ __ __ __ __ __
>   (Agency-assigned)

(M0020) Patient ID Number: __ __ __ __ __ __ __ __ __ __ __ __ __ __ __ __ __ __ __

(M0030) Start of Care Date: __ __ / __ __ / __ __ __ __
                            month day   year

(M0032) Resumption of Care Date: __ __ / __ __ / __ __ __ __   ☐ **NA – Not Applicable**
                                      month day   year

(M0040) Patient Name:

__ __ __ __ __ __ __ __ __ __ __ __   __ __ __ __ __ __ __ __ __ __ __ __ __ __ __ __ __ __ __   __ __ __
(First)   (MI) (Last)   (Suffix)

(M0050) Patient State of Residence: __ __

(M0060) Patient Zip Code: __ __ __ __ __ __ __ __ __

(M0063) Medicare Number: __ __ __ __ __ __ . __ __ __ __ __   ☐ **NA – No Medicare**
                             (including suffix)

(M0064) Social Security Number: __ __ __ - __ __ - __ __ __ __   ☐ **UK – Unknown or Not Available**

(M0065) Medicaid Number: __ __ __ __ __ __ __ __ __ __ __ __ __   ☐ **NA – No Medicaid**

(M0066) Birth Date: __ __ / __ __ / __ __ __ __
                   month day   year

(M0069) Gender:

    1 - Male
    2 - Female

(M0072) Primary Referring Physician ID:

    — — — — — — — —   **UK – Unknown or Not Available**

(M0080) Discipline of Person Completing Assessment:

    1-RN   2-PT   3-SLP/ST   4-OT

(M0090) Date Assessment Completed: __ __ / __ __ / __ __ __ __
                                            month day   year

(M0100) This Assessment is Currently Being Completed for the Following Reason:

Start/Resumption of Care
    1 – Start of care—further visits planned
    2 – Start of care—no further visits planned
    3 – Resumption of care (after inpatient stay)
Follow-Up
    4 – Recertification (follow-up) reassessment [Go to *M0150*]
    5 – Other follow-up [Go to *M0150*]

Transfer to an Inpatient Facility
    6 – Transferred to an inpatient facility—patient not discharged from agency [Go to *M0150*]
    7 – Transferred to an inpatient facility—patient discharged from agency [Go to *M0150*]
Discharge from Agency — Not to an Inpatient Facility
    8 – Death at home [Go to *M0150*]
    9 – Discharge from agency [Go to *M0150*]
    10 – Discharge from agency—no visits completed after start/resumption of care assessment [Go to *M0150*]

DEMOGRAPHICS AND PATIENT HISTORY

(M0150) Current Payment Sources for Home Care: (Mark all that apply.)

    0 - None; no charge for current services
    1 - Medicare (traditional fee-for-service)
    2 - Medicare (HMO/managed care)
    3 - Medicaid (traditional fee-for-service)
    4 - Medicaid (HMO/managed care)
    5 - Workers' compensation
    6 - Title programs (e.g., Title III, V, or XX)
    7 - Other government (e.g., CHAMPUS, VA, etc.)
    8 - Private insurance
    9 - Private HMO/managed care
    10 - Self-pay
    11 - Other (specify) _____

> If reason for assessment (RFA) for M0100 is 6 or 7, go to *M0830*.
> If RFA for M0100 is 8 or 10, go to *M0906*.
> If RFA for M0100 is 9, go to *M0200*.

(M0200) Medical or Treatment Regimen Change Within Past 14 Days: Has this patient experienced a change in medical or treatment regimen (e.g., medication, treatment, or service change due to new or additional diagnosis, etc.) within the last 14 days?

☐ 0 - No [If No, go to *M0250*]
☐ 1 - Yes

(M0210) List the patient's **Medical Diagnoses** and ICD code categories (three digits required; five digits optional) <u>for those conditions requiring changed medical or treatment regimen</u> (no surgical or V-codes):

Changed Medical Regimen Diagnosis	ICD
a. _____	(__ __ __ . __ __)
b. _____	(__ __ __ . __ __)
c. _____	(__ __ __ . __ __)
d. _____	(__ __ __ . __ __)

(M0220) Conditions Prior to Medical or Treatment Regimen Change Within Past 14 Days: If this patient experienced a change in medical or treatment regimen within the past 14 days, indicate any conditions which existed <u>prior to</u> the change in medical or treatment regimen. **(Mark all that apply.)**

☐ 1 - Urinary incontinence
☐ 2 - Indwelling/suprapubic catheter
☐ 3 - Intractable pain
☐ 4 - Impaired decision-making
☐ 5 - Disruptive or socially inappropriate behavior
☐ 6 - Memory loss to the extent that supervision required
☐ 7 - None of the above

(M0250) Therapies the patient receives <u>at home</u>: **(Mark all that apply.)**

☐ 1 - Intravenous or infusion therapy (excludes TPN)
☐ 2 - Parenteral nutrition (TPN or lipids)
☐ 3 - Enteral nutrition (nasogastric, gastrostomy, jejunostomy, or any other artificial entry into the alimentary canal)
☐ 4 - None of the above

(M0280) Life Expectancy: (Physician documentation is not required.)

☐ 0 - Life expectancy is greater than 6 months
☐ 1 - Life expectancy is 6 months or fewer

(M0290) High Risk Factors characterizing this patient: **(Mark all that apply.)**

☐ 1 - Heavy smoking
☐ 2 - Obesity
☐ 3 - Alcohol dependency
☐ 4 - Drug dependency
☐ 5 - None of the above

LIVING ARRANGEMENTS

(M0300) Current Residence:

- ☐ 1 - Patient's owned or rented residence (house, apartment, or mobile home owned or rented by patient/couple/significant other)
- ☐ 2 - Family member's residence
- ☐ 3 - Boarding home or rented room
- ☐ 4 - Board and care or assisted living facility
- ☐ 5 - Other (specify) _____

(M0310) Structural Barriers in the patient's environment limiting independent mobility: **(Mark all that apply.)**

- ☐ 0 - None
- ☐ 1 - Stairs inside home which <u>must</u> be used by the patient (e.g., to get to toileting, sleeping, eating areas)
- ☐ 2 - Stairs inside home which are used optionally (e.g., to get to laundry facilities)
- ☐ 3 - Stairs leading from inside house to outside
- ☐ 4 - Narrow or obstructed doorways

(M0320) Safety Hazards found in the patient's current place of residence: **(Mark all that apply.)**

- ☐ 0 - None
- ☐ 1 - Inadequate floor, roof, or windows
- ☐ 2 - Inadequate lighting
- ☐ 3 - Unsafe gas/electric appliance
- ☐ 4 - Inadequate heating
- ☐ 5 - Inadequate cooling
- ☐ 6 - Lack of fire safety devices
- ☐ 7 - Unsafe floor coverings
- ☐ 8 - Inadequate stair railings
- ☐ 9 - Improperly stored hazardous materials
- ☐ 10 - Lead-based paint
- ☐ 11 - Other (specify) _____

(M0330) Sanitation Hazards found in the patient's current place of residence: **(Mark all that apply.)**

- ☐ 0 - None
- ☐ 1 - No running water
- ☐ 2 - Contaminated water
- ☐ 3 - No toileting facilities
- ☐ 4 - Outdoor toileting facilities only
- ☐ 5 - Inadequate sewage disposal
- ☐ 6 - Inadequate/improper food storage
- ☐ 7 - No food refrigeration
- ☐ 8 - No cooking facilities
- ☐ 9 - Insects/rodents present
- ☐ 10 - No scheduled trash pickup
- ☐ 11 - Cluttered/soiled living area
- ☐ 12 - Other (specify) _____

(M0340) Patient Lives With: (Mark all that apply.)

☐ 1 - Lives alone
☐ 2 - With spouse or significant other
☐ 3 - With other family member
☐ 4 - With a friend
☐ 5 - With paid help (other than home care agency staff)
☐ 6 - With other than above

SUPPORTIVE ASSISTANCE

(M0350) Assisting Person(s) Other than Home Care Agency Staff: (Mark all that apply.)

☐ 1 - Relatives, friends, or neighbors living outside the home
☐ 2 - Person residing in the home (EXCLUDING paid help)
☐ 3 - Paid help
☐ 4 - None of the above [If None of the above, go to *M0410*]

(M0360) Primary Caregiver taking lead responsibility for providing or managing the patient's care, providing the most frequent assistance, etc. (other than home care agency staff):

☐ 0 - No one person [If No one person, go to *M0410*]
☐ 1 - Spouse or significant other
☐ 2 - Daughter or son
☐ 3 - Other family member
☐ 4 - Friend or neighbor or community or church member
☐ 5 - Paid help

(M0370) How Often does the patient receive assistance from the primary caregiver?

☐ 1 - Several times during day and night
☐ 2 - Several times during day
☐ 3 - Once daily
☐ 4 - Three or more times per week
☐ 5 - One to two times per week
☐ 6 - Less often than weekly

(M0380) Type of Primary Caregiver Assistance: (Mark all that apply.)

☐ 1 - ADL assistance (e.g., bathing, dressing, toileting, bowel/bladder, eating/feeding)
☐ 2 - IADL assistance (e.g., meds, meals, housekeeping, laundry, telephone, shopping, finances)
☐ 3 - Environmental support (housing, home maintenance)
☐ 4 - Psychosocial support (socialization, companionship, recreation)
☐ 5 - Advocates or facilitates patient's participation in appropriate medical care
☐ 6 - Financial agent, power of attorney, or conservator of finance
☐ 7 - Health care agent, conservator of person, or medical power of attorney

SENSORY STATUS

(M0410) **Speech and Oral (Verbal) Expression of Language** (in patient's own language):

☐   0 -   Expresses complex ideas, feelings, and needs clearly, completely, and easily in all situations with no observable impairment.

☐   1 -   Minimal difficulty in expressing ideas and needs (may take extra time; makes occasional errors in word choice, grammar or speech intelligibility; needs minimal prompting or assistance).

☐   2 -   Expresses simple ideas or needs with moderate difficulty (needs prompting or assistance, errors in word choice, organization or speech intelligibility). Speaks in phrases or short sentences.

☐   3 -   Has severe difficulty expressing basic ideas or needs and requires maximal assistance or guessing by listener. Speech limited to single words or short phrases.

☐   4 -   Unable to express basic needs even with maximal prompting or assistance but is not comatose or unresponsive (e.g., speech is nonsensical or unintelligible).

☐   5 -   Patient nonresponsive or unable to speak.

(M0420) **Frequency of Pain** interfering with patient's activity or movement:

☐   0 -   Patient has no pain or pain does not interfere with activity or movement
☐   1 -   Less often than daily
☐   2 -   Daily, but not constantly
☐   3 -   All of the time

(M0430) **Intractable Pain:** Is the patient experiencing pain that is not easily relieved, occurs at least daily, and affects the patient's sleep, appetite, physical or emotional energy, concentration, personal relationships, emotions, or ability or desire to perform physical activity?

☐   0 -   No
☐   1 -   Yes

INTEGUMENTARY STATUS

(M0440) Does this patient have a **Skin Lesion** or an **Open Wound**? This excludes "OSTOMIES."

☐   0 -   No [If No, go to *M0490*]
☐   1 -   Yes

(M0445) Does this patient have a **Pressure Ulcer**?

☐   0 -   No [If No, go to *M0468*]
☐   1 -   Yes

(M0450) Current Number of Pressure Ulcers at Each Stage: (Circle one response for each stage.)

	Pressure Ulcer Stages	Number of Pressure Ulcers				
a)	Stage 1: Nonblanchable erythema of intact skin; the heralding of skin ulceration. In darker-pigmented skin, warmth, edema, hardness, or discolored skin may be indicators.	0	1	2	3	4 or more
b)	Stage 2: Partial thickness skin loss involving epidermis and/or dermis. The ulcer is superficial and presents clinically as an abrasion, blister, or shallow crater.	0	1	2	3	4 or more
c)	Stage 3: Full-thickness skin loss involving damage or necrosis of subcutaneous tissue which may extend down to, but not through, underlying fascia. The ulcer presents clinically as a deep crater with or without undermining of adjacent tissue.	0	1	2	3	4 or more
d)	Stage 4: Full-thickness skin loss with extensive destruction, tissue necrosis, or damage to muscle, bone, or supporting structures (e.g., tendon, joint capsule, etc.)	0	1	2	3	4 or more
e)	In addition to the above, is there at least one pressure ulcer that cannot be observed due to the presence of eschar or a nonremovable dressing, including casts? ☐ 0 - No ☐ 1 - Yes					

(M0460) Stage of Most Problematic (Observable) Pressure Ulcer:

☐ 1 - Stage 1
☐ 2 - Stage 2
☐ 3 - Stage 3
☐ 4 - Stage 4
☐ NA - No observable pressure ulcer

(M0464) Status of Most Problematic (Observable) Pressure Ulcer:

☐ 1 - Fully granulating
☐ 2 - Early/partial granulation
☐ 3 - Not healing
☐ NA - No observable pressure ulcer

(M0468) Does this patient have a **Stasis Ulcer?**

☐ 0 - No [If No, go to *M0482*]
☐ 1 - Yes

(M0470) Current Number of Observable Stasis Ulcer(s):

☐ 0 - Zero
☐ 1 - One
☐ 2 - Two
☐ 3 - Three
☐ 4 - Four or more

(M0474) Does this patient have at least one **Stasis Ulcer that Cannot be Observed** due to the presence of a nonremovable dressing?

☐ 0 - No
☐ 1 - Yes

(M0476) Status of Most Problematic (Observable) Stasis Ulcer:

- ☐ 1 - Fully granulating
- ☐ 2 - Early/partial granulation
- ☐ 3 - Not healing
- ☐ NA - No observable stasis ulcer

(M0482) Does this patient have a **Surgical Wound?**

- ☐ 0 - No [If No, go to *M0490*]
- ☐ 1 - Yes

(M0484) Current Number of (Observable) Surgical Wounds: (If a wound is partially closed but has <u>more</u> than one opening, consider each opening as a separate wound.)

- ☐ 0 - Zero
- ☐ 1 - One
- ☐ 2 - Two
- ☐ 3 - Three
- ☐ 4 - Four or more

(M0486) Does this patient have at least one **Surgical Wound that Cannot be Observed** due to the presence of a nonremovable dressing?

- ☐ 0 - No
- ☐ 1 - Yes

(M0488) Status of Most Problematic (Observable) Surgical Wound:

- ☐ 1 - Fully granulating
- ☐ 2 - Early/partial granulation
- ☐ 3 - Not healing
- ☐ NA - No observable surgical wound

RESPIRATORY STATUS

(M0490) When is the patient dyspneic or noticeably **Short of Breath?**

- ☐ 0 - Never, patient is not short of breath
- ☐ 1 - When walking more than 20 feet, climbing stairs
- ☐ 2 - With moderate exertion (e.g., while dressing, using commode or bedpan, walking distances less than 20 feet)
- ☐ 3 - With minimal exertion (e.g., while eating, talking, or performing other ADLs) or with agitation
- ☐ 4 - At rest (during day or night)

(M0500) Respiratory Treatments utilized at home: **(Mark all that apply.)**

- ☐ 1 - Oxygen (intermittent or continuous)
- ☐ 2 - Ventilator (continually or at night)
- ☐ 3 - Continuous positive airway pressure
- ☐ 4 - None of the above

ELIMINATION STATUS

(M0510) Has this patient been treated for a **Urinary Tract Infection** in the past 14 days?

- ☐ 0 - No
- ☐ 1 - Yes
- ☐ NA - Patient on prophylactic treatment

(M0520) Urinary Incontinence or Urinary Catheter Presence:

☐ 0 - No incontinence or catheter (includes anuria or ostomy for urinary drainage) [If No, go to *M0540*]
☐ 1 - Patient is incontinent
☐ 2 - Patient requires a urinary catheter (i.e., external, indwelling, intermittent, suprapubic) [Go to *M0540*]

(M0530) When does Urinary Incontinence occur?

☐ 0 - Timed-voiding defers incontinence
☐ 1 - During the night only
☐ 2 - During the day and night

(M0540) Bowel Incontinence Frequency:

☐ 0 - Very rarely or never has bowel incontinence
☐ 1 - Less than once weekly
☐ 2 - One to three times weekly
☐ 3 - Four to six times weekly
☐ 4 - On a daily basis
☐ 5 - More often than once daily
☐ NA - Patient has ostomy for bowel elimination

(M0550) Ostomy for Bowel Elimination: Does this patient have an ostomy for bowel elimination that (within the last 14 days) necessitated a change in medical or treatment regimen?

☐ 0 - Patient does not have an ostomy for bowel elimination.
☐ 1 - Patient's ostomy did not necessitate change in medical or treatment regimen.
☐ 2 - The ostomy did necessitate change in medical or treatment regimen.

NEURO/EMOTIONAL/BEHAVIORAL STATUS

(M0560) Cognitive Functioning: (Patient's current level of alertness, orientation, comprehension, concentration, and immediate memory for simple commands.)

☐ 0 - Alert/oriented, able to focus and shift attention, comprehends and recalls task directions independently.
☐ 1 - Requires prompting (cuing, repetition, reminders) only under stressful or unfamiliar conditions.
☐ 2 - Requires assistance and some direction in specific situations (e.g., on all tasks involving shifting of attention), or consistently requires low stimulus environment due to distractibility.
☐ 3 - Requires considerable assistance in routine situations. Is not alert and oriented or is unable to shift attention and recall directions more than half the time.
☐ 4 - Totally dependent due to disturbances such as constant disorientation, coma, persistent vegetative state, or delirium.

(M0570) When Confused (Reported or Observed):

☐ 0 - Never
☐ 1 - In new or complex situations only
☐ 2 - On awakening or at night only
☐ 3 - During the day and evening, but not constantly
☐ 4 - Constantly
☐ NA - Patient nonresponsive

(M0580) When Anxious (Reported or Observed):

- ☐ 0 - None of the time
- ☐ 1 - Less often than daily
- ☐ 2 - Daily, but not constantly
- ☐ 3 - All of the time
- ☐ NA - Patient nonresponsive

(M0590) Depressive Feelings Reported or Observed in Patient: (Mark all that apply.)

- ☐ 1 - Depressed mood (e.g., feeling sad, tearful)
- ☐ 2 - Sense of failure or self reproach
- ☐ 3 - Hopelessness
- ☐ 4 - Recurrent thoughts of death
- ☐ 5 - Thoughts of suicide
- ☐ 6 - None of the above feelings observed or reported

(M0600) Patient Behaviors (Reported or Observed): (Mark all that apply.)

- ☐ 1 - Indecisiveness, lack of concentration
- ☐ 2 - Diminished interest in most activities
- ☐ 3 - Sleep disturbances
- ☐ 4 - Recent change in appetite or weight
- ☐ 5 - Agitation
- ☐ 6 - A suicide attempt
- ☐ 7 - None of the above behaviors observed or reported

(M0610) Behaviors Demonstrated at Least Once a Week (Reported or Observed): (Mark all that apply.)

- ☐ 1 - Memory deficit: failure to recognize familiar persons/places, inability to recall events of past 24 hours, significant memory loss so that supervision is required
- ☐ 2 - Impaired decision-making: failure to perform usual ADLs or IADLs, inability to appropriately stop activities, jeopardizes safety through actions
- ☐ 3 - Verbal disruption: yelling, threatening, excessive profanity, sexual references, etc.
- ☐ 4 - Physical aggression: aggressive or combative to self and others (e.g., hits self, throws objects, punches, dangerous maneuvers with wheelchair or other objects)
- ☐ 5 - Disruptive, infantile, or socially inappropriate behavior (**excludes** verbal actions)
- ☐ 6 - Delusional, hallucinatory, or paranoid behavior
- ☐ 7 - None of the above behaviors demonstrated

(M0620) Frequency of Behavior Problems (Reported or Observed) (e.g., wandering episodes, self abuse, verbal disruption, physical aggression, etc.):

- ☐ 0 - Never
- ☐ 1 - Less than once a month
- ☐ 2 - Once a month
- ☐ 3 - Several times each month
- ☐ 4 - Several times a week
- ☐ 5 - At least daily

(M0630) Is this patient receiving Psychiatric Nursing Services at home provided by a qualified psychiatric nurse?

- ☐ 0 - No
- ☐ 1 - Yes

ADL/IADLs

For M0640-M0800, record what the patient currently is *able to do.*

(M0640) Grooming: Ability to tend to personal hygiene needs (i.e., washing face and hands, hair care, shaving or make up, teeth or denture care, fingernail care).

- 0 - Able to groom self unaided, with or without the use of assistive devices or adapted methods.
- 1 - Grooming utensils must be placed within reach before able to complete grooming activities.
- 2 - Someone must assist the patient to groom self.
- 3 - Patient depends entirely upon someone else for grooming needs.

(M0650) Ability to Dress <u>Upper</u> Body (with or without dressing aids) including undergarments, pullovers, front-opening shirts and blouses, managing zippers, buttons, and snaps:

- 0 - Able to get clothes out of closets and drawers, put them on and remove them from the upper body without assistance.
- 1 - Able to dress upper body without assistance if clothing is laid out or handed to the patient.
- 2 - Someone must help the patient put on upper body clothing.
- 3 - Patient depends entirely upon another person to dress the upper body.

(M0660) Ability to Dress <u>Lower</u> Body (with or without dressing aids) including undergarments, slacks, socks or nylons, shoes:

- 0 - Able to obtain, put on, and remove clothing and shoes without assistance.
- 1 - Able to dress lower body without assistance if clothing and shoes are laid out or handed to the patient.
- 2 - Someone must help the patient put on undergarments, slacks, socks or nylons, and shoes.
- 3 - Patient depends entirely upon another person to dress lower body.

(M0670) Bathing: Ability to wash entire body. **<u>Excludes</u> grooming (washing face and hands only).**

- 0 - Able to bathe self in <u>shower or tub</u> independently.
- 1 - With the use of devices, is able to bathe self in shower or tub independently.
- 2 - Able to bathe in shower or tub with the assistance of another person:
  - (a) for intermittent supervision or encouragement or reminders, <u>OR</u>
  - (b) to get in and out of the shower or tub, <u>OR</u>
  - (c) for washing difficult to reach areas.
- 3 - Participates in bathing self in shower or tub, <u>but</u> requires presence of another person throughout the bath for assistance or supervision.
- 4 - <u>Unable</u> to use the shower or tub and is bathed in <u>bed or bedside chair</u>.
- 5 - Unable to effectively participate in bathing and is totally bathed by another person.

(M0680) Toileting: Ability to get to and from the toilet or bedside commode.

- 0 - Able to get to and from the toilet independently with or without a device.
- 1 - When reminded, assisted, or supervised by another person, able to get to and from the toilet.
- 2 - <u>Unable</u> to get to and from the toilet but is able to use a bedside commode (with or without assistance).
- 3 - <u>Unable</u> to get to and from the toilet or bedside commode but is able to use a bedpan/urinal independently.
- 4 - Is totally dependent in toileting.

(M0690) Transferring: Ability to move from bed to chair, on and off toilet or commode, into and out of tub or shower, and ability to turn and position self in bed if patient is bedfast.

- ☐   0 -   Able to independently transfer.
- ☐   1 -   Transfers with minimal human assistance or with use of an assistive device.
- ☐   2 -   <u>Unable</u> to transfer self but is able to bear weight and pivot during the transfer process.
- ☐   3 -   Unable to transfer self and is <u>unable</u> to bear weight or pivot when transferred by another person.
- ☐   4 -   Bedfast, unable to transfer but is able to turn and position self in bed.
- ☐   5 -   Bedfast, unable to transfer and is <u>unable</u> to turn and position self.

(M0700) Ambulation/Locomotion: Ability to <u>SAFELY</u> walk, once in a standing position, or use a wheelchair, once in a seated position, on a variety of surfaces.

- ☐   0 -   Able to independently walk on even and uneven surfaces and climb stairs with or without railings (i.e., needs no human assistance or assistive device).
- ☐   1 -   Requires use of a device (e.g., cane, walker) to walk alone <u>or</u> requires human supervision or assistance to negotiate stairs or steps or uneven surfaces.
- ☐   2 -   Able to walk only with the supervision or assistance of another person at all times.
- ☐   3 -   Chairfast, <u>unable</u> to ambulate but is able to wheel self independently.
- ☐   4 -   Chairfast, unable to ambulate and is <u>unable</u> to wheel self.
- ☐   5 -   Bedfast, unable to ambulate or be up in a chair.

(M0710) Feeding or Eating: Ability to feed self meals and snacks. **Note: This refers only to the process of <u>eating</u>, <u>chewing</u>, and <u>swallowing</u>, <u>not preparing</u> the food to be eaten.**

- ☐   0 -   Able to independently feed self.
- ☐   1 -   Able to feed self independently but requires:
  (a) meal set-up; <u>OR</u>
  (b) intermittent assistance or supervision from another person; <u>OR</u>
  (c) a liquid, pureed or ground meat diet.
- ☐   2 -   <u>Unable</u> to feed self and must be assisted or supervised throughout the meal/snack.
- ☐   3 -   Able to take in nutrients orally <u>and</u> receives supplemental nutrients through a nasogastric tube or gastrostomy.
- ☐   4 -   <u>Unable</u> to take in nutrients orally and is fed nutrients through a nasogastric tube or gastrostomy.
- ☐   5 -   Unable to take in nutrients orally or by tube feeding.

(M0720) Planning and Preparing Light Meals (e.g., cereal, sandwich) or reheat delivered meals:

- ☐   0 -   (a) Able to independently plan and prepare all light meals for self or reheat delivered meals; <u>OR</u>
  (b) Is physically, cognitively, and mentally able to prepare light meals on a regular basis but has not routinely performed light meal preparation in the past (i.e., prior to this home care admission).
- ☐   1 -   <u>Unable</u> to prepare light meals on a regular basis due to physical, cognitive, or mental limitations.
- ☐   2 -   Unable to prepare any light meals or reheat any delivered meals.

(M0730) Transportation: Physical and mental ability to <u>safely</u> use a car, taxi, or public transportation (bus, train, subway).

- ☐   0 -   Able to independently drive a regular or adapted car; <u>OR</u> uses a regular or handicap-accessible public bus.
- ☐   1 -   Able to ride in a car only when driven by another person; <u>OR</u> able to use a bus or handicap van only when assisted or accompanied by another person.
- ☐   2 -   <u>Unable</u> to ride in a car, taxi, bus, or van, and requires transportation by ambulance.

(M0740) Laundry: Ability to do own laundry -- to carry laundry to and from washing machine, to use washer and dryer, to wash small items by hand.

☐ 0 - (a) Able to independently take care of all laundry tasks; <u>OR</u>
(b) Physically, cognitively, and mentally able to do laundry and access facilities, <u>but</u> has not routinely performed laundry tasks in the past (i.e., prior to this home care admission).

☐ 1 - Able to do only light laundry, such as minor hand wash or light washer loads. Due to physical, cognitive, or mental limitations, needs assistance with heavy laundry such as carrying large loads of laundry.

☐ 2 - <u>Unable</u> to do any laundry due to physical limitation or needs continual supervision and assistance due to cognitive or mental limitation.

(M0750) Housekeeping: Ability to safely and effectively perform light housekeeping and heavier cleaning tasks.

☐ 0 - (a) Able to independently perform all housekeeping tasks; <u>OR</u>
(b) Physically, cognitively, and mentally able to perform <u>all</u> housekeeping tasks but has not routinely participated in housekeeping tasks in the past (i.e., prior to this home care admission).

☐ 1 - Able to perform only <u>light</u> housekeeping (e.g., dusting, wiping kitchen counters) tasks independently.

☐ 2 - Able to perform housekeeping tasks with intermittent assistance or supervision from another person.

☐ 3 - <u>Unable</u> to consistently perform any housekeeping tasks unless assisted by another person throughout the process.

☐ 4 - Unable to effectively participate in any housekeeping tasks.

(M0760) Shopping: Ability to plan for, select, and purchase items in a store and to carry them home or arrange delivery.

☐ 0 - (a) Able to plan for shopping needs and independently perform shopping tasks, including carrying packages; <u>OR</u>
(b) Physically, cognitively, and mentally able to take care of shopping, but has not done shopping in the past (i.e., prior to this home care admission).

☐ 1 - Able to go shopping, but needs some assistance:
(a) By self is able to do only light shopping and carry small packages, but needs someone to do occasional major shopping; <u>OR</u>
(b) <u>Unable</u> to go shopping alone, but can go with someone to assist.

☐ 2 - <u>Unable</u> to go shopping, but is able to identify items needed, place orders, and arrange home delivery.

☐ 3 - Needs someone to do all shopping and errands.

(M0770) Ability to Use Telephone: Ability to answer the phone, dial numbers, and <u>effectively</u> use the telephone to communicate.

☐ 0 - Able to dial numbers and answer calls appropriately and as desired.

☐ 1 - Able to use a specially adapted telephone (i.e., large numbers on the dial, teletype phone for the deaf) and call essential numbers.

☐ 2 - Able to answer the telephone and carry on a normal conversation but has difficulty with placing calls.

☐ 3 - Able to answer the telephone only some of the time or is able to carry on only a limited conversation.

☐ 4 - <u>Unable</u> to answer the telephone at all but can listen if assisted with equipment.

☐ 5 - Totally unable to use the telephone.

☐ NA - Patient does not have a telephone.

MEDICATIONS

(M0780) **Management of Oral Medications:** Patient's ability to prepare and take all prescribed oral medications reliably and safely, including administration of the correct dosage at the appropriate times/intervals. **Excludes injectable and IV medications. (NOTE: This refers to ability, not compliance or willingness.)**

- ☐ 0 - Able to independently take the correct oral medication(s) and proper dosage(s) at the correct times.
- ☐ 1 - Able to take medication(s) at the correct times if:
    (a) individual dosages are prepared in advance by another person; OR
    (b) given daily reminders; OR
    (c) someone develops a drug diary or chart.
- ☐ 2 - Unable to take medication unless administered by someone else.
- ☐ NA - No oral medications prescribed.

(M0790) **Management of Inhalant/Mist Medications:** Patient's ability to prepare and take all prescribed inhalant/mist medications (nebulizers, metered dose devices) reliably and safely, including administration of the correct dosage at the appropriate times/intervals. **Excludes all other forms of medication (oral tablets, injectable and IV medications).**

- ☐ 0 - Able to independently take the correct medication and proper dosage at the correct times.
- ☐ 1 - Able to take medication at the correct times if:
    (a) individual dosages are prepared in advance by another person, OR
    (b) given daily reminders.
- ☐ 2 - Unable to take medication unless administered by someone else.
- ☐ NA - No inhalant/mist medications prescribed.

(M0800) **Management of Injectable Medications:** Patient's ability to prepare and take all prescribed injectable medications reliably and safely, including administration of correct dosage at the appropriate times/intervals. **Excludes IV medications.**

- ☐ 0 - Able to independently take the correct medication and proper dosage at the correct times.
- ☐ 1 - Able to take injectable medication at correct times if:
    (a) individual syringes are prepared in advance by another person, OR
    (b) given daily reminders.
- ☐ 2 - Unable to take injectable medications unless administered by someone else.
- ☐ NA - No injectable medications prescribed.

EQUIPMENT MANAGEMENT

(M0810) **Patient Management of Equipment (includes ONLY oxygen, IV/infusion therapy, enteral/parenteral nutrition equipment or supplies):** Patient's ability to set up, monitor and change equipment reliably and safely, add appropriate fluids or medication, clean/store/dispose of equipment or supplies using proper technique. **(NOTE: This refers to ability, not compliance or willingness.)**

- ☐ 0 - Patient manages all tasks related to equipment completely independently.
- ☐ 1 - If someone else sets up equipment (i.e., fills portable oxygen tank, provides patient with prepared solutions), patient is able to manage all other aspects of equipment.
- ☐ 2 - Patient requires considerable assistance from another person to manage equipment, but independently completes portions of the task.
- ☐ 3 - Patient is only able to monitor equipment (e.g., liter flow, fluid in bag) and must call someone else to manage the equipment.
- ☐ 4 - Patient is completely dependent on someone else to manage all equipment.
- ☐ NA - No equipment of this type used in care [If NA, go to M0830]

(M0820) **Caregiver Management of Equipment (includes <u>ONLY</u> oxygen, IV/infusion equipment, enteral/parenteral nutrition, ventilator therapy equipment or supplies):** <u>Caregiver's ability</u> to set up, monitor, and change equipment reliably and safely, add appropriate fluids or medication, clean/store/dispose of equipment or supplies using proper technique. **(NOTE: This refers to ability, not compliance or willingness.)**

☐ 0 - Caregiver manages all tasks related to equipment completely independently.
☐ 1 - If someone else sets up equipment, caregiver is able to manage all other aspects.
☐ 2 - Caregiver requires considerable assistance from another person to manage equipment, but independently completes significant portions of task.
☐ 3 - Caregiver is only able to complete small portions of task (e.g., administer nebulizer treatment, clean/store/dispose of equipment or supplies).
☐ 4 - Caregiver is completely dependent on someone else to manage all equipment.
☐ NA - No caregiver

EMERGENT CARE

(M0830) **Emergent Care:** Since the last time OASIS data were collected, has the patient utilized any of the following services for emergent care (other than home care agency services)? **(Mark all that apply.)**

☐ 0 - No emergent care services **[If no emergent care, go to *M0855*]**
☐ 1 - Hospital emergency room (includes 23-hour holding)
☐ 2 - Doctor's office emergency visit/house call
☐ 3 - Outpatient department/clinic emergency (includes urgicenter sites)
☐ UK - Unknown **[If UK, go to *M0855*]**

(M0840) **Emergent Care Reason:** For what reason(s) did the patient/family seek emergent care? **(Mark all that apply.)**

☐ 1 - Improper medication administration, medication side effects, toxicity, anaphylaxis
☐ 2 - Nausea, dehydration, malnutrition, constipation, impaction
☐ 3 - Injury caused by fall or accident at home
☐ 4 - Respiratory problems (e.g., shortness of breath, respiratory infection, tracheobronchial obstruction)
☐ 5 - Wound infection, deteriorating wound status, new lesion/ulcer
☐ 6 - Cardiac problems (e.g., fluid overload, exacerbation of CHF, chest pain)
☐ 7 - Hypo/Hyperglycemia, diabetes out of control
☐ 8 - GI bleeding, obstruction
☐ 9 - Other than above reasons
☐ UK - Reason unknown

INPATIENT FACILITY ADMISSION OR AGENCY DISCHARGE

(M0855) To which **Inpatient Facility** has the patient been admitted?

☐ 1 - Hospital **[Go to *M0890*]**
☐ 2 - Rehabilitation facility **[Go to *M0903*]**
☐ 3 - Nursing home **[Go to *M0900*]**
☐ 4 - Hospice **[Go to *M0903*]**
☐ NA - No inpatient facility admission

(M0870) Discharge Disposition: Where is the patient after discharge from your agency? **(Choose only one answer.)**

☐ 1 - Patient remained in the community (not in hospital, nursing home, or rehab facility)
☐ 2 - Patient transferred to a noninstitutional hospice **[Go to *M0903*]**
☐ 3 - Unknown because patient moved to a geographic location not served by this agency **[Go to *M0903*]**
☐ UK - Other unknown **[Go to *M0903*]**

(M0880) After discharge, does the patient receive health, personal, or support **Services or Assistance**? **(Mark all that apply.)**

☐ 1 - No assistance or services received
☐ 2 - Yes, assistance or services provided by family or friends
☐ 3 - Yes, assistance or services provided by other community resources (e.g., meals-on-wheels, home health services, homemaker assistance, transportation assistance, assisted living, board and care)
  Go to *M0903*

(M0890) If the patient was admitted to an acute care **Hospital**, for what **Reason** was he/she admitted?

☐ 1 - Hospitalization for emergent (unscheduled) care
☐ 2 - Hospitalization for urgent (scheduled within 24 hours of admission) care
☐ 3 - Hospitalization for elective (scheduled more than 24 hours before admission) care
☐ UK - Unknown

(M0895) Reason for Hospitalization: (Mark all that apply.)

☐ 1 - Improper medication administration, medication side effects, toxicity, anaphylaxis
☐ 2 - Injury caused by fall or accident at home
☐ 3 - Respiratory problems (SOB, infection, obstruction)
☐ 4 - Wound or tube site infection, deteriorating wound status, new lesion/ulcer
☐ 5 - Hypo/Hyperglycemia, diabetes out of control
☐ 6 - GI bleeding, obstruction
☐ 7 - Exacerbation of CHF, fluid overload, heart failure
☐ 8 - Myocardial infarction, stroke
☐ 9 - Chemotherapy
☐ 10 - Scheduled surgical procedure
☐ 11 - Urinary tract infection
☐ 12 - IV catheter-related infection
☐ 13 - Deep vein thrombosis, pulmonary embolus
☐ 14 - Uncontrolled pain
☐ 15 - Psychotic episode
☐ 16 - Other than above reasons
  Go to *M0903*

(M0900) For what **Reason(s)** was the patient **Admitted** to a **Nursing Home**? **(Mark all that apply.)**

☐ 1 - Therapy services
☐ 2 - Respite care
☐ 3 - Hospice care
☐ 4 - Permanent placement
☐ 5 - Unsafe for care at home
☐ 6 - Other
☐ UK - Unknown

(M0903) **Date of Last (Most Recent) Home Visit:**

       __ __ / __ __ / __ __ __ __
       month day   year

(M0906) **Discharge/Transfer/Death Date:** Enter the date of the discharge, transfer, or death (at home) of the patient.

       __ __ / __ __ / __ __ __ __
       month day   year

Outcome and Assessment Information Set (OASIS-B1)
TRANSFER VERSION
(used for Transfer to an Inpatient Facility)

Items to be Used at This Time Point ---------------- M0010-M0100, M0150, M0830-M0855, M0890-M0906

CLINICAL RECORD ITEMS

(M0010) Agency Medicare Provider Number: __ __ __ __ __ __

(M0012) Agency Medicaid Provider Number: __ __ __ __ __ __ __ __ __ __ __ __ __ __

> **Branch Identification** (Optional, for Agency Use)
>
> **(M0014) Branch State:** __ __
>
> **(M0016) Branch ID Number:** __ __ __ __ __ __ __ __ __ __
> (Agency-assigned)

(M0020) Patient ID Number: __

(M0030) Start of Care Date: __ __ / __ __ / __ __ __ __
month   day   year

(M0032) Resumption of Care Date: __ __ / __ __ / __ __ __ __   ☐ NA – Not Applicable
month   day   year

(M0040) Patient Name:

__ __ __ __ __ __ __ __ __ __ __ __   __ __   __ __ __ __ __ __ __ __ __ __ __ __ __ __ __ __   __ __ __
(First)   (MI)   (Last)   (Suffix)

(M0050) Patient State of Residence: __ __

(M0060) Patient Zip Code: __ __ __ __ __   __ __ __ __

(M0063) Medicare Number: __ __ __ __ __ __ __ __ __ __ __ __   ☐ NA – No Medicare
(including suffix)

(M0064) Social Security Number: __ __ __ - __ __ - __ __ __ __   ☐ UK – Unknown or Not Available

(M0065) Medicaid Number: __ __ __ __ __ __ __ __ __ __ __ __ __   ☐ NA – No Medicaid

(M0066) Birth Date: __ __ / __ __ / __ __ __ __
month   day   year

(M0069) Gender:
- ☐ 1 - Male
- ☐ 2 - Female

(M0072) Primary Referring Physician ID:

__ __ __ __ __ __ __ __ __ __   ☐ UK – Unknown or Not Available

(M0080) Discipline of Person Completing Assessment:

☐ 1-RN   ☐ 2-PT   ☐ 3-SLP/ST   ☐ 4-OT

(M0090) Date Assessment Completed: __ __ / __ __ / __ __ __ __

month   day   year

(M0100) This Assessment is Currently Being Completed for the Following Reason:

Start/Resumption of Care
  1 – Start of care—further visits planned
  2 – Start of care—no further visits planned
  3 – Resumption of care (after inpatient stay)
Follow-Up
  4 – Recertification (follow-up) reassessment [Go to *M0150*]
  5 – Other follow-up [Go to *M0150*]

Transfer to an Inpatient Facility
  6 – Transferred to an inpatient facility—patient not discharged from agency [Go to *M0150*]
  7 – Transferred to an inpatient facility—patient discharged from agency [Go to *M0150*]

Discharge from Agency — Not to an Inpatient Facility
  8 – Death at home [Go to *M0150*]
  9 – Discharge from agency [Go to *M0150*]
  10 – Discharge from agency—no visits completed after start/resumption of care assessment
    [Go to *M0150*]

(M0150) Current Payment Sources for Home Care: (Mark all that apply.)

  0 - None; no charge for current services
  1 - Medicare (traditional fee-for-service)
  2 - Medicare (HMO/managed care)
  3 - Medicaid (traditional fee-for-service)
  4 - Medicaid (HMO/managed care)
  5 - Workers' compensation
  6 - Title programs (e.g., Title III, V, or XX)
  7 - Other government (e.g., CHAMPUS, VA, etc.)
  8 - Private insurance
  9 - Private HMO/managed care
  10 - Self-pay
  11 - Other (specify) _____

EMERGENT CARE

(M0830) Emergent Care: Since the last time OASIS data were collected, has the patient utilized any of the following services for emergent care (other than home care agency services)? **(Mark all that apply.)**

  0 - No emergent care services **[If no emergent care, go to *M0855*]**
  1 - Hospital emergency room (includes 23-hour holding)
  2 - Doctor's office emergency visit/house call
  3 - Outpatient department/clinic emergency (includes urgicenter sites)
  UK - Unknown **[If UK, go to *M0855*]**

(M0840) Emergent Care Reason: For what reason(s) did the patient/family seek emergent care? **(Mark all that apply.)**

- ☐ 1 - Improper medication administration, medication side effects, toxicity, anaphylaxis
- ☐ 2 - Nausea, dehydration, malnutrition, constipation, impaction
- ☐ 3 - Injury caused by fall or accident at home
- ☐ 4 - Respiratory problems (e.g., shortness of breath, respiratory infection, tracheobronchial obstruction)
- ☐ 5 - Wound infection, deteriorating wound status, new lesion/ulcer
- ☐ 6 - Cardiac problems (e.g., fluid overload, exacerbation of CHF, chest pain)
- ☐ 7 - Hypo/Hyperglycemia, diabetes out of control
- ☐ 8 - GI bleeding, obstruction
- ☐ 9 - Other than above reasons
- ☐ UK - Reason unknown

(M0855) To which **Inpatient Facility** has the patient been admitted?

- ☐ 1 - Hospital **[Go to *M0890*]**
- ☐ 2 - Rehabilitation facility **[Go to *M0903*]**
- ☐ 3 - Nursing home **[Go to *M0900*]**
- ☐ 4 - Hospice **[Go to *M0903*]**

INPATIENT FACILITY ADMISSION

(M0890) If the patient was admitted to an acute care **Hospital**, for what **Reason** was he/she admitted?

- ☐ 1 - Hospitalization for <u>emergent</u> (unscheduled) care
- ☐ 2 - Hospitalization for <u>urgent</u> (scheduled within 24 hours of admission) care
- ☐ 3 - Hospitalization for <u>elective</u> (scheduled more than 24 hours before admission) care
- ☐ UK - Unknown

(M0895) Reason for Hospitalization: (Mark all that apply.)

- ☐ 1 - Improper medication administration, medication side effects, toxicity, anaphylaxis
- ☐ 2 - Injury caused by fall or accident at home
- ☐ 3 - Respiratory problems (SOB, infection, obstruction)
- ☐ 4 - Wound or tube site infection, deteriorating wound status, new lesion/ulcer
- ☐ 5 - Hypo/Hyperglycemia, diabetes out of control
- ☐ 6 - GI bleeding, obstruction
- ☐ 7 - Exacerbation of CHF, fluid overload, heart failure
- ☐ 8 - Myocardial infarction, stroke
- ☐ 9 - Chemotherapy
- ☐ 10 - Scheduled surgical procedure
- ☐ 11 - Urinary tract infection
- ☐ 12 - IV catheter-related infection
- ☐ 13 - Deep vein thrombosis, pulmonary embolus
- ☐ 14 - Uncontrolled pain
- ☐ 15 - Psychotic episode
- ☐ 16 - Other than above reasons

| Go to *M0903* |

(M0900) For what **Reason(s)** was the patient **Admitted** to a **Nursing Home?** **(Mark all that apply.)**

☐ 1 - Therapy services
☐ 2 - Respite care
☐ 3 - Hospice care
☐ 4 - Permanent placement
☐ 5 - Unsafe for care at home
☐ 6 - Other
☐ UK - Unknown

(M0903) **Date of Last (Most Recent) Home Visit:**

__ __ / __ __ / __ __ __ __
month   day   year

(M0906) **Discharge/Transfer/Death Date:** Enter the date of the discharge, transfer, or death (at home) of the patient.

__ __ / __ __ / __ __ __ __
month   day   year

Outcome and Assessment Information Set (OASIS-B1)

FOLLOW-UP VERSION

Items to be Used at this Time Point ──────────────── M0010-M0100, M0150, M0175, M0200-M0250,
M0280-M0390, M0410-M0840

CLINICAL RECORD ITEMS

(M0010) Agency Medicare Provider Number: __ __ __ __ __ __

(M0012) Agency Medicaid Provider Number: __ __ __ __ __ __ __ __ __ __ __ __ __

Branch Identification (Optional, for Agency Use)

(M0014) Branch State: __ __

(M0016) Branch ID Number: __ __ __ __ __ __ __ __ __ __
                (Agency-assigned)

(M0020) Patient ID Number: __ __ __ __ __ __ __ __ __ __ __ __ __ __ __ __ __ __

(M0030) Start of Care Date: __ __/__ __/__ __ __ __
               month day   year

(M0032) Resumption of Care Date: __ __/__ __/__ __ __ __   ☐ NA – Not Applicable
                    month day   year

(M0040) Patient Name:

__ __ __ __ __ __ __ __ __ __ __ (MI) (Last) __ __ __ __ __ __ __ __ __ __ __ __ __ __ __ __ __
(First)   (MI) (Last)   (Suffix)

(M0050) Patient State of Residence: __ __

(M0060) Patient Zip Code: __ __ __ __ __ __ __ __ __

(M0063) Medicare Number: __ __ __ __ __ __ __ __ __ __ __   ☐ NA – No Medicare
                  (including suffix)

(M0064) Social Security Number: __ __ __ – __ __ – __ __ __ __   ☐ UK – Unknown or Not Available

(M0065) Medicaid Number: __ __ __ __ __ __ __ __ __ __ __ __   ☐ NA – No Medicaid

(M0066) Birth Date: __ __/__ __/__ __ __ __
             month day   year

(M0069) Gender:

    ☐ 1 - Male
    ☐ 2 - Female

(M0072) Primary Referring Physician ID:

       __ __ __ __ __ __ __ __ __ __   ☐ UK – Unknown or Not Available

(M0080) Discipline of Person Completing Assessment:

         ☐ 1-RN   ☐ 2-PT   ☐ 3-SLP/ST   ☐ 4-OT

(M0090) Date Assessment Completed: _ _ / _ _ / _ _ _ _
                                    month day   year

(M0100) This Assessment is Currently Being Completed for the Following Reason:

Start/Resumption of Care
    1 – Start of care—further visits planned
    2 – Start of care—no further visits planned
    3 – Resumption of care (after inpatient stay)
Follow-Up
    4 – Recertification (follow-up) reassessment [Go to M0150]
    5 – Other follow-up [Go to M0150]
Transfer to an Inpatient Facility
    6 – Transferred to an inpatient facility—patient not discharged from agency [Go to M0150]
    7 – Transferred to an inpatient facility—patient discharged from agency [Go to M0150]
Discharge from Agency — Not to an Inpatient Facility
    8 – Death at home [Go to M0150]
    9 – Discharge from agency [Go to M0150]
    10 – Discharge from agency—no visits completed after start/resumption of care assessment
        [Go to M0150]

DEMOGRAPHICS AND PATIENT HISTORY

(M0150) Current Payment Sources for Home Care: (Mark all that apply.)

    0 - None; no charge for current services
    1 - Medicare (traditional fee-for-service)
    2 - Medicare (HMO/managed care)
    3 - Medicaid (traditional fee-for-service)
    4 - Medicaid (HMO/managed care)
    5 - Workers' compensation
    6 - Title programs (e.g., Title III, V, or XX)
    7 - Other government (e.g., CHAMPUS, VA, etc.)
    8 - Private insurance
    9 - Private HMO/managed care
    10 - Self-pay
    11 - Other (specify) _____

(M0175) From which of the following **Inpatient Facilities** was the patient discharged <u>during the past 14 days</u>? **(Mark all that apply.)**

    1 - Hospital
    2 - Rehabilitation facility
    3 - Skilled nursing facility
    4 - Other nursing home
    5 - Other (specify) _____
    NA - Patient was not discharged from an inpatient facility **[If NA, go to M0200]**

(M0200) Medical or Treatment Regimen Change Within Past 14 Days: Has this patient experienced a change in medical or treatment regimen (e.g., medication, treatment, or service change due to new or additional diagnosis, etc.) within the last 14 days?

    0 - No **[If No, go to M0220]**
    1 - Yes

(M0210) List the patient's **Medical Diagnoses** and ICD code categories (three digits required; five digits optional) <u>for those conditions requiring changed medical or treatment regimen</u> (no surgical or V-codes):

Changed Medical Regimen Diagnosis	ICD
a. _____	(___ ___ . ___ ___)
b. _____	(___ ___ . ___ ___)
c. _____	(___ ___ . ___ ___)
d. _____	(___ ___ . ___ ___)

(M0220) **Conditions Prior to Medical or Treatment Regimen Change or Inpatient Stay Within Past 14 Days:** If this patient experienced an inpatient facility discharge or a change in medical or treatment regimen within the past 14 days, indicate any conditions which existed <u>prior to</u> the inpatient stay or change in medical or treatment regimen. **(Mark all that apply.)**

☐ 1 - Urinary incontinence
☐ 2 - Indwelling/suprapubic catheter
☐ 3 - Intractable pain
☐ 4 - Impaired decision-making
☐ 5 - Disruptive or socially inappropriate behavior
☐ 6 - Memory loss to the extent that supervision required
☐ 7 - None of the above
☐ NA - No inpatient facility discharge <u>and</u> no change in medical or treatment regimen in past 14 days
☐ UK - Unknown

(M0230/M0240) **Diagnoses and Severity Index:** List each medical diagnosis or problem for which the patient is receiving home care and ICD code category (three digits required; five digits optional – no surgical or V-codes) and rate them using the following severity index. (Choose one value that represents the most severe rating appropriate for each diagnosis.)

0 - Asymptomatic, no treatment needed at this time
1 - Symptoms well controlled with current therapy
2 - Symptoms controlled with difficulty, affecting daily functioning; patient needs ongoing monitoring
3 - Symptoms poorly controlled, patient needs frequent adjustment in treatment and dose monitoring
4 - Symptoms poorly controlled, history of rehospitalizations

(M0230) Primary Diagnosis	ICD	Severity Rating
a. _____	(___ ___ . ___ ___)	☐ 0 ☐ 1 ☐ 2 ☐ 3 ☐ 4

(M0240) Other Diagnoses	ICD	Severity Rating
b. _____	(___ ___ . ___ ___)	☐ 0 ☐ 1 ☐ 2 ☐ 3 ☐ 4
c. _____	(___ ___ . ___ ___)	☐ 0 ☐ 1 ☐ 2 ☐ 3 ☐ 4
d. _____	(___ ___ . ___ ___)	☐ 0 ☐ 1 ☐ 2 ☐ 3 ☐ 4
e. _____	(___ ___ . ___ ___)	☐ 0 ☐ 1 ☐ 2 ☐ 3 ☐ 4
f. _____	(___ ___ . ___ ___)	☐ 0 ☐ 1 ☐ 2 ☐ 3 ☐ 4

(M0250) **Therapies** the patient receives <u>at home</u>: **(Mark all that apply.)**

☐ 1 - Intravenous or infusion therapy (excludes TPN)
☐ 2 - Parenteral nutrition (TPN or lipids)
☐ 3 - Enteral nutrition (nasogastric, gastrostomy, jejunostomy, or any other artificial entry into the alimentary canal)
☐ 4 - None of the above

(M0280) Life Expectancy: (Physician documentation is not required.)

☐ 0 - Life expectancy is greater than 6 months
☐ 1 - Life expectancy is 6 months or fewer

(M0290) High Risk Factors characterizing this patient: **(Mark all that apply.)**

☐ 1 - Heavy smoking
☐ 2 - Obesity
☐ 3 - Alcohol dependency
☐ 4 - Drug dependency
☐ 5 - None of the above

LIVING ARRANGEMENTS

(M0300) Current Residence:

☐ 1 - Patient's owned or rented residence (house, apartment, or mobile home owned or rented by patient/couple/significant other)
☐ 2 - Family member's residence
☐ 3 - Boarding home or rented room
☐ 4 - Board and care or assisted living facility
☐ 5 - Other (specify) _____

(M0310) Structural Barriers in the patient's environment limiting independent mobility: **(Mark all that apply.)**

☐ 0 - None
☐ 1 - Stairs inside home which <u>must</u> be used by the patient (e.g., to get to toileting, sleeping, eating areas)
☐ 2 - Stairs inside home which are used optionally (e.g., to get to laundry facilities)
☐ 3 - Stairs leading from inside house to outside
☐ 4 - Narrow or obstructed doorways

(M0320) Safety Hazards found in the patient's current place of residence: **(Mark all that apply.)**

☐ 0 - None
☐ 1 - Inadequate floor, roof, or windows
☐ 2 - Inadequate lighting
☐ 3 - Unsafe gas/electric appliance
☐ 4 - Inadequate heating
☐ 5 - Inadequate cooling
☐ 6 - Lack of fire safety devices
☐ 7 - Unsafe floor coverings
☐ 8 - Inadequate stair railings
☐ 9 - Improperly stored hazardous materials
☐ 10 - Lead-based paint
☐ 11 - Other (specify) _____

(M0330) Sanitation Hazards found in the patient's current place of residence: **(Mark all that apply.)**

- ☐ 0 - None
- ☐ 1 - No running water
- ☐ 2 - Contaminated water
- ☐ 3 - No toileting facilities
- ☐ 4 - Outdoor toileting facilities only
- ☐ 5 - Inadequate sewage disposal
- ☐ 6 - Inadequate/improper food storage
- ☐ 7 - No food refrigeration
- ☐ 8 - No cooking facilities
- ☐ 9 - Insects/rodents present
- ☐ 10 - No scheduled trash pickup
- ☐ 11 - Cluttered/soiled living area
- ☐ 12 - Other (specify) _____

(M0340) Patient Lives With: (Mark all that apply.)

- ☐ 1 - Lives alone
- ☐ 2 - With spouse or significant other
- ☐ 3 - With other family member
- ☐ 4 - With a friend
- ☐ 5 - With paid help (other than home care agency staff)
- ☐ 6 - With other than above

SUPPORTIVE ASSISTANCE

(M0350) Assisting Person(s) Other than Home Care Agency Staff: (Mark all that apply.)

- ☐ 1 - Relatives, friends, or neighbors living outside the home
- ☐ 2 - Person residing in the home (EXCLUDING paid help)
- ☐ 3 - Paid help
- ☐ 4 - None of the above **[If None of the above, go to *M0390*]**

(M0360) Primary Caregiver taking <u>lead</u> responsibility for providing or managing the patient's care, providing the most frequent assistance, etc. (other than home care agency staff):

- ☐ 0 - No one person **[If No one person, go to *M0390*]**
- ☐ 1 - Spouse or significant other
- ☐ 2 - Daughter or son
- ☐ 3 - Other family member
- ☐ 4 - Friend or neighbor or community or church member
- ☐ 5 - Paid help

(M0370) How Often does the patient receive assistance from the primary caregiver?

- ☐ 1 - Several times during day and night
- ☐ 2 - Several times during day
- ☐ 3 - Once daily
- ☐ 4 - Three or more times per week
- ☐ 5 - One to two times per week
- ☐ 6 - Less often than weekly

(M0380) Type of Primary Caregiver Assistance: (Mark all that apply.)

- ☐ 1 - ADL assistance (e.g., bathing, dressing, toileting, bowel/bladder, eating/feeding)
- ☐ 2 - IADL assistance (e.g., meds, meals, housekeeping, laundry, telephone, shopping, finances)
- ☐ 3 - Environmental support (housing, home maintenance)
- ☐ 4 - Psychosocial support (socialization, companionship, recreation)
- ☐ 5 - Advocates or facilitates patient's participation in appropriate medical care
- ☐ 6 - Financial agent, power of attorney, or conservator of finance
- ☐ 7 - Health care agent, conservator of person, or medical power of attorney

SENSORY STATUS

(M0390) Vision with corrective lenses if the patient usually wears them:

- ☐ 0 - Normal vision: sees adequately in most situations; can see medication labels, newsprint.
- ☐ 1 - Partially impaired: cannot see medication labels or newsprint, but <u>can</u> see obstacles in path, and the surrounding layout; can count fingers at arm's length.
- ☐ 2 - Severely impaired: cannot locate objects without hearing or touching them <u>or</u> patient nonresponsive.

(M0410) Speech and Oral (Verbal) Expression of Language (in patient's own language):

- ☐ 0 - Expresses complex ideas, feelings, and needs clearly, completely, and easily in all situations with no observable impairment.
- ☐ 1 - Minimal difficulty in expressing ideas and needs (may take extra time; makes occasional errors in word choice, grammar or speech intelligibility; needs minimal prompting or assistance).
- ☐ 2 - Expresses simple ideas or needs with moderate difficulty (needs prompting or assistance, errors in word choice, organization or speech intelligibility). Speaks in phrases or short sentences.
- ☐ 3 - Has severe difficulty expressing basic ideas or needs and requires maximal assistance or guessing by listener. Speech limited to single words or short phrases.
- ☐ 4 - <u>Unable</u> to express basic needs even with maximal prompting or assistance but is not comatose or unresponsive (e.g., speech is nonsensical or unintelligible).
- ☐ 5 - Patient nonresponsive or unable to speak.

(M0420) Frequency of Pain interfering with patient's activity or movement:

- ☐ 0 - Patient has no pain or pain does not interfere with activity or movement
- ☐ 1 - Less often than daily
- ☐ 2 - Daily, but not constantly
- ☐ 3 - All of the time

(M0430) Intractable Pain: Is the patient experiencing pain that is <u>not easily relieved</u>, occurs at least daily, and affects the patient's sleep, appetite, physical or emotional energy, concentration, personal relationships, emotions, or ability or desire to perform physical activity?

- ☐ 0 - No
- ☐ 1 - Yes

INTEGUMENTARY STATUS

(M0440) Does this patient have a **Skin Lesion** or an **Open Wound**? This excludes "OSTOMIES."

☐ 0 - No [**If No, go to** *M0490*]
☐ 1 - Yes

(M0445) Does this patient have a **Pressure Ulcer**?

☐ 0 - No [**If No, go to** *M0468*]
☐ 1 - Yes

(M0450) **Current Number of Pressure Ulcers at Each Stage:** (Circle one response for each stage.)

	Pressure Ulcer Stages	Number of Pressure Ulcers				
a)	Stage 1: Nonblanchable erythema of intact skin; the heralding of skin ulceration. In darker-pigmented skin, warmth, edema, hardness, or discolored skin may be indicators.	0	1	2	3	4 or more
b)	Stage 2: Partial thickness skin loss involving epidermis and/or dermis. The ulcer is superficial and presents clinically as an abrasion, blister, or shallow crater.	0	1	2	3	4 or more
c)	Stage 3: Full-thickness skin loss involving damage or necrosis of subcutaneous tissue which may extend down to, but not through, underlying fascia. The ulcer presents clinically as a deep crater with or without undermining of adjacent tissue.	0	1	2	3	4 or more
d)	Stage 4: Full-thickness skin loss with extensive destruction, tissue necrosis, or damage to muscle, bone, or supporting structures (e.g., tendon, joint capsule, etc.)	0	1	2	3	4 or more
e)	In addition to the above, is there at least one pressure ulcer that cannot be observed due to the presence of eschar or a nonremovable dressing, including casts? ☐ 0 - No ☐ 1 - Yes					

(M0460) **Stage of Most Problematic (Observable) Pressure Ulcer:**

☐ 1 - Stage 1
☐ 2 - Stage 2
☐ 3 - Stage 3
☐ 4 - Stage 4
☐ NA - No observable pressure ulcer

(M0464) **Status of Most Problematic (Observable) Pressure Ulcer:**

☐ 1 - Fully granulating
☐ 2 - Early/partial granulation
☐ 3 - Not healing
☐ NA - No observable pressure ulcer

(M0468) Does this patient have a **Stasis Ulcer?**

☐ 0 - No [**If No, go to** *M0482*]
☐ 1 - Yes

    (M0470) **Current Number of Observable Stasis Ulcer(s):**

    ☐ 0 - Zero
    ☐ 1 - One
    ☐ 2 - Two
    ☐ 3 - Three
    ☐ 4 - Four or more

    (M0474) Does this patient have at least one **Stasis Ulcer that Cannot be Observed** due to the presence of a nonremovable dressing?

    ☐ 0 - No
    ☐ 1 - Yes

    (M0476) **Status of Most Problematic (Observable) Stasis Ulcer:**

    ☐ 1 - Fully granulating
    ☐ 2 - Early/partial granulation
    ☐ 3 - Not healing
    ☐ NA - No observable stasis ulcer

(M0482) Does this patient have a **Surgical Wound?**

☐ 0 - No [**If No, go to** *M0490*]
☐ 1 - Yes

    (M0484) **Current Number of (Observable) Surgical Wounds:** (If a wound is partially closed but has <u>more</u> than one opening, consider each opening as a separate wound.)

    ☐ 0 - Zero
    ☐ 1 - One
    ☐ 2 - Two
    ☐ 3 - Three
    ☐ 4 - Four or more

    (M0486) Does this patient have at least one **Surgical Wound that Cannot be Observed** due to the presence of a nonremovable dressing?

    ☐ 0 - No
    ☐ 1 - Yes

    (M0488) **Status of Most Problematic (Observable) Surgical Wound:**

    ☐ 1 - Fully granulating
    ☐ 2 - Early/partial granulation
    ☐ 3 - Not healing
    ☐ NA - No observable surgical wound

RESPIRATORY STATUS

(M0490) When is the patient dyspneic or noticeably **Short of Breath**?

- ☐ 0 - Never, patient is not short of breath
- ☐ 1 - When walking more than 20 feet, climbing stairs
- ☐ 2 - With moderate exertion (e.g., while dressing, using commode or bedpan, walking distances less than 20 feet)
- ☐ 3 - With minimal exertion (e.g., while eating, talking, or performing other ADLs) or with agitation
- ☐ 4 - At rest (during day or night)

(M0500) **Respiratory Treatments** utilized at home: **(Mark all that apply.)**

- ☐ 1 - Oxygen (intermittent or continuous)
- ☐ 2 - Ventilator (continually or at night)
- ☐ 3 - Continuous positive airway pressure
- ☐ 4 - None of the above

ELIMINATION STATUS

(M0510) Has this patient been treated for a **Urinary Tract Infection** in the past 14 days?

- ☐ 0 - No
- ☐ 1 - Yes
- ☐ NA - Patient on prophylactic treatment

(M0520) **Urinary Incontinence or Urinary Catheter Presence:**

- ☐ 0 - No incontinence or catheter (includes anuria or ostomy for urinary drainage) **[If No, go to M0540]**
- ☐ 1 - Patient is incontinent
- ☐ 2 - Patient requires a urinary catheter (i.e., external, indwelling, intermittent, suprapubic) **[Go to M0540]**

(M0530) When does **Urinary Incontinence** occur?

- ☐ 0 - Timed-voiding defers incontinence
- ☐ 1 - During the night only
- ☐ 2 - During the day and night

(M0540) **Bowel Incontinence Frequency:**

- ☐ 0 - Very rarely or never has bowel incontinence
- ☐ 1 - Less than once weekly
- ☐ 2 - One to three times weekly
- ☐ 3 - Four to six times weekly
- ☐ 4 - On a daily basis
- ☐ 5 - More often than once daily
- ☐ NA - Patient has ostomy for bowel elimination

(M0550) **Ostomy for Bowel Elimination:** Does this patient have an ostomy for bowel elimination that (within the last 14 days): a) was related to an inpatient facility stay, <u>or</u> b) necessitated a change in medical or treatment regimen?

- ☐ 0 - Patient does <u>not</u> have an ostomy for bowel elimination.
- ☐ 1 - Patient's ostomy was <u>not</u> related to an inpatient stay and did <u>not</u> necessitate change in medical or treatment regimen.
- ☐ 2 - The ostomy <u>was</u> related to an inpatient stay or <u>did</u> necessitate change in medical or treatment regimen.

NEURO/EMOTIONAL/BEHAVIORAL STATUS

(M0560) Cognitive Functioning: (Patient's current level of alertness, orientation, comprehension, concentration, and immediate memory for simple commands.)

☐ 0 - Alert/oriented, able to focus and shift attention, comprehends and recalls task directions independently.

☐ 1 - Requires prompting (cuing, repetition, reminders) only under stressful or unfamiliar conditions.

☐ 2 - Requires assistance and some direction in specific situations (e.g., on all tasks involving shifting of attention), or consistently requires low stimulus environment due to distractibility.

☐ 3 - Requires considerable assistance in routine situations. Is not alert and oriented or is unable to shift attention and recall directions more than half the time.

☐ 4 - Totally dependent due to disturbances such as constant disorientation, coma, persistent vegetative state, or delirium.

(M0570) When Confused (Reported or Observed):

☐ 0 - Never
☐ 1 - In new or complex situations only
☐ 2 - On awakening or at night only
☐ 3 - During the day and evening, but not constantly
☐ 4 - Constantly
☐ NA - Patient nonresponsive

(M0580) When Anxious (Reported or Observed):

☐ 0 - None of the time
☐ 1 - Less often than daily
☐ 2 - Daily, but not constantly
☐ 3 - All of the time
☐ NA - Patient nonresponsive

(M0590) Depressive Feelings Reported or Observed in Patient: (Mark all that apply.)

☐ 1 - Depressed mood (e.g., feeling sad, tearful)
☐ 2 - Sense of failure or self reproach
☐ 3 - Hopelessness
☐ 4 - Recurrent thoughts of death
☐ 5 - Thoughts of suicide
☐ 6 - None of the above feelings observed or reported

(M0600) Patient Behaviors (Reported or Observed): (Mark all that apply.)

☐ 1 - Indecisiveness, lack of concentration
☐ 2 - Diminished interest in most activities
☐ 3 - Sleep disturbances
☐ 4 - Recent change in appetite or weight
☐ 5 - Agitation
☐ 6 - A suicide attempt
☐ 7 - None of the above behaviors observed or reported

(M0610) Behaviors Demonstrated <u>at Least Once a Week</u> (Reported or Observed): (Mark all that apply.)

1 - Memory deficit: failure to recognize familiar persons/places, inability to recall events of past 24 hours, significant memory loss so that supervision is required
2 - Impaired decision-making: failure to perform usual ADLs or IADLs, inability to appropriately stop activities, jeopardizes safety through actions
3 - Verbal disruption: yelling, threatening, excessive profanity, sexual references, etc.
4 - Physical aggression: aggressive or combative to self and others (e.g., hits self, throws objects, punches, dangerous maneuvers with wheelchair or other objects)
5 - Disruptive, infantile, or socially inappropriate behavior (**excludes** verbal actions)
6 - Delusional, hallucinatory, or paranoid behavior
7 - None of the above behaviors demonstrated

(M0620) Frequency of Behavior Problems (Reported or Observed) (e.g., wandering episodes, self abuse, verbal disruption, physical aggression, etc.):

0 - Never
1 - Less than once a month
2 - Once a month
3 - Several times each month
4 - Several times a week
5 - At least daily

(M0630) Is this patient receiving **Psychiatric Nursing Services** at home provided by a qualified psychiatric nurse?

0 - No
1 - Yes

ADL/IADLs

For M0640-M0800, record what the patient currently is *able to do.*

(M0640) Grooming: Ability to tend to personal hygiene needs (i.e., washing face and hands, hair care, shaving or make up, teeth or denture care, fingernail care).

0 - Able to groom self unaided, with or without the use of assistive devices or adapted methods.
1 - Grooming utensils must be placed within reach before able to complete grooming activities.
2 - Someone must assist the patient to groom self.
3 - Patient depends entirely upon someone else for grooming needs.

(M0650) Ability to Dress <u>Upper</u> Body (with or without dressing aids) including undergarments, pullovers, front-opening shirts and blouses, managing zippers, buttons, and snaps:

0 - Able to get clothes out of closets and drawers, put them on and remove them from the upper body without assistance.
1 - Able to dress upper body without assistance if clothing is laid out or handed to the patient.
2 - Someone must help the patient put on upper body clothing.
3 - Patient depends entirely upon another person to dress the upper body.

(M0660) Ability to Dress <u>Lower</u> Body (with or without dressing aids) including undergarments, slacks, socks or nylons, shoes:

0 - Able to obtain, put on, and remove clothing and shoes without assistance.
1 - Able to dress lower body without assistance if clothing and shoes are laid out or handed to the patient.
2 - Someone must help the patient put on undergarments, slacks, socks or nylons, and shoes.
3 - Patient depends entirely upon another person to dress lower body.

(M0670) Bathing: Ability to wash entire body. <u>Excludes</u> grooming (washing face and hands only).

- ☐ 0 - Able to bathe self in <u>shower or tub</u> independently.
- ☐ 1 - With the use of devices, is able to bathe self in shower or tub independently.
- ☐ 2 - Able to bathe in shower or tub with the assistance of another person:
  (a) for intermittent supervision or encouragement or reminders, <u>OR</u>
  (b) to get in and out of the shower or tub, <u>OR</u>
  (c) for washing difficult to reach areas.
- ☐ 3 - Participates in bathing self in shower or tub, <u>but</u> requires presence of another person throughout the bath for assistance or supervision.
- ☐ 4 - <u>Unable</u> to use the shower or tub and is bathed in <u>bed or bedside chair</u>.
- ☐ 5 - Unable to effectively participate in bathing and is totally bathed by another person.

(M0680) Toileting: Ability to get to and from the toilet or bedside commode.

- ☐ 0 - Able to get to and from the toilet independently with or without a device.
- ☐ 1 - When reminded, assisted, or supervised by another person, able to get to and from the toilet.
- ☐ 2 - <u>Unable</u> to get to and from the toilet but is able to use a bedside commode (with or without assistance).
- ☐ 3 - <u>Unable</u> to get to and from the toilet or bedside commode but is able to use a bedpan/urinal independently.
- ☐ 4 - Is totally dependent in toileting.

(M0690) Transferring: Ability to move from bed to chair, on and off toilet or commode, into and out of tub or shower, and ability to turn and position self in bed if patient is bedfast.

- ☐ 0 - Able to independently transfer.
- ☐ 1 - Transfers with minimal human assistance or with use of an assistive device.
- ☐ 2 - <u>Unable</u> to transfer self but is able to bear weight and pivot during the transfer process.
- ☐ 3 - Unable to transfer self and is <u>unable</u> to bear weight or pivot when transferred by another person.
- ☐ 4 - Bedfast, unable to transfer but is able to turn and position self in bed.
- ☐ 5 - Bedfast, unable to transfer and is <u>unable</u> to turn and position self.

(M0700) Ambulation/Locomotion: Ability to <u>SAFELY</u> walk, once in a standing position, or use a wheelchair, once in a seated position, on a variety of surfaces.

- ☐ 0 - Able to independently walk on even and uneven surfaces and climb stairs with or without railings (i.e., needs no human assistance or assistive device).
- ☐ 1 - Requires use of a device (e.g., cane, walker) to walk alone <u>or</u> requires human supervision or assistance to negotiate stairs or steps or uneven surfaces.
- ☐ 2 - Able to walk only with the supervision or assistance of another person at all times.
- ☐ 3 - Chairfast, <u>unable</u> to ambulate but is able to wheel self independently.
- ☐ 4 - Chairfast, unable to ambulate and is <u>unable</u> to wheel self.
- ☐ 5 - Bedfast, unable to ambulate or be up in a chair.

(M0710) Feeding or Eating: Ability to feed self meals and snacks. **Note: This refers only to the process of <u>eating, chewing,</u> and <u>swallowing, not preparing</u> the food to be eaten.**

- ☐ 0 - Able to independently feed self.
- ☐ 1 - Able to feed self independently but requires:
  (a) meal set-up; <u>OR</u>
  (b) intermittent assistance or supervision from another person; <u>OR</u>
  (c) a liquid, pureed or ground meat diet.
- ☐ 2 - <u>Unable</u> to feed self and must be assisted or supervised throughout the meal/snack.
- ☐ 3 - Able to take in nutrients orally <u>and</u> receives supplemental nutrients through a nasogastric tube or gastrostomy.
- ☐ 4 - <u>Unable</u> to take in nutrients orally and is fed nutrients through a nasogastric tube or gastrostomy.
- ☐ 5 - Unable to take in nutrients orally or by tube feeding.

(M0720) Planning and Preparing Light Meals (e.g., cereal, sandwich) or reheat delivered meals:

☐   0 -   (a) Able to independently plan and prepare all light meals for self or reheat delivered meals; <u>OR</u>
       (b) Is physically, cognitively, and mentally able to prepare light meals on a regular basis but has not routinely performed light meal preparation in the past (i.e., prior to this home care admission).

☐   1 -   <u>Unable</u> to prepare light meals on a regular basis due to physical, cognitive, or mental limitations.

☐   2 -   Unable to prepare any light meals or reheat any delivered meals.

(M0730) Transportation: Physical and mental ability to <u>safely</u> use a car, taxi, or public transportation (bus, train, subway).

☐   0 -   Able to independently drive a regular or adapted car; <u>OR</u> uses a regular or handicap-accessible public bus.

☐   1 -   Able to ride in a car only when driven by another person; <u>OR</u> able to use a bus or handicap van only when assisted or accompanied by another person.

☐   2 -   <u>Unable</u> to ride in a car, taxi, bus, or van, and requires transportation by ambulance.

(M0740) Laundry: Ability to do own laundry — to carry laundry to and from washing machine, to use washer and dryer, to wash small items by hand.

☐   0 -   (a) Able to independently take care of all laundry tasks; <u>OR</u>
       (b) Physically, cognitively, and mentally able to do laundry and access facilities, <u>but</u> has not routinely performed laundry tasks in the past (i.e., prior to this home care admission).

☐   1 -   Able to do only light laundry, such as minor hand wash or light washer loads. Due to physical, cognitive, or mental limitations, needs assistance with heavy laundry such as carrying large loads of laundry.

☐   2 -   <u>Unable</u> to do any laundry due to physical limitation or needs continual supervision and assistance due to cognitive or mental limitation.

(M0750) Housekeeping: Ability to safely and effectively perform light housekeeping and heavier cleaning tasks.

☐   0 -   (a) Able to independently perform all housekeeping tasks; <u>OR</u>
       (b) Physically, cognitively, and mentally able to perform <u>all</u> housekeeping tasks but has not routinely participated in housekeeping tasks in the past (i.e., prior to this home care admission).

☐   1 -   Able to perform only <u>light</u> housekeeping (e.g., dusting, wiping kitchen counters) tasks independently.

☐   2 -   Able to perform housekeeping tasks with intermittent assistance or supervision from another person.

☐   3 -   <u>Unable</u> to consistently perform any housekeeping tasks unless assisted by another person throughout the process.

☐   4 -   Unable to effectively participate in any housekeeping tasks.

(M0760) Shopping: Ability to plan for, select, and purchase items in a store and to carry them home or arrange delivery.

☐   0 -   (a) Able to plan for shopping needs and independently perform shopping tasks, including carrying packages; <u>OR</u>
       (b) Physically, cognitively, and mentally able to take care of shopping, but has not done shopping in the past (i.e., prior to this home care admission).

☐   1 -   Able to go shopping, but needs some assistance:
       (a) By self is able to do only light shopping and carry small packages, but needs someone to do occasional major shopping; <u>OR</u>
       (b) <u>Unable</u> to go shopping alone, but can go with someone to assist.

☐   2 -   <u>Unable</u> to go shopping, but is able to identify items needed, place orders, and arrange home delivery.

☐   3 -   Needs someone to do all shopping and errands.

(M0770) Ability to Use Telephone: Ability to answer the phone, dial numbers, and <u>effectively</u> use the telephone to communicate.

- ☐ 0 - Able to dial numbers and answer calls appropriately and as desired.
- ☐ 1 - Able to use a specially adapted telephone (i.e., large numbers on the dial, teletype phone for the deaf) and call essential numbers.
- ☐ 2 - Able to answer the telephone and carry on a normal conversation but has difficulty with placing calls.
- ☐ 3 - Able to answer the telephone only some of the time or is able to carry on only a limited conversation.
- ☐ 4 - <u>Unable</u> to answer the telephone at all but can listen if assisted with equipment.
- ☐ 5 - Totally unable to use the telephone.
- ☐ NA - Patient does not have a telephone.

MEDICATIONS

(M0780) Management of Oral Medications: <u>Patient's ability</u> to prepare and take <u>all</u> prescribed oral medications reliably and safely, including administration of the correct dosage at the appropriate times/intervals. **<u>Excludes</u> injectable and IV medications. (NOTE: This refers to ability, not compliance or willingness.)**

- ☐ 0 - Able to independently take the correct oral medication(s) and proper dosage(s) at the correct times.
- ☐ 1 - Able to take medication(s) at the correct times if:
  - (a) individual dosages are prepared in advance by another person; <u>OR</u>
  - (b) given daily reminders; <u>OR</u>
  - (c) someone develops a drug diary or chart.
- ☐ 2 - <u>Unable</u> to take medication unless administered by someone else.
- ☐ NA - No oral medications prescribed.

(M0790) Management of Inhalant/Mist Medications: <u>Patient's ability</u> to prepare and take <u>all</u> prescribed inhalant/mist medications (nebulizers, metered dose devices) reliably and safely, including administration of the correct dosage at the appropriate times/intervals. **<u>Excludes</u> all other forms of medication (oral tablets, injectable and IV medications).**

- ☐ 0 - Able to independently take the correct medication and proper dosage at the correct times.
- ☐ 1 - Able to take medication at the correct times if:
  - (a) individual dosages are prepared in advance by another person, <u>OR</u>
  - (b) given daily reminders.
- ☐ 2 - <u>Unable</u> to take medication unless administered by someone else.
- ☐ NA - No inhalant/mist medications prescribed.

(M0800) Management of Injectable Medications: <u>Patient's ability</u> to prepare and take <u>all</u> prescribed injectable medications reliably and safely, including administration of correct dosage at the appropriate times/intervals. **<u>Excludes</u> IV medications.**

- ☐ 0 - Able to independently take the correct medication and proper dosage at the correct times.
- ☐ 1 - Able to take injectable medication at correct times if:
  - (a) individual syringes are prepared in advance by another person, <u>OR</u>
  - (b) given daily reminders.
- ☐ 2 - <u>Unable</u> to take injectable medications unless administered by someone else.
- ☐ NA - No injectable medications prescribed.

EQUIPMENT MANAGEMENT

(M0810) Patient Management of Equipment (includes <u>ONLY</u> oxygen, IV/infusion therapy, enteral/parenteral nutrition equipment or supplies): <u>Patient's ability</u> to set up, monitor and change equipment reliably and safely, add appropriate fluids or medication, clean/store/dispose of equipment or supplies using proper technique. **(NOTE: This refers to ability, not compliance or willingness.)**

- ☐ 0 - Patient manages all tasks related to equipment completely independently.
- ☐ 1 - If someone else sets up equipment (i.e., fills portable oxygen tank, provides patient with prepared solutions), patient is able to manage all other aspects of equipment.
- ☐ 2 - Patient requires considerable assistance from another person to manage equipment, but independently completes portions of the task.
- ☐ 3 - Patient is only able to monitor equipment (e.g., liter flow, fluid in bag) and must call someone else to manage the equipment.
- ☐ 4 - Patient is completely dependent on someone else to manage all equipment.
- ☐ NA - No equipment of this type used in care **[If NA, go to *M0825*]**

(M0820) Caregiver Management of Equipment (includes <u>ONLY</u> oxygen, IV/infusion equipment, enteral/parenteral nutrition, ventilator therapy equipment or supplies): <u>Caregiver's ability</u> to set up, monitor, and change equipment reliably and safely, add appropriate fluids or medication, clean/store/dispose of equipment or supplies using proper technique. **(NOTE: This refers to ability, not compliance or willingness.)**

- ☐ 0 - Caregiver manages all tasks related to equipment completely independently.
- ☐ 1 - If someone else sets up equipment, caregiver is able to manage all other aspects.
- ☐ 2 - Caregiver requires considerable assistance from another person to manage equipment, but independently completes significant portions of task.
- ☐ 3 - Caregiver is only able to complete small portions of task (e.g., administer nebulizer treatment, clean/store/dispose of equipment or supplies).
- ☐ 4 - Caregiver is completely dependent on someone else to manage all equipment.
- ☐ NA - No caregiver

THERAPY NEED

(M0825) Therapy Need: Does the care plan of the Medicare payment period for which this assessment will define a case mix group indicate a need for therapy (physical, occupational, or speech therapy) that meets the threshold for a Medicare high-therapy case mix group?

- ☐ 0 - No
- ☐ 1 - Yes
- ☐ NA - Not applicable

EMERGENT CARE

(M0830) Emergent Care: Since the last time OASIS data were collected, has the patient utilized any of the following services for emergent care (other than home care agency services)? **(Mark all that apply.)**

- ☐ 0 - No emergent care services **[If no emergent care, skip *M0840*]**
- ☐ 1 - Hospital emergency room (includes 23-hour holding)
- ☐ 2 - Doctor's office emergency visit/house call
- ☐ 3 - Outpatient department/clinic emergency (includes urgicenter sites)
- ☐ UK - Unknown **[If UK, skip *M0840*]**

(M0840) Emergent Care Reason: For what reason(s) did the patient/family seek emergent care? **(Mark all that apply.)**

☐ 1 - Improper medication administration, medication side effects, toxicity, anaphylaxis

☐ 2 - Nausea, dehydration, malnutrition, constipation, impaction

☐ 3 - Injury caused by fall or accident at home

☐ 4 - Respiratory problems (e.g., shortness of breath, respiratory infection, tracheobronchial obstruction)

☐ 5 - Wound infection, deteriorating wound status, new lesion/ulcer

☐ 6 - Cardiac problems (e.g., fluid overload, exacerbation of CHF, chest pain)

☐ 7 - Hypo/Hyperglycemia, diabetes out of control

☐ 8 - GI bleeding, obstruction

☐ 9 - Other than above reasons

☐ UK - Reason unknown

Appendix F

Home Health Advance Beneficiary Notice

Part A providers furnishing Part B services may bill a patient for services denied by Medicare as not reasonable and necessary under Medicare program standards. However, providers must inform the patient before furnishing the services that Medicare will likely deny payment for the services. The home health advance beneficiary notice (HHABN) provides a format to do so.

Note: The following form was revised and approved by the Health Care Financing Administration on December 4, 2000, and became effective on March 1, 2001.

HHA Letterhead

Date of Notice:

Beneficiary name: _____   Medicare # (HICN):_____

Attending physician: _____   Physician's telephone number: _____

HOME HEALTH ADVANCE BENEFICIARY NOTICE (HHABN)

☐ We expect Medicare will not pay for **any** home health services for you.

☐ We expect Medicare will stop paying for **some** of your home health services.

☐ We expect Medicare will stop paying for **all** home health services for you.

Why Won't Medicare Pay For Your Services?

Medicare only pays for your home health services if you qualify under Medicare program rules. You must be homebound, under the care of a physician, and require intermittent skilled nursing care or therapy, or continue to need occupational therapy. All home health services must be medically necessary for the care of your condition and be ordered by a physician. We, _____, have looked at your medical records and condition. We expect Medicare **will not pay for:** _____

_____

_____ because:_____

_____.

This is our opinion based on our understanding of Medicare's home health coverage rules. Talk to your doctor, family, and us about your need for those specified services.

What Does This Mean for You?

You still can get the specified home health services if you think that you need them. We expect that you will have to pay for those services yourself or through any other insurance that you may have. We estimate that all of those services will cost about $_____.

Only Medicare can make the official decision about Medicare payment.
You can ask Medicare for an official decision if you:

- Request that we provide the specified services pending Medicare's decision.

- Instruct us to submit a claim to Medicare so that Medicare can decide if it will pay for those services. You may give us additional evidence to submit with the claim supporting your need for those services, like a letter from your doctor.

- Choose **Option A** on the next page.

If your home health services are paid for by Medicare and/or by your other insurance, you will be refunded any amounts that you are due.

If you do not hear from Medicare within 90 days you can call Medicare at : (___)_____.
Medicare TTY/TDD for the hearing and speech impaired: (____)_____.

If you have questions, please call us at: (___)_____.   **TTY/TDD:** (___)_____.

OMB Approval No. 0938-0781. Form No. HCFA-R-296

What Can You Do If Medicare Decides Not to Pay for Your Services?

You have the right to appeal Medicare's decision not to pay for your home health services. Medicare will send you notice of its official decision not to pay that explains its decision in your case. That notice will explain how you can appeal Medicare's decision not to pay.

What Do You Do Right Now?

1. Choose an option (check only **one** box below).

☐ **A. I want to receive the specified home health services and obtain a Medicare official decision.** Please submit a claim, with any supporting evidence that I include, to Medicare for its official decision. Please bill my other health insurance (_____
_____) if necessary. I understand that, if I have no insurance other than Medicare, I might have to pay for these services while Medicare is making its decision. If Medicare or another insurer does decide to pay and I have made any payments, I will be refunded any amounts that I am due. I agree to be fully and personally responsible for payment of any amount for which Medicare and my other insurance will not pay.

☐ **B. I do not want to receive the specified home health services.**

☐ **C. I want to receive the specified home health services.** I do not want you to submit a claim or any health information to Medicare for an official decision. I know that I will be fully responsible for payment.

---

2. Sign and date the form, to authorize the option you chose.

On (date) _____, I received this notice explaining to me that Medicare may not pay for some or all of my home health services.

_____   _____
Date of signature   Signature of beneficiary or person acting on beneficiary's behalf

3. Return the form to us at our address below.

HHA Address Block

NOTE: Your health information will be kept confidential. Any information that we collect about you on this form will be kept with your personal medical records at our offices. If a claim is submitted to Medicare, your health information on this form may be shared with Medicare. Your health information which Medicare sees will be kept confidential by Medicare.

This is a Medicare Approved Notice.

OMB Approval No. 0938-0781. Form No. HCFA-R-296

Appendix G

Clinical Note and Care Plan Update, and Hospice Care Plan AD PACK and Plan of Treatment

The hospice care plan AD PACK and plan of treatment form and the clinical note and care plan update form were developed by Allina Hospitals and Clinics. The black triangles on the four corners of the first page are anchors used to scan documents into the optical imaging system that indexes and stores all clinical record documents.

RN PN

56214

| HOSPICE CLINICAL NOTE AND CARE PLAN UPDATE |
| ORIGINAL - MEDICAL RECORDS   COPY - CLINICIAN |

SOCIAL SECURITY NUMBER

CLIENT NAME					BR.
BILLABLE	YES	NO	PAYROLL	YES	NO	74
ACTIVITY ID	RNV 760	CSV 760			75
	RNV 740	ETV 740	LNV 740		76
	RNV 745	ETV 760	LNV 760		
	RNV 750	CSV 740			

MONTH   DAY   YEAR

TIME IN   TIME OUT

NCS® MM105621-4 654321   Printed in U.S.A.   Please fill in ovals completely. Write numbers centered in boxes. Use a blue or black ink pen.

| T | P | ○ REGULAR ○ IRREGULAR | R | BP LEFT | BP RIGHT | ○ SITTING | ○ STANDING | ○ LYING | WEIGHT |

A: ASSESSMENT CODES: 1 = PROGRESSING   2 = RESPONDING TO TREATMENT   3 = DECLINING   4 = INITIAL EVALUATION

UNIVERSAL PRECAUTIONS MUST BE FOLLOWED, WHEN APPROPRIATE, USE GOWN, GLOVES, AND/OR MASK

	WNL	ABN	CODE	EXPLANATION
PULMONARY VENTILATION				○ RALES ○ RHONCHI ○ WHEEZE ○ DIMINISHED ○ COUGH ○ DYSPNEA ○ O₂ AT ____
CV / CIRCULATION				○ CHEST PAIN ○ EDEMA ____
NEURO / COMPREHENSION / MENTAL STATUS				○ LETHARGIC ○ CONFUSED ○ SEMI-COMATOSE ○ COMA ○ SEDATED ○ A + O
GI / ELIMINATION				○ ASCITES ○ DISTENSION ○ CONSTIPATED ○ DIARRHEA ○ INCONTINENT ○ NAUSEA ○ BS ○ EMESIS
GU / ELIMINATION				○ DISTENSION ○ INCONTINENCE ○ CLOUDY ○ ODOR ○ CONCENTRATED ○ COLOR ○ CATHETER ____
MUSCULOSKELETAL / MOBILITY / ENDUR				○ GAIT ____ ○ MOBILITY ____ ○ ADLS ____
SKIN WOUND				○ COLOR ____ ○ OPEN AREA ____ ○ WOUND CARE ____
PAIN / DISCOMFORT: (0-10 SCALE) 0=NO PAIN 5=MODERATE 10=WORST PAIN 3=MILD 8=SEVERE				○ LOCATION ____ ○ INTENSITY ____ ○ MEDICATION ____ ○ DURATION ____ ○ RESPONSE ____

| ACTION CODES | S = SUPERVISION T = TEACHING A = ASSESS | C = CARE GIVEN D = DISCUSSION | 1 = IMPROVED 2 = NO CHANGE 3 = DECLINED | 4 = NEEDS CONTINUED INTERVENTION 5 = VERBALIZES/DEMONSTRATES UNDERSTANDING 6 = TEACHING COMPLETE | 7 = LACK OF COMPLIANCE | OUTCOME CODES |

	PROBLEM	DOCUMENT: PROBLEM, ACTION, CARE PLAN CODE, INTERVENTION & OUTCOME
1.	ADJ TO PROGNOSIS/DX	
2.	ALTERATION IN COMFORT	
3.	MEDICATION ADMINISTRATION	
4.	ALT. IN SENSORY/PERCEPTUAL	
5.	POTENTIAL FOR INJURY	
6.	ALT. IN SKIN INTEGRITY	
7.	ALT. IN RESPIRATORY STATUS	
8.	IMPAIRED NUTRITION	
9.	NAUSEA/VOMITING	
10.	ALT. IN ORAL MUCOSA	
11.	ALT. IN BOWEL FUNCTION	
12.	ALT. IN URINARY ELIMINATION	
13.	IMMINENT DEATH	
14.	SPIRITUAL SUPPORT	
15.	ALT. IN FAMILY COPING	
16.	GRIEF/ANXIETY ISSUES	
17.	MANAGEMENT OF STRESS	
18.	IMPAIRED HOME MANAGEMENT	#3
19.	VOLUNTEER SUPPORT	○ DISPOSED OF NARCOTICS / DRUGS: (WHAT, HOW & AMT.) ____ ○ MEDS REVIEWED ____
20.	SUPPORT THRU GRIEVING	○ INSTRUCTED USE, DOSE, SIDE EFFECTS OF: ____
21.	OTHER	○ REFILLS ORDERED: ____

SUPERVISORY VISIT ○ RN ○ LPN ○ HHA ○ INDIRECT ○ DIRECT ○ HOMEMAKER

(DOCUMENT EVERY 14 DAYS) EMPLOYEE: ____

YES NO		YES NO	
○ ○	DEMONSTRATES COMPETENT SKILLS / EXPERTISE	○ ○	ADHERES TO AGENCY POLICIES / PROCEDURES
○ ○	SATISFACTORY CLIENT RESPONSE TO TREATMENT	○ ○	ARRIVES FOR APPOINTMENTS AS SCHEDULED
○ ○	FOLLOWS ASSIGNMENT / PLAN OF CARE	○ ○	COMPLIES WITH AGENCY DRESS CODE
○ ○	DEMONSTRATES ADEQUATE COMMUNICATION SKILLS	○ ○	ASSIGNMENT UPDATED OR REVIEWED

P: ○ CONTINUE TEACHING ACCORDING TO CARE PLAN
CONFERENCE WITH:
○ MD ○ MSW ○ HHA ○ PCC
○ PT ○ CHAPLAIN ○ CASE MANAGER
○ BEREAVEMENT COORD. ○ PHARMACIST
○ CHANGE ORDER ○ VOLUNTEER COORD.
○ OTHER

| EMPLOYEE SIG. | FIRST | MIDDLE INITIAL | LAST | TITLE |

EMPLOYEE ID   EMPLOYEE TYPE

(5/99)

Reprinted with permission from Allina Hospitals and Clinics, Minnesota, © 2001.

Hospice Care Plan
AD PACK and Plan of Treatment

Patient Name: «Patient» **SS#:** «SS» **SOC:** «SOC»

| Initial plan of care | Initiated by: | | Additional team members: | |

Date problem Identified/ Initials	Problem/Opportunities	Intervention	Date initiated/ completed/Initials
	Patient has a terminal illness and has been referred to hospice	1. Inform regarding hospice services; determine appropriateness of admission	

END RESULT OUTCOMES: Self determined life closure; Safe and Comfortable Dying; and Effective Grieving

PATIENT DISEASE STATE (PD)

Goal: Treat distressing symptoms and side effects of symptom management. Prevent unnecessary hospitalizations.
Prevent increase in severity of symptoms. Prevent symptoms from occurring.
Prevent side effects of treating symptoms.

Date problem Identified/Initials		Date problem Identified/Initials	
Primary Diagnosis: _____		Medication related disorder(s): (Such as, allergies, toxicities, etc) _____	
Secondary Diagnoses and common co-morbidity factors: ☐ Morbid weight loss ☐ Smoking habit ☐ Suppressed immunity ☐ Weakness _____		Psychological or behavioral disorder(s) (Such as, anxiety, depression, substance abuse): _____ _____ _____	
Frank disease(s): (such as emphysema, hypertension, diabetes, the anemia's) _____ _____		Trauma injury(ies): _____ _____	
Infections(s): _____			

Patient: «Patient» SS# «SS»

PATIENT MEDICAL STATE (MS)

Goals:

Treat distressing symptoms and side effects of symptom management

Prevent side effects of treating symptoms

Prevent symptoms from occurring

Prevent increase in severity of symptoms

Prevent unnecessary hospitalizations

Support optimal level of consciousness

Date problem identified/ Initials	Problem/Opportunities	Date problem resolved/ Initials	Date initiated/ initials	Interventions (Check Interventions Initiated)	Date completed Initials
	Pain Problems: Sensory/neurologic			**Pain Interventions** ☐ Initiate and maintain standard approach to pain assessment • Complete pain assessment with each visit • Include location, intensity (0-10 scale), duration and contributing factors of symptoms. • Determine type of pain patient has to institute appropriate pain interventions • Identify patient goals for acceptable pain levels • Assess family ability and/or willingness to comply with a medication regime • Assess psychosocial and spiritual distress as it may relate to pain • Evaluate effectiveness of medication and make changes as per order • Consult with physician as needed	
	Abdominal			☐ Pharmacologic pain management • Evaluate effectiveness of medication and make changes as per orders • Assess family ability and/or willingness to comply with a medication regime • Change route of medication administration, if needed • Instruct regarding dose/action/schedule/administration/contraindications and side effects of meds • See medication sheets/transfer summary for patient specific orders	
	Integumentary				
	Cardiac/circulatory				
	Pulmonary				
	Urinary				
	Musculo-skeletal			☐ Start bowel protocol with the initiation of opioids ☐ Initiate and teach regarding alternative comfort measures ☐ Monitor physical changes and instruct regarding disease progression ☐ Provide oxygen therapy (see medication/treatment sheet) ☐ Refer to volunteer services to provide massage, healing touch or music ☐ Adaptive equipment as needed. (more interventions on next pg.)	
	Reproductive System				
	Other _____			☐ Provide teaching regarding pain management including:	

Patient: «Patient»   SS# «SS»

Date problem Identified/ initials	Problem/Opportunities	Date problem resolved/ initials	Date Initiated /Initials	Interventions (Check Interventions Initiated)	Date completed Initials
	Sensory/Neurologic Problems: □ Agitation □ Anxiety □ Aphasia-(inability to express oneself through speech, or loss of verbal comprehension) □ Ataxia-(muscular incoordination, esp. when voluntary muscular movements are attempted) □ Blindness □ Chills □ Coma □ Confusion □ Cramps □ Deafness □ Delirium-(disorientation for time and place, usually with illusions and hallucinations) □ Depression □ Diplopia-(double vision) □ Dysphasia-(Impairment of speech resulting from a brain lesion) □ Fever □ Foot drop-(failure to maintain the foot in a normally flexed position) □ Hemianopsia-(blindness in half the field of vision in one or both eyes) □ Hiccoughs □ Hyperesthesia-(unusual sensitivity to sensory stimuli, such as pain or touch.) □ Insomnia- (inability to sleep) □ Myoclonus-(twitching or spasm of a muscle) □ Numbness □ Paresthesia-(abnormal sensation without objective cause, such as numbness, prickling, and tingling) *(More on next page)*			• Dose/action/schedule/administration and side effects of meds. • Use of narcotic medications including the risks and benefits of taking narcotics • Written medication instructions • Obtaining medications • Evaluate understanding of instructions • Contraindications **Sensory/Neurologic Interventions** □ Pharmacologic symptom management • Evaluate effectiveness of medication and make changes as per orders • Assess family ability and/or willingness to comply with a medication regime • Change route of medication administration, if needed • Instruct regarding dose/action/schedule/administration/ contraindications and side effects of meds • See medication sheets/transfer summary for patient specific orders □ Assess and instruct on methods to provide ADL's □ Assess communication issues • Assess history of ability to communicate • Assess ability to communicate in an alternative method • Instruct patient and family on alternate methods of communication if needed. □ Initiate and teach regarding alternative comfort measures □ Instruct regarding caring for patient with cognitive impairment • Provide calm, supportive atmosphere • Treat patient as an adult with dignity and respect • Help patient remain autonomous • Maintain set routine • Use reality orientation, as appropriate □ Instruct regarding safety measures □ Refer to speech, occupational or rehab therapist □ Refer to a mental health provider □ Adaptive equipment as needed. □ Offer Oxygen therapy:_____ □ Refused oxygen therapy □ Initiated oxygen therapy *(More on next page)*	

Patient: «Patient»   SS# «SS»

Date problem identified/ initials	Problem/Opportunities	Date problem resolved/ initials	Date Initiated/ Initials	Interventions (Check Interventions Initiated)	Date completed Initials
	Sensory/Neurologic Problems (cont): ☐ Sedation–(drug induced calm) ☐ Seizure activity ☐ Stupor–a state of lessened responsiveness ☐ Syncope-fainting ☐ Terminal restlessness ☐ Tinnitus–ringing in the ears ☐ Vertigo–dizziness Inflammation (such as Shingles):			**Sensory/Neurologic Interventions (cont)** ☐Monitor changes and instruct re: disease progression ☐Other _____	
	Nutritional Problems: ☐ Anorexia/decreased intake ☐ Cultural/familial issues related to feeding/nutrition ☐ Dysphagia–(difficulty swallowing) ☐ NPO status Special problem(s) related to diagnosis _____ Special problem(s) related to body mechanics: _____ **Common Fluid and Metabolic Problems:** ☐ Dehydration ☐ Hemorrhage(systemic) ☐ Hypervolemia ☐ Hypovolemia Edema: ☐ Ascites–(excessive accumulation of serous fluid in the peritoneal cavity) ☐ Pedal–(foot)_____ ☐ Leg–_____ ☐ anasarca–(severe generalized edema) ☐ pulmonary Blood chemistry abnormality(ies): ☐ hyperglycemia ☐ hypoglycemia			**Nutritional, fluid, metabolic, GI and elimination interventions** ☐Assess level of intake of food/fluids ☐Assess patient's perception of appetite in relationship to quality of life. ☐Assess cause of decreased appetite ☐Assess bowel status at each visit ☐Assess and instruct regarding oral cares to promote hygiene and alleviate dryness ☐Assess respiratory status on each visit ☐Assess and instruct regarding oral cares to promote hygiene and alleviate dryness ☐Instruct regarding dietary supplement ☐Instruct and support changing nutritional needs as disease progresses ☐Instruct and support changing hydration needs as disease progresses ☐Instruct regarding signs of imminent death ☐Instruct regarding the benefits and burdens of IV fluids/TPN/tube feedings ☐Instruct regarding positioning patient for comfort and reduction of pedal edema ☐Instruct regarding normal bowel function including effects of decreased intake, decreased activity, and/or side effects of medication ☐Refer to Diabetic Nurse Educator	

Patient: «Patient»   SS# «SS»

Date problem Identified/ initials	Problem/Opportunities	Date problem resolved/ initials	Date Initiated/ Initials	Interventions (Check Interventions Initiated)	Date completed Initials
	Gastro-Intestinal and Elimination Problems: ☐ Abdominal distension ☐ Constipation ☐ Diarrhea ☐ Dyspepsia-(indigestion) ☐ Emesis ☐ Esophageal reflux ☐ Fecal incontinence ☐ Hematemesis-vomiting of blood ☐ Hiccoughs ☐ Impaction ☐ Melena-(bloody/tarry stools) ☐ Nausea ☐ Rectal prolapse ☐ Hemorrhoids ☐ Stomatitis Stoma(s): _____ Obstruction(s): _____ Urinary ☐ Bladder catheter ☐ Bladder spasms ☐ Hematuria-(blood in urine) ☐ Nocturia-(excessive urination at night) ☐ Urine frequency ☐ Urine incontinence ☐ Urine retention ☐ Anuria-(not producing urine) Other: _____			☐ Refer to Enterostomal nurse ☐ Refer to dietician ☐ Refer to speech therapist for swallowing evaluation ☐ Pharmacologic symptom management • Evaluate effectiveness of medication and make changes as per orders • Assess family ability and/or willingness to comply with a medication regime • Change route of medication administration, if needed • Instruct regarding dose/action/schedule/administration/ contraindications and side effects of meds ☐ Evaluate and manage nausea/vomiting • Determine cause of nausea/vomiting • Eliminate non-essential drugs • Evaluate need for antiemetic • Evaluate need for change in pain med or route of administration ☐ Provide support and teaching regarding care of ostomy • Assess patient and family knowledge and ability to care for ostomy • Assess skin integrity around stoma at each visit • Instruct patient and family proper ostomy care • Instruct patient and family to report change in ostomy function ☐ Determine urinary history and assess current status at each visit ☐ Instruct regarding disease progression and effects on urinary function ☐ Insert Foley catheter and instruct family on care of catheter ☐ Insert Foley catheter to check for residual (straight cath) ☐ Monitor physical changes and instruct regarding disease progression	

Patient: «Patient» SS# «SS»

Date problem identified/initials	Problem/Opportunities	Date problem resolved/initials	Date Initiated/initials	Interventions (Check Interventions Initiated)	Date completed Initials
	Integumentary Problems: ☐ Cellulitis-(inflammation of cellular of connective tissue) ☐ Diaphoresis-(profuse sweating) ☐ Erythema-(skin redness) ☐ Jaundice-(yellowness of skin and white of eye) ☐ Necrosis-(death of areas of body tissue) ☐ Nodules-(a knot or swelling of tissue) ☐ Photosensitivity-(sensitive to light) ☐ Polyps- ☐ Pruritis-(itching) ☐ Rash ☐ Uremic frost-(urea from sweat crystallized on the skin) Decubitus(i): _____ Dryness: _____ Hemorrhage, site: _____ Inflammation: _____ Lesion(s), wound(s), and excoriation(s): _____			**Integumentary Interventions** ☐ Assess skin integrity at each visit ☐ Instruct regarding good skin care and evaluate learning ☐ Provide therapies for itching ☐ Provide wound care per doctors orders • Assess patient and family ability to do wound care • Teach patient and/or family wound care and signs and symptoms of infection • see medication/treatment sheet for details ☐ Instruct patient/family on the potential for bleeding • Instruct family to have dark towels or bedding available in the event of major hemorrhage • Instruct patient/family on techniques to control bleeding • Instruct regarding safety measures to prevent hemorrhaging from surface tumors ☐ Provide specialized mattress or skin protection : ☐ Instruct regarding infection control practices.	

Patient: «Patient»   SS# «SS»

Reprinted with permission from Allina Hospitals and Clinics, Minnesota, © 2001.

Date problem identified/initials	Problem/Opportunities	Date problem resolved/initials	Date Initiated/initials	Interventions (Check Interventions Initiated)	Date completed/initials
	Cardiac/Circulatory Problems: ☐ Angina–(chest pain) ☐ Arrhythmia–(irregular heart rhythm) ☐ Claudication–(severe pain in an exercising muscle to inadequate blood supply) ☐ Cyanosis–(bluish, grayish color of skin) ☐ Hypertension ☐ Orthostatic Hypotension–(blood pressure drops when standing) ☐ Tachycardia–(rapid heart rate) ☐ Thrombosis–(blood clot) Hemorrhage, site: _____ Inflammation: _____ **Respiratory Problems:** ☐ Apnea–(cessation of breathing) ☐ Cough ☐ Dyspnea ☐ air hunger ☐ Hemoptysis—(coughing bloody sputum) ☐ Hypoxemia–(below normal level of oxygen in the blood) ☐ Mucositis–inflamation of the mucosa ☐ Orthopnea–only able to breathe when upright ☐ Terminal congestion–congestion experienced at end of life ☐ Tracheostomy ☐ Smoking in home **Musculoskeletal Problems:** ☐ Atrophy/wasting ☐ Contracture(s)–(muscle "frozen") ☐ Deformity ☐ Diminished strength and endurance ☐ Diminished mobility			**Cardiac/Circulatory /Respiratory Interventions** ☐ Offer Oxygen therapy:_____ ☐ Refused oxygen therapy ☐ Initiated oxygen therapy ☐ Pharmacologic symptom management • Evaluate effectiveness of medication and make changes as per orders • Assess family ability and/or willingness to comply with a medication regime • Change route of medication administration, if needed • Instruct regarding dose/action/schedule/administration/ contraindications and side effects of meds ☐ Instruct regarding positions promoting circulation and comfort. ☐ Instruct regarding infection control practices ☐ Provide tracheostomy care ☐ Assess and instruct regarding oral cares to promote hygiene and alleviate dryness ☐ Instruct regarding positions to promote breathing and comfort. ☐ Instruct regarding effect of smoking on respiratory status and safety ☐ Offer assistive devices; reassess at each visit ☐ Refused assistive devices ☐ Teach regarding safe use of assistive devices **Musculo-skeletal Interventions** ☐ Monitor physical changes and instruct regarding disease progression	

Patient: «Patient»   SS# «SS»

Date problem Identified/ initials	Problem/Opportunities	Date problem resolved/ initials	Date Initiated /Initials	Interventions (Check Interventions Initiated)	Date completed Initials
	□ Fat emboli □ Hernia □ Limited ROM(range of motion) □ Muscle spasms Inflammation: _____ Pathologic fracture (potential): _____ **Reproductive System Problems:** □ Dysmenorrhea-(painful or difficult menstruation) □ Genital Hygiene □ Impotence □ Uterine prolapse Note: Cysts, erosions and polyps are categorized as problems of the integument; infections and STD's are considered secondary diagnoses.			□Instruct regarding providing ADL's □refer to Volunteer services to provide massage or healing touch **Reproductive System Interventions** □Monitor physical changes and instruct regarding disease progression □Instruct regarding providing ADL's □Instruct regarding infection control practices □Instruct regarding good skin care and evaluate learning □Provide therapies for itching □Provide wound care per doctors orders • Assess patient and family ability to do wound care • Teach patient and/or family wound care and signs and symptoms of infection	

Patient: «Patient»   SS# «SS»

Patient/Family Functional State (FS): A person's physical, cognitive and /or social capacity to communicate, learn, and carry out activities of daily living or care requirements.

Goals:	Patient

(check appropriate goals)
- ☐ Promote optimal mobility based on interest and capacity
- ☐ Address treatment compliance problems
- ☐ Promote a safe environment

Goals:	Family

(check appropriate goals)
- ☐ Prepare caregivers for imminent death and/or management of death in home
- ☐ Provide additional support for caregivers with limited capacity to safely support patient.
- ☐ Monitor and address caregiver fatigue

Date problem identified/initials	Problem/Opportunities	Date problem resolved/initials	Date initiated/initials	Interventions (Check Interventions Initiated)	Date completed initials
	Care and Safety Problems:			☐ P ☐ F Instruct regarding procedure at time of death.	
	☐ No family			☐ P ☐ F Instruct regarding use of hospice team to assist with coping.	
	☐ Inadequate number of caregivers			☐ P ☐ F Written instructions to reinforce teaching.	
	☐ Family lives in distant location			☐ P ☐ F Discuss hospice literature.	
	☐ Patient's care and treatment needs not met			• Instruct regarding enhancing coping skills.	
	☐ Patient uncooperative with plan of care			☐ Instruct regarding balance of sleep, rest & activity.	
	☐ Patient lives alone			☐ Instruct regarding effects of chemicals, drugs, and alcohol use.	
	☐ Other			☐ Instruct regarding effect of good nutrition.	
	Treatment Compliance problems:			☐ Instruct regarding use of ordered medication.	
	☐ P ☐ F Illiterate			☐ P ☐ F Refer to dietitian.	
	☐ P ☐ F Impaired understanding due to age			☐ P ☐ F Initiate psychiatric assessment.	
	☐ Child			☐ P ☐ F Follow up with existing mental health provider.	
	☐ Adolescent				
	☐ Elderly Adult			☐ P ☐ F Adaptive equipment as needed.	
	☐ P ☐ F Impaired access to information			☐ P ☐ F Instruct on methods to provide ADL's.	
	☐ P ☐ F Impaired learning ability			• Manage patient/family dynamics.	
	☐ P ☐ F Language barrier			☐ P ☐ F Clarify patient/family goals.	
	☐ P ☐ F Communication barrier other than language			☐ P ☐ F Set limits and guidelines to maintain hospice involvement.	
	☐ P ☐ F Unwilling/unmotivated to learn			☐ P ☐ F Monitor emotional status.	
	☐ P ☐ F Cultural/social barrier			☐ P ☐ F Acknowledge and educate regarding current and potential losses as appropriate.	
	☐ P ☐ F Health care beliefs and practices			☐ P ☐ F Support each person's grieving process.	
	☐ P ☐ F Denial				
	☐ P ☐ F Stress				

Careplan   03/23/01   Page 9

Patient: «Patient»   SS# «SS»

Date problem Identified/ initials	Problem/Opportunities	Date problem resolved/ initials	Date initiated /initials	Interventions (Check Interventions Initiated)	Date completed Initials

	Caregiver capacity problems:
	☐ Physical capacity limitations
	☐ Mental capacity limitations
	
	☐ Ongoing care requirements creating caregiver fatigue
	☐ Unable to drive/restrictions on transportation
	☐ Time limitations, conflicts in demands
	☐ Family conflict
	
	☐ Concurrent life crisis
	☐ Substance abuse
	
	☐ Other _____
				• Reassess caregiver stress at each visit
				
				• Assess and coordinate additional resources.
				  ☐ Lifeline
				  ☐ Meals on wheels
				  ☐ Transportation
				  ☐ County service
				  ☐ Handicap parking
				  ☐ Interpreter
				  ☐ Legal
				  ☐ Financial
				  ☐ Cancer Society
				  ☐ Children's Resources
				  ☐ Other _____
				
				• Volunteer assigned to provide support:
				  ☐ Interpreter
				  ☐ Transportation
				  ☐ Delivery
				  ☐ Other _____
				
				☐ Home Health Aide assigned to provide assistance
				  • HHA supervision every 14 days
				
				• Discuss back-up plan
				  ☐ Respite care discussed
				  ☐ Respite care initiated.
				  ☐ Continuous care discussed
				  ☐ Continuous care initiated.
				  ☐ Acute hospitalization discussed
				  ☐ Acute hospitalization initiated
				  ☐ Alternative placement discussed
				  ☐ Alternative placement initiated
				  ☐ Involve additional family members.
				  ☐ Family conference
				  ☐ Discuss hiring private duty nursing care/long hours of care
				  ☐ Initiate private duty nursing care
				
				• Other: _____	

Reprinted with permission from Allina Hospitals and Clinics, Minnesota, © 2001.

PATIENT/FAMILY ADAPTATION STATE (AS): A person's ability to emotionally or spiritually adjust to changing environmental conditions or life circumstances.

Goals:

Patient	Family/Caregiver	Date completed/Initials
☐ Assist with treatment of problems related to coping and grieving ☐ Support optimal level of awareness ☐ Prevent/address treatment compliance problems ☐ Promote autonomy ☐ Assist patient in emotional and/or spiritual adjustment to changing life circumstances ☐ Redefine concept of wellness as it relates to dying ☐ Promote opportunities for growth	☐ Assist with the treatment of problems associated with coping and grieving ☐ Assist family members' emotional adjustment to the changing role in relation to patient and within family system. ☐ Promote opportunites for growth	

Date problem identified/initials	Problem/Opportunities	Date problem resolved/initials	Date initiated/initials	Interventions (Check Interventions Initiated)
	Problems in Loss & Grieving: ☐P ☐F Loss of self ☐P ☐F Feeling separate from God/Community ☐P ☐F Difficulty letting go ☐P ☐F Feeling victimized by God/Others/World ☐P ☐F Unresolved grief/death experiences ☐P ☐F Disenfranchised grief ☐P ☐F Relational changes e.g. loss of role, decreased ability or desire to interrelate ☐P ☐F Loss of dreams/vision for the future Other: **Existential & Spiritual Growth Issues:** ☐P ☐F Loss/absence of meaning and purpose ☐P ☐F Sense of injustice ☐P ☐F Despair/Hopelessness ☐P ☐F Loneliness ☐P ☐F Guilt/Shame/Sense of unworthiness **Separation/Alienation from:** ☐P ☐F God ☐P ☐F Spouse/Significant other ☐P ☐F Family ☐P ☐F Friends			☐ Initial spiritual care contact by phone/visit • Identify and assess spiritual needs and resources • Offer spiritual support and/or explain spiritual care services • Remain available to provide spiritual care ☐ Patient/family decline initial contact ☐ Crisis intervention precluded initial contact/assessment ☐ Patient died before assessment completed ☐P ☐F Contact current faith community per request ☐ Coordinate spiritual care needs with community clergy • Continue to monitor and assess spiritual care needs and resources ☐P ☐F Follow up phone calls and/or staff consultations ☐P ☐F Weekly team reports ☐P ☐F Visits/care conferences/family meetings • Provide spiritual support/counseling: ☐P ☐F Explore spiritual issues as appropriate ☐P ☐F Encourage sharing of life stories ☐P ☐F Reflective listening/supportive presence ☐P ☐F Assess spiritual practices. ☐P ☐F Spiritual direction ☐P ☐F Inspirational reading, sacred scripture as requested or appropriate

Patient: «Patient» SS# «SS»

Date problem identified/ initials	Problem/Opportunities	Date problem resolved/initials	Date initiated/initials	Interventions (Check Interventions Initiated)	Date completed initials
	□P □F Community □P □F Spiritual community □P □F Anger at God/religious tradition □P □F Sense of abandonment by God/others □P □F Absence of meaningful spiritual support ▪ Fear of: □P □F Suffering □P □F Death □P □F Dependency, being a burden □P □F The unknown □P □F Other: ▪ Forgiveness/Reconciliation in relation to: □P □F God □P □F Spouse/Significant other □P □F Family □P □F Friends □P □F Community □P □F Spiritual Community ▪ Difficulty accepting □P □F Impending death □P □F Self worthiness /one's life □P □F Help/Support and assistance □P □F Individual grieving processes □P □F Changes – physical, emotional, and spiritual Other **Coping Problems:** □P □F Unwillingness to communicate or feel emotion □P □F Maladaptive denial □P □F Suicidal ideation □P □F Impairment of desired sexual expression □P □F Inadequate or inaccurate information □P □F Loss of role □P □F Persistent anxiety			□P □F Prayer □P □F Sacrament □P □F Other____ ▪ Manage family dynamics: □P □F Clarify patient/family goals. □P □F Set limits and guidelines to maintain hospice involvement. □P □F Monitor emotional status. □P □F Acknowledge and educate regarding current and potential losses as appropriate. □P □F Acknowledge and support each person's grieving process. □P □F Empower decision making by providing information and options. □P □F Facilitate improvement in communication among family members □ Refer to Hospice Grief Counselor □ Assess and monitor for volunteer needs □ Died/Discharged before call was made □ Offer Volunteer services □Declined Volunteer services □Accepted Volunteer services ▪ Volunteer assigned to provide: □P □F Caregiver respite □P □F Companionship □P □F Emotional Support □P □F Healing touch □P □F Music □P □F Massage Other____ □ Social Work assessment completed ▪ Offer and provide psychosocial support □P □F Counseling - Home visits. □P □F Counseling - Phone calls □P □F Reflective listening □P □F Family conference □P □F Encourage patient to share life stories □P □F Educate and support around emotional issues	

Patient: «Patient»   SS# «SS»

Reprinted with permission from Allina Hospitals and Clinics, Minnesota, © 2001.

Date problem identified/ initials	Problem/Opportunities	Date problem resolved/initials	Date initiated/initials	Interventions (Check Interventions Initiated)	Date completed initials
	□ P □ F Unremitting depression □ P □ F Family members not aligned around primary decisions □ P □ F Disruption in community support □ P □ F Developmentally unprepared □ P □ F Anxiety about fiscal issues □ P □ F Anxiety about legal issues □ P □ F Other: ___			▪ Social Work assessment not completed because: □ Patient/family declined participation in assessment □ Crisis intervention precluded assessment □ Patient died before assessment completed ▪ If no social work involvement requested, continue to reassess for unmet social work needs: □ P □ F Follow up phone call/s □ P □ F Team reports □ P □ F During each visit/care conference • Other ___	

Patient: «Patient»   SS# «SS»

Family/Patient Resource State (R): The scope of a patient/family unit's environmental and financial resources, related to provision of patient care and future family health.

Goals:
- ☐ Address financial, legal and/or environmental problems, which compromise safe care of patient and welfare of the family.
- ☐ Identify problems associated with personal business and family welfare problems to prevent crisis
- ☐ Define system for timely response to emergencies

Date problem identified/ initials	Problem/Opportunities	Date problem resolved/initials	Date initiated/initials	Interventions (Check Interventions Initiated)	Date completed Initials
	Safety Problems:			☐ P ☐ F Encourage interdisciplinary team involvement to maximize team and family resources.	
	• Shelter			☐ P ☐ F Contact community clergy or spiritual leader regarding additional church resources.	
	☐ Unsafe conditions				
	☐ Phone system absent for emergency communications			☐ P ☐ F Empower decision making by providing information and options.	
	☐ Family unable to remain at home after death				
	☐ Patient or family member threaten others			☐ P ☐ F Adaptive equipment as needed.	
	☐ No shelter			☐ P ☐ F Instruct regarding safety if smoking occurs with O2 use	
	• Inadequate finances			☐ P ☐ F Discuss back-up plan	
	☐ Patient's current care and treatment needs not met			☐ Respite care discussed and initiated.	
	☐ Family's current basic needs (food, clothing) not met			☐ Continuous care discussed and initiated. ☐ Acute hospitalization. ☐ Alternative placement discussed and initiated.	
	☐ Care costs put family at risk in future			☐ Involve additional family members. ☐ Family conference ☐ Hire private duty nursing care	
	☐ Other			☐ P ☐ F Manage family dynamics. ☐ Clarify patient/family goals.	
	General Safety Issues			☐ Set limits and guidelines to maintain hospice involvement.	
	☐ Patient or family members threaten others			☐ Monitor emotional status and caregiver stress.	
	☐ Home has dangerous pets			☐ Acknowledge and educate regarding current and potential losses as appropriate.	
	☐ Staff safety issues exist in home			☐ Support each person's grieving process.	
	☐ Smoking with Oxygen in the home				

Patient: «Patient»   SS# «SS»

Date problem Identified/ Initials	Problem/Opportunities	Date problem resolved/Initials	Date Initiated/Initials	Interventions (Check Interventions Initiated)	Date completed Initials
	Personal Business, Family Welfare and End-of-Life Issues:			□ P □ F Assess and coordinate additional resources.	
	☐ Unresolved will and estate plans ☐ Unresolved funeral arrangements ☐ Unresolved financial arrangements/trusts ☐ Unresolved custody issues ☐ **Unresolved issues regarding end-of-life decisions, and advance directives/ DNR/DNI** _____			☐ Lifeline ☐ Meals on wheels ☐ Transportation ☐ County service ☐ Donated Funds ☐ Free Care ☐ Handicap parking ☐ Interpreter ☐ Legal ☐ Financial ☐ Cancer Society ☐ Telephone ☐ Air conditioner ☐ Other	
	• Other unresolved legal issues: ☐ Citizenship ☐ Next-of-kin status is unclear ☐ Other: _____			• Assist with additional Health Care Funding options ☐ Apply for Medical Assistance ☐ Use MedEligible ☐ Other_____	
	♦ Other_____ _____ _____ _____			• Instruct regarding personal safety issues as identified by patient/staff and family. ☐ Security escort. ☐ Set limits re: animals in the home. ☐ Co-visits with team members. ☐ Other	
				♦ Other_____ _____ _____	

Patient: «Patient»   SS# «SS»

Appendix H

Home Care-Path Visit 1—
Wound and Pain

Bonnie Davis, RN, BSN, and Sheila Hawley, RN, MSN, worked together to develop and design the following sample care path for basic wound care and pain management. These forms were designed to meet PPS documentation requirements and JCAHO pain assessment standards.

BASIC WOUNDS

Patient Name: _____ ID #: _____ VISIT _____

C=Complete I=Incomplete

Nursing Assessment of Signs & Symptoms: Problem (+) No Problem (−) NA= Not Applicable EM= Educational Material

WOUNDS GROUP

CG=Caregiver P=Patient B=Both

INTERVENTIONS

1. Instruct on medications dose/purpose/administration/side effects 1 & 2 (Meds)
2. Instruct on Pathophysiology of wound healing (Patho)
3. Instruct on infection control measures (S/I)
4. Instruct on pain control for the dressing change as needed (Mgt)
5. Instruct on dressing change as ordered (Tx)
6. Instruct a proper activity level (Act)

PATIENT RESPONSE

Verbally returns meds for dose/purpose/administration/side effects

Verbalizes understanding of pathophysiology of wound healing

States 3 infection control measures

States pain is tolerable and verbalizes understanding of pain control measures

Verbalizes/Demonstrates steps in dressing change

States a proper activity level

OTHER:

PLAN:

COMMENTS:

Interdisciplinary communication/referral
MD PT ST HHA SS other: _____

VARIANCES:

Intervention #	Code	Response #	Code

A. Pt. too sick B. RN decision
C. Pt. decision D. CG decision
E. Cognitive status F. Lack of CG
G. Lack of Equip. H. Co-Morbidity
I. Other:

TIME IN: TIME OUT:
DATE: PT/CG INITIAL

RN SIGNATURE:

NEUROLOGICAL
Alert & Oriented x ___
Anxious
Confused
Disoriented
Lethargic
Vertigo
Sensory deficit

VITAL SIGNS
Temp.
Pulse
Resp.
B/P
G.I.

Nausea/Vomiting
Anorexia
Diarrhea
Constipation
Bowel sounds
Last BM

DIET/HYDRATION
Regular
ADA
Blood sugar
Appetite G-F-P
Weight

SKIN
Color
Turgor
Dry
Wound:
Length
Width
Depth
Drainage
Odor
Am't

RESPIRATORY
Crackles
Rhonchi
Cough
Productive
Wheezes
O₂
SOB
DOE
Incentive Spirometry
Other

CARDIOVASCULAR
Arrhythmia
Chest pain
Peripheral Pulse
RUE ___ LUE ___
RLE ___ LLE ___

G.U.
Burning/pain
Frequency/urgency
Hesitancy
Distention/retention
Incontinent
Catheter

MED COMPLIANCE
New
Changes
Adverse Drug Reaction
Med. Safety/Compliance
Other:

INFECTION CONTROL
Appropriate Hygiene techniques
Appropriate Infection control techniques
S/S of infection

SAFETY
Inside
Outside
Staff Safety

MUSCULO/SKELETAL
Weakness
Bed/chair bound
Balance/gait unsteady
Functional status
Independent
Assist
Dependent
Assistive Device
Cane
Walker
Wheelchair
Ambulate
x ___ feet

PAIN
Location
Intensity 0-10
Relieved/Not relieved

HHA SERVICE Y N
Patient satisfaction
HHA to continue
HHA POC revised
HHA following assignment
Patient satisfaction with Aid
Patient satisfaction with Homecare service

PSYCHOSOCIAL
Strengths:
Family Support
Willing
Available
Able
S/S abuse/neglect

NEXT MD APPT.
Date: _____
OTHER:

© 1998 Hawley-Davis, Inc. SF 4/98   BasicWounds PM 6.5

PAIN MANAGEMENT

Patient Name: _____ ID #: _____

Nursing Assessment of Signs & Symptoms: Problem (+) No Problem (-) EM= Educational Material NA= Not Applicable C=Complete I=Incomplete

VISIT ___ 1 ___

PAIN MANAGEMENT

CG=Caregiver P=Patient B=Both

INTERVENTIONS	C	I
1. Instruct on medications dose/purpose/administration/side effects 1 & 2 (Med)		
2. Instruct on pathophysiology of disease (Patho)		
3. Instruct on proper nutrition and hydration (N)		
4. Instruct on the use of a pain flow sheet (Mgt)		
5. Establish a pain baseline using a pain assessment (Mgt)		
6. Instruct [on] pathophysiology of the pain (Patho)		
7. Instruct [on] safety factors related to pain med[ica]tion (Sf)		

OTHER: _____

PATIENT RESPONSE	C	I
Verbally returns meds for dose/purpose/administration/side effects		
Verbalizes understanding of pathophysiology of disease		
States proper nutrition and hydration		
Demonstrates use of pain flow sheet		
Establish a pain baseline using a pain assessment		
Verbalizes understanding of pathophysiology of the pain		
States 3 safety factors related to pain med		

OTHER: _____

PLAN: _____

Interdisciplinary communication/referral
MD PT OT ST HHA SS other: _____

VARIANCES:

COMMENTS: _____

Intervention #	Code	Response #	Code

A. Pt. too sick   B. RN decision
C. Pt. decision   D. CG decision
E. Cognitive status   F. Lack of CG
G. Lack of Equip.   H. Co-Morbidity
I. Other: _____

TIME IN:	TIME OUT:
DATE:	PT/CG INITIAL:

RN SIGNATURE: _____

NEUROLOGICAL
☐ Alert & Oriented x _____
☐ Anxious
☐ Confused
☐ Disoriented
☐ Lethargic
☐ Vertigo
☐ Sensory deficit

VITAL SIGNS
☐ Temp.
☐ Pulse
☐ Resp.
☐ B/P

G.I.
☐ Nausea/Vomiting
☐ Anorexia
☐ Diarrhea
☐ Constipation
☐ Bowel sounds
☐ Last BM _____

DIET/HYDRATION
☐ Regular
☐ ADA
☐ Blood sugar _____
☐ Appetite G-F-P
☐ Weight _____

SKIN
☐ Color
☐ Turgor
☐ Dry
☐ Wound:
  Length _____
  Width _____
  Depth _____
  Drainage _____
  Odor _____
  Am't _____

RESPIRATORY
☐ Crackles _____
☐ Rhonchi _____
☐ Cough
☐ Pro_____
☐ Wheezes
☐ O₂ _____
☐ OB
☐ [illegible]
☐ Incentive Sp_____
☐ Other _____

CARDIOVASCULAR
☐ Arrhythmia
☐ Chest pain
☐ Peripheral Pulses
☐ Edema:
  RUE _____ LUE _____
  RLE _____ LLE _____

G.U.
☐ Burning/pain
☐ Frequency/urgency
☐ Hesitancy
☐ Distention/retention
☐ Incontinent
☐ Catheter

MED COMPLIANCE
☐ New
☐ Changes
☐ Adverse Drug Reaction
☐ Med. Safety/Compliance
☐ Other:

INFECTION CONTROL
☐ Appropriate Hygiene techniques
☐ Appropriate Infection control techniques
☐ S/S of Infection _____

SAFETY
☐ Inside
☐ Outside
☐ Staff Safety

MUSCULO/SKELETAL
☐ Weakness
☐ Bed/chair bound
☐ Balance/gait unsteady
☐ Functional status
  ☐ Independent
  ☐ Assist
  ☐ Dependent
☐ Assistive Device
☐ C_____
☐ W_____ch
☐ [illegible]
☐ X_____

☐ PAIN
  Location _____
  Intensity _____
  0-10
☐ Pain Med. Effectiveness
  0-10

HHA SERVICE   Y   N
Patient satisfaction   ☐ ☐
HHA to continue   ☐ ☐
HHA POC revised   ☐ ☐
HHA following assignment ☐ ☐
Patient satisfaction with Aid ☐
Patient satisfaction with Homecare service ☐

PSYCHOSOCIAL
Strengths:
☐ Family Support
  ☐ Willing
  ☐ Available
  ☐ Able
☐ S/S abuse/neglect

☐ NEXT MD APPT.
  Date: _____
☐ OTHER:

© 1998 Hawley-Davis, Inc. SF 4/98

PAINMANAGEMENT PM 6.5

Appendix I

Case Conference Summaries

The home health case conference summary can be used to record home case conferences. The hospice interdisciplinary plan of care update can be used to document patient, family, and caregiver updates or team conferences.

Organization's Name Press hard for multiple copies.				**HOME HEALTH CASE CONFERENCE SUMMARY**

SYMPTOMS/SEVERITY
- ☐Unchanged
- ☐Deteriorating
- ☐Stable
- ☐Unstable

PRIMARY REASON FOR CARE

ORDERED FREQUENCY
- ☐No Changes

PROGRESS TOWARDS GOALS
- ☐Progressing
- ☐Not progressing

EFFECTIVENESS OF TEACHING
- ☐Patient/Client ☐PCG
- ☐Verbalizes and demonstrates understanding of care plan
- ☐Patient/Client unable to participate in care activities

DISCHARGE PLAN

CURRENT FREQUENCY

SN	
HHA	
MSW	
PT	
ST	
OT	
OTHER:	
Next Review Date:	

Visit Frequency is:
☐Adequate ☐Inadequate

Progress towards goals is
☐Adequate ☐Inadequate

Care plan needs
☐Changes ☐No Changes

PHYSICIAN'S ORDER
☐Summary only, no changes in orders required

Report Completed by _____ Date _____

Physician-Please sign and return within 48 hours

Attending Physician Signature _____ Date _____

White - Clinical Record   Yellow - Physician Name: _____ **Pink - Case Manager**

Patient/Client Name *(Last, First, MI -PLEASE PRINT)*   ID #

tcgcds\caseconf.frp

Organization's Name Press hard for multiple copies.		**HOSPICE INTERDISCIPLINARY PLAN OF CARE UPDATE**	

SYMPTOMS/SEVERITY	LEVEL OF CARE	MEDICATION CHANGES	VISIT CHANGES
☐No changes ☐Deteriorating ☐Stable ☐Unstable	☐No changes ☐Return to home care ☐Inpatient respite ☐Inpatient general ☐Continuous care	☐No changes	☐No changes

TREATMENT/PROCEDURES	PATIENT/FAMILY CONSULTATIONS	SPIRITUAL SUPPORT	BEREAVEMENT SUPPORT
☐No changes	☐None since last update	☐None at present	☐None at present

CURRENT FREQUENCY	CONFERENCE DETERMINATION	RECOMMENDED CHANGES TO POC
SN HHA MSW OTHER: Next Review Date:	Visit Frequency is ☐Adequate ☐Inadequate Progress towards goals is ☐Adequate ☐Inadequate Care plan needs ☐Changes ☐No Changes	

PHYSICIAN'S ORDER

☐Summary only, no changes in orders required

Report Completed by _____   Date _____

Physician-Please sign and return within 48 hours

Attending Physician Signature _____   Date _____

White - Clinical Record	**Yellow - Physician Name:** _____	**Pink - Case Manager**
Patient/Client Name *(Last, First, MI -PLEASE PRINT)*		ID #

tcgcds\ipocu.frp

Appendix J

Home Health Certification and Plan of Care

The home health certification and plan of care is also known as form HCFA-485 and plan of treatment. Standardized data collection facilitates accurate coverage decisions, helps to ensure correct payment for covered services, and promotes compliance with federal laws and regulations. Form HCFA-485 meets regulatory and national survey requirements for the physician's plan of care, certification, and recertification. However, home health organizations may submit any documentation that is signed and dated by the physician that contains all of the required components of the plan of care.

The following 1994 form is available at the Health Care Financing Administration Web site: www.hcfa.gov/forms/default.asp.

Department of Health and Human Services
Health Care Financing Administration

Form Approved
OMB No. 0938-0357

HOME HEALTH CERTIFICATION AND PLAN OF CARE

1. Patient's HI Claim No.	2. Start Of Care Date	3. Certification Period From: To:		4. Medical Record No.	5. Provider No.

6. Patient's Name and Address	7. Provider's Name, Address and Telephone Number

8. Date of Birth	9. Sex ☐ M ☐ F	10. Medications: Dose/Frequency/Route (N)ew (C)hanged

11. ICD-9-CM	Principal Diagnosis	Date
12. ICD-9-CM	Surgical Procedure	Date
13. ICD-9-CM	Other Pertinent Diagnoses	Date

14. DME and Supplies	15. Safety Measures:
16. Nutritional Req.	17. Allergies:

18.A. Functional Limitations

1 ☐ Amputation	5 ☐ Paralysis	9 ☐ Legally Blind				
2 ☐ Bowel/Bladder (Incontinence)	6 ☐ Endurance	A ☐ Dyspnea With Minimal Exertion				
3 ☐ Contracture	7 ☐ Ambulation	B ☐ Other (Specify)				
4 ☐ Hearing	8 ☐ Speech					

18.B. Activities Permitted

1 ☐ Complete Bedrest	6 ☐ Partial Weight Bearing	A ☐ Wheelchair
2 ☐ Bedrest BRP	7 ☐ Independent At Home	B ☐ Walker
3 ☐ Up As Tolerated	8 ☐ Crutches	C ☐ No Restrictions
4 ☐ Transfer Bed/Chair	9 ☐ Cane	D ☐ Other (Specify)
5 ☐ Exercises Prescribed		

19. Mental Status:

1 ☐ Oriented	3 ☐ Forgetful	5 ☐ Disoriented	7 ☐ Agitated
2 ☐ Comatose	4 ☐ Depressed	6 ☐ Lethargic	8 ☐ Other

20. Prognosis:

1 ☐ Poor	2 ☐ Guarded	3 ☐ Fair	4 ☐ Good	5 ☐ Excellent

21. Orders for Discipline and Treatments (Specify Amount/Frequency/Duration)

22. Goals/Rehabilitation Potential/Discharge Plans

23. Nurse's Signature and Date of Verbal SOC Where Applicable:	25. Date HHA Received Signed POT

24. Physician's Name and Address	26. I certify/recertify that this patient is confined to his/her home and needs intermittent skilled nursing care, physical therapy and/or speech therapy or continues to need occupational therapy. The patient is under my care, and I have authorized the services on this plan of care and will periodically review the plan.
27. Attending Physician's Signature and Date Signed	28. Anyone who misrepresents, falsifies, or conceals essential information required for payment of Federal funds may be subject to fine, imprisonment, or civil penalty under applicable Federal laws.

Form HCFA-485 (C-4) (02-94) (Print Aligned)
790-0150

1-PROVIDER

Privacy Act Statement

Sections 1812, 1814, 1815, 1816, of the Social Security Act authorize collection of this information. The primary use of this information is to process and pay Medicare benefits to or on behalf of eligible individuals. Disclosure of this information may be made to: Peer Review Organizations and Quality Review Organizations in connection with their review of claims, or in connection with studies or other review activities, conducted pursuant to Part B of Title XI of the Social Security Act; State Licensing Boards for review of unethical practices or nonprofessional conduct; A congressional office from the record of an individual in response to an inquiry from the congressional office at the request of that individual.

Where the individual's identification number is his/her Social Security Number (SSN), collection of this information is authorized by Executive Order 9397. Furnishing the information on this form, including the SSN, is voluntary, but failure to do so may result in disapproval of the request for payment of Medicare benefits.

Paper Work Burden Statement

Public reporting burden for this collection of information is estimated to average 15 minutes per response and recordkeeping burden is estimated to average 15 minutes per response. This includes time for reviewing instructions, searching existing data sources, gathering and maintaining data needed, and completing and reviewing the collection of information. Send comments regarding this burden estimate or any other aspect of this collection of information, including suggestions for reducing the burden, to Health Care Financing Administration, P.O. Box 26684, Baltimore, Maryland 21207, and to the Office of Information and Regulatory Affairs, Office of Management and Budget, Washington, D.C. 20503. Paperwork Reduction Project 0938-0357.

Appendix K

Nursing Clinical Progress Note

The nursing clinical progress note is designed to document all specific care, services, and actions provided by the nurse. The form also includes a section for the documentation of home health aide supervision.

NURSING CLINICAL NOTES

ADDRESSOGRAPH

T _____ **R** _____

P _____

- ❑ Radial ❑ Regular
- ❑ Apical ❑ Irregular

Cardiovascular:
- ❑ +/- Radial/Pedal pulses
- Edema - Pitting
- 0 Tr. 1+ 2+ 3+ 4+
- Location _____
- ❑ Color satisfactory
- ❑ Cyanosis ❑ Dizziness
- ❑ Chest Pain _____

- ❑ Palpitations
- ❑ Calf Tenderness
- Homans ❑+ ❑- ❑N/A

Respiratory: ❑ No SOB
- Lungs ❑ Clear
- ❑ Rales ❑ Diminished
- ❑ Wheezes ❑ Rhonchi
- ❑ SOB/exert. ❑ SOB/rest
- ❑ Cough ❑ Sputum

- ❑ Oxygen _____ L/min
- S₄O₂ _____
- ❑ RA

Additional Assessment Findings: _____

Musculoskeletal:
Gait:
- ❑ Steady without assist
- ❑ Steady with assist
- ❑ Unsteady
- ❑ Hemiplegia   R L
- ❑ Paraplegia
- ❑ Quadriplegia
- ❑ ROM Limitations
- ❑ Contractures
- Other _____

Psychosocial Behavior:
- ❑ Cooperative
- ❑ Agitated ❑ Tearful
Affect / Mood:
- ❑ Normal ❑ Anxious
- ❑ Labile ❑ Flat
- ❑ Depressed
- ❑ Withdrawn
Poor coping with: _____

Neurological:
- ❑ PERRL
- ❑ Oriented
- ❑ Person ❑ Place ❑ Time
- ❑ Confused
- ❑ Tremors
- ❑ Tinnitus
- ❑ Syncope
- ❑ Hand Grip Equal ❑ N/A
Deficit

Weight ❑ Unable
- ❑ Actual ❑ Stated
RBS _____ hrs PP
CBG/FBS
- ❑ Actual ❑ Stated ❑ N/A
- ❑ B ❑ NB

Gastrointestinal:
- ❑ ABD soft ❑ Distended
- ❑ Bowel Sounds +/-
- ❑ Dysphagia
- ❑ Nausea ❑ Vomiting
- ❑ Diarrhea Stools/day _____
- ❑ Constipation
- ❑ Colostomy ❑ Ileostomy
Stoma size: _____ ❑Ostomy Care
Last BM

Nutritional:
Appetite:
- ❑ Good ❑ Fair ❑ Poor
- ❑ PEG/Gastrostomy/NG/J Tube

Fluids _____
Feeding/Diet _____
- ❑ Noncompliant with diet

Genitourinary:
- ❑ Voiding, no complaints
Urine Color:
- ❑ Clear ❑ Cloudy ❑ Odor
- ❑ Nocturia ❑ Incontinence
- ❑ Retention ❑ Freq/Urgency
- ❑ Hematuria ❑ Dysuria
- ❑ Urostomy Stoma Size: _____
- ❑ Ostomy Care
- ❑ Suprapubic ❑ Foley
Size: _____ CC
- ❑ Irrigation _____

Blood Pressure: (Orthostatic B/P only as indicated or ordered)
Lying   Sitting   Standing
R ____ L ____   R ____ L ____   R ____ L ____

IV Site ❑ N/A ❑ Peripheral Line
- ❑ PICC ❑Midline ❑Central line
- ❑ Implantable Port
- ❑ Other _____
- ❑ Flush Protocol
- ❑ Flushed
- ❑ Site Complications
- ❑ Site Care/Dreg Change

Integumentary
Skin: ❑ Intact ❑ Warm/Dry
- ❑ Pallor ❑ Diaphoretic
- ❑ Red ❑ Ecchymosis
Turgor: ❑Good ❑ Tenting
Wound:
- ❑ Pressure ❑ N/A
- ❑ Surgical ❑ Stasis
- ❑ Sutures ❑ Staples
- ❑ Skin Tear ❑ Steristrip
- ❑ Burn
Location: _____

- ❑ See Wound Sheet
Plan Next Visit: _____

Discharge Plan: _____

Pain and Pain Management:
- ❑ Denies
Location/Character _____

Intensity: 0   1   2
            3   4   5   6   7
            8   9   10
Onset
- ❑ Acute ❑ Chronic
- ❑ Infrequent ❑ Intermittent
- ❑ Continuous
Analgesia
Frequency of use:
- ❑ Effective ❑ Noneffective
Alleviates _____

Exacerbates _____

Additional Skilled Nursing Instruction: _____

Response to Skilled Nursing Instruction: ❑ Pt. / CG / SO verbalize/demonstrate understanding of
- ❑ Poor understanding-repeat all   content - no review necessary
- ❑ Unable to teach-describe   ❑ Pt. / CG / SO needs reinforcement
- ❑ Other-Specify   ❑ S.O. / CG involvement necessary
- ❑ Return Demonstration of Skilled Nursing Instruction

MD Visit _____ ❑ None Scheduled

Safety: ❑ Universal Precautions Used
- ❑ No Safety issues identified
- ❑ Other: _____
Skilled Nursing Service: _____

Lab Test: _____
Site: _____ Needle Size: _____
- ❑ Pressure Dressing Lab
Resp. to Treatment: ❑ Tolerated Well ❑ Tolerated Poorly

Skilled Nursing Instruction: ❑ See Medication Profile
Medications: _____

- ❑ Dose/Frequency/Route ❑ Indication/Action
- ❑ Side effects ❑ Drug/Food Interaction ❑ Refills
- ❑ Complaint ❑ Noncompliant ❑ Storage
Comprehension: ❑ Good ❑ Fair ❑ Poor
Person Instructed: ❑ Patient ❑ CG ❑ Other _____
Medication analysis / Interactions completed for:
- ❑ New Medication ❑ Changed Medication
- ❑ F/U needed with MD/Pt
Supplies Delivered _____

Supplies needed next visit: _____

Coordination of Plan of Care: ❑ Phone/Voice ❑ Discussed with _____ Copy of note to:
- ❑ Patient ❑ Caregiver ❑ Physician ❑ MSW ❑ PT ❑ OT
- ❑ ST ❑ HCA ❑ Primary RN ❑ Coordinator ❑ Pharmicist ❑ DME
- ❑ ET ❑ Insurance Company ❑ Other: _____
MD Contacted
- ❑ See Communication note/order ❑ Care Plan meets Patient needs ❑ Changes made to Care Plan
- ❑ See Care Step _____

HCA Supervision ❑ N/A ❑ Joint ❑ Nonjoint ❑ Q14D ❑ 60 days
- ❑ Performs Personal Care as outlined on Plan of Treatment - Care Plan
- ❑ Shows an awareness of basic infection control procedures ❑ CPR Pocket Mask
- ❑ Patient/Caregiver pleased with care plan ❑ Name Badge On
- ❑ Anticipates and responds to patient needs
- ❑ Plan of Care meets patient needs ❑ Changes Made HCA Signature: _____
- ❑ CG/SO unable / unwilling to assist with care

Homebound: (Check all that apply)
- ❑ Nonambulatory ❑ Bedbound ❑ Chairbound
- ❑ Needs assist of at least one person to leave house
- ❑ Maximum assist at all times ❑ Requires assistive Device
- ❑ Unable to safely negotiate _____ Entry Steps
- ❑ Endurance - dyspnea on exertion/rest ❑ Home IV therapy in lieu of hospitalization
- ❑ Extreme fatigue after advancing (feet) _____
- ❑ Severely Restricted ROM due to _____
- ❑ Open Draining Wound ❑ O₂ dependent
- ❑ Uncontrolled/intolerable pain
- ❑ Confused, disoriented, lacks judgement, needs supervision
- ❑ Other _____

Disaster Priority Code: Changed ❑ ❑A ❑B ❑C ❑D

Sun M T W Th F Sa   SK   NSK   PRN

Clinician Signature _____
HH - 11   2800077 rev 1/01

Date: _____ Time in: _____ Time out: _____

Appendix L

Initial Bereavement Assessment and Bereavement Care Plan

The following bereavement forms are designed to be used for initial assessments and follow-up.

INBE

710411

	INITIAL BEREAVEMENT ASSESSMENT
	ORIGINAL - MEDICAL RECORDS COPY 1 - BEREAVEMENT COORD. COPY 2 - VOLUNTEER

Page 1

PATIENT NAME

BEREAVED

CONTACT: ☐ PHONE ☐ VISIT   LENGTH OF CONTACT

PHONE NO.

SOCIAL SECURITY NUMBER

☐☐☐-☐☐-☐☐☐☐

DATE OF DEATH: MONTH   DAY   YEAR
☐☐-☐☐-☐☐☐☐

1. Seems open to verbalizing grief-related feelings and issues: ☐ Yes   ☐ Somewhat   ☐ Not very

2. Feelings and issues verbalized:

3. Physical status verbalized:

4. Activities verbalized:

5. Responsibilities/pressures verbalized:

☐ Children at home   ☐ Financial issues   ☐ Social isolation   ☐ Expectations of others
☐ Care giver for other(s)   ☐ Transportation   ☐ Work   ☐ Other _____

Comments:

6. Support system (check):

☐ Family   Describe _____
☐ Friends   Describe _____
☐ Social group(s)   Describe _____
☐ Community of faith   Describe _____
☐ Work setting/colleagues   Describe _____
☐ Other   Describe _____

Special needs or difficulties affecting bereaved's support:

7. Attitude toward future:

8. Memories verbalized:

9. Faith/spiritual issues, struggles, experiences verbalized:

10. Additional losses verbalized: (recent, concurrent, past, anticipated)

H71-041 (7/00)

▲ INBE   **INITIAL BEREAVEMENT ASSESSMENT**   ▲

710411   ORIGINAL - MEDICAL RECORDS   COPY 1 - BEREAVEMENT COORD.   COPY 2 - VOLUNTEER

Page 2

SOCIAL SECURITY NUMBER

PATIENT NAME

MONTH   DAY   YEAR

DATE
OF
DEATH:

ACTION TAKEN: (Affirmations or concerns addressed, resources offered, referrals suggested, grief education offered, etc.)

☐ Offered encouragement regarding grieving process

☐ Affirmed grief experiences to this point

☐ Helped name or clarify grief-related feelings/issues

☐ Discussed:

☐ Encouraged verbalizing of hospice/death/care giving experiences

☐ Offered listening support

☐ Offered and/or reiterated resources and services

    ☐ Grief support group(s)   Specify _____

    ☐ Grief counseling   Referral _____

    ☐ Children and grief resources   Date sent _____

    ☐ Book(s) suggested or offered   Specify _____

    ☐ Volunteer support offered

    ☐ Mailings described

    ☐ Other

GENERAL ASSESSMENT/COMMENTS:

☐ Bereaved seems to be grieving appropriately at this time

☐ Concerns   Describe _____

☐ Other _____

CARE CATEGORY RECOMMENDED:

☐ #1 (Recommend professional follow-up) ☐ #2 (Recommend volunteer assignment) ☐ #3 (Recommend continued follow-up by mail)

   1. Severe complicated grieving
      Violent death
      Current mental health/chemical dependency issues
      Pronounced spiritual struggles
      Need for professional referral
      Children/adolescents at home

   2. Moderately complicated grieving
      Need for additional grief education
      Limited support/isolation
      Previous volunteer assignment

   3. Uncomplicated grieving or declines additional phone/volunteer support
      Good support; good understanding of grieving process

NAME

▲ H71-041 (7/00)   ▲

Reprinted with permission from Allina Hospitals and Clinics, Minnesota, © 2001.

BE CP

710321

ORIGINAL - MEDICAL RECORD   COPY 1 - BEREAVEMENT COORDINATOR   COPY 2 - VOLUNTEER

BEREAVEMENT CARE PLAN

PATIENT		SOCIAL SECURITY NO.

SURVIVOR		DATE OF DEATH
		MONTH DAY YEAR

RELATIONSHIP TO PATIENT	PHONE NO.	LENGTH OF CONTACT

TIME OF CONTACT:
☐ 2 weeks   ☐ 9 months
☐ 30-45 days ☐ 1 year
☐ 3 months   ☐ Other
☐ 6 months _____

TYPE OF CONTACT:
☐ PHONE CALL   Attempts _____
☐ HOME VISIT   _____
☐ FUNERAL/VISITATION _____
☐ OTHER   _____

RISK ASSESSMENT:
#1   #2   #3

PLAN:

☐ AWAIT CONTACT (LEFT MESSAGE) FROM _____ (NAME) FOR FOLLOW-UP

☐ HOME VISIT TO _____ DATE/TIME _____

☐ SEND LETTER NOTIFYING _____ (NAME) OF UNSUCCESSFUL ATTEMPTS TO CONTACT, OFFERING ENCOURAGEMENT IN THEIR GRIEF, AND REITERATING BEREAVEMENT SERVICES AVAILABLE

☐ BEREAVEMENT FOLLOW-UP SUPPORT WILL BE PROVIDED BY MAIL AND BY _____ (NAME) BY PHONE OR VISIT AS NEEDED, BUT AT LEAST QUARTERLY
FIRST QUARTER _____   SECOND QUARTER _____
THIRD QUARTER _____   FOURTH QUARTER _____
13TH MONTH _____

☐ CONTACT HOSPICE VOLUNTEER COORDINATOR _____ (NAME) FOR ASSIGNMENT OF A VOLUNTEER
DATE OF CONTACT _____

☐ MONITOR VOLUNTEER DOCUMENTATION

☐ BEREAVEMENT FOLLOW-UP BY MAIL ONLY (5 CONTACTS PER YEAR)

NOTES: (May include brief assessment or volunteer recommendations)

NAME	DATE
	(See above for attempts)

H71-032 (Rev 12/99)

Appendix M

Record Review Forms

The record review forms are intended for use in performing routine and focused quantitative record reviews. The forms are set to be updated once home health providers supply feedback from external auditors on additional documentation needs.

CONFIDENTIAL / Attorney Client Work Product Privilege

Billing Compliance Review Tool

Beneficiary Name: _____ Reviewer Signature _____

SOC/DC Dates: _____ Date _____

Medical Record Number _____

Medicare # if Applicable _____

Check List	Yes	No	N/A
1. Homebound status met			
2. Need for skilled care documented			
3. Visit frequency matches physician orders			
4. Verbal orders obtained for start of care			
5. Visit documented			
6 Physician signature obtained prior to billing			

MONTH:	RN	PT	ST	OT	MSW	HHA	Bill Date	Error Code
Visits on Invoice								
Potential visit disallowances								

MONTH:	RN	PT	ST	OT	MSW	HHA	Bill Date	Error Code
Visits on Invoice								
Potential visit disallowances								

MONTH:	RN	PT	ST	OT	MSW	HHA	Bill Date	Error Code
Visits on Invoice								
Potential visit disallowances								

MONTH:	RN	PT	ST	OT	MSW	HHA	Bill Date	Error Code
Visits on Invoice								
Potential visit disallowances								

MONTH:	RN	PT	ST	OT	MSW	HHA	Bill Date	Error Code
Visits on Invoice								
Potential visit disallowances								

MONTH:	RN	PT	ST	OT	MSW	HHA	Bill Date	Error Code
Visits on Invoice								
Potential visit disallowances								

TOTAL:	RN	PT	ST	OT	MSW	HHA		
Visits on Invoice								
Potential visit disallowances								

ERROR CODE LEGEND	Primary reasons for potential disallowance
1	Homebound not documented
2	Skilled care not documented
3	Visit frequency inconsistent with physician orders
4	Verbal orders for start of care not documented
5	Visits billed but not documented or match visits in record
6	No physician signature prior to billing

Focused Medical Review Compliance Audit

Client Name _____ Account # _____ Billing Period Requested _____

SOC Date _____ Recert Date_____ DC Date_____

Documentation requested for the following services (circle): RN   PT   ST   OT   MSW   HHA

		YES	NO	N/A	COMMENTS
A	**QUALIFYING CRITERIA**				
	1. Homebound Status Indicated				
	2. Need for Intermittent Skill (RN, PT, or ST) documented				
	3. Medical necessity evident				
B	**PLAN OF CARE (485)**				
	1. VO for SOC present and dated				
	2. Non-routine supplies indicated on orders				
	3. 485 signed/dated by MD prior to billing. If not dated by MD, date received by Agency indicated (#25).				
	4. 485 signed/dated by nurse				
	5. Subsequent Verbal Orders signed and dated by nurse.				
	6. Subsequent Verbal Orders signed and dated by MD prior to billing.				
	7. Endpoint to daily vs on 485 or VO.				
	8. Skilled observation beyond 3 weeks				
C	**RECERT (485)**				
	1. Signed/dated by MD prior to billing				
	2. Signed/dated by nurse (#23)				
D	**PROGRESS/CLINICAL NOTES**				
	1. Visit frequency consistent with orders				
	2. SVCS consistent with Plan of Care (485)				
	3. Notes signed and dated				
E	**HOME HEALTH AIDES**				
	1. Personal care documented each visit				
	2. Visit frequency consistent with orders				
	3. Notes signed & dated				
	4. Supervisory visits evident every 2 weeks				
F	**UB '92**				
	1. Visits documented match vs. billed				
	2. Supplies ordered & used match supplies billed				

General Comments:_____

_____

_____

Billing Recommendations: _____

_____

_____

_____   _____   _____   _____
Nurses Reviewer's Signature   Date   TCG Reviewer's Signature   Date

Med. Rec #				Patient's Initials:				
SOC From: To:								
Physician Order Changes (Include Date)				Frequency of Visits by Work				
				SN				
				HHA				
				PT				
				ST				
				OT				
				MSW				
				Lab Orders:				

Day	Su	M	Tu	W	Th	F	Sa	Service Frequency Below	
Wk 1								RN PT OT Lab	HHA ST MSW
Wk 2								RN PT OT Lab	HHA ST MSW
Wk 3								RN PT OT Lab	HHA ST MSW
Wk 4								RN PT OT Lab	HHA ST MSW
Wk 5								RN PT OT Lab	HHA ST MSW
Wk 6								RN PT OT Lab	HHA ST MSW
Wk 7								RN PT OT Lab	HHA ST MSW
Wk 8								RN PT OT Lab	HHA ST MSW
Wk 9								RN PT OT Lab	HHA ST MSW

* RN Supervisory Visit Necessary Every 14 days

Appendix N

Criteria for Acute and Chronic Conditions

In 1994, the Center for Health Policy and Services Research defined a *quality indicator group* (QUIG), now commonly referred to as acute or chronic conditions, as a grouping of similar patient conditions that relate to or influence the nature of quality measures. QUIGs describe both acute and chronic conditions based on responses to items in the OASIS data set. The final report, *Quality Monitoring Using Case Mix and Adverse Event Outcome Reports,* lists all acute and chronic conditions.

The following extract comes from the Health Care Financing Administration's *Appendix: Guidelines for Reviewing Case Mix and Adverse Event Outcome Reports* (January 2001). The entire appendix can be accessed at www.hcfa.gov/medicaid/oasis/obqm3.pdf.

Acute Conditions

On the second page of case-mix reports, prevalence values are given for patients categorized with acute conditions. The inclusion of patients in these groups is based on the following criteria. Categories are not mutually exclusive.

Orthopedic conditions: Patients who were discharged from a hospital, rehabilitation facility, or nursing home within 14 days of start or resumption of care (SOC/ROC), or who experienced a medical or treatment regimen change within 14 days of SOC/ROC, are included in this group if any medical diagnosis pertaining to those events is related to the musculoskeletal system. This also includes disorders of cartilage or other connective and soft tissues.

Neurologic conditions: Patients who were discharged from a hospital, rehabilitation facility, or nursing home within 14 days of SOC/ROC, or who experienced a medical or treatment regimen change within 14 days of SOC/ROC, are included in this group if any medical diagnosis pertaining to those events relates to the nervous system.

Open wounds or lesions: Patients are included in this group if they have an open wound or skin lesion. Also, patients who were discharged from a hospital, rehabilitation facility, or nursing home within 14 days of SOC/ROC, or who experienced a medical or treatment regimen change within 14 days of SOC/ROC, are included in this group if any medical diagnosis pertaining to those events relates to an open wound or skin lesion.

Terminal conditions: Patients who have a life expectancy of six months or less are included in this group. These patients usually are receiving palliative care for terminal illnesses, such as malignant neoplasms, end-stage cardiopulmonary disease, or end-stage renal disease.

Cardiac/peripheral vascular conditions: Patients who were discharged from a hospital, rehabilitation facility, or nursing home within 14 days of SOC/ROC, or who experienced a medical or treatment regimen change within 14 days of SOC/ROC, are included in this group if any medical diagnosis pertaining to those events relates to the circulatory system.

Pulmonary conditions: Patients who were discharged from a hospital, rehabilitation facility, or nursing home within 14 days of SOC/ROC, or who experienced a medical or treatment regimen change within 14 days of SOC/ROC, are included in this group if any medical diagnosis pertaining to those events relates to respiratory function.

Diabetes mellitus: Patients who were discharged from a hospital, rehabilitation facility, or nursing home within 14 days of SOC/ROC, or who experienced a medical or treatment regimen change within 14 days of SOC/ROC, are included in this group if any medical diagnosis pertaining to those events is diabetes mellitus.

Acute gastrointestinal disorders: Patients who were discharged from a hospital, rehabilitation facility, or nursing home within 14 days of SOC/ROC, or who experienced a medical or treatment regimen change within 14 days of SOC/ROC, are included in this group if any medical diagnosis pertaining to those events is related to the digestive system.

Contagious/communicable conditions: Patients who were discharged from a hospital, rehabilitation facility, or nursing home within 14 days of SOC/ROC, or who experienced a medical or treatment regimen change within 14 days of SOC/ROC, are included in this group if any medical diagnosis pertaining to those events is related to infections or parasitic diseases.

Acute urinary incontinence/catheter: Patients who were discharged from a hospital, rehabilitation facility, or nursing home within 14 days of SOC/ROC, or who experienced a medical or treatment regimen change within 14 days of SOC/ROC, are included in this group if the patient is incontinent of urine or if the patient has a new indwelling catheter.

Acute mental/emotional conditions: Patients receiving psychiatric nursing services at home are included in this group.

Oxygen therapy: Patients receiving either intermittent or continuous oxygen therapy at home are included in this group.

IV/infusion therapy: Patients receiving intravenous or infusion therapy at home, such as hydration, or intravenous, subcutaneous, or intrathecal therapy for pain control, are included in this group.

Enteral/parenteral nutrition therapy: Patients receiving enteral or parenteral nutrition at home, such as gastrostomy tube feedings or hyperalimentation, are included in this group.

Ventilator therapy: Patients receiving continuous or intermittent ventilation therapy at home are included in this group.

Chronic Conditions

Patients who were not discharged from an inpatient facility (hospital, rehabilitation facility, or nursing home) within 14 days of SOC/ROC, and who did not experience a change in medical or treatment regimen within 14 days of SOC/ROC, are assigned to a chronic group if they meet specified levels of dependency (or conditions for membership) for that group. Patients who were discharged from an inpatient facility within 14 days of SOC/ROC, or who did experience a change in medical or treatment regimen within 14 days of SOC/ROC, are assigned to a chronic group if, and only if, they met the specified levels of dependency/conditions for membership for that condition prior to the inpatient stay/medical regimen change.

The inclusion of patients in these groups is based on the following criteria. These categories are not mutually exclusive.

Dependence in living skills: Patients who meet the criteria for inclusion in chronic conditions are assigned to this group if they are unable to prepare main meals on a regular basis and require the assistance of another person for at least two of the following: laundry, transportation, housekeeping, shopping, or ability to use the telephone. The assistance required is necessary for routine or normal performance of the activity.

Dependence in personal care: Patients who meet the criteria for inclusion in chronic conditions are assigned to this group if they require the assistance of another person for bathing; or if they require assistance for grooming (combing or brushing hair, shaving or applying makeup, cleaning teeth or dentures, or trimming fingernails) plus dressing of the upper or lower body.

Impaired ambulation/mobility: Patients who meet the criteria for inclusion in chronic conditions are assigned to this group if they require the routine assistance of another person for toileting, transferring, or ambulation.

Eating disability: Patients who meet the criteria for inclusion in chronic conditions are assigned to this group if they are unable to feed themselves without constant supervision or assistance, or if they receive nutrients through a nasogastric or gastrostomy tube.

Urinary incontinence/catheter use: Patients who meet the criteria for inclusion in chronic conditions are assigned to this group if they are incontinent of urine or have an indwelling/suprapubic catheter.

Dependence in medication administration: Patients who meet the criteria for inclusion in chronic conditions are assigned to this group if they require the assistance of another person for taking oral medications, inhalant medications, or injectable medications.

Chronic pain: Patients who meet the criteria for inclusion in chronic conditions are assigned to this group if they are experiencing intractable pain.

Chronic cognitive/mental/behavioral problems: Patients who meet the criteria for inclusion in chronic conditions are assigned to this group if they demonstrate one or more of the following behaviors at least once a week:

- Memory deficit
- Impaired decision making

- Verbal disruption

- Physical aggression

- Disruptive, infantile, or socially inappropriate behavior (excludes verbal actions)

- Delusions, hallucinations, or paranoid ideations

Chronic condition with caregiver: Patients are included in this group if they have been assigned to one or more chronic conditions and an assisting person (caregiver) resides in the home.

Diagnoses for which patients are receiving home care: Patients are assigned to each of these diagnostic categories if they are receiving home care for a diagnosis belonging to that category (excluding diagnoses that are currently asymptomatic). A patient may have several home care diagnoses and may, therefore, belong to more than one diagnosis category.

Appendix O

Home Health Rules and Regulations

The prospective payment system (PPS) described in rules and regulations of the July 3, 2000, *Federal Register,* replaced the retrospective reasonable-cost–based system previously used by Medicare for the payment of home health services under Part A and Part B. The following pages were excerpted from the final rule:

Readers can download the entire document at www.access.gpo.gov/su_docs/aces/aces 140.html.

A national effort is underway to have a cross-section of home care leaders recommend best practice strategies for how an agency can best manage under the PPS. In the 3M Ground Point Zero Project, over 60 home care leaders met to review the realities of PPS and recommend ways agencies could better manage in the new environment.

The following findings and regulations are excerpted from the Ground Point Zero Project:

1. Utilize the integrated planning model in planning for the future of your agency.

2. Identify and manage outcome measures and performance indicators.

3. Develop and implement a marketing plan to create the desired case mix for your agency.

4. Review and refine admission criteria and identify who has authority to admit patients.

5. Educate staff to accurately complete the OASIS assessment.

6. Develop utilization guidelines for each HHRG based on the agency's cost per visit.

7. Create a clinical review function that determines the accuracy of the OASIS assessments.

8. Update and streamline care pathways to incorporate recognition of the utilization guidelines for each HHRG.

9. Incorporate alternative services and alternative products as part of the plan of care.

10. Implement an interdisciplinary team structure.

11. Clinical staff with care management responsibilities should be paid on a salary basis, not pay per visit.

12. Refine clinical productivity to include quality measures and other measures.

13. Strengthen the agencies' compliance programs.

14. Make the use of data a strong agency value.

15. Make accountability a norm in the agency.

The full report includes graphs, charts, 25 performance indicators, and other information related to findings. Also included is a brief history of the project, along with an overview of how the project was operated and how the leaders were identified. A free copy of the report can be obtained at the Fazzi Associates Web site (www.Fazzi.com).

41128 Federal Register / Vol. 65, No. 128 / Monday, July 3, 2000 / Rules and Regulations

DEPARTMENT OF HEALTH AND HUMAN SERVICES

Health Care Financing Administration

42 CFR Parts 409, 410, 411, 413, 424, and 484

[HCFA–1059–F]

RIN 0938–AJ24

Medicare Program; Prospective Payment System for Home Health Agencies

AGENCY: Health Care Financing Administration (HCFA), HHS.

ACTION: Final rule.

SUMMARY: This final rule establishes requirements for the new prospective payment system for home health agencies as required by section 4603 of the Balanced Budget Act of 1997, as amended by section 5101 of the Omnibus Consolidated and Emergency Supplemental Appropriations Act for Fiscal Year 1999 and by sections 302, 305, and 306 of the Medicare, Medicaid, and SCHIP Balanced Budget Refinement Act of 1999. The requirements include the implementation of a prospective payment system for home health agencies, consolidated billing requirements, and a number of other related changes. The prospective payment system described in this rule replaces the retrospective reasonable-cost-based system currently used by Medicare for the payment of home health services under Part A and Part B.

EFFECTIVE DATE: These regulations are effective October 1, 2000.

FOR FURTHER INFORMATION CONTACT:
Bob Wardwell (Project Manager), (410) 786–3254
Susan Levy (Payment Policy), (410) 786–9364
Debbie Chaney (Data), (410) 786–8164
Randy Throndset (Data), (410) 786–0131

SUPPLEMENTARY INFORMATION:
Copies: To order copies of the **Federal Register** containing this document, send your request to: New Orders, Superintendent of Documents, P.O. Box 371954, Pittsburgh, PA 15250–7954. Specify the date of the issue requested and enclose a check or money order payable to the Superintendent of Documents, or enclose your Visa or Master Card number and expiration date. Credit card orders can also be placed by calling the order desk at (202) 512–1800 or by faxing to (202) 512–2250. The cost for each copy is $8. As an alternative, you can view and photocopy the Federal Register document at most libraries designated as Federal Depository Libraries and at many other public and academic libraries throughout the country that receive the **Federal Register**.

This Federal Register document is also available from the Federal Register online database through GPO Access, a service of the U.S. Government Printing Office. The Website address is: http://www.access.gpo.gov/nara/index.html.

To assist readers in referencing sections contained in this document, we are providing the following table of contents.

Table of Contents

In addition, because of the many terms to which we refer by abbreviation in this rule, we are listing these abbreviations and their corresponding terms in alphabetical order below:

ADL	Activities of Daily Living
BBA	Balanced Budget Act of 1997
BBRA	Medicare, Medicaid, and SCHIP Balanced Budget Refinement Act of 1999
COPs	Conditions of participation

Therefore, the final rule model continues to define three levels: stage 1 or 2 (score=15), stage 3 or 4 (score=36), and all other (including no pressure ulcer and no observable pressure ulcer) (score=0). In addition, we tested whether the number of pressure ulcers made an independent contribution to explaining resource use. We found that having more than one pressure ulcer was a significant predictor of resource use when the multiple ulcers were stage 3 or 4. Therefore, the model in the final rule includes a variable adding 17 points if the patient has two or more stage 3 or 4 pressure ulcers.

We tested a general variable that measured the presence of any kind of open wound, decubitus ulcer, stasis ulcer, or surgical wound, based on an affirmative answer to M0445 (does patient have a pressure ulcer?), M0468 (does patient have a stasis ulcer?), M0482 (does patient have a surgical wound), or reporting of wound diagnosis codes in M0230 (primary home care diagnosis). This variable did not contribute statistically significant explanatory power when added to the model containing the other wound variables. However, we also tested separately a variable identifying burn or trauma patients with skin lesions or open wounds, identified from M0230 (primary diagnosis) and M0440 (does this patient have a skin lesion or an open wound?). This variable did contribute significantly and has been added to the model. The score for this variable is 21. The burn and trauma diagnosis code categories are shown in Table 8B.

In addition, we examined the impact of selected diagnoses that may be associated with difficult-to-heal wounds, including diabetes, atherosclerosis, peripheral vascular disease, and heart failure. We tested whether patients with these diagnoses should be assigned a higher score for their wound severity. Most results were not statistically significant. A few results were inconsistent across measures of wound severity. We also tested a variable measuring whether limited mobility results in higher cost impact for severe pressure ulcers, but this variable did not contribute significantly to the model after all other variables were included. The reasons for the weak results and inconsistency are unclear, and we did not make any of these changes to the clinical dimension. We will continue to study these types of issues during further refinement work on larger samples with more detailed diagnostic data.

Differences between the clinical dimension scores in the proposed rule

and the final rule are generally small. Differences that do exist are attributable to our use of an augmented sample and the use of new variables related to wounds. In our model-building methodology, the scores in the functional dimension depend on results of the regression for deriving the clinical dimension scores. New scores for the functional dimension are very similar to the proposed-rule functional scores. Differences that do exist are attributable to the above-mentioned changes to the clinical dimension. The changes in functional scoring lead to a slightly different set of severity-score level intervals compared to the functional scoring in the proposed rule. The functional severity-score intervals are now minimal severity: 0–2; low severity: 3–15; moderate severity: 16–23; high severity: 24–29; maximum severity: 30+. The frequency distribution of the sample observations across the functional severity levels is essentially unchanged.

We validated the revised scoring for the clinical and functional dimensions using the validation subsample of the final, augmented sample. The results supported the scoring system developed with the learning subsample.

Re-examination of severity levels in clinical dimension. In response to several comments on wound-care patients, we refined the severity-score intervals in the clinical dimension to better differentiate patients who are clinically most severe from remaining patients. The revised score intervals are as follows: minimal severity: 0–7; low severity: 8–19; moderate severity: 20–40; high severity: 41+. To determine the refined severity-score intervals, we used the same process we followed in developing the case-mix system initially. We examined the array of scores for natural clustering and the impact of alternative sets of intervals on the proportion of variation explained by the model (R-squared). We also considered increases in the imbalance of the population across severity levels. The refined severity score intervals do result in more imbalance. The relative frequencies in the Abt sample for the revised clinical severity levels are 30 percent, 36 percent, 28 percent, 6 percent, for minimal, low, moderate, and high clinical severity, respectively. In contrast, the previous model's corresponding percentages were 30 percent, 30 percent, 23 percent, 17 percent. However, this change has also generally resulted in higher case-mix relative weights for the case-mix groups involving moderate and high clinical severity, where the most severe wound patients are likely to be found. It has

also resulted in a wider range of weights for therapy-threshold case-mix groups and non-therapy-threshold case-mix groups.

Comparison with the earlier model. All combined, the refinements made to the case-mix model cause a modest improvement in explanatory power. The proportion of variation explained (R-squared) is now .34, compared to .32 for the model in the proposed rule. The model now provides for more adequate payment for wound care patients. Some of these high-cost patients would have been assigned to a different group under the model we presented in the proposed rule. Their removal from those earlier groups potentially results in a lower average cost, and lower case-mix weight, for those groups. We examined the impact on the array of relative case-mix weights across the case-mix groups. For the most part, we find generally small changes in the individual weights other than the weights for groups involving the moderate and high clinical severity levels.

The case-mix system will continue to be studied and refined in future years. Larger and better data resources, and information accumulated from users like those who commented, will both contribute to the evolution of the system.

2. Diagnosis Coding Changes in the Revised Case-Mix Model

When we published the proposed rule, we listed ICD–9–CM three-digit diagnosis category codes to identify orthopedic, neurologic, and diabetes diagnoses recognized in the clinical dimension. The scores associated with these diagnoses were based on analysis of the OASIS primary diagnosis item (M0230). A commenter pointed out that certain diagnoses within the category codes we listed should never be reported as primary diagnoses, according to ICD–9–CM coding rules and official coding guidelines. These diagnoses must be used with a higher-coded diagnosis that indicates the underlying disease. The affected category codes are 711, 712, 713, 720, 730, 731, 320, 321, 323, 330, 331, 334, 336, 337, 357, 358.

Accordingly, we have revised the diagnosis coding list. The revised list shows the complete code for the affected category codes, and is divided into two sections, one for primary diagnoses and one for secondary diagnoses (see Table 8A). The case-mix system will recognize the appropriate score for a diagnosis that should never be reported as a primary diagnosis, provided that the diagnosis appears as the first OASIS secondary diagnosis

41194 **Federal Register** / Vol. 65, No. 128 / Monday, July 3, 2000 / Rules and Regulations

(line b, under OASIS M0240) and that the code shows all digits required by ICD–9–CM coding guidelines. Remaining diagnoses from the affected categories must appear as the primary diagnosis (line a, under OASIS M0230) and the code must show all digits required by ICD–9–CM coding rules. The case-mix system will not recognize remaining diagnoses from the affected categories if they appear as a secondary diagnosis on the OASIS record. Nor will it recognize diagnoses that must never be reported as primary if they are placed on the primary diagnosis line (line a, M0230).

The refined case-mix system recognizes burns and trauma primary diagnoses, if the OASIS item M0440 shows the patient has a skin lesion or open wound. The diagnosis code categories for burns and trauma diagnoses included in the case-mix system are shown in Table 8B.

A lack of specificity in diagnosis code assignment may be a hindrance to case-mix refinement. Agencies that voluntarily code all diagnoses to the complete four- or five-digit level in accordance with ICD–9–CM coding rules would help us in subsequent review and examination of the case-mix methodology.

TABLE 7.—HOME HEALTH RESOURCE GROUP CASE-MIX CLASSIFICATION DECISION TREE LOGIC

Clinical severity domain			
OASIS+ Item	Description	Value	Scoring
M0230/M0240	Primary home care diagnosis (or initial secondary diagnosis ONLY for selected ICD-9 manifestation codes).	—credit *only* the single highest value: If Orthopedic diagnostic group (DG)*, add 11 to score If Diabetes DG*, add 17 to score If Neurological DG*, add 20 to score	Min = 0–7 Low = 8–19 Mod = 20–40 High = 41+
M0250	IV/Infusion/Parenteral/Enteral Therapies.	—credit *only* the single highest value: If box 1, add 14 to score If box 2, add 20 to score If box 3, add 24 to score	
M0390	Vision	If box 1 or 2, add 6 to score	
M0420	Pain	If box 2 or 3, add 5 to score	
M0440	Wound/Lesion	If box 1 and M0230 is Burn/Trauma DG*, add 21 to score	
M0450	Multiple pressure ulcers	If 2 or more stage 3 or 4 pressure ulcers, add 17 to score	
M0460	Most problematic pressure ulcer stage.	If box 1 or 2, add 15 to score If box 3 or 4, add 36 to score	
M0476	Stasis ulcer status	If box 2, add 14 to score If box 3, add 22 to score	
M0488	Surgical wound status	If box 2, add 7 to score If box 3, add 15 to score	
M0490	Dyspnea	If box 2, 3 or 4, add 5 to score	
M0530	Urinary incontinence	If box 1 or 2, add 6 to score	
M0540	Bowel incontinence	If box 2–5, add 9 to score	
M0550	Bowel ostomy	If box 1 or 2, add 10 to score	
M0610	Behavioral Problems	If box 1–6, add 3 to score	

*See table for ICD9–CM codes included in each diagnosis group (DG)

Functional status domain			
OASIS+ Item	Description	Value	Scoring
M0650 (current) M0660 (current)	Dressing	If M0650 = box 1, 2 or 3 Or } add 4 to score M0660 = box 1, 2 or 3	Min = 0–2 Low = 3–15 Mod = 16–23
M0670 (current)	Bathing	If box 2, 3, 4 or 5 add 8 to score	High = 24–29
M0680 (current)	Toileting	If box 2–4, add 3 to score	Max = 30+
M0690 (current)	Transferring	If box 1, add 3 to score If box 2–5, add 6 to score	
M0700 (current)	Locomotion	If box 1 or 2, add 6 to score If box 3–5, add 9 to score	

Service utilization domain			
Variable	Description	Value	Scoring
M0170—line 1	No Hospital discharge past 14 days.	If box 1 IS BLANK, add 1 to score	Min = 0–2
M0170—line 2 or 3	Inpatient rehab/SNF discharge past 14 days.	If box 2 or 3, add 2 to score	Low = 3
Receipt of Therapy	10 or more therapy visits	If yes, add 4 to score	Mod = 4–6 High = 7

347

TABLE 8A.—DIAGNOSIS GROUPS IN THE CLINICAL DIMENSION

[Note: Codes shown at the 3-digit level include all the related 4- and 5-digit codes. Diagnoses coded with 4 or 5 digits must be coded as shown to receive a score in the clinical dimension.]

Diagnosis group	ICD–9–CM Code	Description
Primary Diagnoses		
DM	250	DIABETES MELLITUS
NEURO	013	CNS TUBERCULOSIS
NEURO	045	ACUTE POLIOMYELITIS
NEURO	046	CNS SLOW VIRUS INFECTION
NEURO	047	ENTEROVIRAL MENINGITIS
NEURO	048	OTH ENTEROVIRAL CNS DIS
NEURO	049	OTH NONARTHROPOD CNS VIR
NEURO	191	MALIGNANT NEOPLASM BRAIN
NEURO	192	MAL NEO NERVE NEC/NOS
NEURO	225	BENIGN NEO NERVOUS SYST
NEURO	320.0	HEMOPHILUS MENINGITIS
NEURO	320.1	PNEUMOCOCCAL MENINGITIS
NEURO	320.2	STREPTOCOCCAL MENINGITI
NEURO	320.3	STAPHYLOCOCC MENINGITIS
NEURO	320.81	ANAEROBIC MENINGITIS
NEURO	320.82	MNINGTS GRAM-NEG BCT NEC
NEURO	320.89	MENINGITIS OTH SPCF BAC
NEURO	320.9	BACTERIAL MENINGITIS NOS
NEURO	322	MENINGITIS, UNSPECIFIED
NEURO	323.5	POSTIMMUNIZAT ENCEPHALI
NEURO	323.8	ENCEPHALITIS NEC
NEURO	323.9	ENCEPHALITIS NOS
NEURO	324	CNS ABSCESS
NEURO	325	PHLEBITIS INTRCRAN SINU
NEURO	326	LATE EFF CNS ABSCESS
NEURO	330.0	LEUKODYSTROPHY
NEURO	330.1	CEREBRAL LIPIDOSES
NEURO	330.8	CEREB DEGEN IN CHILD NEC
NEURO	330.9	CEREB DEGEN IN CHILD NOS
NEURO	331.0	ALZHEIMER'S DISEASE
NEURO	331.1	PICK'S DISEASE
NEURO	331.2	SENILE DEGENERAT BRAIN
NEURO	331.3	COMMUNICAT HYDROCEPHALU
NEURO	331.4	OBSTRUCTIV HYDROCEPHALU
NEURO	331.81	REYE'S SYNDROME
NEURO	331.89	CEREB DEGENERATION NEC
NEURO	331.9	CEREB DEGENERATION NOS
NEURO	332	PARKINSON'S DISEASE
NEURO	333	EXTRAPYRAMIDAL DIS NEC
NEURO	334.0	FRIEDREICH'S ATAXIA
NEURO	334.1	HERED SPASTIC PARAPLEGI
NEURO	334.2	PRIMARY CEREBELLAR DEGE
NEURO	334.3	CEREBELLAR ATAXIA NEC
NEURO	334.8	SPINOCEREBELLAR DIS NEC
NEURO	334.9	SPINOCEREBELLAR DIS NOS
NEURO	335	ANT HORN CELL DISEASE
NEURO	336.0	SYRINGOMYELIA
NEURO	336.1	VASCULAR MYELOPATHIES
NEURO	336.8	MYELOPATHY NEC
NEURO	336.9	SPINAL CORD DISEASE NOS
NEURO	337.0	IDIOPATH AUTO NEUROPATH
NEURO	337.20	UNSP RFLX SYMPTH DYSTRP
NEURO	337.21	RFLX SYM DYSTRPH UP LIM
NEURO	337.22	RFLX SYM DYSTRPH LWR LM
NEURO	337.29	RFLX SYM DYSTRPH OTH ST
NEURO	337.3	AUTONOMIC DYSREFLEXIA
NEURO	337.9	AUTONOMIC NERVE DIS NEC
NEURO	340	MULTIPLE SCLEROSIS
NEURO	341	OTHER CNS DEMYELINATION
NEURO	342	HEMIPLEGIA
NEURO	343	INFANTILE CEREBRAL PALSY
NEURO	344	OTH PARALYTIC SYNDROMES
NEURO	347	CATAPLEXY AND NARCOLEPS
NEURO	348	OTHER BRAIN CONDITIONS
NEURO	349	CNS DISORDER NEC/NOS
NEURO	352	DISORDER CRAN NERVE NEC
NEURO	356	HERED PERIPH NEUROPATHY
NEURO	357.0	AC INFECT POLYNEURITIS

41196   Federal Register / Vol. 65, No. 128 / Monday, July 3, 2000 / Rules and Regulations

TABLE 8A.—DIAGNOSIS GROUPS IN THE CLINICAL DIMENSION—Continued

[Note: Codes shown at the 3-digit level include all the related 4- and 5-digit codes. Diagnoses coded with 4 or 5 digits must be coded as shown to receive a score in the clinical dimension.]

Diagnosis group	ICD–9–CM Code	Description
NEURO	357.5	ALCOHOLIC POLYNEUROPATH
NEURO	357.6	NEUROPATHY DUE TO DRUGS
NEURO	357.7	NEURPTHY TOXIC AGENT NEC
NEURO	357.8	INFLAM/TOX NEUROPTHY NEC
NEURO	357.9	INFLAM/TOX NEUROPTHY NOS
NEURO	358.0	MYASTHENIA GRAVIS
NEURO	358.2	TOXIC MYONEURAL DISORDE
NEURO	358.8	MYONEURAL DISORDERS NEC
NEURO	358.9	MYONEURAL DISORDERS NOS
NEURO	392	RHEUMATIC CHOREA
NEURO	430	SUBARACHNOID HEMORRHAGE
NEURO	431	INTRACEREBRAL HEMORRHAG
NEURO	432	INTRACRANIAL HEM NEC/NOS
NEURO	433	PRECEREBRAL OCCLUSION
NEURO	434	CEREBRAL ARTERY OCCLUS
NEURO	435	TRANSIENT CEREB ISCHEMIA
NEURO	436	CVA
NEURO	437	OTH CEREBROVASC DISEASE
NEURO	741	SPINA BIFIDA
NEURO	742	OTH NERVOUS SYSTEM ANOM
NEURO	851	CEREBRAL LACER/CONTUSION
NEURO	852	MENINGEAL HEM FOLLOW INJ
NEURO	853	OTH TRAUMATIC BRAIN HEM
NEURO	854	OTHER BRAIN INJURY
NEURO	907	LATE EFF NERV SYSTEM INJ
NEURO	950	INJ OPTIC NERV/PATHWAYS
NEURO	951	CRANIAL NERVE INJURY NEC
NEURO	952	SPINAL CORD INJ W/O FX
NEURO	953	INJ NERVE ROOT/SPIN PLEX
NEURO	954	INJURY OTH TRUNK NERVE
NEURO	955	INJ PERIPH NERV SHLD/ARM
NEURO	956	INJ PERIPH NERV PELV/LEG
ORTHO	170	MAL NEO BONE/ARTIC CART
ORTHO	171	MAL NEO SOFT TISSUE
ORTHO	213	BEN NEO BONE/ARTIC CART
ORTHO	274	GOUT
ORTHO	710	DIFF CONNECTIVE TISS DIS
ORTHO	711.00	PYOGEN ARTHRITIS—UNSPEC
ORTHO	711.01	PYOGEN ARTHRITIS—SHLDER
ORTHO	711.02	PYOGEN ARTHRITIS—UP/ARM
ORTHO	711.03	PYOGEN ARTHRITIS—FOREAR
ORTHO	711.04	PYOGEN ARTHRITIS—HAND
ORTHO	711.05	PYOGEN ARTHRITIS—PELVIS
ORTHO	711.06	PYOGEN ARTHRITIS—L/LEG
ORTHO	711.07	PYOGEN ARTHRITIS—ANKLE
ORTHO	711.08	PYOGEN ARTHRITIS NEC
ORTHO	711.09	PYOGEN ARTHRITIS—MULT
ORTHO	711.90	INF ARTHRITIS NOS—UNSPE
ORTHO	711.91	INF ARTHRITIS NOS—SHLDE
ORTHO	711.92	INF ARTHRITIS NOS—UP/AR
ORTHO	711.93	INF ARTHRIT NOS—FOREARM
ORTHO	711.94	INF ARTHRIT NOS—HAND
ORTHO	711.95	INF ARTHRIT NOS—PELVIS
ORTHO	711.96	INF ARTHRIT NOS—L/LEG
ORTHO	711.97	INF ARTHRIT NOS—ANKLE
ORTHO	711.98	INF ARTHRIT NOS—OTH SIT
ORTHO	711.99	INF ARTHRITIS NOS—MULT
ORTHO	712.80	CRYST ARTHROP NEC—UNSPE
ORTHO	712.81	CRYST ARTHROP NEC—SHLDE
ORTHO	712.82	CRYST ARTHROP NEC—UP/AR
ORTHO	712.83	CRYS ARTHROP NEC—FOREAR
ORTHO	712.84	CRYST ARTHROP NEC—HAND
ORTHO	712.85	CRYST ARTHROP NEC—PELVI
ORTHO	712.86	CRYST ARTHROP NEC—L/LEG
ORTHO	712.87	CRYST ARTHROP NEC—ANKLE
ORTHO	712.88	CRY ARTHROP NEC—OTH SIT
ORTHO	712.89	CRYST ARTHROP NEC—MULT
ORTHO	712.90	CRYST ARTHROP NOS—UNSPE
ORTHO	712.91	CRYST ARTHROP NOS—SHLDR
ORTHO	712.92	CRYST ARTHROP NOS—UP/AR

TABLE 8A.—DIAGNOSIS GROUPS IN THE CLINICAL DIMENSION—Continued

[Note: Codes shown at the 3-digit level include all the related 4- and 5-digit codes. Diagnoses coded with 4 or 5 digits must be coded as shown to receive a score in the clinical dimension.]

Diagnosis group	ICD–9–CM Code	Description
ORTHO	712.93	CRYS ARTHROP NOS—FOREAR
ORTHO	712.94	CRYST ARTHROP NOS—HAND
ORTHO	712.95	CRYST ARTHROP NOS—PELVI
ORTHO	712.96	CRYST ARTHROP NOS—L/LEG
ORTHO	712.97	CRYST ARTHROP NOS—ANKLE
ORTHO	712.98	CRY ARTHROP NOS—OTH SIT
ORTHO	712.99	CRYST ARTHROP NOS—MULT
ORTHO	714	OTH INFLAMM POLYARTHROP
ORTHO	716	ARTHROPATHIES NEC/NOS
ORTHO	717	INTERNAL DERANGEMNT KNEE
ORTHO	718	OTHER JOINT DERANGEMENT
ORTHO	720.0	ANKYLOSING SPONDYLITIS
ORTHO	720.1	SPINAL ENTHESOPATHY
ORTHO	720.2	SACROILIITIS NEC
ORTHO	720.89	INFLAM SPONDYLOPATHY NEC
ORTHO	720.9	INFLAM SPONDYLOPATHY NOS
ORTHO	721	SPONDYLOSIS ET AL
ORTHO	722	INTERVERTEBRAL DISC DIS
ORTHO	723	OTHER CERVICAL SPINE DIS
ORTHO	724	BACK DISORDER NEC & NOS
ORTHO	725	POLYMYALGIA RHEUMATICA
ORTHO	728	DIS OF MUSCLE/LIG/FASCIA
ORTHO	730.00	AC OSTEOMYELITIS—UNSP
ORTHO	730.01	AC OSTEOMYELITIS—SHLDER
ORTHO	730.02	AC OSTEOMYELITIS—UP/ARM
ORTHO	730.03	AC OSTEOMYELITIS—FOREAR
ORTHO	730.04	AC OSTEOMYELITIS—HAND
ORTHO	730.05	AC OSTEOMYELITIS—PELVIS
ORTHO	730.06	AC OSTEOMYELITIS—L/LEG
ORTHO	730.07	AC OSTEOMYELITIS—ANKLE
ORTHO	730.08	AC OSTEOMYELITIS NEC
ORTHO	730.09	AC OSTEOMYELITIS—MULT
ORTHO	730.10	CHR OSTEOMYELITIS—UNSP
ORTHO	730.11	CHR OSTEOMYELIT—SHLDER
ORTHO	730.12	CHR OSTEOMYELIT—UP/ARM
ORTHO	730.13	CHR OSTEOMYELIT—FOREARM
ORTHO	730.14	CHR OSTEOMYELIT—HAND
ORTHO	730.15	CHR OSTEOMYELIT—PELVIS
ORTHO	730.16	CHR OSTEOMYELIT—L/LEG
ORTHO	730.17	CHR OSTEOMYELIT—ANKLE
ORTHO	730.18	CHR OSTEOMYELIT NEC
ORTHO	730.19	CHR OSTEOMYELIT—MULT
ORTHO	730.20	OSTEOMYELITIS NOS—UNSPE
ORTHO	730.21	OSTEOMYELITIS NOS—SHLDE
ORTHO	730.22	OSTEOMYELITIS NOS—UP/AR
ORTHO	730.23	OSTEOMYELIT NOS—FOREARM
ORTHO	730.24	OSTEOMYELITIS NOS—HAND
ORTHO	730.25	OSTEOMYELITIS NOS—PELVI
ORTHO	730.26	OSTEOMYELITIS NOS—L/LEG
ORTHO	730.27	OSTEOMYELITIS NOS—ANKLE
ORTHO	730.28	OSTEOMYELIT NOS—OTH SIT
ORTHO	730.29	OSTEOMYELITIS NOS—MULT
ORTHO	730.30	PERIOSTITIS—UNSPEC
ORTHO	730.31	PERIOSTITIS—SHLDER
ORTHO	730.32	PERIOSTITIS—UP/ARM
ORTHO	730.33	PERIOSTITIS—FOREARM
ORTHO	730.34	PERIOSTITIS—HAND
ORTHO	730.35	PERIOSTITIS—PELVIS
ORTHO	730.36	PERIOSTITIS—L/LEG
ORTHO	730.37	PERIOSTITIS—ANKLE
ORTHO	730.38	PERIOSTITIS NEC
ORTHO	730.39	PERIOSTITIS—MULT
ORTHO	730.90	BONE INFEC NOS—UNSP SIT
ORTHO	730.91	BONE INFECT NOS—SHLDER
ORTHO	730.92	BONE INFECT NOS—UP/ARM
ORTHO	730.93	BONE INFECT NOS—FOREARM
ORTHO	730.94	BONE INFECT NOS—HAND
ORTHO	730.95	BONE INFECT NOS—PELVIS
ORTHO	730.96	BONE INFECT NOS—L/LEG
ORTHO	730.97	BONE INFECT NOS—ANKLE

41198   Federal Register / Vol. 65, No. 128 / Monday, July 3, 2000 / Rules and Regulations

TABLE 8A.—DIAGNOSIS GROUPS IN THE CLINICAL DIMENSION—Continued

[Note: Codes shown at the 3-digit level include all the related 4- and 5-digit codes. Diagnoses coded with 4 or 5 digits must be coded as shown to receive a score in the clinical dimension.]

Diagnosis group	ICD–9–CM Code	Description
ORTHO	730.98	BONE INFECT NOS—OTH SIT
ORTHO	730.99	BONE INFECT NOS—MULT
ORTHO	731.0	OSTEITIS DEFORMANS NOS
ORTHO	731.2	HYPERTROPH OSTEOARTHROP
ORTHO	732	OSTEOCHONDROPATHIES
ORTHO	781	NERV/MUSCULSKEL SYS SYMP
ORTHO	800	SKULL VAULT FRACTURE
ORTHO	801	SKULL BASE FRACTURE
ORTHO	802	FRACTURE OF FACE BONES
ORTHO	803	OTHER SKULL FRACTURE
ORTHO	804	MULT FX SKULL W OTH BONE
ORTHO	805	VERTEBRL FX W/O CORD INJ
ORTHO	806	VERTEBRAL FX W CORD INJ
ORTHO	807	FX RIB/STERN/LARYN/TRACH
ORTHO	808	PELVIC FRACTURE
ORTHO	809	FRACTURE OF TRUNK BONES
ORTHO	810	CLAVICLE FRACTURE
ORTHO	811	SCAPULA FRACTURE
ORTHO	812	HUMERUS FRACTURE
ORTHO	813	RADIUS & ULNA FRACTURE
ORTHO	814	CARPAL FRACTURE
ORTHO	815	METACARPAL FRACTURE
ORTHO	816	FRACTURE PHALANGES, HAND
ORTHO	817	MULTIPLE HAND FRACTURES
ORTHO	818	FRACTURE ARM MULT/NOS
ORTHO	819	FX ARMS W RIB/STERNUM
ORTHO	820	FRACTURE NECK OF FEMUR
ORTHO	821	OTHER FEMORAL FRACTURE
ORTHO	822	PATELLA FRACTURE
ORTHO	823	TIBIA & FIBULA FRACTURE
ORTHO	824	ANKLE FRACTURE
ORTHO	825	FX OF TARSAL/METATARSAL
ORTHO	827	LOWER LIMB FRACTURE NEC
ORTHO	828	FX LEGS W ARM/RIB
ORTHO	831	SHOULDER DISLOCATION
ORTHO	832	ELBOW DISLOCATION
ORTHO	833	WRIST DISLOCATION
ORTHO	835	DISLOCATION OF HIP
ORTHO	836	DISLOCATION OF KNEE
ORTHO	837	DISLOCATION OF ANKLE
ORTHO	838	DISLOCATION OF FOOT
ORTHO	846	SPRAIN SACROILIAC REGION
ORTHO	847	SPRAIN OF BACK NEC/NOS
ORTHO	887	TRAUMATIC AMPUT ARM/HAND
ORTHO	896	TRAUMATIC AMPUTAT FOOT
ORTHO	897	TRAUMATIC AMPUTATION LEG
ORTHO	927	CRUSHING INJ UPPER LIMB
ORTHO	928	CRUSHING INJURY OF LEG

Secondary Diagnoses

The following diagnoses should never be used as primary diagnoses, according to ICD–9–CM coding guidelines. The case-mix system will recognize them in the clinical dimension if they appear as the first secondary diagnosis (line b, M0240 on the OASIS record). Diagnoses coded with 4 or 5 digits must be coded as shown to be recognized in the clinical dimension.

	ICD–9–CM Code	Description
NEURO	320.7	MENINGITIS IN OTH BAC
NEURO	321.0	CRYPTOCOCCAL MENINGITIS
NEURO	321.1	MENING IN OTH FUNGAL DI
NEURO	321.2	MENING IN OTH VIRAL DIS
NEURO	321.3	TRYPANOSOMIASIS MENINGI
NEURO	321.4	MENINGIT D/T SARCOIDOSI
NEURO	321.8	MENING IN OTH NONBAC DI
NEURO	323.0	ENCEPHALIT IN VIRAL DIS
NEURO	323.1	RICKETTSIAL ENCEPHALITI
NEURO	323.2	PROTOZOAL ENCEPHALITIS
NEURO	323.4	OTH ENCEPHALIT D/T INFE
NEURO	323.6	POSTINFECT ENCEPHALITIS
NEURO	323.7	TOXIC ENCEPHALITIS
NEURO	330.2	CEREB DEGEN IN LIPIDOSI
NEURO	330.3	CERB DEG CHLD IN OTH DI

TABLE 8A.—DIAGNOSIS GROUPS IN THE CLINICAL DIMENSION—Continued

[Note: Codes shown at the 3-digit level include all the related 4- and 5-digit codes. Diagnoses coded with 4 or 5 digits must be coded as shown to receive a score in the clinical dimension.]

Diagnosis group	ICD–9–CM Code	Description
NEURO	331.7	CEREB DEGEN IN OTH DIS
NEURO	334.4	CEREBEL ATAX IN OTH DIS
NEURO	336.2	COMB DEG CORD IN OTH DI
NEURO	336.3	MYELOPATHY IN OTH DIS
NEURO	337.1	AUT NEUROPTHY IN OTH DI
NEURO	357.1	NEURPTHY IN COL VASC DI
NEURO	357.2	NEUROPATHY IN DIABETES
NEURO	357.3	NEUROPATHY IN MALIG DIS
NEURO	357.4	NEUROPATHY IN OTHER DIS
NEURO	358.1	MYASTHENIA IN OTH DIS
ORTHO	711.10	REITER ARTHRITIS—UNSPEC
ORTHO	711.11	REITER ARTHRITIS—SHLDER
ORTHO	711.12	REITER ARTHRITIS—UP/ARM
ORTHO	711.13	REITER ARTHRITIS—FOREAR
ORTHO	711.14	REITER ARTHRITIS—HAND
ORTHO	711.15	REITER ARTHRITIS—PELVIS
ORTHO	711.16	REITER ARTHRITIS—L/LEG
ORTHO	711.17	REITER ARTHRITIS—ANKLE
ORTHO	711.18	REITER ARTHRITIS NEC
ORTHO	711.19	REITER ARTHRITIS—MULT
ORTHO	711.20	BEHCET ARTHRITIS—UNSPEC
ORTHO	711.21	BEHCET ARTHRITIS—SHLDER
ORTHO	711.22	BEHCET ARTHRITIS—UP/ARM
ORTHO	711.23	BEHCET ARTHRITIS—FOREAR
ORTHO	711.24	BEHCET ARTHRITIS—HAND
ORTHO	711.25	BEHCET ARTHRITIS—PELVIS
ORTHO	711.26	BEHCET ARTHRITIS—L/LEG
ORTHO	711.27	BEHCET ARTHRITIS—ANKLE
ORTHO	711.28	BEHCET ARTHRITIS NEC
ORTHO	711.29	BEHCET ARTHRITIS—MULT
ORTHO	711.30	DYSENTER ARTHRIT—UNSPEC
ORTHO	711.31	DYSENTER ARTHRIT—SHLDER
ORTHO	711.32	DYSENTER ARTHRIT—UP/ARM
ORTHO	711.33	DYSENTER ARTHRIT—FOREAR
ORTHO	711.34	DYSENTER ARTHRIT—HAND
ORTHO	711.35	DYSENTER ARTHRIT—PELVIS
ORTHO	711.36	DYSENTER ARTHRIT—L/LEG
ORTHO	711.37	DYSENTER ARTHRIT—ANKLE
ORTHO	711.38	DYSENTER ARTHRIT NEC
ORTHO	711.39	DYSENTER ARTHRIT—MULT
ORTHO	711.40	BACT ARTHRITIS—UNSPEC
ORTHO	711.41	BACT ARTHRITIS—SHLDER
ORTHO	711.42	BACT ARTHRITIS—UP/ARM
ORTHO	711.43	BACT ARTHRITIS—FOREARM
ORTHO	711.44	BACT ARTHRITIS—HAND
ORTHO	711.45	BACT ARTHRITIS—PELVIS
ORTHO	711.46	BACT ARTHRITIS—L/LEG
ORTHO	711.47	BACT ARTHRITIS—ANKLE
ORTHO	711.48	BACT ARTHRITIS NEC
ORTHO	711.49	BACT ARTHRITIS—MULT
ORTHO	711.50	VIRAL ARTHRITIS—UNSPEC
ORTHO	711.51	VIRAL ARTHRITIS—SHLDER
ORTHO	711.52	VIRAL ARTHRITIS—UP/ARM
ORTHO	711.53	VIRAL ARTHRITIS—FOREARM
ORTHO	711.54	VIRAL ARTHRITIS—HAND
ORTHO	711.55	VIRAL ARTHRITIS—PELVIS
ORTHO	711.56	VIRAL ARTHRITIS—L/LEG
ORTHO	711.57	VIRAL ARTHRITIS—ANKLE
ORTHO	711.58	VIRAL ARTHRITIS NEC
ORTHO	711.59	VIRAL ARTHRITIS—MULT
ORTHO	711.60	MYCOTIC ARTHRITIS—UNSPE
ORTHO	711.61	MYCOTIC ARTHRITIS—SHLDE
ORTHO	711.62	MYCOTIC ARTHRITIS—UP/AR
ORTHO	711.63	MYCOTIC ARTHRIT—FOREARM
ORTHO	711.64	MYCOTIC ARTHRITIS—HAND
ORTHO	711.65	MYCOTIC ARTHRITIS—PELVI
ORTHO	711.66	MYCOTIC ARTHRITIS—L/LEG
ORTHO	711.67	MYCOTIC ARTHRITIS—ANKLE
ORTHO	711.68	MYCOTIC ARTHRITIS NEC
ORTHO	711.69	MYCOTIC ARTHRITIS—MULT

41200   Federal Register / Vol. 65, No. 128 / Monday, July 3, 2000 / Rules and Regulations

TABLE 8A.—DIAGNOSIS GROUPS IN THE CLINICAL DIMENSION—Continued

[Note: Codes shown at the 3-digit level include all the related 4- and 5-digit codes. Diagnoses coded with 4 or 5 digits must be coded as shown to receive a score in the clinical dimension.]

Diagnosis group	ICD–9–CM Code	Description
ORTHO	711.70	HELMINTH ARTHRIT—UNSPEC
ORTHO	711.71	HELMINTH ARTHRIT—SHLDER
ORTHO	711.72	HELMINTH ARTHRIT—UP/ARM
ORTHO	711.73	HELMINTH ARTHRIT—FOREAR
ORTHO	711.74	HELMINTH ARTHRIT—HAND
ORTHO	711.75	HELMINTH ARTHRIT—PELVIS
ORTHO	711.76	HELMINTH ARTHRIT—L/LEG
ORTHO	711.77	HELMINTH ARTHRIT—ANKLE
ORTHO	711.78	HELMINTH ARTHRIT NEC
ORTHO	711.79	HELMINTH ARTHRIT—MULT
ORTHO	711.80	INF ARTHRITIS NEC—UNSPE
ORTHO	711.81	INF ARTHRITIS NEC—SHLDE
ORTHO	711.82	INF ARTHRITIS NEC—UP/AR
ORTHO	711.83	INF ARTHRIT NEC—FOREARM
ORTHO	711.84	INF ARTHRITIS NEC—HAND
ORTHO	711.85	INF ARTHRITIS NEC—PELVI
ORTHO	711.86	INF ARTHRITIS NEC—L/LEG
ORTHO	711.87	INF ARTHRITIS NEC—ANKLE
ORTHO	711.88	INF ARTHRIT NEC—OTH SIT
ORTHO	711.89	INF ARTHRITIS NEC—MULT
ORTHO	712.10	DICALC PHOS CRYST—UNSPE
ORTHO	712.11	DICALC PHOS CRYST—SHLDE
ORTHO	712.12	DICALC PHOS CRYST—UP/AR
ORTHO	712.13	DICALC PHOS CRYS—FOREAR
ORTHO	712.14	DICALC PHOS CRYST—HAND
ORTHO	712.15	DICALC PHOS CRYST—PELVI
ORTHO	712.16	DICALC PHOS CRYST—L/LEG
ORTHO	712.17	DICALC PHOS CRYST—ANKLE
ORTHO	712.18	DICALC PHOS CRY—SITE NE
ORTHO	712.19	DICALC PHOS CRYST—MULT
ORTHO	712.20	PYROPHOSPH CRYST—UNSPEC
ORTHO	712.21	PYROPHOSPH CRYST—SHLDER
ORTHO	712.22	PYROPHOSPH CRYST—UP/ARM
ORTHO	712.23	PYROPHOSPH CRYST—FOREAR
ORTHO	712.24	PYROPHOSPH CRYST—HAND
ORTHO	712.25	PYROPHOSPH CRYST—PELVIS
ORTHO	712.26	PYROPHOSPH CRYST—L/LEG
ORTHO	712.27	PYROPHOSPH CRYST—ANKLE
ORTHO	712.28	PYROPHOS CRYST—SITE NEC
ORTHO	712.29	PYROPHOS CRYST—MULT
ORTHO	712.30	CHONDROCALCIN NOS—UNSPE
ORTHO	712.31	CHONDROCALCIN NOS—SHLDE
ORTHO	712.32	CHONDROCALCIN NOS—UP/AR
ORTHO	712.33	CHONDROCALC NOS—FOREARM
ORTHO	712.34	CHONDROCALCIN NOS—HAND
ORTHO	712.35	CHONDROCALCIN NOS—PELVI
ORTHO	712.36	CHONDROCALCIN NOS—L/LEG
ORTHO	712.37	CHONDROCALCIN NOS—ANKLE
ORTHO	712.38	CHONDROCALC NOS—OTH SIT
ORTHO	712.39	CHONDROCALCIN NOS—MULT
ORTHO	713.0	ARTHROP W ENDOCR/MET DI
ORTHO	713.1	ARTHROP W NONINF GI DIS
ORTHO	713.2	ARTHROPATH W HEMATOL DI
ORTHO	713.3	ARTHROPATHY W SKIN DIS
ORTHO	713.4	ARTHROPATHY W RESP DIS
ORTHO	713.5	ARTHROPATHY W NERVE DIS
ORTHO	713.6	ARTHROP W HYPERSEN REAC
ORTHO	713.7	ARTHROP W SYSTEM DIS NE
ORTHO	713.8	ARTHROP W OTH DIS NEC
ORTHO	720.81	SPONDYLOPATHY IN OTH DI
ORTHO	730.70	POLIO OSTEOPATHY—UNSPEC
ORTHO	730.71	POLIO OSTEOPATHY—SHLDER
ORTHO	730.72	POLIO OSTEOPATHY—UP/ARM
ORTHO	730.73	POLIO OSTEOPATHY—FOREAR
ORTHO	730.74	POLIO OSTEOPATHY—HAND
ORTHO	730.75	POLIO OSTEOPATHY—PELVIS
ORTHO	730.76	POLIO OSTEOPATHY—L/LEG
ORTHO	730.77	POLIO OSTEOPATHY—ANKLE
ORTHO	730.78	POLIO OSTEOPATHY NEC
ORTHO	730.79	POLIO OSTEOPATHY—MULT

TABLE 8A.—DIAGNOSIS GROUPS IN THE CLINICAL DIMENSION—Continued

[Note: Codes shown at the 3-digit level include all the related 4- and 5-digit codes. Diagnoses coded with 4 or 5 digits must be coded as shown to receive a score in the clinical dimension.]

Diagnosis group	ICD–9–CM Code	Description
ORTHO	730.80	BONE INFECT NEC—UNSPEC
ORTHO	730.81	BONE INFECT NEC—SHLDER
ORTHO	730.82	BONE INFECT NEC—UP/ARM
ORTHO	730.83	BONE INFECT NEC—FOREARM
ORTHO	730.84	BONE INFECT NEC—HAND
ORTHO	730.85	BONE INFECT NEC—PELVIS
ORTHO	730.86	BONE INFECT NEC—L/LEG
ORTHO	730.87	BONE INFECT NEC—ANKLE
ORTHO	730.88	BONE INFECT NEC—OTH SIT
ORTHO	730.89	BONE INFECT NEC—MULT
ORTHO	731.1	OSTEITIS DEF IN OTH DIS
ORTHO	731.8	BONE INVOLV IN OTH DIS

TABLE 8B.—BURNS AND TRAUMA DIAGNOSES

[Note: Codes shown at the 3-digit level include all of the related 4- and 5-digit codes. Burns and trauma diagnoses are included in the clinical dimension if the diagnosis is the primary diagnosis and if box 1 of the OASIS item M0440 is checked.]

ICD–9–CM code	Description
870	OCULAR ADNEXA OPEN WOUND
872	OPEN WOUND OF EAR
873	OTHER OPEN WOUND OF HEAD
874	OPEN WOUND OF NECK
875	OPEN WOUND OF CHEST
876	OPEN WOUND OF BACK
877	OPEN WOUND OF BUTTOCK
878	OPEN WOUND GENITAL ORGAN
879	OPEN WOUND SITE NEC
880	OPN WND SHOULDR/UPPR ARM
881	OPEN WOUND OF LOWER ARM
882	OPEN WOUND OF HAND
883	OPEN WOUND OF FINGER
884	OPEN WOUND ARM MULT/NOS
885	TRAUM AMPUTATION THUMB
886	TRAUM AMPUTATION FINGER
890	OPEN WOUND OF HIP/THIGH
891	OPEN WND KNEE/LEG/ANKLE
892	OPEN WOUND OF FOOT
893	OPEN WOUND OF TOE
894	OPEN WOUND OF LEG NEC
895	TRAUMATIC AMPUTATION TOE
941	BURN OF HEAD/FACE/NECK
942	BURN OF TRUNK
943	BURN OF ARM
944	BURN OF HAND & WRIST
945	BURN OF LEG
946	BURN OF MULTIPLE SITE
948	BURN BY % BODY SURFACE
949	BURN UNSPECIFIED

3. Determining the Case-Mix Indices

Calculation of the case-mix relative weights. We derived the relative weights for the case-mix groups from a straightforward multiple regression

analysis. The data for the regression came from the Abt sample episodes with more than four visits (the same sample used to develop and validate the case-mix model).

The coefficients that resulted from the regression equation are shown below. The multiple regression coefficients are estimates of the average addition to resource cost due to each severity level above the lowest-severity case-mix group (C0F0S0). For each case-mix group, the average resource cost is calculated from the sum of the appropriate regression coefficients. In the example below, the average resource cost for case-mix group C3F0S3 is the sum of the average resource cost for the base group (C0F0S0) plus the average additional cost due to C3 plus the average additional cost due to S3. We then used the computed case-mix-group average resource costs to find the relative case-mix weights. Specifically, the case-mix group averages (that is, sum of appropriate regression coefficients) are divided by the overall average resource cost. The case-mix weights are shown in Table 9.

The methodology for calculating the case-mix weights is the same one we used to find the case-mix weights in the proposed rule, except that we did not use weighted regression for the final rule. We determined that the distribution of the unweighted Abt Associates data better resembled the 1998 episode file distribution than did the weighted Abt Associates data. Thus, unweighted regression was the appropriate methodology. As stated in the proposed rule, we plan to refine the case-mix weights to adjust for changes in patient population, actual changes in home health care practice patterns, and changes in the coding or classification of patients that do not reflect real changes in case-mix.

Regression Coefficients for Calculating Case-Mix Relative Weights

Intercept*—$1,271.95
C1—$230.98
C2—$652.42
C3—$1,620.75
F1—$229.14
F2—$479.30
F3—$571.20
F4—$976.08
S1—$195.53
S2—$2,315.15
S3—$2,923.22

Example:

Calculate case-mix relative weight for group C3F0S3
Overall average resource cost (scaled to national average episode cost): $2,416.00
Relative weight = average resource cost for group C3F0S3 divided by overall average resource cost = (base group cost +C3 increment +S3 increment)/overall average resource cost = (1271.95 + 1620.75 + 2923.22)/2416.00 = 2.4073

Below we show the average resource cost calculated from the regression coefficients for each case-mix group.

Regression coefficient	Average resource cost
C0F0S0	$1,271.95
C0F0S1	1,467.48
C0F0S2	3,587.10
C0F0S3	4,195.17
C0F1S0	1,501.09
C0F1S1	1,696.62
C0F1S2	3,816.24
C0F1S3	4,424.31
C0F2S0	1,751.25
C0F2S1	1,946.77
C0F2S2	4,066.40
C0F2S3	4,674.46
C0F3S0	1,843.15
C0F3S1	2,038.68
C0F3S2	4,158.30

* Intercept value is the average resource cost for the base group, C0F0S0.

41202 Federal Register / Vol. 65, No. 128 / Monday, July 3, 2000 / Rules and Regulations

Regression coefficient	Average resource cost	Regression coefficient	Average resource cost	Regression coefficient	Average resource cost
COF3S3	4,766.37	C1F4S2	4,794.16	C3F0S1	3,088.23
COF4S0	2,248.03	C1F4S3	5,402.23	C3F0S2	5,207.85
COF4S1	2,443.56	C2F0S0	1,924.37	C3F0S3	5,815.92
COF4S2	4,563.18	C2F0S1	2,119.90	C3F1S0	3,121.84
COF4S3	5,171.25	C2F0S2	4,239.52	C3F1S1	3,317.37
C1F0S0	1,502.93	C2F0S3	4,847.59	C3F1S2	5,436.99
C1F0S1	1,698.46	C2F1S0	2,153.51	C3F1S3	6,045.06
C1F0S2	3,818.08	C2F1S1	2,349.04	C3F2S0	3,372.00
C1F0S3	4,426.15	C2F1S2	4,468.66	C3F2S1	3,567.52
C1F1S0	1,732.07	C2F1S3	5,076.73	C3F2S2	5,687.15
C1F1S1	1,927.60	C2F2S0	2,403.67	C3F2S3	6,295.22
C1F1S2	4,047.22	C2F2S1	2,599.19	C3F3S0	3,463.91
C1F1S3	4,655.29	C2F2S2	4,718.82	C3F3S1	3,659.43
C1F2S0	1,982.23	C2F2S3	5,326.89	C3F3S2	5,779.06
C1F2S1	2,177.75	C2F3S0	2,495.57	C3F3S3	6,387.12
C1F2S2	4,297.38	C2F3S1	2,691.10	C3F4S0	3,868.79
C1F2S3	4,905.45	C2F3S2	4,810.72	C3F4S1	4,064.31
C1F3S0	2,074.13	C2F3S3	5,418.79	C3F4S2	6,183.94
C1F3S1	2,269.66	C2F4S0	2,900.45	C3F4S3	6,792.00
C1F3S2	4,389.28	C2F4S1	3,095.98		
C1F3S3	4,997.35	C2F4S2	5,215.61		
C1F4S0	2,479.01	C2F4S3	5,823.67		
C1F4S1	2,674.54	C3F0S0	2,892.70		

Construction of the Relative Weights for the HHRGs

TABLE 9.—RELATIVE CASE-MIX WEIGHTS CORRESPONDING TO HOME HEALTH RESOURCE GROUPS

HHRG group	HHRG description	Case-mix weight
COF0S0	"Clinical=Min, Functional=Min, Service=Min"	0.5265
COF0S1	"Clinical=Min, Functional=Min, Service=Low"	0.6074
COF0S2	"Clinical=Min, Functional=Min, Service=Mod"	1.4847
COF0S3	"Clinical=Min, Functional=Min, Service=High"	1.7364
COF1S0	"Clinical=Min, Functional=Low, Service=Min"	0.6213
COF1S1	"Clinical=Min, Functional=Low, Service=Low"	0.7022
COF1S2	"Clinical=Min, Functional=Low, Service=Mod"	1.5796
COF1S3	"Clinical=Min, Functional=Low, Service=High"	1.8313
COF2S0	"Clinical=Min, Functional=Mod, Service=Min"	0.7249
COF2S1	"Clinical=Min, Functional=Mod, Service=Low"	0.8058
COF2S2	"Clinical=Min, Functional=Mod, Service=Mod"	1.6831
COF2S3	"Clinical=Min, Functional=Mod, Service=High"	1.9348
COF3S0	"Clinical=Min, Functional=High, Service=Min"	0.7629
COF3S1	"Clinical=Min, Functional=High, Service=Low"	0.8438
COF3S2	"Clinical=Min, Functional=High, Service=Mod"	1.7212
COF3S3	"Clinical=Min, Functional=High, Service=High"	1.9728
COF4S0	"Clinical=Min, Functional=Max, Service=Min"	0.9305
COF4S1	"Clinical=Min, Functional=Max, Service=Low"	1.0114
COF4S2	"Clinical=Min, Functional=Max, Service=Mod"	1.8887
COF4S3	"Clinical=Min, Functional=Max, Service=High"	2.1404
C1F0S0	"Clinical=Low, Functional=Min, Service=Min"	0.6221
C1F0S1	"Clinical=Low, Functional=Min, Service=Low"	0.7030
C1F0S2	"Clinical=Low, Functional=Min, Service=Mod"	1.5803
C1F0S3	"Clinical=Low, Functional=Min, Service=High"	1.8320
C1F1S0	"Clinical=Low, Functional=Low, Service=Min"	0.7169
C1F1S1	"Clinical=Low, Functional=Low, Service=Low"	0.7978
C1F1S2	"Clinical=Low, Functional=Low, Service=Mod"	1.6752
C1F1S3	"Clinical=Low, Functional=Low, Service=High"	1.9269
C1F2S0	"Clinical=Low, Functional=Mod, Service=Min"	0.8205
C1F2S1	"Clinical=Low, Functional=Mod, Service=Low"	0.9014
C1F2S2	"Clinical=Low, Functional=Mod, Service=Mod"	1.7787
C1F2S3	"Clinical=Low, Functional=Mod, Service=High"	2.0304
C1F3S0	"Clinical=Low, Functional=High, Service=Min"	0.8585
C1F3S1	"Clinical=Low, Functional=High, Service=Low"	0.9394
C1F3S2	"Clinical=Low, Functional=High, Service=Mod"	1.8168
C1F3S3	"Clinical=Low, Functional=High, Service=High"	2.0684
C1F4S0	"Clinical=Low, Functional=Max, Service=Min"	1.0261
C1F4S1	"Clinical=Low, Functional=Max, Service=Low"	1.1070
C1F4S2	"Clinical=Low, Functional=Max, Service=Mod"	1.9843
C1F4S3	"Clinical=Low, Functional=Max, Service=High"	2.2360
C2F0S0	"Clinical=Mod, Functional=Min, Service=Min"	0.7965
C2F0S1	"Clinical=Mod, Functional=Min, Service=Low"	0.8774
C2F0S2	"Clinical=Mod, Functional=Min, Service=Mod"	1.7548
C2F0S3	"Clinical=Mod, Functional=Min, Service=High"	2.0065
C2F1S0	"Clinical=Mod, Functional=Low, Service=Min"	0.8914

TABLE 9.—RELATIVE CASE-MIX WEIGHTS CORRESPONDING TO HOME HEALTH RESOURCE GROUPS—Continued

HHRG group	HHRG description	Case-mix weight
C2F1S1	"Clinical=Mod, Functional=Low, Service=Low"	0.9723
C2F1S2	"Clinical=Mod, Functional=Low, Service=Mod"	1.8496
C2F1S3	"Clinical=Mod, Functional=Low, Service=High"	2.1013
C2F2S0	"Clinical=Mod, Functional=Mod, Service=Min"	0.9949
C2F2S1	"Clinical=Mod, Functional=Mod, Service=Low"	1.0758
C2F2S2	"Clinical=Mod, Functional=Mod, Service=Mod"	1.9532
C2F2S3	"Clinical=Mod, Functional=Mod, Service=High"	2.2048
C2F3S0	"Clinical=Mod, Functional=High, Service=Min"	1.0329
C2F3S1	"Clinical=Mod, Functional=High, Service=Low"	1.1139
C2F3S2	"Clinical=Mod, Functional=High, Service=Mod"	1.9912
C2F3S3	"Clinical=Mod, Functional=High, Service=High"	2.2429
C2F4S0	"Clinical=Mod, Functional=Max, Service=Min"	1.2005
C2F4S1	"Clinical=Mod, Functional=Max, Service=Low"	1.2814
C2F4S2	"Clinical=Mod, Functional=Max, Service=Mod"	2.1588
C2F4S3	"Clinical=Mod, Functional=Max, Service=High"	2.4105
C3F0S0	"Clinical=High, Functional=Min, Service=Min"	1.1973
C3F0S1	"Clinical=High, Functional=Min, Service=Low"	1.2782
C3F0S2	"Clinical=High, Functional=Min, Service=Mod"	2.1556
C3F0S3	"Clinical=High, Functional=Min, Service=High"	2.4073
C3F1S0	"Clinical=High, Functional=Low, Service=Min"	1.2922
C3F1S1	"Clinical=High, Functional=Low, Service=Low"	1.3731
C3F1S2	"Clinical=High, Functional=Low, Service=Mod"	2.2504
C3F1S3	"Clinical=High, Functional=Low, Service=High"	2.5021
C3F2S0	"Clinical=High, Functional=Mod, Service=Min"	1.3957
C3F2S1	"Clinical=High, Functional=Mod, Service=Low"	1.4766
C3F2S2	"Clinical=High, Functional=Mod, Service=Mod"	2.3540
C3F2S3	"Clinical=High, Functional=Mod, Service=High"	2.6056
C3F3S0	"Clinical=High, Functional=High, Service=Min"	1.4337
C3F3S1	"Clinical=High, Functional=High, Service=Low"	1.5147
C3F3S2	"Clinical=High, Functional=High, Service=Mod"	2.3920
C3F3S3	"Clinical=High, Functional=High, Service=High"	2.6437
C3F4S0	"Clinical=High, Functional=Max, Service=Min"	1.6013
C3F4S1	"Clinical=High, Functional=Max, Service=Low"	1.6822
C3F4S2	"Clinical=High, Functional=Max, Service=Mod"	2.5596
C3F4S3	"Clinical=High, Functional=Max, Service=High"	2.8113

H. Consolidated Billing

1. Background

Under the HHA consolidated billing requirement established by sections 4603(c)(2)(B) and (c)(2)(C) of the BBA, the HHA that establishes the home health plan of care has the Medicare billing responsibility for all of the Medicare-covered home health services listed in section 1861(m) of the Act that the patient receives and are ordered by the physician in the plan of care. Section 305 of BBRA of 1999 amended the consolidated billing language governing home health PPS by eliminating DME covered as a home health service from the consolidated billing requirements.

2. HHA Consolidated Billing Legislation

Specific Provisions of the Legislation. Sections 4603(c)(2)(B) and (c)(2)(C) of the BBA amend sections 1842(b)(6) and 1862(a) of the Act, respectively, to require a new consolidated billing and bundling of all home health services while a beneficiary is under the plan of care. The statute now requires payment for all items and services to be made to

an agency. As stated above, section 305 of BBRA of 1999 excludes DME covered as a home health service from the consolidated billing requirements.

Specifically, the law requires, "in the case of home health services (including medical supplies described in section 1861(m)(5), but excluding durable medical equipment to the extent provided for in such section) furnished to an individual who (at the time the item or service is furnished) is under the plan of care of a home health agency, payment shall be made to the agency (without regard to whether or not the item or service was furnished by the agency, by others under arrangement with them made by the agency, or when any other contracting or consulting arrangement, or otherwise)."

Moreover, there will be separate payment for DME items and services provided under the home health benefit, which are under the DME fee schedule. As discussed previously, under the HHA PPS, DME covered as a home health service as part of the Medicare home health benefit will continue to be paid under the DME fee schedule and will also be excluded from the

consolidated billing requirements. In addition to the prospective payment amount for home health services a separate payment amount will be made for DME currently covered as a home health service under the PPS.

3. Types of Services That Are Subject to the Provision

Under the consolidated billing requirement, we require that the HHA must submit all Medicare claims for all home health services included in section 1861(m) of the Act (including medical supplies described in section 1861(m)(5)) of the Act, but excluding DME to the extent provided for in such section), while the beneficiary is under the home health plan of care established by a physician and eligible for the home health benefit. The home health services included in consolidated billing are:

• Part-time or intermittent skilled nursing care.
• Part-time or intermittent home health aide services.
• Physical therapy.
• Speech-language pathology.
• Occupational therapy, medical social services.

• Routine and nonroutine medical supplies.

• A covered osteoporosis drug (as defined in section 1861(kk) of the Act- (not paid under PPS rate, see 1833(a)(2)(A)), but excluding other drugs and biologicals).

• Medical services provided by an intern or resident- in-training of the hospital, under an approved teaching program of the hospital in the case of an HHA that is affiliated or under common control with a hospital.

• Services at hospitals, SNFs, or rehabilitation centers when they involve equipment too cumbersome to bring to the home.

4. Effects of This Provision

HHAs will no longer be able to "unbundle" services to an outside supplier that can then submit a separate bill directly to the Part B carrier. Instead, the HHA itself will have to furnish the home health services (except DME) either directly or under an arrangement with an outside supplier in which the HHA itself, rather than the supplier, bills Medicare. With the exception of DME, the outside supplier must look to the HHA rather than to Medicare Part B for payment. Beneficiaries receiving DME prior to establishment of a home health plan of care, can continue the relationship with that same DME supplier. The consolidated billing requirement eliminates the potential for duplicative billings for the same services to the RHHI by the HHA and to the Part B carrier by an outside supplier. All covered home health services listed in section 1861(m) of the Act, (including medical supplies described in section 1861(m)(5) of the Act, but excluding DME to the extent provided in such section) ordered in the patient's plan of care must be billed by the HHA.

As discussed in the proposed rule published on October 28, 1999, the responsibility for consolidated billing moves to the transfer HHA. The consolidated billing requirement enhances the HHA's capacity to meet its existing responsibility to oversee and coordinate the Medicare- covered home health services that each of its patients receives.

Consistent with SNF PPS consolidated billing, the beneficiary exercises his or her freedom of choice for the entire home health benefit of services listed in section 1861(m) of the Act, including medical supplies described in section 1861(m)(5) of the Act, but excluding DME as a home health service by choosing the HHA. Once a home health patient chooses a particular HHA, he or she has clearly exercised freedom of choice with respect to all items and services included within the scope of the Medicare home health benefit (except DME). The HHA's consolidated billing role supersedes all other billing situations the beneficiary may wish to establish for home health services covered under the scope of the home health benefit during the certified episode.

Current law is silent regarding the specific terms of an HHA's payment to an outside supplier, and does not authorize the Medicare program to impose any requirements in this regard. We remain concerned, however, over the potential for the provision of unnecessary services, and will continue to evaluate approaches addressing this concern. One appropriate way to address any abusive practices would be through more vigorous enforcement of existing statutes and regulations (such as medical review procedures). Furthermore, since under current law, an HHA's relationship with its supplier is essentially a private contractual matter, the terms of the supplier's payment by the HHA must be arrived through direct negotiations between the two parties themselves. Accordingly, we believe that the most effective way for a supplier to address any concerns that it may have about the adequacy or timeliness of the HHA's payment would be for the supplier to ensure that any terms to which it agrees in such negotiations satisfactorily address those concerns. Finally, we note that matters relating to the enforcement of the statutory anti-kickback provisions lie exclusively within the purview of the Office of the Inspector General, and any questions or concerns in this area should be directed to the attention of that agency.

5. Effective Date for Consolidated Billing

The effective date for consolidated billing is October 1, 2000.

V. Provisions of the Final Rule

We are adopting the provisions of the proposed rule with the following revisions:

Section 409.43

We revised paragraph (c) to clarify that the request for anticipated payment for the initial percentage payment is not a Medicare claim under the Act and subject to the requirement that the physician sign the plan of care before the HHA bills for the initial percentage payment. The request for anticipated payment for the initial percentage episode payment may be based on verbal orders that are copied into the plan of care with the plan of care being immediately submitted to the physician. However, the requests for anticipated payments may be modified or withheld in order to protect Medicare program integrity. However, the final percentage payment is a claim subject to the current physician signature requirements. We revised current paragraph (c) governing physician signature of the plan of care. Specifically, paragraph (c)(1) of this section specifies, "If the physician signed plan of care is not available, the request for anticipated payment of the initial percentage payment must be based on—

• A physician's verbal order that—

++ Is recorded in the plan of care;

++ Includes a description of the patient's condition and the services to be provided by the home health agency;

++ Includes an attestation (relating to the physician's orders and the date received) signed and dated by the registered nurse or qualified therapist (as defined in 42 CFR 484.4) responsible for furnishing or supervising the ordered service in the plan of care; and

++ Is copied into the plan of care and the plan of care is immediately submitted to the physician; or

• A referral prescribing detailed orders for the services to be provided that is signed and dated by a physician."

In paragraph (c)(2) of this section, we specify that "HCFA has the authority to reduce or disapprove requests for anticipated payments in situations when protecting Medicare program integrity warrants this action. Since the request for anticipated payment is based on verbal orders as specified in paragraphs (c)(1)(i) and/or a prescribing referral as specified in (c)(1)(ii) of this section and is not a Medicare claim for purposes of the Act (although it is a "claim" for purposes of Federal, civil, criminal, and administrative law enforcement authorities, including but not limited to the Civil Monetary Penalties Law (as defined in 42 U.S.C. 1320a–7a (i) (2)), the Civil False Claims Act (as defined in 31 U.S.C. 3729(c)), and the Criminal False Claims Act (18 U.S.C. 287)), the request for anticipated payment will be canceled and recovered unless the claim is submitted within the greater of 60 days from the end of the episode or 60 days from the issuance of the request for anticipated payment."

Paragraph (c)(3) of this section specifies that "The plan of care must be signed and dated—

• By a physician as described who meets the certification and recertification requirements of § 424.22 of this chapter and;

• Before the claim for each episode for services is submitted for the final percentage payment."

Paragraph (c)(4) of this section specifies that "Any changes in the plan must be signed and dated by a physician."

Section 409.43

We revised the paragraph (e) of this section to clarify that the plan of care must be reviewed by the physician at least every 60 days or more frequently when there is a beneficiary elected transfer, significant change in condition, or discharge and return to the same HHA during the same 60-day episode.

We also made a conforming change in paragraph (f) of this section regarding the termination of the plan of care by replacing "62-day" with "60-day." We amended this paragraph to specify that if specific services are not provided to the beneficiary at least once every 60-days, the plan of care is terminated unless the physician documents that the interval without this care is appropriate to the treatment of the beneficiary's condition.

Sections 409.100(a)(2), 410.150(b)(19), and 411.15(q)

We revised the regulations at §§ 409.100(a)(2), 410.150(b)(19), and 411.15(q) to conform to the BBRA revisions that eliminate DME from the consolidated billing requirements.

Section 413.64

We revised § 413.1(h) to clarify that durable medical equipment and the covered osteoporosis drug as defined in section 1861(m) of the Act are not included in the HHA PPS rate.

We deleted § 413.64(h)(2)(iv). This corresponds to our revision in the proposed rule to remove Part A and Part B home health services from § 413.64(h)(1). PIP is eliminated for home health services upon implementation of PPS.

Section 424.22

We are not adopting proposed paragraph (a)(1)(v) that would have required the physician to certify the correct HHRG.

Section 484.1(a)

We amended this section by adding a new paragraph (3) to include the provision under the Act that provides the basis for establishing the new prospective payment system for home health services covered under Medicare.

Section 484.18

We revised the paragraph (b) to clarify that the plan of care must be reviewed

by the physician at least every 60 days or more frequently when there is a beneficiary elected transfer, significant change in condition, or discharge and return to the same HHA during the same 60-day episode.

Section 484.55

We revised paragraph (d)(1) to specify that the update to the comprehensive assessment is required the last five days of every 60 days beginning with the start of care date unless there is an applicable payment adjustment. This clarification parallels the current OASIS requirements governing the timeframe of the update.

Section 484.202

We amended this section by removing the term "clinical model" from the list of definitions because we did not use the term in this subpart.

Section 484.205

We revised paragraph (a)(1) and (b) to clarify that the PPS payments are based on a predetermined rate for a home health service previously paid on a reasonable cost basis and that the osteoporosis drug covered under the home health benefit is the only home health service listed in section 1861(m) of the Act that continues to be paid on a reasonable cost basis under PPS. The revised language will read, "The national 60-day episode payment represents payment in full for all costs associated with furnishing a home health service paid on a reasonable cost basis (except the osteoporosis drug listed in section 1861(m) of the Act as defined in section 1861(kk) of the Act) as of August 5, 1997 * * *"

We also clarify in paragraph (b) that all payments under this system must be subject to a medical review adjustment reflecting beneficiary eligibility, medical necessity determinations, and the HHRG assignment.

We added paragraphs (b)(1) and (b)(2) that provides for the requirements governing the final split percentage payment approach. New paragraph (b)(1) governs the split percentage payment approach for initial episodes. The initial percentage payment for initial episodes is paid at 60 percent of the case-mix and wage adjusted 60 day episode rate. The residual final payment for initial episodes is paid at 40 percent of the case-mix and wage adjusted 60 day episode rate. New paragraph (b)(2) governs the split percentage payment approach for subsequent episodes. The initial percentage payment for subsequent episodes is paid at 50 percent of the case-mix and wage adjusted 60 day episode rate. The

residual final payment for subsequent episodes is paid at 50 percent of the case-mix and wage adjusted 60 day episode rate.

We revised paragraph (d) of this section to clarify that PEP adjustments do not apply in situations of transfer among HHAs of common ownership as defined in § 424.22. Those situations would be considered services provided under arrangement on behalf of the originating HHA by the receiving HHA with the common ownership interest for the balance of the 60-day episode. The common ownership exception to the transfer PEP adjustment does not apply if the beneficiary moves to a different MSA or Non-MSA during the 60-day episode before the transfer to the receiving HHA. The transferring HHA in situations of transfers among HHAs of common ownership not only serves as a billing agent, but must also exercise professional responsibility over the arranged-for services in order for services provided for under arrangements to be paid.

Section 484.215

We renamed the heading of section 484.215 to clarify that the calculation reflects the initial establishment of the PPS rates. Section 484.215 has been revised to read "Initial establishment of the calculation of the national 60-day episode payment." We revised paragraph (d)(4) to reflect the amounts that are added to the nonstandardized episode amount for the OASIS adjustment for the one time implementation costs associated with assessment scheduling form changes and amounts for Part B therapies that could have been unbundled to Part B prior to PPS implementation.

Section 424.220

We revised § 484.220 to specify that HCFA adjusts the national 60-day episode payment rate to account for geographic differences in wage levels using an appropriate wage index based on the site of the service for the beneficiary.

Section 484.225(c)

We revised paragraph (c) to reflect that for each of FYs 2002 *and* 2003 the rates are updated by the applicable home health market basket minus 1.1 percentage points.

Section 484.230

We revised the language in this section to reflect the higher per-visit amounts that will be used to calculate the LUPA payments. The amounts will be referred to as national per-visit amounts. We also clarified that the wage

41206   **Federal Register** / Vol. 65, No. 128 / Monday, July 3, 2000 / Rules and Regulations

index are based on the site of service for the beneficiary.

Section 484.235

We revised paragraph (b) to reflect the use of billable visit dates as the defining points for the PEP adjustment. The following phrase will be added to the end of the sentence, "* * * based on the first billable visit date through and including the last billable visit date."

Section 484.237

We revised paragraphs (b)(1) and (b)(2) governing the SCIC adjustment to reflect the use of billable visit dates to define the span of days used to calculate the proportional payments both before and after a patient experiences a significant change in condition. In §§ 484.237(b)(1) and (b)(2) we inserted the phrase "(the first billable visit date through and including the last billable visit date)" after the phrase "span of days."

Section 484.240

We revised paragraph (d) to reflect the higher per- visit amounts that will be used to calculate the imputed costs for each episode for outlier payment determination. The amounts are referred to as national per-visit amounts.

Section 484.245

We added new § 484.245 that sets forth the processes involving accelerated payment requests by an HHA under PPS if there is a delay by the intermediary in making payment.

VI. Collection of Information Requirements

Under the Paperwork Reduction Act of 1995, we are required to provide 60-day notice in the **Federal Register** and solicit public comment before a collection of information requirement is submitted to the Office of Management and Budget (OMB) for review and approval. In order to fairly evaluate whether an information collection should be approved by OMB, section 3506(c)(2)(A) of the Paperwork Reduction Act of 1995 requires that we solicit comment on the following issues:

• The need for the information collection and its usefulness in carrying out the proper functions of our agency.

• The accuracy of our estimate of the information collection burden.

• The quality, utility, and clarity of the information to be collected.

• Recommendations to minimize the information collection burden on the affected public, including automated collection techniques.

However, the requirements summarized below are currently approved as indicated by the appropriate OMB control number.

Section 409.43   Plan of Care Requirements

Section 409.43(c) states that a plan of care must be signed and dated by a physician and meets the certification and recertification requirements of § 424.22 of this chapter, before the episode claim for services is submitted for the final percentage payment. This provision also states that any changes in the plan must be signed and dated by the physician. The requirements and burden associated with the plan of care are currently approved under OMB control numbers 0938–0357, with a current expiration date of 11/30/2000, 0938–0760 with a current expiration date of 09/30/2000, and 0938–0761 with a current expiration date of 09/30/2000.

Section 409.43(e) states that a plan of care must be reviewed, signed, and dated by the physician who reviews the plan of care (as specified in § 409.42(b)) in consultation with agency professional personnel at least every 60 days. The requirements and burden associated with the plan of care are currently approved under OMB control numbers 0938–0357, with a current expiration date of 11/30/2000, 0938–0760 with a current expiration date of 09/30/2000, and 0938–0761 with a current expiration date of 09/30/2000.

Section 424.22   Requirements for Home Health Services

Section 424.22(b) states that a recertification is required at least every 60 days, preferably at the time the plan is reviewed, and must be signed by the physician who reviews the plan of care. The requirements and burden associated with the plan of care are currently approved under OMB control numbers 0938–0357, with a current expiration date of 11/30/2000, 0938–0760 with a current expiration date of 09/30/2000, and 0938–0761 with a current expiration date of 09/30/2000.

Section 484.55   Comprehensive Assessment of Patients

Section 484.55 states that an HHA must update the comprehensive assessment by completing the appropriate OASIS schedule the last five days of every 60 days beginning with the start of care date unless there is a PEP adjustment or SCIC adjustment. The new requirement replaces the current language regarding "every second calendar month" with every 60 days." The requirements and burden associated with the plan of care are currently approved under OMB control numbers 0938–0357, with a current

expiration date of 11/30/2000, 0938–0760 with a current expiration date of 09/30/2000, and 0938–0761 with a current expiration date of 09/30/2000.

Section 484.250   Patient Assessment Data.

Section 484.250 states that an HHA must submit OASIS data to HCFA as described at § 484.55(b)(1) and (d)(1) to administer the payment rate methodologies described in §§ 484.215, 484.230, 484.235, and 484.237. The requirements and burden associated with the plan of care are currently approved under OMB control numbers 0938–0357, with a current expiration date of 11/30/2000, 0938–0760 with a current expiration date of 09/30/2000, and 0938–0761 with a current expiration date of 09/30/2000.

VII. Regulatory Impact Analysis

Section 804(2) of title 5, United States Code (as added by section 251 of Public Law 104–121), specifies that a "major rule" is any rule that the Office of Management and Budget finds is likely to result in—

• An annual effect on the economy of $100 million or more;

• A major increase in costs or prices for consumers, individual industries, Federal, State, or local government agencies, or geographic regions; or

• Significant adverse effects on competition, employment, investment productivity, innovation, or on the ability of United States based enterprises to compete with foreign based enterprises in domestic and export markets.

We estimate, based on a simulation model, that the redistributional effects on HHAs participating in the Medicare program associated with this final rule would range from a positive $428 million for freestanding not-for-profit agencies to a negative $363 million for freestanding for-profit agencies in FY 2001. Therefore, this rule, is a major rule as defined in Title 5, United States Code, section 804(2).

We have examined the impacts of this final rule as required by Executive Order 12866, the Unfunded Mandates Reform Act of 1995, (Public Law 104–4), and the Regulatory Flexibility Act (RFA) (Public Law 96–354). Executive Order 12866 directs agencies to assess all costs and benefits of available regulatory alternatives and, when regulation is necessary, to select regulatory approaches that maximize net benefits (including potential economic, environmental, public health and safety effects, distributive impacts, and equity). A regulatory impact analysis (RIA) must be prepared for

Federal Register / Vol. 65, No. 128 / Monday, July 3, 2000 / Rules and Regulations **41207**

major rules with economically significant effects ($100 million or more annually). Section 1895(b)(3)(A)(i) of the Act requires that the total amounts payable under the HHA PPS be equal to the total amount that would have been paid if this system had not been in effect. Section 302 of the BBRA amends section 1895(b)(3)(A)(ii) of the Act and delays the application of a 15 percent reduction in HHA PPS payment amounts until 1 year after its implementation. Section 306 of the BBRA amends section 1895(b)(3)(B)(ii) of the Act to require the standard prospective payment amounts to be increased by a factor equal to the home health market basket minus 1.1 percentage points for each of FYs 2002 and 2003. In addition, for subsequent fiscal years, the law requires the rates to be increased by the applicable home health market basket index change. Thus, subject to these adjustments, the statutory construction of this final rule is budget neutral. However, we are aware that there would be a number of organizational accommodations that must be made by HHAs in order to make the transition from the cost-based/interim payment system environment to a prospective payment environment that would result in costs to these entities. On that basis, we are preparing this RIA.

Section 202 of the Unfunded Mandates Reform Act of 1995 requires that agencies prepare an assessment of anticipated costs and benefits for any rule that may result in an expenditure by State, local, or tribal governments, in the aggregate, or by the private sector, of $100 million in any given year. We believe that the costs associated with this final rule that apply to these governmental sectors would fall below this threshold. Therefore, the law does not apply and we have not prepared an assessment of anticipated costs and benefits of this final rule.

The RFA requires agencies to analyze options for regulatory relief of small businesses. For purposes of the RFA, small entities include small businesses, nonprofit organizations, and governmental agencies. Most HHAs are considered small entities, either by nonprofit status or by having revenues of $5 million or less annually.

Table 10 illustrates the distribution of HHAs by provider type participating in Medicare as of March 16, 2000.

TABLE 10.—NUMBER OF HHAs BY PROVIDER TYPE

HHA Provider Type	Number of HHAs
Visiting Nurse Association	451

TABLE 10.—NUMBER OF HHAs BY PROVIDER TYPE

HHA Provider Type	Number of HHAs
Combination of Government & Voluntary	35
Official Health Agency	910
Rehabilitation Facility Based	0
Hospital Based	2,278
Skilled Nursing Facility Based	161
Other	3,801
Total	7,636

Source: HCFA—On Line Survey Certification and Reporting System Standard Report 10—March 16, 2000.

The following RIA/RFA analysis, together with the rest of this preamble, explains the rationale for and purposes of this final rule.

A. Background

This final rule establishes requirements for the new prospective payment system for home health agencies as required by section 4603 of the Balanced Budget Act of 1997, as amended by section 5101 of OCESAA and sections 302, 305, and 306 of BBRA. The requirements include the implementation of a prospective payment system for home health agencies and a number of other related changes. The prospective payment system described in this rule would replace the retrospective reasonable cost-based system currently used by Medicare for the payment of home health services under Part A and Part B. This final rule sets forth a prospective payment system for all costs of home health services under section 1895 of the Act.

B. Revisions to the Proposed Rule

Below are listed a number of the significant changes to the proposed rule that are reflected in the final rule.

Section 409.100

Section 305 of the BBRA excludes DME covered as a home health service from the consolidated billing requirements. Specifically, the law requires, "in the case of home health services (including medical supplies described in section 1861(m)(5), but excluding durable medical equipment to the extent provided for in such section) furnished to an individual who (at the time the item or service is furnished) is under the plan of care of a home health agency, payment shall be made to the agency (without regard to whether or not the item or service was furnished by the agency, by others under arrangement with them made by the agency, or when

any other contracting or consulting arrangement, or otherwise)."

However, under HHA PPS there is a separate payment for DME items and services currently provided as a home health service and paid under the DME fee schedule. As discussed earlier, under the HHA PPS, DME covered as a home health service as part of the Medicare home health benefit will continue to be paid under the DME fee schedule. Further, in accordance with the statue, as amended by section 305 of BBRA, DME is also excluded from the consolidated billing requirements. A separate payment amount in addition to the prospective payment amount for home health services will be made for DME currently covered as a home health service under the PPS.

HHAs will no longer be able to "unbundle" home health services (other than DME) to an outside supplier that can then submit a separate bill directly to the Part B carrier or DMERC. Instead, the HHA itself will have to furnish the home health services (except DME) either directly or under an arrangement with an outside supplier in which the HHA itself, rather than the supplier, bills Medicare. The outside supplier must look to the HHA rather than to Medicare Part B for payment, except in the case of DME. Beneficiaries receiving DME prior to establishment of a home health plan of care can continue the relationship with that same DME supplier. The consolidated billing requirement eliminates the potential for duplicative billings for the same services to the RHHI by the HHA and to the Part B carrier by an outside supplier. All covered home health services listed in section 1861(m) (including medical supplies described in section 1861(m)(5), but excluding DME to the extent provided in such section) of the Act under a plan of care must be billed by the HHA.

Section 484.205

• We revised paragraph (a)(1) and (b) to clarify that the osteoporosis drug covered under the home health benefit is the only home health service listed in section 1861(m) of the Act that continues to be paid on a reasonable cost basis under PPS.

• We added paragraphs (b)(1) and (b)(2) that provides for the requirements governing the final split percentage payment approach. New paragraph (b)(1) governs the split percentage payment approach for initial episodes. The initial percentage payment for initial episodes is paid at 60 percent of the case-mix and wage adjusted 60 day episode rate. The residual final payment for initial episodes is paid at 40 percent of the case-mix and wage adjusted 60 day episode rate. New paragraph (b)(2) governs the split percentage payment approach for subsequent episodes. The initial percentage payment for subsequent episodes is paid at 50 percent of the case-mix and wage adjusted 60 day episode rate. The residual final payment for subsequent episodes is paid at 50 percent of the case-mix and wage adjusted 60 day episode rate.

Section 484.215

We revised paragraph (d)(4) to reflect the amounts that are added to the nonstandardized episode amount for the OASIS adjustment for the one time implementation costs associated with assessment scheduling form changes and amounts for Part B therapies that could have been unbundled to Part B prior to PPS implementation.

Section 484.225

We revised paragraph (c) to reflect that for each of FYs 2002 and 2003 the rates are updated by the applicable home health market basket minus 1.1 percentage points.

Section 484.230

We revised the language in this section to reflect the higher per-visit amounts that will be used to calculate the LUPA payments.

Section 484.235

We revised paragraph (b) to reflect the use of billable visit dates as the defining points for the PEP adjustment.

Section 484.237

We revised paragraphs (b)(1) and (b)(2) governing the SCIC adjustment to reflect the use of billable visit dates to define the span of days used to calculate the proportional payments both before and after a patient experiences a significant change in condition.

Section 484.240

We revised paragraph (d) to reflect the higher per-visit amounts that will be used to calculate the imputed costs for each episode for outlier payment determination.

C. Effects of This Final Rule

Section 1895(b)(3)(A)(i) of the Act requires the computation of a standard prospective payment amount to be initially based on the most recent audited cost-report data available to the Secretary. In accordance with this section of the Act, the primary data source in developing the cost basis for the 60-day episode payments was the audited cost-report sample of HHAs whose cost reporting periods ended in fiscal year 1997 (that is, ending on or after October 1, 1996 through September 30, 1997). We also adopted the most current complete utilization data available from 1998.

Table 11 below illustrates the proportion of HHAs that are likely to be affected. This table reflects how agencies would be paid under PPS versus how they would be paid under IPS. The limits under IPS were determined by updating the per-visit limits in effect for FY 2000 by the market basket minus 1.1 percent and updating each agency's per-beneficiary cap for FY 2000 by this same percentage. For each agency in the audited cost report data set, we updated their costs from FY 1997 to FY 2001 by our best estimate of HHA cost increases during this period. We then compared each agency's FY 2001 costs to the IPS limits to determine their IPS payment in FY 2001. To determine each agency's payment under PPS, we translated the cost report data into 60-day episodes and used the average case-mix for urban/rural and provider type as a proxy. We extrapolated the audited cost report data to reflect the total Medicare HHA distribution. We obtained average case-mix values based on the type of provider and whether the HHA was urban or rural from the Abt data set. We then multiplied the agency's expected number of episodes in FY 2001 by the wage-adjusted and case-mix-adjusted episode payment to obtain the agency's expected PPS payment. The PPS payment was then compared to the IPS payment.

TABLE 11.—IMPACT OF THE HOME HEALTH PROSPECTIVE PAYMENT AMOUNTS ON HOME HEALTH AGENCIES BY TYPE AND LOCATION FOR THE 563 AUDITED COST REPORT SAMPLE AGENCIES

Type of agency	Percentage change from IPS to PPS
All Agencies	0.0
By Urban/Rural and Provider Type:	
Rural:	
Freestanding: For-Profit	−7.50
Governmental	29.98
Non-Profit	13.28
Provider Based	5.31
Urban:	
Freestanding: For-Profit	−14.25
Governmental	20.58
Non-Profit	18.89
Provider Based	−2.50
By Provider Type:	
Freestanding: For-Profit	−12.77
Governmental	26.50
Non-Profit	17.88
Provider Based	−1.03
By Urban/Rural:	
Rural Agencies	5.94
Urban Agencies	−0.08
By Region:	
Midwest States	14.77
Northeast States	15.37
Southern States	−16.75
Western States	17.84

Appendix P

AHIMA's Domains, Subdomains, and Task Competencies RHIA, RHIT, and CCS

AHIMA's domains, subdomains, and task competencies are provided so that home care and hospice administrators can be fully aware of the capabilities of credentialed health information management professionals. This information includes the skills that these professionals can bring to an organization.

Registered Health Information Administrator (RHIA)

Domain: Healthcare Data

1.1. **Subdomain:** Data Structure, Content, and Use

    1.1.1.   Verify timeliness, completeness, accuracy, and appropriateness of data and data sources (for example, patient care, management, billing reports, or databases).

    1.1.2.   Conduct qualitative analysis to ensure documentation in the health record supports the diagnosis and reflects the progress, clinical findings, and discharge status.

    1.1.3.   Assist in the facility's billing processes.

    1.1.4.   Validate coding accuracy using clinical information found in the health record.

1.2. **Subdomain:** Clinical Classification Systems—ICD-9-CM Coding

    1.2.1.   Assign diagnosis/procedure codes using ICD-9-CM.

1.3. **Subdomain:** Clinical Classification Systems—CPT Coding

    1.3.1.   Assign procedure codes using CPT/HCPCS

Domain: Health Information Analysis

2.1. **Subdomain:** Healthcare Statistics and Research

    2.1.1.   Abstract records for department indices/databases/registries.

    2.1.2.   Collect data for quality management, utilization management, risk management, and other patient care related studies.

    2.1.3.   Calculate and interpret healthcare statistics.

    2.1.4.   Present data in verbal and written forms.

2.2.   **Subdomain:** Clinical Quality Assessment and Performance

      2.2.1.   Participate in facility-wide quality management program.

      2.2.2.   Analyze clinical data to identify trends.

Domain: Healthcare Environment

3.1.   **Subdomain:** Healthcare Delivery Systems

      3.1.1.   Interpret and apply laws and accreditation, licensure, and certification standards; monitor changes; and communicate information-related changes to others in the facility.

      3.1.2.   Understand the role of various providers and disciplines throughout the continuum of healthcare services.

3.2.   **Subdomain:** Legal Issues

      3.2.1.   Release patient-specific data to authorized users.

      3.2.2.   Request patient-specific information from other sources.

      3.2.3.   Summarize patient encounter data for release to authorized users.

      3.2.4.   Develop policies and procedures to protect unauthorized access to patient records.

      3.2.5.   Assist in developing facility-wide confidentiality policies.

3.3.   **Subdomain:** Healthcare Information Requirements and Standards

      3.3.1.   Assist in developing health record documentation guidelines.

      3.3.2.   Perform quantitative analysis of health records to evaluate compliance with regulations and standards.

      3.3.3.   Perform qualitative analysis of health records to evaluate compliance.

      3.3.4.   Assist in preparing the facility for an accreditation, licensing, or certification survey.

      3.3.5.   Develop and demonstrate HIM service compliance with relevant regulations and accreditation standards.

      3.3.6.   Ensure facility-wide adherence to health information services' compliance with regulatory requirements (for example, ICD-9-CM Cooperating parties coding guidelines, HCFA Compliance Plan, Correct Coding Initiative).

Domain: Information Technology and Systems

4.1.   **Subdomain:** Information Technology

      4.1.1.   Use common software packages (for example, spreadsheets, databases, word processing, graphics, presentation, statistical, e-mail).

      4.1.2.   Use electronic and imaging technology to store health records.

      4.1.3.   Query facility-wide databases to retrieve information.

      4.1.4.   Generate reports from various databases.

      4.1.5.   Protect data integrity and validity using software or hardware technology.

      4.1.6.   Enforce confidentiality and security measures to protect electronic information

      4.1.7.   Identify common software problems.

      4.1.8.   Design data quality controls and edits.

      4.1.9.   Participate in development of strategic and operational plans for facility-wide information systems.

4.2. **Subdomain:** Health Information Systems

4.2.1. Collect and report data on incomplete records and timeliness of record completion.

4.2.2. Maintain filing and retrieval systems for paper-based patient records.

4.2.3. Maintain integrity of master patient/client index.

4.2.4. Maintain integrity of patient numbering and filing systems.

4.2.5. Design forms, computer input screens, and other health record documentation tools.

4.2.6. Evaluate software packages to determine that they meet user needs.

Domain: Organization and Supervision

5.1. **Subdomain:** Human Resources Management

5.1.1.   Interview prospective employees.

5.1.2.   Hire new employees.

5.1.3.   Develop and implement new staff orientation and training programs.

5.1.4.   Supervise staff.

5.1.5.   Collect data on employee performance.

5.1.6.   Conduct performance appraisals.

5.1.7.   Counsel, discipline, and terminate staff.

5.1.8.   Perform job analysis.

5.1.9.   Develop job descriptions.

5.1.10. Conduct in-service education programs on topics related to health information services.

5.1.11. Develop and support work teams.

5.2. **Subdomain:** Health Information Services Management

5.2.1.   Monitor staffing levels, turnaround time, productivity, and workflow.

5.2.2.   Assign projects and tasks to appropriate staff.

5.2.3.   Develop productivity and control measures.

5.2.4.   Benchmark staff performance data in relation to departmental and facility performance standards.

5.2.5.   Determine resources (equipment and supplies) to meet workload needs.

5.2.6.   Develop departmental policies and procedures.

5.2.7.   Develop strategic plans, goals, and objectives for area of responsibility and communicate to staff.

5.2.8.   Participate on intradepartmental teams and committees.

5.2.9.   Participate on facility-wide teams and committees responsible for health information services issues.

5.2.10. Coordinate interdepartmental and intradepartmental services.

5.2.11. Provide consultation, education, and training to users of health information services.

5.2.12. Prepare budgets with accompanying justification and monitor adherence.

5.2.13. Evaluate effectiveness of departmental operations and services.

5.2.14. Develop quality control and improvement systems for departmental processes, and use quality improvement tools and techniques to improve processes.

5.2.15. Manage special projects.

5.2.16. Plan and conduct meetings.

5.2.17. Resolve customer complaints.

5.2.18. Identify departmental resource requirements, determine costs and benefits, communicate requirements to vendors, and evaluate vendor proposals.

5.2.19. Assist in redesigning and reengineering departmental services and operations.

5.2.20. Prioritize department functions and services.

Registered Health Information Technician (RHIT)

Domain: Healthcare Data

1.1. **Subdomain:** Data Structure, Content, and Use

1.1.1. Verify timeliness, completeness, accuracy, and appropriateness of data and data sources (for example, patient care, management, billing reports, or databases).

1.1.2. Conduct qualitative analysis to ensure that documentation in the health record supports the diagnosis and reflects the progress, clinical findings, and discharge status.

1.1.3. Assist in the facility's billing processes.

1.1.4. Validate coding accuracy using clinical information found in the health record.

1.2. **Subdomain:** Clinical Classification Systems—ICD-9-CM Coding

1.2.1. Assign diagnosis/procedure codes using ICD-9-CM.

1.3. **Subdomain:** Clinical Classification Systems—CPT Coding

1.3.1. Assign procedure codes using CPT/HCPCS.

Domain: Health Information Analysis

2.1. Abstract records for department indices/databases/registries.

2.2. Collect data for quality management, utilization management, risk management, and other patient care related studies.

2.3. Participate in facility-wide quality management program.

2.4. Calculate and interpret descriptive healthcare statistics.

2.5. Present data in verbal and written forms.

Domain: Healthcare Environment

3.1. **Subdomain:** Healthcare Delivery Systems

3.1.1. Interpret and apply laws and accreditation, licensure, and certification standards; monitor changes; and communicate information-related changes to other people in the facility.

3.1.2. Understand the role of various providers and disciplines throughout the continuum of healthcare services.

3.2. **Subdomain:** Legal Issues

3.2.1. Release patient-specific data to authorized users.

3.2.2. Request patient-specific information from other sources.

3.2.3.   Summarize patient encounter data for release to authorized users.

3.2.4.   Maintain and enforce patient health record confidentiality requirements.

3.3.   Subdomain: Healthcare Information Requirements and Standards

3.3.1.   Assist in developing health record documentation guidelines.

3.3.2.   Perform quantitative analysis of health records to evaluate compliance with regulations and standards.

3.3.3.   Perform qualitative analysis of health records to evaluate compliance.

3.3.4.   Assist in preparing the facility for an accreditation, licensing, and/or certification survey.

3.3.5.   Ensure facility-wide adherence to health information services' compliance with regulatory requirements (for example, ICD-9-CM Cooperative parties coding guidelines, HCFA Compliance Plan, Correct Coding Initiative).

Domain: Information Technology and Systems

4.1.   Subdomain: Information Technology

4.1.1.   Use common software packages (for example, spreadsheets, databases, word processing, graphics, presentation, statistical, e-mail).

4.1.2.   Use electronic and imaging technology to store health records.

4.1.3.   Query facility-wide databases to retrieve information.

4.1.4.   Generate reports from various databases.

4.1.5.   Protect data integrity and validity using software or hardware technology.

4.1.6.   Identify common software problems.

4.2.   Subdomain: Health Information Systems

4.2.1.   Collect and report data on incomplete records and timeliness of record completion.

4.2.2.   Maintain filing and retrieval systems for paper-based patient records.

4.2.3.   Maintain integrity of master patient/client index.

4.2.4.   Maintain integrity of patient numbering and filing systems.

4.2.5.   Design forms, computer input screens, and other health record documentation tools.

Domain: Organization and Supervision

5.1.   Monitor staffing levels, turnaround time, productivity and workflow for supervisory purposes.

5.2.   Determine resources (equipment and supplies) to meet workload needs.

5.3.   Develop departmental procedures.

5.4.   Develop strategic plans, goals, and objectives for area of responsibility.

5.5.   Participate on intradepartmental teams/committees.

5.6.   Participate on facility-wide teams/committees responsible for health information services issues.

5.7.   Provide consultation, education, and training to users of health information services.

5.8.   Use quality improvement tools and techniques to improve departmental processes.

5.9.   Plan and conduct meetings.

5.10.   Resolve customer complaints.
5.11.   Prioritize department functions and services.
5.12.   Implement staff orientation and training programs.
5.13.   Manage special projects.

Certified Coding Specialist (CCS)

Competency: Data Identification

1. Read and interpret health record documentation to identify all diagnoses and procedures that affect the current inpatient stay/outpatient encounter visit.

2. Assess the adequacy of health record documentation to ensure that it supports all diagnoses and procedures to which codes are assigned.

3. Apply knowledge of anatomy and physiology, clinical disease processes, pharmacology, and diagnostic and procedural terminology to assign accurate codes to diagnoses and procedures.

4. Apply knowledge of disease processes and surgical procedures to assign nonindexed medical terms to the appropriate class in the classification/nomenclature system.

Competency: Coding Guidelines

1. Apply knowledge of current approved ICD-9-CM Coding Guidelines* to assign and sequence the correct diagnosis and procedure codes for hospital inpatient services.

2. Apply knowledge of current Diagnostic Coding and Reporting Guidelines for Outpatient Services.*

3. Apply knowledge of CPT format, guidelines, and notes to locate the correct codes for all services and procedures performed during the encounter/visit and sequence them correctly.

4. Apply knowledge of procedural terminology to recognize when an unlisted procedure code must be used in CPT.

Competency: Regulatory Guidelines

1. Apply Uniform Hospital Discharge Data Set (UHDDS) definitions to select the principal diagnosis, principal procedure, complications, comorbid conditions, other diagnoses, and significant procedures which require coding.

2. Select the appropriate principal diagnosis for episodes of care in which determination of principal diagnosis is not clear because the patient has multiple problems.

3. Apply knowledge of the Prospective Payment System to confirm DRG assignment that ensures optimal reimbursement.

4. Refuse to fraudulently maximize reimbursement by assigning codes that do not conform to approved coding principles/guidelines.*

5. Refuse to unfairly maximize reimbursement by unbundling services and codes that do not conform to CPT basic coding principles.

6. Apply knowledge of the Ambulatory Surgery Center Payment Groups to confirm ASC assignment that ensures optimal reimbursement.

7. Apply policies and procedures on health record documentation, coding and claims processing, and appeal.

8. Use the HCFA Common Procedural Coding System (HCPCS) to appropriately assign HCPCS codes for outpatient Medicare reimbursement.

Competency: Coding

1. Exclude from coding diagnoses, conditions, problems, and procedures related to an earlier episode of care that have no bearing on the current episode of care.

2. Exclude from coding ICD-9-CM nonsurgical, noninvasive procedures that carry no operative or anesthetic risk.

3. Exclude from coding information, such as symptoms or signs characteristic of diagnosis, findings from diagnostic studies, or localized conditions, that has no bearing on the current management of the patient.

4. Apply knowledge of ICD-9-CM instructional notations and conventions to locate and assign the correct diagnostic and procedural codes and sequence them correctly.

5. Facilitate data retrieval by recognizing when more than one code is required to adequately classify a given condition.

6. Exclude from coding those procedures which are component parts of an already assigned CPT procedure code.

Competency: Data Quality

1. Clarify conflicting, ambiguous, or nonspecific information appearing in a health record by consulting the appropriate physician.

2. Participate in quality assessment to ensure continuous improvement in ICD-9-CM and CPT coding and collection of quality health data.

3. Demonstrate ability to recognize potential coding quality issues from an array of data.

4. Apply policies and procedures on health record documentation and coding that are consistent with Official Coding Guidelines.*

5. Contribute to development of facility-specific coding policies and procedures.

---

* The cooperating parties (the American Health Information Management Association, the American Hospital Association, the Health Care Financing Administration, and the National Center for Health Statistics) publish official guidelines in the *Coding Clinic for ICD-9-CM,* available from the American Hospital Association. These guidelines are also available in the ICD-9-CM CD-ROM offered by the U.S. Government Printing Office. "ICD-9-CM Coding and Reporting Official Guidelines" and "Diagnostic Coding and Reporting Guidelines for Outpatient Services (Hospital-Based and Physician Offices)" published in Fourth Quarter, *1995 Coding Clinic for ICD-9-CM* (Volume 7, No. 1).

Appendix Q

Sample Health Record

The following pages contain a complete health record from a recent home care and hospice admission. Actual patient and physician names have been omitted to protect confidentiality. This appendix provides a practical look at the various documents and forms used in the home care and hospice record.

PHYSICIAN'S ORDERS

Client ████████████████████████
                      Last   First

~~ID:~~
~~SS#:~~ _____

Dear Dr. ████████████ _____ MD Phone ████████████

PROFESSIONAL WORKER'S COMMENTS:

Orders Received from Ann RN 81-4940

████ _____ Professional Worker's Signature/Phone ████████████████
Date

Please document any change in TREATMENT OR MEDICATIONS. Return to Home Care office.

MD COMMENTS / TELEPHONE ORDERS:

8/7/00

Dr. over Home Care needs ████████████████████
I.D. ████████████████████████████

_____ _____
Date MD Signature

Please sign and return within 48 hours

122001 (10/99)   White - Home Care Record   Yellow/Pink - Medical Records   Blue - Case Manager

```
┌─────────────────────────┐
│                         │        Patient: ██████████████████████
│                         │        ~~SS#~~: ████████████████████████
│      Consent Form       │
│                         │        DOB: ██████████████████████
└─────────────────────────┘
```

1. **CONSENT FOR HOME HEALTH SERVICES**

   I voluntarily give my consent for   Home and Community-based Services to provide home care and hospice and/or pharmaceutical services as ordered by my physician. I am aware that health care is not an exact science and I acknowledge that no guarantees have been made to me as the result of home health services. In the event a health care worker sustains exposure to my blood or body fluids, I give permission for a sample of my blood to be tested for infectious disease.

2. **BILL OF RIGHTS**

   I have received and I understand the Home Care Patient Bill of Rights. I understand that I have the right to register a complaint without fear of retribution if my rights are violated.

3. **PATIENT SELF DETERMINATION ACT**

   I have received written information regarding the Patient Self Determination Act of 1990.

4. **GUARANTEE OF ACCOUNT**

   ☑   **Medicare Authorization**
   I certify that the information given by me in applying for payment under Title XVIII of the Social Security Act is correct. I authorize any holder of medical or other information about me to release to the Social Security Administration or its intermediaries or carriers any information needed for this or a related Medicare claim. I request that payment of authorized benefits be made on my behalf.

   ☐   **Insurance Authorization**
   I hereby authorize payment directly to   for the insurance benefits allowed to me but not to exceed Fairview regular charges for these services. I understand that **EXACT INSURANCE BENEFITS CANNOT BE DETERMINED UNTIL THE INSURANCE COMPANY RECEIVES THE CLAIM. ANY REMAINING PORTION OF THE BILL WILL BE MY RESPONSIBILITY.** I further authorize the release of any medical information necessary to determine benefits.

5. **AUTHORIZATION TO RELEASE MEDICAL RECORDS**

   I authorize _____████████████████_____ to release to   Home and Community-based Services my most recent History and Physical and Discharge Summary and other records or orders, if applicable, which are necessary and reasonable concerning my case.

   I also agree that   may release their information to other health care/medical agencies providing care to me. A photocopy of the authorization shall be considered as valid as the original.

   ████████████████████████████████████

   SIGNATURE (Patient or Authorized Representative)   DATE

   ████████████████████████████████████

   WITNESS   DATE

   61-9673

   White: Medical Record   Yellow: Home File

Service Agreement

Patient:
Cust ID:

Service	Refused Services	Anticipated Schedule (Frequency/duration)	Primary Goal/Care Plan	Expected Payor ☐ Card Verified	Expected Patient Charges*
Skilled Nursing ☑RN ☐Visits ☐Hourly ☐LPN ☐Visits ☐Hourly		1-3 wk x 4 w	safety Diagnosis	M DC 12	-0-
Medical Supplies					
Pharmacy					
Rehab Services ☑PT ☑OT ☐ST		3/wk	Transfer & safety	M OC R	-0-
Social Services		1 visit	community service	M DC R	0
Chaplain ☐Volunteer					
Home Health Aide ☐Visits ☐Hourly					
Supervisory Visits ☐RN ☐Therapist					

*I understand that the information on payment for services is a preliminary estimate which is based on the information I have provided to FHCH at the time of my admission for services I understand that actual payment by my insurance company cannot be determined until home care bills have been submitted to them. I understand that I am responsible for all charges that are not reimbursed by my insurance company. A placement fee of $2,000.00 will be charged if I hire a FHCH employee within 90 days of receiving services.

In the case of a change in condition, FHCH should call my Emergency Contact: _____ **Relationship:** _____ (W) _____

Emergency Preparedness Plan - a plan to ensure the safety of patients in the event of an environmental or agency emergency which may interrupt patient services from FHCH.
☑*Non-essential Services* - A patient who has the ability and/or has caregivers available to provide care for a short period of time. This could include the ability to self-medicate, manage bowel and bladder needs, get nutrition, manage transfers and access 911/emergency services.

☐*Essential Services* - A patient with immediate needs who cannot safely forfeit care and requires health care intervention regardless of other conditions. Patients in this category may include: patients with no qualified caregiver available; patients who are on life sustaining equipment or life sustaining infusion therapy; insulin dependent diabetic patients who are unable to self-inject; patients with significant cognitive impairment.

Contingency Plan
List Essential Services by Discipline: ☐Skilled Nursing ☐Pharmacy ☐Home Health Aide   Patient able to access 911: ☑Yes ☐No
My Primary Caregiver for Essential Services is: _____ Relationship: _____ (H) _____ (W) _____

A representative from _____ **can be reached at** _____ **, 24 hours per day OR** _____
I understand that emergency services will not be summoned during a life threatening emergency when there is a written physician's order for DNR/DNI in my record that reflect my wishes according to the Adult Health Care Decisions Act and home death has been pre-arranged. I have had the opportunity to participate in the development of this service agreement. I have read this agreement, understand it and agree to abide by its terms.

_____   _____   _____
Signature (Patient or Authorized Representative)   Witness   Date

White: Patient   Yellow: Chart   Pink: Home Chart   122013

Verbal Orders For: MR #:

                                                             Episode ID:

       Please review,   **Home Care**   DOB:
    sign, and return to:

|||||||||||||||||||||||||||||||

Verbal Order #   2002800695New order for SN - SKILLED NURSING VISITS:
                              HOME CARE ORDERS FOR CERT PERIOD 8 8 2000 TO 10 8 2000
08/08/2000   SN 1 TO 3 XWX4W   TEACH SAFETY MED USE   OB AND ASSESS   LEFT
                              ANKLE STATUS   CMS   CAST   TEACH PAIN CONTROL   AND CAST CARE

|||||||||||||||||||||||||||||||

Verbal Order #   2002800696New order for SW - SOCIAL WORKER:
                              SW 2 VISITS TO CONNECT TO COMMUNITY SERVICES
`8/08/2000   SW 2X4X

|||||||||||||||||||||||||||||||

Verbal Order #   2002800697New order for OT - OCCUPATIONAL THERAPY:
                              OT VISITS OB AND EVAL FOR SAFETY TRANSFER TECHNIQUES   SOME
08/08/2000   EXERCISES AS POSS
                                  QT EVAL AND TX 1X1 AND CALL
                                       CLIENT HAS PROGRESSIVE CHRONIC CONDITION

                    Verbal Order
                      Employee ▆▆▆▆▆▆▆▆▆▆▆▆▆▆▆▆ _____ Date ▆▆▆▆▆▆

Physician's
Order
                    Physician _____▆▆▆▆▆▆▆▆_____ Date ▆▆▆▆▆

Page 1 of 1

Printed: 08/09/2000
        7:32:34AM

```
Verbal Orders For:                                          MR #:

                                                           Episode ID:

         Please review,     Home Care                       DOB:
    sign, and return to:
```

|‖█‖‖‖█‖‖█‖█‖‖█‖|

Verbal Order #   2002800695New order for SN - SKILLED NURSING VISITS:
08/08/2000   HOME CARE ORDERS FOR CERT PERIOD 8 8 2000 TO 10 8 2000
                               SN 1 TO 3 XWX4W   TEACH SAFETY MED USE   OB AND ASSESS   LEFT
                           ANKLE STATUS   CMS   CAST   TEACH PAIN CONTROL   AND CAST CARE

|‖█‖‖‖█‖‖█‖█‖‖█‖|

Verbal Order #   2002800696New order for SW - SOCIAL WORKER:
'8/08/2000   SW 2 VISITS TO CONNECT TO COMMUNITY SERVICES
                           SW 2X4X

|‖█‖‖‖█‖‖█‖█‖‖█‖|

Verbal Order #   2002800697New order for OT - OCCUPATIONAL THERAPY:
08/08/2000   OT VISITS OB AND EVAL FOR SAFETY TRANSFER TECHNIQUES   SOME
                           EXERCISES AS POSS
                               QT EVAL AND TX 1X1 AND CALL
                                   CLIENT HAS PROGRESSIVE CHRONIC CONDITION

```
                    Verbal Order
                       Employee _____ Date_____

Physician's
Order
                       Physician _____ Date_____

Page 1 of 1

Printed: 08/29/2000
         8:50:24AM
```

Occupational Therapy Evaluation/Plan of Care

Client _____
Last _____ First _____

Cust ID _____ Date _____

Doctor _____ Phone Numbe _____

DOB 4/5/28 Age: _____ Sex M. (F)

PERSONAL DATA

Diagnosis Fx (L) ankle · c̄ repair 5/5/00

Hx/Precautions IBM; Musc. Dystrophy

Support Persons - Caregivers pt's dtrs. Lives with close.

Work Avocation disability; retired.

ENVIROMENTAL DESCRIPTION

Carpet + linoleum Throghout; Laundry in basement.

ENVIRONMENTAL PROBLEM

See above.

Equipment In Use: w/c.

quipment Needs:

CLINICAL PICTURE

A = Abnormal	N/A = Not applicable
WNL = Within normal limits	N/E = Not evaluated
WFL = Within functional limts	Pain (0-10) = 0=No Pain, 10 = Intense
S/C = Safety concern	

MMT 0/5 no contraction
1/5 Trace
2/5 full ROM gravity eliminated
3/5 full ROM against gravity

4/5 able to resist applied force
5/5 normal

JOINT	A ROM		MMT				R	L	
	R	L	R	L			R		L	
Shoulder	WFL	WFL	4/5	4/5	Grasp		R	4+/5	L	3+/5
Elbow					Coordination - fine motor, 9 hole peg		R	A	L	A
Forearm					Coordination - gross motor, finger - nose		R	WFL	L	WFL
Wrist					Sensation		R	↓	L	↓
Hand	✓	✓	✓	✓	Hearing					
Dominance	X				Vision					
					Pain - 1 2 3 4 5 6 7 8 9 10 Location:					

Comments:

Pt attempting to go to SNF for 6 wks. She feels she can't manage at home by herself.

Call placed to SW referral / C entral intake.

61-9359

White: Medical Records   Yellow: OT

Initials: _____

Page 1 of 3

Occupational Therapy Eval/Plan of Care					Client

ACTIVITES OF DAILY LIVING

I = Independent   SBA = Stand by Assist   MIN = Minimal Assist
MOD = Moderate Assist   U = Unable   MAX = Maximum Assist
N/A = Not Applicable   N/E = Not Evaluated
Area of Concern

Comments

ACTIVITES OF DAILY LIVING	Prior	Prevent	Observe	Reported	Comments
SKILL					
1. Self Feeding	I	I		x	
2. Grooming/Oral Hygiene/Hair Care	I	I		x	
3. Dressing U/L/Ex					
a. On/off	I	A		x	
b. Fastners	I	I	x		
4. Bathing	I	A		x	
5. Toileting	I	A		x	daughter.
6. Homemaking					
a. Kitchen food prep	I	A		x	
b. Yard	M	A		→	
c. Cleaning	A	A		x	
d. Laundry	I	A		x	
e. Shopping	I	A		x	
7. Mobility					
a. In home	I	A	x		
b. Carry/reach objects	I	I	x		
c. Mode of transport					
8. Transfers					
a. Tub/shower	I	A		x	
b. Toilet	I	A		x	
c. Bed & mobility	I	A		✓	
d. Chair/couch	I	A	x		
9. Personal Affairs	I	I		x	
10. Communication					
a. Written	I	I	Y		
b. Reading	I	I	Y		
c. Oral	I	I	x		
d. Phone use	I	I		✓	
11. Cognitive/Psycosocial					
a. Orientation					person, place, time
b. Memory LT					appears intact
c. Memory ST					
d. Attention span					focused, distracted, preoccupied
e. Follow directions					1 Step 2 Step
f. Understands Limitations					appears to understand.
g. Behavior/Emotions					Anxious, depressed, frustrated, alert, pleasant, angry, confused, flat, passive, fearful, labile, agitated, compliant, cooperative, impulsive

Claudia Allen Score _____   Initials _____

61-9359

OT Plan of Care

Client _____ Last _____ First

Problem	Short Term Goals	Plan	Duration
① *Functional transfer*	Pt ① transfer *ind by p/c*	transfer training	2 wks.
② ↓ LE Dressing	Pt ① LE Dressing by p/c	ADL	↓

LTG:

HOMEBOUND DUE TO:
- ☐ Bedbound
- ☐ Emotional disorder
- ☐ Other/comments.

- ☐ Poor endurance
- ☐ Req. assist of person/device to leave

- ☐ Chairbound
- ☐ Severe Pain

- ☐ Considerable & taxing effort
- ☐ Medically contraindicated

PLAN:
1. ADL training
2. Adaptive equipment/training ✓
3. Safety
4. Joint protection
5. Home exercise program
6. Transfer training ✓
7. Orthotic referral
8. Patient education
9. Progressive resistive exercises
10. Progressive aerobic exercises
11. Home modifications
12. Compensatory techniques
13. Endurance
14. Family teaching
15. Work simplification/Energy conservation
16. Needs further assessment:
17. Other
18. Discharge no need for OT now

Rehab potential to complete OT goals.   Excellent   Good   ⟨Fair⟩   Poor

Frequency and Duration: 1 *pr in 2 wks*.

Signature _____

White: Medical Records   Yellow: OT

9/95   61-9359

inclusive body myositis

_____ AND HOSPICE
SKILLED NURSING VISIT REPORT
☑ Skilled Care
☐ Maintenance Care

DATE 8/10/00

| TIME OF DAY | HOUR : MIN 4:05p |
| Time in Home | 5:2b |

Patient Name _____
(Last, First)

| T 98.3 | PA | ☐ Reg ☐ Irreg | PR 60 | ☐ Reg ☑ Irreg | R 16 | BP 124/70 | WT. |

HOMEBOUND DUE TO:
☐ Bedbound
☐ Chairbound
☑ Considerable & taxing effort
☐ Req. assist of person/device to leave
☐ Poor endurance
☐ Medically contraindicated
☐ Severe Pain
☐ Mental/Emotional Disorder
☐ Other/Comments:

NOT ASSESSED	SYSTEM	NO CHANGE	WNL	OBSERVATIONS-SUBJECTIVE/OBJECTIVE
	E.E.N.T.		✓	
	Cardiovascular			see below
	Respiratory		✓	
	Gastro-Intestinal			↑ water intake, stool softeners prn
	Endocrine			
	Genito Urinary			adv to ↑ water intake
	Neuro Muscular			see
	Skin Integrity		✓	
	Rest/Comfort		✓	not requiring pain med except HS + early AM
	Cognitive/Mental		✓	
	Psycho-Social		✓	
	ADL's			Needs HHA p cleared by PT

PROBLEM(S) (If new problem specify goal)	NURSING INTERVENTIONS O/E, Treatments, Teaching, etc.	EVALUATION OF CARE Patient/Family Response Progress Toward Goal(s)	CARE PLAN UPDATE N.C. = No Change in plan P.R. = Problem Resolved (Goal Met) Specify Any Changes in Plan
alt CV	Pt has irreg HR which she is unaware of. She has no blood thinner ordered. Teaching re a-fib vs v-fib - S/s of ea. color good, no dyspnea or cough		- get PT eval - get HHA - start ASA
alt neuro	→ Pt extremely weak 2° IBM, unable to transfer even c assistance of experienced daughter. Good circulation to toes. Teaching re S/s of DVT.		

HHA SUPERVISION/ORIENTATION:

	GOOD	FAIR	POOR
Aide Appearance			
Relationship to Patient			
Reliability/Punctuality			
Task Completion			
Task Observed:			

☐ Indirect   ☐ Direct
HHA Name _____
Care Plan Update: ☐ Current Care plan meeting needs
☐ Care plan changes _____

LAB RESULTS: _____ ☐ Called to MD
CARE CONFERENCE: _____

ORDER CHANGES: ☐ See MD Order   ☐ See Medication Profile Update   ☐ Patient/Caregiver Instructed
NEXT SN VISIT: NEXT MD APPT:

SIGNATURE _____   TITLE _____

122015   White: Medical Record   Yellow: Case Manager

380

PHYSICIAN'S ORDERS

Patient Name: ▓▓▓▓▓▓▓▓▓▓ ✓
(Last,First)

Cust. ID: ▓▓▓▓▓▓▓▓▓▓

Dear Dr. ▓▓▓▓▓▓▓▓▓▓
(Last,First)

MD Phone ▓▓▓▓▓▓▓▓▓▓

PROFESSIONAL WORKER'S COMMENTS:

OT eval completed. OT rec 4 PRN visits in 2 wks for transfer training

Date 8/10/00

Professional Worker's Signature/Phone ▓▓▓▓▓▓▓▓

Please document any change in TREATMENT OR MEDICATIONS. Return to Home Care office.

MD COMMENTS / TELEPHONE ORDERS:

8/14/00 T.O. received from ▓▓▓▓▓▓▓▓ for OT 4 PRN visits in 2 wks.

Date ▓▓▓▓▓▓

MD Signature ▓▓▓▓▓▓

Please sign and return within 48 hours

122001 REV 3/00   White - Home Care Record   Yellow/Pink - Medical Records   Blue - Case Manager

Service Agreement

Patient: _____

Cust ID: _____

03-15-00 P 12:54

Service	Refused Services	Anticipated Schedule (frequency/duration)	Primary Goal/Care Plan	Expected Payor ☐ Card Verified	Expected Patient Charges*
Skilled Nursing ☐RN ☐Visits ☐Hourly / ☐LPN ☐Visits ☐Hourly					
Medical Supplies					
Pharmacy					
Rehab Services ☐PT ☐OT ☐ST					
Social Services		1 eval visit to provide info in locally in length	to provide info on community resources for managing long-term	medicare 100 %	0
Chaplain ☐Volunteer					
Home Health Aide ☐Visits ☐Hourly					
Supervisory Visits ☐RN ☐Therapist					

*I understand that the information on payment for services is a preliminary estimate which is based on the information I have provided to FHCH at the time of my admission for services. I understand that actual payment by my insurance company cannot be determined until home care bills have been submitted to them. I understand that I am responsible for all charges that are not reimbursed by my insurance company. A placement fee of $2,000.00 will be charged if I hire a FHCH employee within 90 days of receiving services.

In the case of a change in condition, FHCH should call my Emergency Contact: _____ Relationship: _____ (H) _____ (W) _____

Emergency Preparedness Plan - *a plan to ensure the safety of patients in the event of an environmental or agency emergency which may interrupt patient services from FHCH.*
☐ *Non-essential Services* - A patient who has the ability and/or has caregivers available to provide care for a short period of time. This could include the ability to self-medicate, manage bowel and bladder needs, get nutrition, manage transfers and access 911/emergency services.

☐ *Essential Services* - A patient with immediate needs who cannot safely forfeit care and requires health care intervention regardless of other conditions. Patients in this category may include: patients with no qualified caregiver available; patients who are on life sustaining equipment or life sustaining infusion therapy; insulin dependent diabetic patients who are unable to self-inject; patients with significant cognitive impairment.
Contingency Plan
List Essential Services by Discipline: ☐Skilled Nursing ☐Pharmacy ☐Home Health Aide   Patient able to access 911: ☐Yes ☐No
My Primary Caregiver for Essential Services is: _____ Relationship: _____ (H) _____ (W) _____

A representative from _____ can be reached at _____ , 24 hours per day OR _____
I understand that emergency services will not be summoned during a life threatening emergency when there is a written physician's order for DNR/DNI in my record that reflect my wishes according to the Adult Health Care Decisions Act and home death has been pre-arranged. I have had the opportunity to participate in the development of this service agreement. I have read this agreement, understand it and agree to abide by its terms.

Signature/(Patient or Authorized Representative) _____   Witness _____   Date _____

White: Patient   Yellow: Chart   Pink: Home Chart   122013

Client _____
Cust ID _____
Date _____

MEDICAL SOCIAL SERVICE ASSESSMENT

DIAGNOSIS: osteoporosis, Inclusion body myositis, fx. trimalleolar - open dislocation ankle

NAME/RELATIONSHIP		PHONE	FAMILY/SOCIAL/OCCUPATIONAL HISTORY
Household Members:	pt lives alone but living c her to help.		Pt. divorced. Pt. has lived in current condo for 2 yrs. dtr will be returning to teaching in wks but still available overnights
Others:			Dtr. doesn't work b. hu. k.

ASSESSMENT - CODES: G = GOOD F = FAIR P = POOR

BEHAVIOR/PSYCH/ SOCIAL	Client	Caregiver	PHYSICAL	Client	Caregiver
Memory	F-G	G	Ability to Manage ADLs	P	G
Comprehension	G	(	Appetite/Wt Management	F	
...gement/Decision Making	G	)	Sleep	F	
...nunication Skills	G	)	Energy	P. F	✓
Health Status Knowledge	G				
Motivation to Resolve Needs	G	✓			

EMOTIONAL/MENTAL	CLIENT RESPONSE	CAREGIVER RESPONSE
Orientation	G	G
	G	G
Mood	depressed but on meds	G
ETOH/Drug Use/Treatment	0 cigs / glass of wine/day	N/A
Attention Span	G	G
Compliance with Treatment/Needs	G	G
...gness to Accept Help	G	G
...sentation	G	G
Mental Health Diagnosis/Treatment	depression - on meds.	N/A

ENVIRONMENT	DESCRIPTION	VULNERABLE ADULT PLAN
Odor	NO	☐ Level of care provided by caregiver is appropriate to safely meet clients needs.
Dirt/Clutter	(	☑ Facilitate community services that will assist client/caregiver in managing their environment and decrease safety concerns.
Infestation	)	
Waste		☐ Refer to adult protection.
Repair	✓	

FUNCTIONAL STATUS	PSYCH/SOCIAL STATUS	SOCIALIZATION/RECREATION	COUNSELING/SUPPORT NEEDS
☐ SAME AS BEFORE	☑ STABLE	☐ ACTIVE	☐ AGING
☐ MORE ALERT	☐ UNSTABLE	☐ BORED	☐ FAMILY
☐ LESS ALERT	☑ REALISTIC	☐ LONELY	☐ DISABILITY
☐ ...RE INDEPENDENT	☐ UNREALISTIC	☑ ISOLATED	☐ MARRIAGE
S INDEPENDENT	☐ FUNCTIONAL	INTERESTS:	☐ GRIEF
...DDEN ACTIVITY LOSS	☐ DYSFUNCTIONAL		☐ PSYCHIATRIC
☐ GRADUAL ACTIVITY LOSS	☐ SUICIDAL/DEATH THOUGHTS		FAMILY SUPPORT: as above

Initials _____
Page 1 of 3

Original - Medical Record   Yellow - SW   Pink - Case Manager

1-9664

Client _____

3ESSMENT/PROBLEMS	RESOURCES	INTERVENTIONS					PLAN
		In Place	Pend	Refuse	Refer	Inform	
HUUSING Type: 1-Level Levels: 2 Steps: 2 NH ☐ Needed ☐ Willing ☐ Waiting List Where _____ Client choice _____	Senior Housing					✓	Goals: Client/Caregiver verbalizes an awareness of: accessible home and no need to move from that stand point but wondering if NH
	Relative		•				
	Nursing Home					✓	Intervention: MSS will nuded due to dt educate help no longer avail as stated
	Utility bill assist						Comments: during the day in 2 weeks.
	Shared Housing						
	Subsidized						
ADVANCED DIRECTIVE ☐ Needed ☑ Has ☐ Agent/Proxy	DNR/DNI						Goals: Client/Caregiver verbalizes an awareness of:
	Living Will			•			
	Durable POA Health Care						Intervention: MSS will
	Psych Living Will						
	Guardianship/ Conservatorship						Comments:
	Other						
TRANSPORTATION ☐ Needed Not Needed	Senior Transportation	American Red Cross				✓	Goals: Client/Caregiver verbalizes an awareness of: need for ast.
	Transportation Co's						
	Disabled Parking Permit	✓					Intervention: MSS will educate as stated
	Metro Mobility	application		left	✓		Comments:
	Other						
IIPMENT ☐ Needed ☐ Not Needed	Walker	✓					Goals: Client/Caregiver verbalizes an awareness of: need for sliding board + transfer belt
	W/C	✓					
	Commode	✓					Intervention: MSS will discuss c̄ PT
	Bath Bench	✓					
	Other toilet seat	✓					Comments:
PERSONAL CARE/ HOUSEKEEPING ☐ Self-independent ☐ Self-with difficulty ☑ Needs Assistance ☐ Needs Total Care ☐ Elderly/ill caregiver ☐ Employed caregiver ☐ Caregiver able/willing ☑ Caregiver unable/ unwilling ☐ Cannot afford to hire	Family Care	✓					Goals: Client/Caregiver verbalizes an awareness of: need for ast. c̄ personal care + household
	Extended Hours					✓	
	Protective Services						Intervention: MSS will educate as stated
	Senior Companion						
	Lifeline						Comments: has a cleaning lady 1x/mo r may increase this.
	Respite						
	Adult Day Care					✓	Considering adult day extended hrs. + neighbors. when dt not avail.
	Chore Services					✓	
	Other						

Client _____

ASSESSMENT/PROBLEMS	RESOURCES	INTERVENTIONS					PLAN
		In Place	Pend	Refuse	Refer	Inform	
OOD/MEALS Jequate ☑ Yes ☐ No ☐ Self ☑ Caregiver ☐ Client/Caregiver unable to prepare meals ☐ Inadequate Income ☑ Inability to shop for groceries	Food Stamps						**Goals:** Client/Caregiver verbalizes an awareness of: need for ast. when dtr.'s availability changes **Intervention:** MSS will educate as stated **Comments:**
	Store to Door	brochure left				✓	
	Meals on Wheels					✓	
	Congregate Meals				✓		
	Family/Caregiver	✓					
	Extended Hours					✓	
	Other						
FINANCIAL $ Income approx 2000/m Source _____ Concerns _____ .sets _____ .nances Managed ☑ Self ☐ Spouse ☐ Caregiver ☐ POA	Medical Assistance						**Goals:** Client/Caregiver verbalizes an awareness of: rising costs of medical care, especially when not avaialable to ast. **Intervention:** MSS will educate as stated + assess pt eligibility for govt ast. **Comments:** over income + assets
	Soc Sec Disability						
	AFDC						
	General Assistance						
	Charitable Donation						
	Legal Services						
	VA Pension						
	PAS / ACC					✓	
	Other Pharm. Ast.					✓	

MSS INTERVENTION AFFECTING RATE OF RECOVERY: Home Visit. This worker met c pt + dtr. to assess need + ast of community resources for managing long-term. Pt. cannot transfer w/out ast + therefore someone needs to be with her 24°/day, available + capable of assisting. Dtr. has been caregiver + will continue to be available during non-work hrs but returns to work approx

CARE COORDINATION: 6am–4pm M-F in 2 weeks. Pt. interested in info rel options for caregiving. Community Resource info as stated above shared c pt/dtr. It sounds as though pt has ruled out NH due to cost + is going to devise careplan likely to include adult day

OTHER: care 3-3x /wk + the ast of d neighbors other days. This worker recommended PT provide caregiver teaching to T safety. Pt may also hire extended hours of HHA some days.

Pt + family to consider options + this worker to follow up + ast as needed in Case Conference.

Signature/Title _____
Page 3 of 3

61-9664   Original - Medical Record   Yellow - SW   Pink - Case Manager

Verbal Orders For: MR #:

                                                                      Episode ID:

          Please review,   **Home Care**   DOB:
     sign, and return to:

Verbal Order #   2006200465New order for PT - PHYSICAL THERAPY:
                              PHYSICAL THERAPY EVAL AND TREAT FOR SAFE TRANSFERS
08/11/2000
                              PLEASE EVALUATE AND CLEAR FOR HOME HEALTH AID

Verbal Order #   2006200466New order for HA - HOME HEALTH AIDE VISITS:
                              HOME HEALTH AID 3XW X 9 WKS TO ASSIST WITH BATH AND PRSONAL
8/11/2000   CARES IF AND WHEN CLEARED BY PHYSICAL THERAPY

Verbal Order
      Employee _____ Date▮▮▮▮▮

**Physician's
Order**

      Physician _____ Date▮▮▮▮▮

Page **1** of **1**

Printed: **08/14/2000**
        7:57:01AM

Service Agreement

Patient: _____

Cust ID: _____

Service	Refused Services	Anticipated Schedule (frequency/duration)	Primary Goal/Care Plan	Expected Payor ☐ Card Verified	Expected Patient Charges*
☐Skilled Nursing ☐RN ☐Visits ☐Hourly / ☐LPN ☐Visits ☐Hourly					
☐Medical Supplies			(I) transfers	MDCR	∅
☐Pharmacy			(I) gait ½ RW		
☒Rehab Services ☒PT ☐OT ☐ST		1-3 a9 wks			
☐Social Services					
☐Chaplain ☐Volunteer					
☐Home Health Aide ☐Visits ☐Hourly					
☐Supervisory Visits ☐RN ☐Therapist					

*I understand that the information on payment for services is a preliminary estimate which is based on the information I have provided to FHCH at the time of my admission for services I understand that actual payment by my insurance company cannot be determined until home care bills have been submitted to them. I understand that I am responsible for all charges that are not reimbursed by my insurance company. A placement fee of $2,000.00 will be charged if I hire a FHCH employee within 90 days of receiving services.

In the case of a change in condition, FHCH should call my Emergency Contact: ▮▮▮▮▮▮▮▮▮ Relationship: ▮▮▮▮▮▮ (H) ▮▮▮▮▮ (W) ▮▮▮▮

Emergency Preparedness Plan - *a plan to ensure the safety of patients in the event of an environmental or agency emergency which may interrupt patient services from FHCH.*
☒*Non-essential Services* - A patient who has the ability and/or has caregivers available to provide care for a short period of time. This could include the ability to self-medicate, manage bowel and bladder needs, get nutrition, manage transfers and access 911/emergency services.

☐*Essential Services* - A patient with immediate needs who cannot safely forfeit care and requires health care intervention regardless of other conditions. Patients in this category may include: patients with no qualified caregiver available; patients who are on life sustaining equipment or life sustaining infusion therapy; insulin dependent diabetic patients who are unable to self-inject; patients with significant cognitive impairment.

Contingency Plan
List Essential Services by Discipline: ☐Skilled Nursing ☐Pharmacy ☐Home Health Aide
My Primary Caregiver for Essential Services is: ▮▮▮▮▮▮▮▮ Relationship: ▮▮▮▮▮▮ (H) ▮▮▮▮ (W) ▮▮▮▮

A representative from ▮▮▮▮▮▮▮▮▮ can be reached at ▮▮▮▮▮▮▮ , 24 hours per day OR ▮▮▮▮▮▮▮▮

I understand that emergency services will not be summoned during a life threatening emergency when there is a written physician's order for DNR/DNI in my record that reflect my wishes according to the Adult Health Care Decisions Act and home death has been pre-arranged. I have had the opportunity to participate in the development of this service agreement. I have read this agreement, understand it and agree to abide by its terms.   Patient able to access 911: ☐Yes ☐No

▮▮▮▮▮▮▮▮▮▮▮ /	▮▮▮▮▮▮▮	122013
Signature (Patient or Authorized Representative)	Witness	Date

White: Patient   Yellow: Chart   Pink: Home Chart

Home Care and Hospice
Physical Therapy Evaluation

Patient: _____
(Last, First - Legal Name)

DOB: 4.5.28

Branch ○ Metro   Princeton   Billable ○ Yes   No
Department ● Skilled   Hospice

SOCIAL SECURITY

ID 00 035032

HOMEBOUND STATUS DUE TO:
Bed bound/chair bound
● Considerable and taxing effort
Mental/emotional disorder
Requires assist of person/device to leave
Other

Diagnosis, Date of Onset: ORIF 12.5.00 (L) ankle
Pain, Prior Functional Status, Comments:
PMHx: IBM inclusive body myocyti.
30 yrs - makes her weak & poor balance
Fx ankle 1 week ago - op ratu - came
home - WC.
Has had difficulty getting up from low surfaces.

ROM, Document for Exception: Pt reports she can't
HOP on (R) LE - couldn't do it B/4 surgery

Manual Muscle Function (Tone, quality, strength, coordination) document for exception:

ACTIVITY DATE

Month	Day	Year
Jan		97
Feb	1 2	98
Mar		99
Apr		00
May		
Jun		
Jul		
Aug		
Sep		
Oct		
Nov		
Dec		

Vital Signs: B.P.   Pulse   R.R.

Sensory/Cognitive Screen:

Sensory Loss   Yes   ● No
Preprioceptive Loss   Yes   No

Cognition - *Oriented to:*
● Person   ● Place   ● Time
Disoriented   Confused

Behavior: ● Cooperative   Uncooperative
Impulsive   Labile   Combative

Safety Awareness   ● Intact   Impaired

Performs   ○   Step Commands

DME/Home Adaptations:
WC bedside commode

	IND = Independent	MOD = Moderate
	CG = Close Guard	MAX = Maximum
	MIN = Minimum	

LEVEL OF ASSIST

	IND	CG	MIN	MOD	MAX
Bed Mob	✓				
SUP ← → SIT	✓				
SIT ← → STAND					
CHAIR ← → BED			✓		
TOILET			✓		
TUB					
WC LOCOMOTION				✓	

N/A

GAIT - level   NON amb - at present time
stair   has a R.W. but can't use
quality   it.

TINETTI   Balance ___/16   Gait ___/12   Total ___/28

TIME
Hrs. Min.
1 10

Problem List:
● Bed Mobility
● Transfers
● Ambulation
Pain
ROM
● Muscle Function
Skin Integrity
Other

Goals:
● Ind/Assisted/Safe Bed Mobility ___ 2-4 wks
● Ind/Assisted/Safe Transfers ___ 2-4 wk
● Ind/Assisted/Safe Ambulation Level/Stairs with ___ 2-4 wks
Manageable Pain Level for Functional Mobility ___
ROM ___
Muscle Function ___
● Independent in Home Exercise Program ___
Able to Progress to O.P. Status ___
Other ___

Time Frame:

Plan of Care - Treatment Codes

B1 - Evaluation	● B4 - Home Program	B7 - Prosthetic Training
● B2 - Therapeutic Exercise	● B5 - Gait Training	B8 - Other
● B3 - Transfer Training	B6 - Pain Management	

Frequency/Duration:
2-3 wk
4 wks

Care Coordination: RN/LPN   HHA   PT/PTA   OT/COTA   SLP   SW   MD   SO

TIME
Hrs. Min.

Visit Verification Signature: _____
Signature of Therapist: _____

Verbal Orders For: MR #:

                                                     Episode ID:

         Please review,   **Home Care**   DOB: **4/5/28**
     sign, and return to:

‖‖‖‖‖‖‖‖‖‖‖‖‖‖‖‖‖

Verbal Order #   2007800160New order for PT - PHYSICAL THERAPY:
                             PT 2 TO 3XWX4W FOR EX GAIT AND TRANSFER TRAINING
    08/12/2000   PATIENT NEEDS MODERATE ASSIST FOR TRANSFERS
                             UNABLE TO AMBULATE DUE TO NWB STATUS AND WEAKNESS OF ARMS

                    Verbal Order
                       Employee _____ Date **08/16/2000**
Physician's
Order
                       Physician _____ Date 8/26/00

Page 1 of 1

Printed: **08/16/2000**
        8:44:52AM

Verbal Orders For: MR #:

                                                                  Episode ID:

            Please review,   **Home Care**   DOB: **4/5/28**
      sign, and return to:

||||||||||||||||||||||||||||

Verbal Order #   2007800160New order for PT - PHYSICAL THERAPY:
                              PT 2 TO 3XWX4W FOR EX GAIT AND TRANSFER TRAINING
   08/12/2000   PATIENT NEEDS MODERATE ASSIST FOR TRANSFERS
                              UNABLE TO AMBULATE DUE TO NWB STATUS AND WEAKNESS OF ARMS

                    Verbal Order
                     Employee _____ Date _____

**Physician's
Order**
                      Physician _____ Date 9/17/00

Page **1** of **1**

Printed: **08/29/2000**
          8:50:24AM

SKILLED NURSING VISIT REPORT

DATE 8/14/00

☑ Skilled Care
☐ Maintenance Care

(Last, First)

TIME OF DAY — HOUR : MIN 11:55
Time in Home 12:55

T 98.9	PA	☐ Reg ☐ Irreg PR 72	☐ Reg ☑ Irreg R 18	BP 134/70	WT.

HOMEBOUND DUE TO:
☐ Bedbound
☐ Chairbound
☐ Req. assist of person/device to leave

☐ Poor endurance
☑ Considerable & taxing effort
☐ Medically contraindicated

☐ Severe Pain
☐ Mental/Emotional Disorder
☐ Other/Comments:

NOT ASSESSED	SYSTEM	NO CHANGE	WNL	OBSERVATIONS-SUBJECTIVE/OBJECTIVE
	E.E.N.T.		✓	
	Cardiovascular	✓	✓	irreg HR, no SX
	Respiratory		✓	
	Gastro-Intestinal			eating & BMs - good
	Endocrine		✓	
	Genito Urinary			see below
	Neuro Muscular			see below
	Skin Integrity			bruising & ecchymosis of (L) leg
	Rest/Comfort	✓		pain pill @ noc only
	Cognitive/Mental		✓	
	Psycho-Social		✓	
	ADL's			

PROBLEM(S) (If new problem specify goal)	NURSING INTERVENTIONS O/E, Treatments, Teaching, etc.	EVALUATION OF CARE Patient/Family Response Progress Toward Goal(s)	CARE PLAN UPDATE N.C. = No Change in plan P.R. = Problem Resolved (Goal Met) Specify Any Changes in Plan
alt neuro -	Pt still very weak. using sliding board & it works much better. Pt states back doesn't hurt. Also feel like transfer belt helpful.		
alt GU -	up to urinate @ noc & has ↓ water intake. Teaching re: UTI & water Pt/fam verb understanding		

HHA SUPERVISION/ORIENTATION:

☐ Indirect   ☐ Direct

	GOOD	FAIR	POOR
Aide Appearance			
Relationship to Patient			
Reliability/Punctuality			
Task Completion			
Task Observed:			

HHA Name _____
Care Plan Update: ☐ Current Care plan meeting needs
☐ Care plan changes _____

LAB RESULTS: ☐ Called to MD
CARE CONFERENCE:

ORDER CHANGES: ☐ See MD Order   ☐ See Medication Profile Update   ☐ Patient/Caregiver Instructed
NEXT SN VISIT: _____   NEXT MD APPT: _____

SIGNATURE _____   TITLE _____

122015   White: Medical Record   Yellow: Case Manager

Service Agreement

Patient: _____

Cust ID: _____

Service	Refused Services	Anticipated Schedule (frequency/duration)	Primary Goal/Care Plan	Expected Payor ☐ Card Verified	Expected Patient Charges*
Skilled Nursing ☐RN ☐Visits ☐Hourly ☐LPN ☐Visits ☐Hourly					
☐Medical Supplies					
☐Pharmacy					
Rehab Services ☐PT ☐OT ☐ST					
Social Services		(2 additional with 1 co)	to ast c appropte community resources to ↑ safely.	medi care 100%	Ø
Chaplain ☐Volunteer					
Home Health Aide ☐Visits ☐Hourly					
Supervisory Visits ☐RN ☐Therapist					

*I understand that the information on payment for services is a preliminary estimate which is based on the information I have provided to FHCH at the time of my admission for services I understand that actual payment by my insurance company cannot be determined until home care bills have been submitted to them. I understand that I am responsible for all charges that are not reimbursed by my insurance company. A placement fee of $2,000.00 will be charged if I hire a FHCH employee within 90 days of receiving services.

In the case of a change in condition, FHCH should call my Emergency Contact: _____ Relationship: _____ (H) _____ (W)

Emergency Preparedness Plan - *a plan to ensure the safety of patients in the event of an environmental or agency emergency which may interrupt patient services from FHCH.*
☐*Non-essential Services* - A patient who has the ability and/or has caregivers available to provide care for a short period of time. This could include the ability to self-medicate, manage bowel and bladder needs, get nutrition, manage transfers and access 911/emergency services.

☐*Essential Services* - A patient with immediate needs who cannot safely forfeit care and requires health care intervention regardless of other conditions. Patients in this category may include: patients with no qualified caregiver available; patients who are on life sustaining equipment or life sustaining infusion therapy; insulin dependent diabetic patients who are unable to self-inject; patients with significant cognitive impairment.

Contingency Plan
List Essential Services by Discipline: ☐Skilled Nursing ☐Pharmacy ☐Home Health Aide
My Primary Caregiver for Essential Services is: _____ Relationship: _____

Patient able to access 911: ☐Yes ☐No

A representative _____ **can be reached at** _____ , **24 hours per day OR**

I understand that emergency services will not be summoned during a life threatening emergency when there is a written physician's order for DNR/DNI in my record that reflect my wishes according to the Adult Health Care Decisions Act and home death has been pre-arranged. I have had the opportunity to participate in the development of this service agreement. I have read this agreement, understand it and agree to abide by its terms.

Signature (Patient or Authorized Representative) _____ Witness _____ Date _____

White: Patient   Yellow: Chart   Pink: Home Chart   122013

Home Health Aide Care Plan

Patient Name: ▮▮▮▮▮▮▮ First
Cust. ID: ▮▮▮▮▮▮▮ Phone ▮▮▮
Address: ▮▮▮▮▮▮▮ Street City Zip
Payor Source: _mcp_

Please check appropriate boxes

Emergency Contact: Phone:
☐ Essential - Reason:
Time Range:

Frequency of visits / hourly services: 3x(w)
☐ DNR / DNI ☐ Hospice Language Spoken:
Directions to Home: ▮▮▮▮▮▮▮
Allergies:

Diagnosis / Health Problems (Notify case manager of changes in patient condition): ▮▮▮▮▮▮▮
Fx Lt ankle

Pets in Home: Small dog
Does patient smoke? ☐ Yes ☒ No
Patient prefers non-smoker? ☒ Yes ☐ No

Mental Status
☒ Alert & Oriented
☐ Lethargic
☐ Forgetful
☐ Depressed
☐ Agitated ☐ Combative
☐ Comatose
☐ Confused
Special Instructions:

Impairments
☐ Hearing
☐ Blind
☐ Contractures
☐ Paralysis ☐ Aphasia
Adaptive Device
☐ Hearing aid ☐ L ☐ R
☐ Glasses ☐ Contacts
☐ Dentures
☐ Prosthesis
Special Instructions:

Elimination
☒ Toilet
☐ Commode
☐ Bedpan
☐ Urinal
☐ Incontinence Briefs
Bowel
☒ Continent
☐ Incontient
☐ Record BMs
Ostomy Type:
☐ Ostomy care

Bladder
☒ Continent
☐ Incontinent
Catheter Type:
☐ Condom
☐ Intermittent self
☐ Indwelling (Foley)
☐ Suprapubic
☐ Pericare
☐ Catheter care
☐ Empty bag
☐ Clean equipment

Diet Ordered
☐ MOW
☐ Encourage Fluids
☐ Set up and assist
☐ Total feed

Vital Signs (Call case manager if outside range)
☐ T ☐ P ☐ R Frequency:
☐ BP (stethoscope & cuff left in home) Frequency:
☐ WT Frequency:

Oral Hygiene
☐ Brush Teeth
☐ Denture Cleaning
☐ Upper ☐ Lower
☐ Oral Swab
☐ Other
Skin Care
☐ Lotion
☐ Back Rub
☐ Reposition
Hand Care
☐ Fingernail Care (Clean, Trim, File)
☐ Soak

Grooming
☐ Comb / Brush Hair
☒ Shampoo Hair PRA
☐ Set Hair
☐ Shave
☐ Dressing
☐ Assist ☐ Total
Foot Care
☐ Toenail Care
(Clean, Trim, File)
☐ Elevate when Sitting
☐ Assist w/ Ted Socks / Ace Wraps / Braces
☐ Other

Incidental Services
☐ Make Bed
☐ Change Linens
☐ Tidy Bedroom
☐ Tidy Bathroom
☐ Prepare Meal:
 ☐ B ☐ L ☐ D ☐ Snack
☐ Laundry
☐ See Homemaker Plan of Services
☐ Errands
☐ Other

Transfers
☒ Transfer Belt PRN
☐ Standby Assist
☐ Pivot
☐ Total Assist
☒ Sliding Board
☐ Hoyer Lift
Exercises
☐ Follow instructions in folder
Bath (Observe transfer on initial visit)
☐ Bed ☐ Sponge ☒ Shower ☐ Tub
☒ Bench (in home) ☐ Pericare

Ambulation
☐ Bedrest
☐ Bedbound
☐ Wt Bearing
☐ Walker
☐ Crutches
☐ Cane
☐ Wheelchair
☐ Assistance Needed

Medication Assistance (see addendum) ☐ Verbal Reminder ☐ Administration Assist
Outcomes
☒ Personal Care Needs will be Met
☒ Promote Self Care
☒ Assure Safety, Comfort & Cleanliness
Special Instructions:

Case Manager Name (please print): ▮▮▮
RN / Therapist Signature ▮▮▮ Date
Voice Mail: ▮▮▮

Patient Signature ▮▮▮

White: Medical Record Yellow: Staffing Pink: Home

61-9065

z:\user\common\hhcadmin\hhaadl4.doc

Home Care and Hospice
Physical Therapy Visit Note

Pathway ○ Yes ⊘ No
(If yes, see Pathway documentation)

Patient: ▓▓▓▓▓▓▓▓▓▓▓▓▓▓▓▓▓▓▓
(Last, First - Legal Name)

Branch ⊘ Metro ○ Princeton **Billable** ○ Yes ○ No
Department ⊘ Skilled ○ Hospice

HOMEBOUND STATUS UPDATE:
⊘ Unchanged
○ Changed Explain:_____

SOCIAL SECURITY

S: C/o inability to transfer — dtr has
back pain and from assist. very
O: frustrated by weakness

SUPERVISORY VISIT ○ PTA ○ HHA ○ DIRECT ○ INDIRECT

EMPLOYEE _____

Yes	No	
○	○	Demonstrates competent skills/expertise
○	○	Satisfactory patient response to treatment
○	○	Follows assignment/Plan of Care
○	○	Demonstrates adequate communication skills
○	○	Adheres to Agency Policies/Procedures
○	○	Arrives for appointments as scheduled
○	○	Complies with agency dress code
○	○	Employee present
○	○	Assignment updated or reviewed
○	○	Results conveyed to Case Mgr./Supervisor

ACTIVITY DATE

Month	Day	Year
Jan		97
Feb	① ⑤	98
Mar	⓪ ⓪	99
Apr	① ①	
May	② ②	2000
Jun	③ ③	
Jul	④	
Aug	⑤	
Sep	⑥	
Oct	⑦	
Nov	⑧	
Dec	⑨	

THERAPY ACTION A = Assessment C = Care given T = Teaching

ACTION	INTERVENTION		EXPLANATION
TC	Exercise		given Theraband resist ex
	Gait	Device___ Distance___ Assist___	and strength
		Deviations ○ Yes ○ No	
	Stairs	Device___ Distance___	
	Transfer	Bed___	instructed in slide board
TC		Toilet___	to tub bench — mod +
TC		Tub___	asst.
		Chair___	chair ↔ w/c — attempts
	Balance Activities		to initiate push c RLE
	Massage/Myofascial Release/Modalities		back protection instruction to
T	Safety		Caregiver
T	ADLs		
T	Home Program		
	Discharge Planning		
	Pain Management Techniques		
	Other		

THERAPY OUTCOME Improved Stabilization Decline 1 = 2 = 3 =

ACTIVITY	OUTCOME	PROGRESSION TOWARD GOAL
1. Bed Mobility		
2. Transfers	2	
3. Ambulation		
4. ROM		
5. Muscle Function	3	transfers improving
6. ADLs		
7. Pain Management	1	
8. Other		

☒ Continues current service(s) and frequency 2-3 times a week.
☐ Changes in services and frequency have been discussed with patient/caregiver.
☐ Service _____ Frequency _____
☐ Discharge to care of:_____ with continued medical follow-up.
☐ Other _____

Care Coordination:
○ RN/LPN ○ HHA ○ PT/PTA ○ OT/COTA ○ SLP ○ SW ○ MD ○ SO

TIME

VISIT	Hrs.	Min.
	⓪ ⓪ 30
	① ⑤ 35
	② ⑩ 40
	③ ⑮ 45
	④ ⑳ 50
	⑤ ㉕ 55
	⑥
	⑦
	⑧
	⑨

TRAVEL	Hrs.	Min.
	0	0 30
	1	5 35
	2	10 40
	3	15 45
	4	20 50
	5	25 55
	6	
	7	
	8	
	9	

CASE MGMT	Hrs.	Min.
	0	0 30
	1	5 35
	2	10 40
	3	15 45
	4	20 50
	5	25 55
	6	
	7	
	8	
	9	

Visit Verification Signature: _____
Signature of Therapist: _____

White: Billing/Medical Records   Yellow: Patient

Mark Reflex by NCS MM211762-1   65432   PE21   Printed in U.S.A.

Verbal Orders For: MR #:

                                                            Episode ID:

        Please review,   **Home Care**   DOB: **4/5/28**
   sign, and return to:

‖‖‖‖‖‖‖‖‖‖‖‖‖‖‖‖‖‖

Verbal Order #   2004800029New order for SW - SOCIAL WORKER:
                        08 15 00   1 TO 2 ADDITIONAL SW VISITS IN 1 MONTH TO ASSIST
08/15/2000   WITH EDUCATION AND LINKAGE WITH APPROPRIATE RESOURCES TO
                        ENHANCE PATIENT SAFETY AND ABILITY TO MANAGE LONG TERM   CERT
                        PERIOD 08 08 2000 THRU 10 08 2000

                  Verbal Order
                     Employee ▨ ✐ ▮▮▮   ▶_____ Date **08/29/2000**
Physician's
Order
                   Physician _____⊥_____ Date _9/17/00_

Page **1** of **1**

Printed: **08/29/2000**
         8:50:24AM

Home Health Aide Activity Report
612-721-2491

Patient or Facility Name: _____

SS#: _____

Patient Team: ☒ EAST ☐ WEST ☐ HOSPICE
☒ Visit ☐ Bath visit ☐ Ext. Hours/County
☐ Continuous Care (Hospice only) ☐ Live In

Employee Name: _____

☒ Benefited Hours	☐ Casual
☒ Mileage 22.2	☐ Travel Charge
☒ Drive Time 45	

Employee # _____

Employee Team: ☒ EAST ☐ WEST ☐ HOSPICE

Service Date	Time In	Time Out	Total Time	Circle Day of Week
8-16-00	1045 Military Time	1145 Military Time	1:00	SU M T (W) TH F S

Payor Source: ☐ MA ☐ Private Pay ☐ County ☐ Insurance ☐ Foundation ☐ Other ☒ MEDICARE

Non-Billable: ☐ No Answer ☐ Refused ☐ Hospitalized ☐ Assisted Living Shift-Pay Only ☐ HO Per Diem ☐ Other ___

Indirect Pay Only: ☐ Meeting ☐ Orientation ☐ Other: _____

☐ Inservice/Competency (explain): _____

Patient or Facility Signature: _____

Name of Case Manager Notified:
_____ Date: _____ Time: _____

Comments/Change in status:
_____

Elimination

☒ Toilet	
☐ Commode	
☐ Bedpan	
☐ Urinal	
☐ Incontinence Briefs	

Bowel
☒ Continent
☐ Incontinent
☐ Last BM

Ostomy
☐ Ostomy care

Bladder
☒ Continent
☐ Incontinent

Catheter
☐ Condom
☐ Intermittent self cath
☐ Indwelling (Foley)
☐ Suprapubic
☐ Peri care
☐ Catheter care
☐ Empty bag
☐ Clean equipment

Nutrition
☐ Encourage Fluids ☐ Set up and assist
☐ Appetite good fair poor (circle one) ☐ Total feed

Vital Signs (Call case manager if outside range)
Temp: ___ Pulse: ___ Respiration: ___
Blood Pressure: ___ Weight: ___

Oral Hygiene	Grooming	Incidental Services	Transfers	Ambulation
☐ Brush Teeth	☐ Comb ☐ Brush Hair	☐ Make Bed	☐ Transfer Belt	☐ Bedrest
☐ Denture Cleaning ☐ Upper ☐ Lower	☒ Shampoo Hair	☐ Change Linens	☒ Standby Assist	☐ Bedbound turn/ position
☐ Oral Swab	☐ Set Hair	☐ Tidy Bedroom	☐ Pivot	☐ Wt Bearing
☐ Other	☐ Shave	☒ Tidy Bathroom	☒ Total Assist	☐ Walker
	☒ Dressing ☒ Undressing	☐ Prepare Meal:	☒ Sliding Board	☐ Crutches
Skin Care	☒ Assist ☐ Total	☐ B ☐ L ☐ D ☐ Snack	☐ Hoyer Lift	☐ Cane
☒ Lotion	**Foot Care**	**Laundry**	☐ ROM ☐ PROM	☒ Wheelchair
☒ Back Rub	☐ Toenail Care	☐ Currency Exchange	☐ Exercise-Per Rehab care	☒ Assistance Needed
☐ Reposition	Clean, Trim, File (circle one)	Yes No (circle one)	plan	
☐ Dressing Change (Dry Gauze only)				
Hand Care	☐ Elevate when Sitting	☐ Errands	**Bath**	
☐ Fingernail Care	☐ Ted Socks /	☐ Other	☐ Bed ☐ Sponge ☐ Tub	
Clean, Trim, File (circle)	☐ Ace Wraps ☐ Braces		☒ Shower ☒ Bench ☐ Peri care	
☐ Soak	☐ Other			

Medication Assistance (see addendum) ☐ Verbal Reminder ☐ Administration Assist

CURRENCY EXCHANGE						
Date	Amount Given	Pt. Initials	Change Received	Pt. Initials	Receipt Received	Pt. Initials

☐ Oriented to Care Plan on Visit or by phone

Employee Signature: _____ Title: _____

160452   White- Medical Record   Yellow- Data Entry   Pink- Home   ☒ RECONCILED

OT D/c Note (No visit)

Date	Time of Day	Supervisory Visit	Care Plan Update	Care Coordination	☐ SN ☐ PT ☒ OT ☐ SW ☐ ST ☐ Dietician ☐ Chaplain **Progress Notes** Client ▓▓▓ Last ▓▓ First SS# ▓▓▓
8/17/00					OT d/c this date 2° pt chooses not to utilize homecare OT at this time. Pt intends on Admission to SNF or inpt. rehab 2° not being able to manage at home. SN; CM notified of pt's intent. ∞ OT d/c.

Signature _____ Title _____

Date	Time of Day	Supervisory Visit	Care Plan Update	Care Coordination	☑SN ☐PT ☐OT ☐SW ☐ST Client ██████████ ☐ Dietician ☐ Chaplain Last First SS# ████████
8/17/00					Several attempts to locate pt – left several messages to contact me re: visit scheduled today. Did not receive call back. Made arrangements for HHA noon til 10p on Mon 8/18/00. Will check to see if pt went to hosp or NH.

Signature _____ Title _____ RN, CM

White: Medical Record   Yellow: Case Manager

Transfer to Inpatient Facility (B1)

Author: Completed: 8/21/2000

Transfer To Inpatient Facility

Observation	**Result**
M0010 Agency Medicare ID	
M0012 Agency Medicaid ID	
M0014 Branch State	
M0016 Branch ID Number	
M0020 Patient ID Number	
M0030 Start of Care Date	
M0032 Resumption of Care Date	*NA - Not Applicable*
M0040 Patient Name	
M0050 Patient State of Residence	
M0060 Patient Zip Code	
M0063 Medicare Number	
M0064 Patient Social Security Number	
M0065 Medicaid Number	*NA - No Medicaid*
M0066 Patient Date of Birth	
M0069 Patient Gender	*2 - Female*
M0072 Primary Referring Physician ID	
M0080 Discipline of Person Completing Assessment	*1 - RN*
M0090 Date Assessment Completed	*08/21/2000*
M0100 Reason for Assessment	*7 - Transferred to an inpatient facility - patient discharged from agency [Go to M0830]*
M0830 Emergent Care	*0 - No emergency care services [Go to M0855]*
M0855 Inpatient Facility	*3 - Nursing home [Go to M0900]*
M0900 Admitted to Nursing Home	*5 - Unsafe for care at home*
M0903 Date of Last Home Visit	*08/17/2000*
M0906 Discharge, Transfer, Death Date	*08/21/2000*

Author: Date: __

Home Care

Start of Care/Resumption of Care (B1-H2)

Author: _____   Completed: 8/13/2000

SOC Demographics/General

Observation	Result
M0010 Agency Medicare ID	
M0012 Agency Medicaid ID	
M0014 Branch State	
M0016 Branch ID Number	
M0020 Patient ID Number	
M0030 Start of Care Date	
M0032 Resumption of Care Date	*NA - Not Applicable*
M0040 Patient Name	
M0050 Patient State of Residence	
M0060 Patient Zip Code	
M0063 Medicare Number	
M0064 Patient Social Security Number	
M0065 Medicaid Number	*NA - No Medicaid*
M0066 Patient Date of Birth	
M0069 Patient Gender	*2 - Female*
M0072 Primary Referring Physician ID	
M0080 Discipline of Person Completing Assessment	*1 - RN*
M0090 Date Assessment Completed	*08/08/2000*
M0100 Reason for Assessment	*1 - Start of care (further visits planned)*
Consent For Treatment Signed by:	*Patient*
M0140 Patient Race/Ethnicity	*6 - White*
M0150 Current Payment Sources for Home Care	*1 - Medicare (traditional fee-for-service)*
M0160 Limiting Financial Factors	*0 - None*
M0170 From which of the following Inpatient facilities was the patient discharged during the past 14 days	*1 - Hospital*
M0180 Most Recent Inpatient Discharge Date	*08/07/2000*
M0190 Inpatient Stay Diagnoses within Last 14 Days	*TRIMALLEOLAR FRACTURE, OPEN*
	8247
	CLOSED DISLOCATION OF FOOT, UNSPECIFIED PART
	83800
M0200 Medical or Treatment Regimen: Change in Past 14 Days	*1 - Yes*
M0210 Regimen Change	*TRIMALLEOLAR FRACTURE, OPEN*
	8247
	CLOSED DISLOCATION OF FOOT, UNSPECIFIED PART

Start of Care/Resumption of Care (B1-H2)

Author: ▮▮▮▮▮▮▮▮▮▮▮▮▮▮   Completed: 8/13/2000

83800

M0220 Prior Condition	*3 - Intractable pain*
M0230 Primary Diagnosis	*TRIMALLEOLAR FRACTURE, OPEN*
	8247
	(A) 3 - Symptoms poorly controlled patient needs frequent adjustment in treatment and dose monitoring treatment and dose monitoring
M0240 Other Diagnosis 1	*OPEN DISLOCATION OF ANKLE*
	8371
	(B) 2 - Symptoms controlled with difficulty affecting daily functioning patient needs ongoing monitoring
M0240 Other Diagnosis 2	*OSTEOPOROSIS, UNSPECIFIED*
	73300
	(C) 2 - Symptoms controlled with difficulty affecting daily functioning patient needs ongoing monitoring
M0250 Therapies Received at Home	*4 - None of the above*
M0260 Overall Prognosis for Recovery from This Episode	*1 - Good/Fair: partial to full recovery is expected*
Prognosis	*3 - Fair*
M0270 Rehabilitative Prognosis	*1 - Good: marked improvement in functional status is expected*
M0280 Life Expectancy	*0 - Life expectancy is greater than 6 months*
M0290 High Risk Factors Characterizing This Patient	*5 - None of the above*
M0300 Current Residence	*1 - Patient's owned or rented residence (house/apartment or mobile home owned or rented by patient/couple/significant other)*
M0310 Structural Barriers	*0 - None*
M0320 Safety Hazards	*0 - None*
M0330 Sanitation Hazards	*0 - None*
Environment (Home) Suitable For Home Care	*Yes - Environment (home) is suitable for home care.*
Adaptations Required	*Adaptations Required Minor*
Safety Measures	*1 - Establish emergency plan*
	4 - Implement a falls prevention program (e.g. remove throw rugs/teach safe use of assist/safety devices)
	5 - Teach weight-bearing precautions
	8 - Teach proper/safe use of medications
M0340 Patient Lives With	*1 - Lives alone*
M0350 Assisting Person	*1 - Relatives/friends or neighbors living outside the home*
M0360 Primary Caregiver	*2 - Daughter or son*
M0370 Frequency of Primary Caregiver Assistance	*2 - Several times during day*
M0380 Type of Primary Caregiver Assistance	*1 - ADL assistance (e.g. bathing/dressing/toileting/bowel/bladder/eating/feeding)*
	2 - IADL assistance (e.g. meds/meals/housekeeping/laundry/telephone/shopping/finances)
	3 - Environmental support (housing/home maintenance)

Start of Care/Resumption of Care (B1-H2)

Author: ▓▓▓▓▓▓▓▓▓▓▓▓▓   Completed: 8/13/2000

4 - Psychosocial support (socialization/companionship/recreation)

5 - Advocates or facilitates patient's participation in appropriate medical care

Caretaking / Parenting   *1 - Adequate - No problems noted*

Unusual Home / Social Environment   *None*

Abuse/Neglect   *No signs of abuse/neglect*

	Home Care

Start of Care/Resumption of Care (B1-H2)

Author: ▓▓▓▓▓▓▓▓▓▓▓▓   Completed: 8/13/2000

SOC Review of Systems

Observation	Result
Systolic Blood Pressure (1)	*122*
Diastolic Blood Pressure (1)	*70*
Blood Pressure taken in which Position (1)	*Sitting*
Blood Pressure taken in which Arm (1)	*Left*
Pulse (1)	*62*
Location Pulse was Taken (1)	*Apical*
Characteristic of Pulse (1)	*Regular*
Respiration	*16*
Temperature	*974*
Height in Feet	*5*
Inches	*7*
Weight in Pounds	*190*
Weight Loss	*Weight loss last 30 days*
M0420 Frequency of Pain	*2 - Daily but not constantly*
M0430 Experiencing Intractable Pain	*0 - No*
Location of Pain (1)	*LT ANKLE*
Pain (1) Is	*Recent Onset*
Pain Intensity (4)	*7*
Precipitating Factors (1)	*DEPENDENT POSITION WALKING*
Pain Control Measures (1)	*Rest*
Pain Control Measures (2)	*Medication*
Best Response to Control Measures (1)	*3*
Pain Expression	*Verbalizes*
	Guarding
	Limited movement
M0390 Vision with Corrective Lenses	*0 - Normal vision: sees adequately in most situations; can see medication labels/newsprint*
M0400 Sensory Status	*0 - No observable impairment. Able to hear and understand complex or detailed instructions and extended or abstract conversation*
Nose	*WNL*
Conditions Affecting Dentition	*WNL*
M0410 Speech and Oral Expression	*0 - Expresses complex ideas/feelings and needs clearly/completely and easily in all situations with no observable impairment*
Patients usual method of communication	*1 - Speech*
M0560 Cognitive Functioning	*0 - Alert/oriented/able to focus and shift attention/comprehends and recalls task directions independently*
Mental Assessment for Certification	*1 - Oriented to:*
	Person

Start of Care/Resumption of Care (B1-H2)

Author: ████████	Completed: 8/13/2000

Mental Assessment for Certification	*Place*
	Time
M0570 When Confused (Reported or Observed)	*0 - Never*
M0580 When Anxious (Reported or Observed)	*0 - None of the time*
M0590 Depressive Feelings	*1 - Depressed mood (e.g. feeling sad/tearful)*
M0600 Behavior	*7 - None of the above behaviors observed or reported*
M0610 Behaviors demonstrated at least once a week	*7 - None of the above behaviors demonstrated*
M0620 Frequency of Behavior Problems	*0 - Never*
M0630 Receives Psychiatric Nursing	*0 - No*
Neurological Status	*WNL*
Location of Musculoskeletal Conditions	*LLE*
Conditions Affecting Musculoskeletal Status	*7 - Decreased Muscle Strength*
Location of Musculoskeletal Conditions	*LLE*
Conditions Affecting Musculoskeletal Status	*8 - Other:*
	9 - Gait/Ambulation disturbance:
	CASTED WITH NO WT BEAR
Activities Permitted	*3 - Up as Tolerated*
	8 - Crutches
	B - Walker
	D - Other (specify):
	NON WT BR
Assistive Devices/DME	*2 - Raised Toilet Seat/Commode*
	6 - Shower Chair/Bench
	9 - Wheelchair
Integumentary Status	*WNL*
M0440 Does This Patient Have a Skin Lesion or Open Wound - This Excludes Ostomies	*0 - No (Go to Cardiovascular)*
Conditions Affecting Cardiovascular Status	*6 - Fatigue*
Right Dorsalis Pedis	*NORMAL*
Capillary Refill	*1 - Less than 3 seconds*
Edema for Left Lower Extremity/Ankle	*2+*
M0490 When Dyspneic	*0 - Never; patient is not short of breath*
M0500 Respiratory Treatments	*4 - None of the above*
Breath Sounds	*Clear Bilaterally*
Conditions Affecting Elimination	*2 - Constipation*
M0540 Bowel Incontinence Frequency	*0 - Very rarely or never has bowel incontinence*
M0550 Ostomy for Bowel Elimination	*0 - Patient does NOT have an ostomy for bowel elimination*
Appetite	*2 - Fair*

Start of Care/Resumption of Care (B1-H2)

Author: ███████████	Completed: 8/13/2000

Nutritional Requirements/Special Diet	*1 - Regular*
Nutritional Evaluation of the Patient	*8 - Takes three or more different prescribed/over the counter drugs*
	10 - Not always able to physically shop/cook/or feed self
Total Nutritional Score (Refer to Legend For Results)	*3*
Actions Initiated	*None Required*
Conditions Affecting Genitourinary Status	*WNL*
M0510 Treated for Urinary Tract Infection in Past 14 Days	*0 - No*
M0520 Urinary Incontinence or Urinary Catheter Present	*0 - No incontinence or catheter (includes anuria or ostomy for urinary drainage) [Go to Reproductive]*

Start of Care/Resumption of Care (B1-H2)

Author: ▮▮▮▮▮▮▮▮   Completed: 8/13/2000

SOC ADL/IADLs

Observation	Result
M0640 Grooming	(Prior) 0- Able to groom self unaided with or without the use of assistive devices or adapted methods
M0640 Current: Grooming	(Current) 1 - Grooming utensils must be placed within reach before able to complete grooming activities
M0650 Dress Upper Body	(Prior) 0 - Able to get clothes out of closets/drawers/put them on and remove them from the upper body without assistance
M0650 Current: Dress Upper Body	(Current) 1 - Able to dress upper body without assistance if clothing is laid out or handed to the patient
M0660 Dress Lower Body	(Prior) 0 - Able to obtain/put on and remove clothing and shoes without assistance
M0660 Current: Dress Lower Body	(Current) 2 - Someone must help the patient put on undergarments/slacks/socks or nylons and shoes
M0670 Bathing	(Prior) 1 - With the use of devices is able to bathe self in shower or tub independently
M0670 Current: Bathing	(Current) 3 - Participates in bathing self in shower or tub BUT requires presence of another person throughout the bath for assistance or supervision
M0680 Toileting	(Prior) 0 - Able to get to and from the toilet independently with or without a device
M0680 Current: Toileting	(Current) 1 - When reminded/assisted or supervised by another person able to get to and from the toilet
M0690 Transferring	(Prior) 1 - Transfers with minimal human assistance or with use of an assistive device
M0690 Current: Transferring	(Current) 2 - UNABLE to transfer self but is able to bear weight and pivot during the transfer process
M0700 Ambulation	(Prior) 1 - Requires use of a device (i.e. cane/walker) to walk alone OR requires human supervision or assistance to negotiate stairs or steps or uneven surfaces
M0700 Current: Ambulation	(Current) 4 - Chairfast-unable to ambulate and is UNABLE to wheel self
M0710 Feeding	(Prior) 0 - Able to independently feed self
M0710 Current: Feeding	(Current) 0 - Able to independently feed self
M0720 Prepare Light Meals	(Prior) 0 - (a) Able to independently plan and prepare all light meals for self or reheat delivered meals OR (b) is physically/cognitively and mentally able to prepare light meals on a regular basis but has not performed light meal preparation
M0720 Current: Prepare Light Meals	(Current) 1 - UNABLE to prepare light meals on a regular basis due to physical/cognitive or mental limitations
M0730 Transportation	(Prior) 1 - Able to ride in a car only when driven by another person OR able to use a bus or handicap van only when assisted or accompanied by another person
M0730 Current: Transportation	(Current) 1 - Able to ride in a car only when driven by another person OR able to use a bus or handicap van only when assisted or accompanied by another person
M0740 Laundry	(Prior) 1 - Able to do only light laundry such as minor hand wash or light washer loads. Due to physical/cognitive or mental limitations needs assistance with heavy laundry such as carrying large loads of laundry
M0740 Current: Laundry	(Current) 2 - UNABLE to do any laundry due to physical limitation or needs continual supervision and assistance due to cognitive or mental limitation

Start of Care/Resumption of Care (B1-H2)

Author: ███████████████   Completed: 8/13/2000

M0750 Housekeeping	*(Prior) 1 - Able to perform only LIGHT housekeeping (e.g. dusting/wiping kitchen counters) tasks independently*
M0750 Current: Housekeeping	*(Current) 4 - Unable to effectively participate in any housekeeping tasks*
M0760 Shopping	*(Prior)2 - UNABLE to go shopping but is able to identify items needed/place orders and arrange home delivery*
M0760 Current: Shopping	*(Current) 2 - UNABLE to go shopping but is able to identify items needed/place orders and arrange home delivery*
M0770 Telephone Use	*(Prior) 0 - Able to dial numbers and answer call appropriately and as desired*
M0770 Current: Telephone Use	*(Current) 0 - Able to dial numbers and answer call appropriately and as desired*
M0780 Management of Oral Medications	*(Prior) UK - Unknown*
M0780 Current: Management of Oral Medications	*(Current) 1 - Able to take medications at the correct times if: (a) Individual dosages are prepared in advance by another person; OR (b) given daily reminders; OR (c) someone develops a drug diary or chart*
M0790 Management of Inhalant Medications	*(Prior) UK - Unknown*
M0790 Current: Management of Inhalant Medications	*(Current) NA - No inhalant/mist medications prescribed*
M0800 Management of Injectable Medications	*(Prior) NA - No injectable medications prescribed*
M0800 Current: Management of Injectable Medications	*(Current) NA - No injectable medications prescribed*
M0810 Patient Management of Equipment	*NA - No equipment of this type in care [Go to Homebound Status]*
Homebound Status	*Yes [Go to Reasons]*
Reason Patient is Homebound	*1 - Limited ambulation*
	2 - Unsteady gait/poor balance
	7 - Wheelchair bound
	8 - Needs assistance with equipment
Functional Limitations	*6 - Endurance*
	7 - Ambulation
	B - Other (specify):
	CASTED LEFT6 ANKLE AND PROGRESSIVE WEAKENING DISEASE
Can the Patient Understand Verbal Instructions	*Yes*
Can the Patient Read and Understand Simple Written Instructions	*Yes*
Patients Rights and Responsibilites	*Discussed*
	Copy left in home
State Home Health Hot Line Numbers	*Discussed*
	Copy left in home
Verification Of Benefits	*Discussed*
Advance Directives	*Discussed*
Home Care Service Agreement	*Discussed*
	Copy left in home
Home Health Visit Schedule	*Discussed*

███████████████████████   Home Care

Start of Care/Resumption of Care (B1-H2)

Author: ████████████████   Completed: 8/13/2000

Copy left in home

Home Health Agency Phone Numbers   _Discussed_

Copy left in home

Instructions / Materials Given To Whom   _Patient_

Emergency Phone Numbers Prominently   _Yes_
Displayed Near Phone

Author: _____████████████████_____   Date: _____████████_____

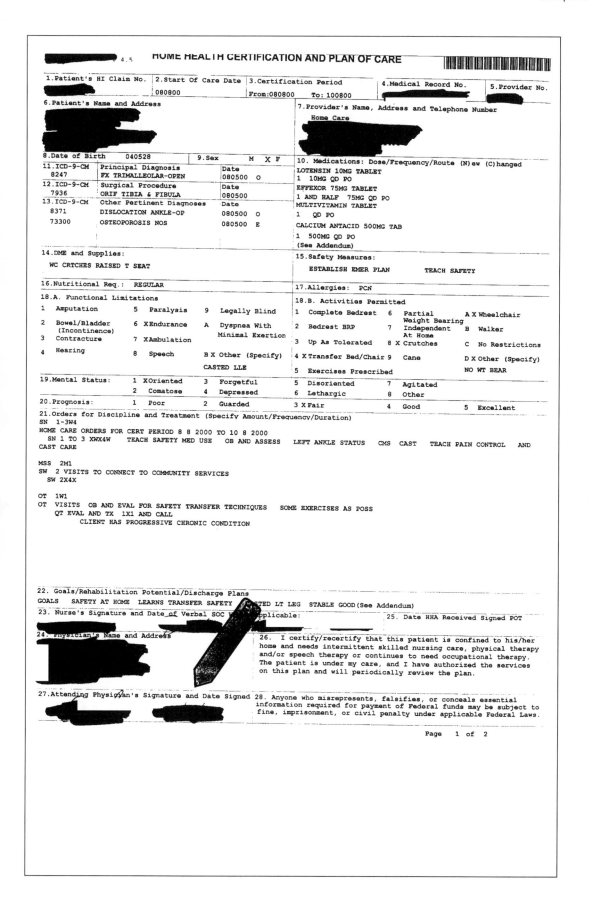

HOME HEALTH CERTIFICATION AND PLAN OF CARE

1.Patient's HI Claim No.	2.Start Of Care Date 080800	3.Certification Period From:080800 To: 100800	4.Medical Record No.	5.Provider No.

6. Patient's Name and Address

7. Provider's Name, Address and Telephone Number
Home Care

8.Date of Birth 040528	9.Sex M X F

11.ICD-9-CM	Principal Diagnosis	Date
8247	FX TRIMALLEOLAR-OPEN	080500 O
12.ICD-9-CM	Surgical Procedure	Date
7936	ORIF TIBIA & FIBULA	080500
13.ICD-9-CM	Other Pertinent Diagnoses	Date
8371	DISLOCATION ANKLE-OP	080500 O
73300	OSTEOPOROSIS NOS	080500 E

10. Medications: Dose/Frequency/Route (N)ew (C)hanged
LOTENSIN 10MG TABLET
1 10MG QD PO
EFFEXOR 75MG TABLET
1 AND HALF 75MG QD PO
MULTIVITAMIN TABLET
1   QD PO
CALCIUM ANTACID 500MG TAB
1 500MG QD PO
(See Addendum)

14.DME and Supplies:
WC CRTCHES RAISED T SEAT

15.Safety Measures:
ESTABLISH EMER PLAN   TEACH SAFETY

16.Nutritional Req.: REGULAR

17.Allergies: PCN

18.A. Functional Limitations

1	Amputation	5	Paralysis	9	Legally Blind
2	Bowel/Bladder (Incontinence)	6	X Endurance	A	Dyspnea With Minimal Exertion
3	Contracture	7	X Ambulation		
4	Hearing	8	Speech	B X	Other (Specify) CASTED LLE

18.B. Activities Permitted

1	Complete Bedrest	6	Partial Weight Bearing	A X	Wheelchair
2	Bedrest BRP	7	Independent At Home	B	Walker
3	Up As Tolerated	8 X	Crutches	C	No Restrictions
4 X	Transfer Bed/Chair	9	Cane	D X	Other (Specify) NO WT BEAR
5	Exercises Prescribed				

19.Mental Status:

| 1 | X Oriented | 3 | Forgetful | 5 | Disoriented | 7 | Agitated |
| 2 | Comatose | 4 | Depressed | 6 | Lethargic | 8 | Other |

20.Prognosis:

| 1 | Poor | 2 | Guarded | 3 X | Fair | 4 | Good | 5 | Excellent |

21.Orders for Discipline and Treatment (Specify Amount/Frequency/Duration)
SN 1-3W4
HOME CARE ORDERS FOR CERT PERIOD 8 8 2000 TO 10 8 2000
  SN 1 TO 3 XWX4W   TEACH SAFETY MED USE   OB AND ASSESS   LEFT ANKLE STATUS   CMS   CAST   TEACH PAIN CONTROL   AND
CAST CARE

MSS 2M1
SW 2 VISITS TO CONNECT TO COMMUNITY SERVICES
  SW 2X4X

OT 1W1
OT   VISITS OB AND EVAL FOR SAFETY TRANSFER TECHNIQUES   SOME EXERCISES AS POSS
     QT EVAL AND TX 1X1 AND CALL
         CLIENT HAS PROGRESSIVE CHRONIC CONDITION

22. Goals/Rehabilitation Potential/Discharge Plans
GOALS   SAFETY AT HOME   LEARNS TRANSFER SAFETY   CASTED LT LEG   STABLE GOOD (See Addendum)

23. Nurse's Signature and Date of Verbal SOC (if applicable:		25. Date HHA Received Signed POT
24. Physician's Name and Address	26. I certify/recertify that this patient is confined to his/her home and needs intermittent skilled nursing care, physical therapy and/or speech therapy or continues to need occupational therapy. The patient is under my care, and I have authorized the services on this plan and will periodically review the plan.	
27. Attending Physician's Signature and Date Signed	28. Anyone who misrepresents, falsifies, or conceals essential information required for payment of Federal funds may be subject to fine, imprisonment, or civil penalty under applicable Federal Laws.	

Page   1 of 2

v 4.5	ADDENDUM TO:	X PLAN OF TREATMENT	_ MEDICAL UPDATE

1. Patient's HI Claim	2. Start Of Care	3. Certification Period	.. Medical Record No.	5. Provider No
▮▮▮▮▮	080800	From: 080800 To: 100800	▮▮▮▮▮	▮▮▮▮▮

6. Patient's Name	7. Provider Name
	Home Care

8. Item No.

10	VITAMIN E 400IU CAPSULE
	1 400U QD PO
	VICODIN 5/500 TABLET (N)
	1 5-500MG Q6 PRN PO

22   COLOR AND TEMP   PAIN CONTROLLED   LEARNS MEDS   RECEIVES COMMUNITY SERVICES INFORMATION TO ACCESS AFTER HOMECARE IS DISCHARGED
LIMITED REHAB POTENTIAL FOR STRENGTHENING   FAIR POTENTIAL FOR WEIGHT BEARING ON LEFT LE
DISCHARGE WHEN SAFE AT HOME WITH ASSISTANCE AND AT OPTIMAL INDEPENENCE
MD SUMMARY   LEFT LE WARM TOES NO NUMBNESS WITH CAST ON   COMPLYING WITH RAISING OF LEG AS MUCH AS POSSIBLE
PAIN IS CONTROLLED DTR PRESENT FOR SEVERAL WEEKS TO ASSIST WITH TRANSFERS UNTIL CLIENT IS SAFE   SHE WILL
NEED ON GOING ASSISTANCE AT HOME FO9R SAFETY AND MONITORING SINCE SHE LIVES ALONE AND WISHES TO STAY IN OWN
HOME   T 974 P 62   HAS SKIPS IN PULSE RATE   BP 122 OVER 70

9. Signature of Physician	10. Date
▮▮▮▮▮	

11. Optional Name/Signature of Nurse/Therapist	12. Date
▮▮▮▮▮	

Addendum   Page   2 of 2

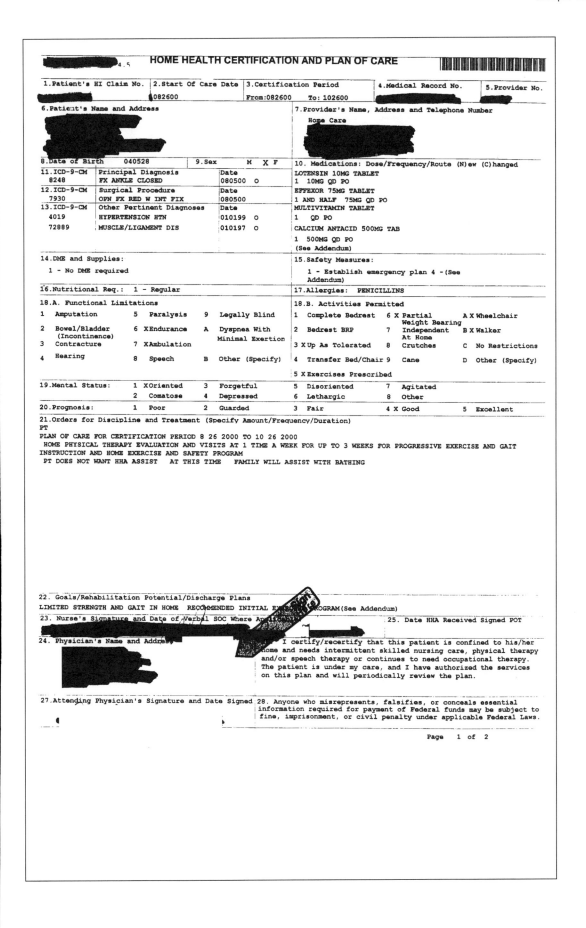

HOME HEALTH CERTIFICATION AND PLAN OF CARE

1.Patient's HI Claim No.	2.Start Of Care Date 082600	3.Certification Period From:082600 To: 102600	4.Medical Record No.	5.Provider No.

6.Patient's Name and Address	7.Provider's Name, Address and Telephone Number Home Care

8.Date of Birth 040528	9.Sex M X F	10. Medications: Dose/Frequency/Route (N)ew (C)hanged

11.ICD-9-CM 8248	Principal Diagnosis FX ANKLE CLOSED	Date 080500 O	LOTENSIN 10MG TABLET 1 10MG QD PO
12.ICD-9-CM 7930	Surgical Procedure OPN FX RED W INT FIX	Date 080500	EFFEXOR 75MG TABLET 1 AND HALF 75MG QD PO
13.ICD-9-CM 4019	Other Pertinent Diagnoses HYPERTENSION HTN	Date 010199 O	MULTIVITAMIN TABLET 1 QD PO
72889	MUSCLE/LIGAMENT DIS	010197 O	CALCIUM ANTACID 500MG TAB 1 500MG QD PO (See Addendum)

14.DME and Supplies: 1 - No DME required	15.Safety Measures: 1 - Establish emergency plan 4 -(See Addendum)

16.Nutritional Req.: 1 - Regular	17.Allergies: PENICILLINS

18.A. Functional Limitations

1	Amputation	5	Paralysis	9	Legally Blind
2	Bowel/Bladder (Incontinence)	6	X Endurance	A	Dyspnea With Minimal Exertion
3	Contracture	7	X Ambulation		
4	Hearing	8	Speech	B	Other (Specify)

18.B. Activities Permitted

1	Complete Bedrest	6 X	Partial Weight Bearing	A X	Wheelchair
2	Bedrest BRP	7	Independent At Home	B X	Walker
3 X	Up As Tolerated	8	Crutches	C	No Restrictions
4	Transfer Bed/Chair	9	Cane	D	Other (Specify)
5 X	Exercises Prescribed				

19.Mental Status:	1 X Oriented	3	Forgetful	5	Disoriented	7	Agitated
	2	Comatose	4	Depressed	6	Lethargic	8	Other

20.Prognosis:	1	Poor	2	Guarded	3	Fair	4 X	Good	5	Excellent

21.Orders for Discipline and Treatment (Specify Amount/Frequency/Duration)
PT
PLAN OF CARE FOR CERTIFICATION PERIOD 8 26 2000 TO 10 26 2000
 HOME PHYSICAL THERAPY EVALUATION AND VISITS AT 1 TIME A WEEK FOR UP TO 3 WEEKS FOR PROGRESSIVE EXERCISE AND GAIT INSTRUCTION AND HOME EXERCISE AND SAFETY PROGRAM
 PT DOES NOT WANT HHA ASSIST   AT THIS TIME   FAMILY WILL ASSIST WITH BATHING

22. Goals/Rehabilitation Potential/Discharge Plans
LIMITED STRENGTH AND GAIT IN HOME   RECOMMENDED INITIAL E___ ___OGRAM(See Addendum)

23. Nurse's Signature and Date of Verbal SOC Where Ap___	25. Date HHA Received Signed POT

24. Physician's Name and Address	I certify/recertify that this patient is confined to his/her home and needs intermittent skilled nursing care, physical therapy and/or speech therapy or continues to need occupational therapy. The patient is under my care, and I have authorized the services on this plan and will periodically review the plan.

27.Attending Physician's Signature and Date Signed	28. Anyone who misrepresents, falsifies, or conceals essential information required for payment of Federal funds may be subject to fine, imprisonment, or civil penalty under applicable Federal Laws.

Page   1 of 2

| v 4.5 | ADDENDUM TO: | X PLAN OF TREATMENT | _ MEDICAL UPDATE |

1. Patient's HI Claim	2. Start Of ___re	3. Certification Period	4. Medical Record No.	5. Provider No.
▉▉▉▉▉	082600	From: 082600 To: 102600	▉▉▉▉▉	▉▉▉▉▉

6. Patient's Name	7. Provider Name
▉▉▉▉▉	Home Care

8. Item No.	
10	VITAMIN E 400IU CAPSULE
	1 400U QD PO
	VICODIN 5/500 TABLET
	1 5-500MG Q6 PRN PO
15	Implement a falls prevention program (e.g. remove throw rugs/teach safe use of assist/safety devices)
22	WHICH WILL REQUIRE UPGRADES ON A WEEKLY BASIS AS STRENGTH AND MOBILITY IMPROVE
	REHAB POTENTIAL IS GOOD
	PLAN TO DISCHARGE TO SELF CARE
	GOALS OF SAFE AND INDEPENDENT IN TRANSFERS SAFE AND INDEPENDENT IN AMBULATION WITH A WALKER FOR UP TO 100
	FT SAFE AND INDEPENDENT IN A HOME EXERCISE PROGRAM

9. Signature of Physician	10. Date
▉▉▉▉▉	

11. Optional Name/Signature of Nurse/Therapist	12. Date
▉▉▉▉▉	

Addendum   **Page**   2 of 2

PatID: 00035032   EpsID: 00128931

Physical Therapy Start of Care (B1)

Author: ▮▮▮▮▮▮▮▮▮▮▮▮   Completed: 8/26/2000

PT SOC/ROC

Observation	Result
M0010 Agency Medicare ID	
M0012 Agency Medicaid ID	
M0014 Branch State	
M0016 Branch ID Number	
M0020 Patient ID Number	
M0030 Start of Care Date	*08/26/2000*
M0032 Resumption of Care Date	*NA - Not Applicable*
M0040 Patient Name	
M0050 Patient State of Residence	
M0060 Patient Zip Code	
M0063 Medicare Number	
M0064 Patient Social Security Number	
M0065 Medicaid Number	*NA - No Medicaid*
M0066 Patient Date of Birth	
M0069 Patient Gender	*2 - Female*
M0072 Primary Referring Physician ID	
M0080 Discipline of Person Completing Assessment	*2 - PT*
M0090 Date Assessment Completed	*08/26/2000*
M0100 Reason for Assessment	*1 - Start of care (further visits planned)*
Consent For Treatment Signed by:	*Patient*
Treatment Consent Date	*08/26/2000*
M0140 Patient Race/Ethnicity	*6 - White*
M0150 Current Payment Sources for Home Care	*1 - Medicare (traditional fee-for-service)*
M0160 Limiting Financial Factors	*0 - None*
M0170 From which of the following Inpatient facilities was the patient discharged during the past 14 days	*3 - Nursing home*
M0180 Most Recent Inpatient Discharge Date	*08/25/2000*
M0190 Inpatient Stay Diagnoses within Last 14 Days	*UNSPECIFIED FRACTURE OF ANKLE, CLOSED*
	8248
	UNSPECIFIED DISORDER OF MUSCLE, LIGAMENT, AND FASCIA
	7289
M0200 Medical or Treatment Regimen: Change in Past 14 Days	*0 - No[Go to M0220]*
M0220 Prior Condition	*7 - None of the above*
M0230 Primary Diagnosis	*UNSPECIFIED FRACTURE OF ANKLE, CLOSED*

Appendix Q

Home Care

Physical Therapy Start of Care (B1)

Author: ▮▮▮▮▮▮▮▮▮▮▮   Completed: 8/26/2000

M0230 Primary Diagnosis	8248
M0240 Other Diagnosis 1	(A) 2 - Symptoms controlled with difficulty affecting daily functioning patient needs ongoing monitoring *UNSPECIFIED ESSENTIAL HYPERTENSION* 4019
M0240 Other Diagnosis 2	(B) 1 - Symptoms well controlled with current therapy *OTHER DISORDER OF MUSCLE, LIGAMENT, AND FASCIA* 72889
M0250 Therapies Received at Home	(C) 2 - Symptoms controlled with difficulty affecting daily functioning patient needs ongoing monitoring 4 - None of the above
M0260 Overall Prognosis for Recovery from This Episode	1 - Good/Fair: partial to full recovery is expected
Prognosis	4 - Good
M0270 Rehabilitative Prognosis	1 - Good: marked improvement in functional status is expected
M0280 Life Expectancy	0 - Life expectancy is greater than 6 months
M0290 High Risk Factors Characterizing This Patient	5 - None of the above
M0300 Current Residence	1 - Patient's owned or rented residence (house/apartment or mobile home owned or rented by patient/couple/significant other)
M0310 Structural Barriers	2 - Stairs inside home which are used optionally (e.g. to get to laundry facilities) 3 - Stairs leading from inside house to outside
M0320 Safety Hazards	0 - None
M0330 Sanitation Hazards	0 - None
Environment (Home) Suitable For Home Care	Yes - Environment (home) is suitable for home care.
Adaptations Required	Adaptations Required None
Safety Measures	1 - Establish emergency plan 4 - Implement a falls prevention program (e.g. remove throw rugs/teach safe use of assist/safety devices)
M0340 Patient Lives With	1 - Lives alone
M0350 Assisting Person	1 - Relatives/friends or neighbors living outside the home
M0360 Primary Caregiver	2 - Daughter or son
M0370 Frequency of Primary Caregiver Assistance	2 - Several times during day
M0380 Type of Primary Caregiver Assistance	1 - ADL assistance (e.g. bathing/dressing/toileting/bowel/bladder/eating/feeding) 2 - IADL assistance (e.g. meds/meals/housekeeping/laundry/telephone/shopping/finances) 3 - Environmental support (housing/home maintenance) 4 - Psychosocial support (socialization/companionship/recreation)
Unusual Home / Social Environment	None
Abuse/Neglect	No signs of abuse/neglect
M0420 Frequency of Pain	2 - Daily but not constantly

Home Care

Physical Therapy Start of Care (B1)

Author: ▮▮▮▮▮▮	Completed: 8/26/2000
M0430 Experiencing Intractable Pain	*0 - No*
Location of Pain (1)	*JOINTS OF LE*
Pain Intensity (4)	*5*
Precipitating Factors (1)	*MOVEMENT*
Pain Control Measures (1)	*Rest*
Pain Control Measures (2)	*Medication*
Best Response to Control Measures (1)	*1*
Visual Correction	*1 - Glasses*
Appropriate Use of Corrective Devices	*Yes*
M0390 Vision with Corrective Lenses	*0 - Normal vision: sees adequately in most situations; can see medication labels/newsprint*
M0400 Sensory Status	*0 - No observable impairment. Able to hear and understand complex or detailed instructions and extended or abstract conversation*
M0410 Speech and Oral Expression	*0 - Expresses complex ideas/feelings and needs clearly/completely and easily in all situations with no observable impairment*
M0560 Cognitive Functioning	*0 - Alert/oriented/able to focus and shift attention/comprehends and recalls task directions independently*
Mental Assessment for Certification	*1 - Oriented to:*
	Person
	Place
	Time
M0570 When Confused (Reported or Observed)	*0 - Never*
M0580 When Anxious (Reported or Observed)	*0 - None of the time*
M0590 Depressive Feelings	*6 - None of the above feelings observed or reported*
M0600 Behavior	*7 - None of the above behaviors observed or reported*
M0610 Behaviors demonstrated at least once a week	*7 - None of the above behaviors demonstrated*
M0620 Frequency of Behavior Problems	*0 - Never*
M0630 Receives Psychiatric Nursing	*0 - No*
Posture/Alignment	*Flattened lumbar lordosis*
	Shoulder protraction
	Knee valgus
Knee valgus	*Right*
Joints	*Stiffness*
Stiffness	*RUE*
	LUE
Flexion - Strength - Right	*3*
Flexion - Strength - Left	*3*
Extension - Strength - Right	*3*
Extension - Strength - Left	*3*

Physical Therapy Start of Care (BI)

Author: ▓▓▓▓▓▓▓	Completed: 8/26/2000

Abduction - Strength - Right	3
Abduction - Strength - Left	3
Adduction - Strength - Right	3
Adduction - Strength - Left	3
Internal Rotation - Strength - Right	3
Internal Rotation - Strength - Left	3
External Rotation - Strength - Right	3
External Rotation - Strength - Left	3
Flexion - Strength - Right	3
Flexion - Strength - Left	3
Extension - Strength - Right	3
Extension - Strength - Left	3
Flexion - Strength - Right	3
Flexion - Strength - Left	2
Extension - Strength - Right	3
Extension - Strength - Left	3
Flexion - Strength - Right	3
Flexion - Strength - Left	3
Extension - Strength - Right	2
Extension - Strength - Left	2
Abduction - Strength - Right	2
Abduction - Strength - Left	2
Adduction - Strength - Right	3
Adduction - Strength - Left	3
Flexion - Strength - Right	3
Flexion - Strength - Left	3
Extension - Strength - Right	3
Extension - Strength - Left	3
Dorsiflexion - Strength - Right	2
Plantarflexion - Strength - Right	2
Coordination/Gross	*WNL*
Muscle Tone/Sensation	*Decreased tone*
Decreased Tone	*RLE*
	LLE
Dermatome	*QUADS AND DORSIFLEXORS RT WEAKER THAN LT*
M0700 Ambulation	*(Prior) 0 - Able to independently walk on even and uneven surfaces and climb stairs with or without railings (i.e. needs no human assistance or assistive device)*
M0700 Current: Ambulation	*(Current) 2 - Able to walk only with the supervision or assistance of another person at all times*

Physical Therapy Start of Care (B1)

Author: ███████████   Completed: 8/26/2000

Level surface (ft.)	35
Uneven surface (ft.)	10
Number of persons to assist - Uneven Surface	One
Stairs with handrails (ft.)	3
Number of persons to assist - Stairs with Handrails	One
LLE	TOUCH DOWN WT BEARING
Devices Currently Used for Ambulation	Wheeled walker
	Other (specify):
Devices Currently Used for Ambulation - Other	ALSO DEPENDENT ON WHEELCHAIR WHEN SHE BECOMES TOO FATIGUED TO AMBULATE
Gait Quality Deficits	Initiating gait
	Step length
	Cadence
	Posture
	Balance
	Turning
	Hip stability
Gait Description	Antalgic
Indoor Surfaces	MI
Outdoor Surfaces	MO
Curbs/barriers	MX
Propel forward	MI
Propel backward	MI
Bed Mobility	WNL
M0690 Transferring	(Prior) 0 - Able to independently transfer
M0690 Current: Transferring	(Current) 1 - Transfers with minimal human assistance or with use of an assistive device
Sit to stand	MI
Sit to Stand Comments	2 HAND PUSH MULTIPLE ATTEMPTS TO COME TO STAND
Stand to Sit	MI
Stand to Sit Comments	FLOPS DOWN INTO CHAIR
Shower/tub	MX
Shower/tub Comments	DTR ABLE TO SAFELY ASSIST
Toilet	MI
Into Car	MX
Out of Car	MX
Static Sitting	Good
Static Standing	Fair
Dynamic Sitting	Good

Appendix Q

Physical Therapy Start of Care (B1)

Author: ████████	Completed: 8/26/2000

Dynamic Standing	*Fair*
Activities Permitted	*3 - Up as tolerated*
	5 - Exercises as prescribed
	6 - Partial weight bearing
	A - Wheelchair
	B - Walker
Assistive Devices/DME	*1 - No DME required*
Integumentary Status	*WNL*
M0440 Does This Patient Have a Skin Lesion or Open Wound - This Excludes Ostomies	*1 - Yes*
M0445 Has Pressure Ulcer	*0 - No [Go to M0468]*
M0468 Has Stasis Ulcer	*0 - No [Go to M0482]*
M0482 Has Surgical Wound	*1 - Yes*
M0484 Number Surgical Wounds	*1 - One*
M0486 Has Unobserved Surgical Wound	*0 - No*
M0488 Status of Most Problematic Surgical Wound	*1 - Fully granulating*
Cardiovascular	*WNL*
M0490 When Dyspneic	*1 - When walking more than 20 feet/climbing stairs*
M0500 Respiratory Treatments	*4 - None of the above*
M0540 Bowel Incontinence Frequency	*0 - Very rarely or never has bowel incontinence*
M0550 Ostomy for Bowel Elimination	*0 - Patient does NOT have an ostomy for bowel elimination*
Intake	*WNL*
Nutritional Requirements/Special Diet	*1 - Regular*
M0510 Treated for Urinary Tract Infection in Past 14 Days	*0 - No*
M0520 Urinary Incontinence or Urinary Catheter Present	*0 - No incontinence or catheter (includes anuria or ostomy for urinary drainage) [Go to Reproductive]*
M0640 Grooming	*(Prior) 0- Able to groom self unaided with or without the use of assistive devices or adapted methods*
M0640 Current: Grooming	*(Current) 1 - Grooming utensils must be placed within reach before able to complete grooming activities*
M0650 Dress Upper Body	*(Prior) 0 - Able to get clothes out of closets/drawers/put them on and remove them from the upper body without assistance*
M0650 Current: Dress Upper Body	*(Current) 1 - Able to dress upper body without assistance if clothing is laid out or handed to the patient*
M0660 Dress Lower Body	*(Prior) 0 - Able to obtain/put on and remove clothing and shoes without assistance*
M0660 Current: Dress Lower Body	*(Current) 2 - Someone must help the patient put on undergarments/slacks/socks or nylons and shoes*
M0670 Bathing	*(Prior) 0 - Able to bathe self in SHOWER OR TUB independently*
M0670 Current: Bathing	*(Current) 2 - Able to bathe in shower or tub with the assistance of another person (a) for intermittent supervision or encouragement or reminders OR (b) to get in and out of the shower or tub OR (c) for washing difficult to reach areas*

Home Care

Physical Therapy Start of Care (B1)

Author: �ꞏꞏꞏꞏꞏꞏꞏꞏꞏ   Completed: 8/26/2000

M0680 Toileting	*(Prior) 0 - Able to get to and from the toilet independently with or without a device*
M0680 Current: Toileting	*(Current) 0 - Able to get to and from the toilet independently with or without a device*
M0710 Feeding	*(Prior) 0 - Able to independently feed self*
M0710 Current: Feeding	*(Current) 0 - Able to independently feed self*
M0720 Prepare Light Meals	*(Prior) 0 - (a) Able to independently plan and prepare all light meals for self or reheat delivered meals OR (b) is physically/cognitively and mentally able to prepare light meals on a regular basis but has not performed light meal preparation*
M0720 Current: Prepare Light Meals	*(Current) 1 - UNABLE to prepare light meals on a regular basis due to physical/cognitive or mental limitations*
M0730 Transportation	*(Prior) 0 - Able to independently drive a regular or adapted car OR uses a regular or handicap-accessible public bus*
M0730 Current: Transportation	*(Current) 1 - Able to ride in a car only when driven by another person OR able to use a bus or handicap van only when assisted or accompanied by another person*
M0740 Laundry	*(Prior) 0 - (a) Able to independently take care of all laundry tasks OR (b) Physically/cognitively and mentally able to do laundry and access facilities BUT has not routinely performed laundry tasks in the past*
M0740 Current: Laundry	*(Current) 2 - UNABLE to do any laundry due to physical limitation or needs continual supervision and assistance due to cognitive or mental limitation*
M0750 Housekeeping	*(Prior) 0 - (a) Able to independently perform all housekeeping tasks OR (b) physically/cognitively and mentally able to perform ALL housekeeping tasks but has not routinely participated in housekeeping tasks in the past*
M0750 Current: Housekeeping	*(Current) 3 - UNABLE to consistently perform any housekeeping tasks unless assisted by another person throughout the process*
M0760 Shopping	*(Prior) 0 - (a) Able to plan for shopping needs and independently perform shopping tasks including carrying packages OR (b) physically/cognitively and mentally able to take care of shopping but has not done shopping in the past*
M0760 Current: Shopping	*(Current) 2 - UNABLE to go shopping but is able to identify items needed/place orders and arrange home delivery*
M0770 Telephone Use	*(Prior) 0 - Able to dial numbers and answer call appropriately and as desired*
M0770 Current: Telephone Use	*(Current) 0 - Able to dial numbers and answer call appropriately and as desired*
M0780 Management of Oral Medications	*(Prior) 0 - Able to independently take the correct oral medication(s) and proper dosage(s) at the correct times*
M0780 Current: Management of Oral Medications	*(Current) 0 - Able to independently take the correct oral medication(s) and proper dosage(s) at the correct times*
M0790 Management of Inhalant Medications	*(Prior) NA - No inhalant/mist medications prescribed*
M0790 Current: Management of Inhalant Medications	*(Current) NA - No inhalant/mist medications prescribed*
M0800 Management of Injectable Medications	*(Prior) NA - No injectable medications prescribed*
M0800 Current: Management of Injectable Medications	*(Current) NA - No injectable medications prescribed*
M0810 Patient Management of Equipment	*NA - No equipment of this type in care [Go to Homebound Status]*
Homebound Status	*Yes [Go to Reasons]*
Reason Patient is Homebound	*1 - Limited ambulation*

	Home Care

Physical Therapy Start of Care (B1)

Author: ███████████   Completed: 8/26/2000

Reason Patient is Homebound	35
	2 - Unsteady gait/poor balance
Reason Patient Leaves Home	*Physician's office*
Functional Limitations	*6 - Endurance*
	7 - Ambulation
Rehabilitation Potential	*1 - Excellent*
Can the Patient Understand Verbal Instructions	*Yes*
Can the Patient Read and Understand Simple Written Instructions	*Yes*
Patients Rights and Responsibilites	*Discussed*
	Copy left in home
State Home Health Hot Line Numbers	*Discussed*
	Copy left in home
Verification Of Benefits	*Discussed*
	Copy left in home
Advance Directives	*Discussed*
	Copy left in home
Home Care Service Agreement	*Discussed*
	Copy left in home
Home Health Visit Schedule	*Discussed*
	Copy left in home
Home Health Agency Phone Numbers	*Discussed*
	Copy left in home
Emergency / Medical Response Plan	*Discussed*
	Copy left in home
Instructions / Materials Given To Whom	*Patient*
Emergency Phone Numbers Prominently Displayed Near Phone	*Yes*
Plan of Care	*Evaluation*
	Transfer training
	Gait training
	Muscle re-education
	Establish/upgrade home exercise program

Author: ███████████   Date: ███████

SS#: _____ DOB: _____ Age: 78 | Team: (No) So Pr _____

Ethnicity: _____ Religion: Lutheran

Start of Care Date: 11 / 3 / 00

Marital Status: ☒ MA ☐ SE ☐ SI ☐ WI ☐ DI

Condition: ☐ Fair ☐ Good ☒ Guarded ☐ Poor

Address: _____

RN: _____
SW: _____

Phone: _____ County: _____

Attending Physician: _____

Facility: _____ FAX: ( )

Phone: _____

Directions to Home: _____

Consultant: _____

Phone: ( ) _____

Last Saw MD: 10/31/00

Caregiver: _____

Hospital: _____

Next of Kin: " Relationship: wife

Primary Diagnosis: Esophageal CA

Address: " Hm Ph ( )
" Wk Ph ( )

DX Code: 150.9 Date: 01 / 04 / 00

☒ Non-Essential Emergency contact: _____

fx: hx. □ chemo & radiation in yr.
Has tracheostomy, open naxx.
uses talking device

Address: _____ Hm Ph ( )
Wk Ph ( )

DNR: ☒ Yes ☐ No ☐ Health Care Directive ☐ DPOA

☐ Essential Primary Caregiver _____

Uses talking device

Address: _____ Hm Ph ( )
_____ Wk Ph ( )

Comments: _____

☒ Medicare Benefit # | ☐ MA Benefit #

Private Insurance: _____ | Per Diem: ☐ Yes ☐ No

Equipment Co: _____ ☐ Bed ☐ OBT ☐ W/C ☐ O2 ☐ Commode ☐ Other: _____

Nursing: Freq: 1-3/wk
Social Work Freq: 1-3/mo
Chaplain: Freq: 1-3/mo ☐ Refused at this time

Hospice Aide: Freq: _____ ☐ Refused at this time
Volunteer: Freq: _____ ☐ Refused at this time
Other: music management Freq: ___

Identified Problem	Intervention	
Pain: _____	assess during visit	Mobility/ADL: arthritis assess mobility as needed
		Skin: intact, has trach site, mark clean assess q. visit
LOC: ☒ alert ☐ II ☐ III ☐ IV (comatose)	AxDx3 Monitor LOC q visit	Sleep: w/m. if takes @ hs assess for effectiveness
Alteration in Nutrition:	monitor q. visit	Alteration in Cardiac/circ: hx □ HTN assess q. visit
Unable to eat liquids d/t Esophageal CA		
Dyspnea: No problem	monitor @ visit	Confusion: AxDx3 monitor as needed
Bowel: constipation	assess bowel status q visit	Anxiety/Depression: assess q. visit
Urinary: No problem	assess as needed	Family Coping: assess q. visit

_____ RN Signature 11/2/00 Date Discussed with ✓ Social Worker ✓ Chaplain

I have reviewed the Plan of Care and provided input. The above orders reflect my approval for hospice care. This patient has _____ Esophageal CA _____, a terminal disease, with a life expectancy of 6 months or less if the disease follows its normal course. The focus of care is palliative rather than curative.

Verbal order from: Dr. _____ Date: 11/2/00

Attending Physician: Dr. _____ Date: 11/13/00 Date Faxed: ( ) _____

team faxed 11/6/2000 act

Appendix Q

VS:	BP _130/70_	Pulse _64_	Resp _16_	Temp _98.1_

Problems Scale Min to Severe 0 to 10	Desired Outcomes	Interventions

PAIN

1) ALTERATION IN PHYSICAL COMFORT

Pt   0 1 2 3 4 5 6 7 8 9 10
Cg   0 1 2 3 4 5 6 7 8 9 10
RN   0 1 2 3 4 5 6 7 8 9 10
LOC I (alert) II III IV (comatose)
☐ Complete Pain Assessment Form

☐ Pt rates pain _0_
☐ Pt reports pain decreased
☐ Pt/Cg reports pain relief
☐ Pt/Cg comply w/med regime
☐ increased activities

☐ Comments _____

☐ Assess LOC q visit
☑ Assess pain q visit
☐ Monitor med effective
☐ Teach importance med regime
☐ Teach med side effects
☐ Teach Cg
☐ Call physician with results

☐ WNL   ☐ Reviewed no problem

NAUSEA/VOMITING

2) ALTERATION IN NUTRITION DUE TO

☐ Anorexia ☐ Nausea ☐ Wt loss ___
☐ Emesis ☐ Dysphagia ☐ Flatulence
☐ NG tube ☐ G tube ☐ Altered taste
☐ Appetite: ☐ Good ☐ Fair ☐ Poor
☐ Diet: ☐ General ☐ Soft ☐ Liquid

☐ Pt maintaining hydration
☐ Pt rates N/V ___
☐ Pt reports decreased nausea
☐ Pt reports decreased emesis
☐ Pt reports increased intake
☑ Pt eats diet as desired
☑ Pt/Cg accept decreased intake as natural process
☐
☐ Comments _____

☐ Assess hydration status
☐ Assess N/V freq. & severity
☑ Small freq. meals
☐ Rest before/after meals
☐ Promote oral hygiene
☐ Dietary consult
☑ Monitor changes
☐ Assess GI process
☐ Irrigate G tube
☐ Meds to control N/V
☐ Meds: ___ change ___ no change

☐ WNL   ☐ Reviewed no problem

DYSPNEA

3) ALTERATION IN RESPIRATORY CLEARANCE/BREATHING PATTERN

☑ Clear R L   ☐ Rales R L
☐ Rhonchi R L ☐ Trache
☐ Hemoptysis ☐ Dyspnea
☐ Decreased BS R L O___ L/M
☐ Smoking Hx ___ Pack per day
☐ Mucous ___ ☐ Cough

☑ Pt resp rate WNL
☑ Pt reports improved respiratory status
☐ Breath sounds improved
☑ Resp status consistent with disease process
☐ Pt/Cg accept resp status
☐ Comments _____

☐ Assess need for oxygen
☑ Assess respiratory status q visit
☐ Promote energy conservation
☐ Monitor changes in resp status due to disease
☐ Teach oxygen therapy
☐ Teach airway patency
☐ Teach med regime
☐ Suction
☐ Meds: ___ change ___ no change

☐ WNL   ☐ Reviewed no problem

CONSTIPATION

4) ALTERATION IN BOWEL ELIMINATION

☐ Constipation ☐ Diarrhea
☐ Obstruction ☐ Impactions
☐ Colostomy/Bag size ___
☐ Incontinent ☐ Stools ___
☐ Bowel sounds ___ BM pattern ___
Last BM date ___

☐ Pt rates constipation ___
☐ Pt rates diarrhea ___
☐ Pt complies with regime
☑ Pt will have BM q ___
☐
☐ Comments _____

☑ Assess status q visit
☐ Pt/Cg comply with regime
☐ Check for impactions
☐ Teach bowel regime
☐ Teach diet/fluids
☐ Meds: ___ change ___ no change

☐ WNL   ☐ Reviewed no problem

*WNL – within normal limits

422

Patient:_____   CustID_____   Page 2 of 6

Problems Scale Min to Severe 0 to 10	Desired Outcomes	Interventions

5) ALTERATION IN URINARY ELIMINATION

Desired Outcomes:
- ☐ Pt reports decreased UTI
- ☐ Pt/Cg report anuria
- ☐ Pt/Cg understand reason for incontinence
- ☐ Pt/Cg accepts incontinence
- ☐ Comments_____

Interventions:
- ☑ Assess status q visit
- ☐ Monitor for S/S UTI
- ☐ Increase fluids
- ☐ Eval need for catheter
- ☐ Teach catheter care
- ☐ Monitor cath & change PRN
- ☐ Instruct to keep pt clean & dry
- ☐ Use chux/diapers/pads
- ☐ Meds: ___change ___no change

Problems:
- ☐ Dysuria ☐ Retention ☐ Burning
- ☐ Hematuria ☐ Urostomy ☐ Incontinent
- ☐ Fluid intake____
- ☐ Cath Ext___ Internal___ Supra Pub___
- ☐ Cath size_____ Change Date_____
- ☐ UTI freq_____ ☐ Genitals_____

☐ WNL   ☐ Reviewed no problem

6) ALTERATION IN PHYSICAL MOBILITY

Desired Outcomes:
- ☑ Pt maintains mobility as long as possible
- ☐ Pt performs ADLs as able
- ☐ Pt remains free from injury
- ☐ Pt/Cg understands decreased mobility & disease process
- ☐ Pt change consistent with disease process
- ☐ Comments_____

Interventions:
- ☑ Assess mobility status
- ☑ Instruct safe use of DME
- ☐ Teach expected changes
- ☑ Teach energy conservation
- ☐ Assist with personal care
- ☐ Eval therapies PT OT
- ☐ Monitor changes in mobility
- ☐ Order DME_____
- ☐ Meds: ___change ___no change

Problems:
- ☐ Ambulates ☐ w/assist ☐ w/o assist
- ☐ Gait ☐ Steady ☐ Unsteady
- ☐ Dizzy ☐ ROM limited ☐ Paresis
- ☐ ADL status
  - ☐ Indep ☐ Semi ☐ Total Care
- ☐ Needs assist with transfers
- ☐ DME already in home
  - DME Company_____

☐ WNL   ☐ Reviewed no problem

7) ALTERATION IN SKIN INTEGRITY

Desired Outcomes:
- ☑ Skin integrity maintains
- ☐ Decubitus decreased in size
- ☐ Cg complies with skin regime
- ☐ Skin free of infection pressures
- ☐ Skin changes consistent with disease process
- ☐ Comments_____

Interventions:
- ☑ Assess skin q visit
- ☑ Instruct preventive measures
- ☐ Use devices to reduce
- ☐ Teach skin care
- ☐ Monitor skin changes
- ☐ Lotion prn
- ☐ Teach to keep clean & dry
- ☐ Meds: ___change ___no change

Problems:
- ☐ Warm ☐ Moist ☐ Dry ☐ Pale
- ☐ Jaundiced ☐ Rash
- ☐ Turgor Good ☐ Fair ☐ Poor
- ☐ Diaphoretic
- ☐ Decubitus ___cm Site
- ☐ Tumor growth
- ☐ Skin assessment completed/score

☐ WNL   ☐ Reviewed no problem

8) ALTERATION IN SLEEP PATTERN

Desired Outcomes:
- ☐ Pt/Cg report improved sleep
- ☑ Pt has_-_ hrs uninterrupted sleep at night
- ☐ Restlessness decreased
- ☐ Pt complies with sleep regime
- ☐ Comments_____

Interventions:
- ☐ Eval pattern pre/post lines
- ☐ Teach relaxation technics
- ☐ Monitor for restlessness
- ☑ Eval need for meds
- ☐ Eval med effectiveness
- ☐ Meds: ___change ___no change

Problems:
- ☐ Insomnia ☐ Nocturia ☐ Pain
- ☐ Restless ☐ Daytime Naps
- ☐ Current pattern ____hrs/night
- ☐ Fear

☐ WNL   ☐ Reviewed no problem

9) ALTERATION IN CARDIAC/CIRC FUNCTION FLUID VOLUME STATUS

Desired Outcomes:
- ☐ Pt edema decreased
- ☐ Pt fluid intake increased
- ☐ Pt/Cg understand dehydration normal dying process q visit
- ☐ Pt/Cg complies with meds
- ☑ Pt without distress
- ☐ Comments_____

Interventions:
- ☑ Assess cardiac status
- ☐ Instruct fluids inc dec
- ☐ Assess edema/dehydration
- ☐ Instruct measures to decrease edema
- ☐ Teach med side effects
- ☐ Monitor med effectiveness
- ☐ Meds: ___change ___no change

Problems:
- ☐ Pulse regular ☐ Irregular
- ☐ Dehydration ☐ Ascites
- ☐ Edema ___ + Sites____
- ☐ Abd girth____ Cap refill____
- ☐ Cyanosis ☐ Hemorrhage
- ☐ Pedal Pulse R____ L____
- ☐ Daily fluid intake____

☐ WNL   ☐ Reviewed no problem

* WNL – within normal limits

forms/hosp06 rev 3/1/2000

423

Patient:_____ _____CustID_____ Page 3 of 6

Problems	Desired Outcomes	Interventions

10) ALTERATION IN MENTAL/NEURO FUNCTION - CONFUSION

Desired Outcomes:
- ☑ Pt maintains LOC as desired
- ☑ Pt aware of surroundings as long as possible
- ☐ Pt remains free from injury
- ☐ Pt responds to reality as long as possible
- ☐ Pt/Cg understands disease progression
- ☐
- ☐ Comments_____

LOC I (alert) II III IV (comatose)

- ☐ Alert   ☐ Oriented   ☐ Confused
- ☐ Restless   ☐ Drowsy   ☐ Agitated
- ☐ Somnolent ☐ Coma   ☐ Semi-coma
- ☐ Speech unclear ☐ Hearing_____
- ☐ Pupils equal   ☐ Pupils unequal
- ☐ Vision_____   ☐ Seizures
- ☐ Diminished thought processes

☐ WNL   ☐ Reviewed no problem

Interventions:
- ☑ Assess LOC q visit
- ☑ Assess confusion q visit
- ☐ Promote calm, restful environment
- ☐ Teach safety measures
- ☐ Assess ability to follow
- ☐ Monitor changes in LOC
- ☐ Teach side effects of meds
- ☐ Meds: ___change ___no change

11) COPING - PATIENT

Desired Outcomes:
- ☑ Pt acknowledges loss & grief
- ☑ Pt reports calm feelings
- ☑ Pt verbalizes concerns
- ☑ Pt verbalizes feelings about Rx
- ☐ Relaxed facial/body language
- ☐ Enhanced coping skill
- Comments_____

- ☐ Open communications   ☐ Closed
- ☐ Withdrawn ☐ Depressed ☐ Upset
- ☐ Anxious ☐ Peaceful   ☐ Accepting
- ☐ Active grieving Stage
- ☐ Prefers not to discuss
- ☐ Church affiliation_____
- ☐ Fearful   ☐ Suicidal

☐ WNL   ☐ Reviewed no problem

Interventions:
- ☑ Assess pt coping skills
- ☑ Assess pt understanding
- ☑ Encourage pt to verbalize feelings/concerns
- ☐ Eval for counseling
- ☐ Identify support systems
- ☐ Refer to_____
- ☐ Assess grief stage
- ☐ Meds: ___change ___no change
- ☐ Reviewed disaster plan

12) COPING - CAREGIVER/FAMILY

Desired Outcomes:
- ☑ Acknowledges loss & grief
- ☑ Cg/Fam verbalizes concerns
- ☑ Cg/Fam verbalizes feelings
- ☑ Cg/Fam anxiety decreased
- ☑ Cg/Fam aware of S/S of approaching death
- ☐ Lessened crisis anxiety
- ☐ Pt needs immediate spiritual care
- ☐ Comments_____

- ☐ Family not present/unknown
- ☐ Open communications ☐ Closed
- ☐ Withdrawn ☐ Depressed ☐ Upset
- ☐ Anxious ☐ Peaceful ☐ Accepting
- ☐ Prefers not to discuss
- ☐ Church affiliation_____
- ☐ Fearful Suicidal

☐ WNL   ☐ Reviewed no problem

Interventions:
- ☑ Assess understanding dx/px
- ☑ Encourage open communication
- ☐ Assess grief stage
- ☐ Teach S/S of approaching death
- ☐ Notify MSW immediately
- ☐ Refer to_____

13) PATIENT CARE MANAGEMENT
- ☐ Dx/Px understood by pt____ Cg____
- ☐ Cg available_____
               Name
- ☐ Home adequate for care y n n/a
- ☐ Home environment safe for staff
- ☐ High crime area ☐ Isolated area
- ☐ Safety hazards_____
- ☐ Animals in household_____

Desired Outcomes:
- ☐ Pt goals *comfort*
- ☐ Cg goals for pt *comfort*
- ☐ Comments_____

*WNL – within normal limits

forms/hoembi rev 3/1/2000

Patient:_____

Problems	Desired Outcomes	Interventions
14) SOCIAL CONCERNS	☐ Reduced conflict in family dynamics	☐ Active listening
	☑ Fam verbalizes concerns & feelings	☑ Facilitate family conference and and counseling
☑ Limited support systems	☑ Fam able to make decisions	☐ Encourage expressing feeling
☐ Financial needs ☐ Legal needs	☐ Fam acknowledges limits	☐ Provide information
☐ Cg/Family health poor	☐ Fam complies w/ care plan	☐ Monitor needs
☐ Family dynamic conflicts	☐ Fam returned to functioning	☐ Assess financial status/need
☐ Family refuses resources	☐ Outcomes achieved	☑ Eval volunteer services
☐ No family	☐ Continue same outcomes	☐ Refer to volunteer services
☐ Lives alone	☐ Observations:_____	☐ Refer to_____
☐ Respite needs		☐ Other_____
☐ Other_____	☐ Other_____	

CHAPLAIN

Problems	Desired Outcomes	Interventions
15) SPIRITUAL CONCERNS	☑ Pt verbalizes belief	☐ Active listening
	☑ Pt at peace with spiritual issues	☑ Assess spiritual needs
	☐ Pt redefines hope	☐ Contact specific clergy as desired by Pt/Fam
☐ Religion preference _La Mean_	☐ Pt anxiety reduced	☐ Arrange for rites
☐ Desire for rites ☐ Desires funeral planning	☐ Pt anger reduced	☑ Offer prayer & scriptures
☐ Desires prayer & scripture	☐ Pt fear reduced	☐ Offer counseling
☐ Prefers not to discuss_____	☐ Pt verbalizes concerns\feelings	☐ Refer to_____
☐ Pt ☐ Angry ☐ Fearful ☐ Anxious	☐ Outcomes achieved	☐ Encourage open communication
☐ Withdrawn ☐ Depressed ☐ Upset ☐ Despair	☐ Continue same outcomes	☐ Life history review
☐ Experiencing major loss_____	☐ Funeral planning complete	☑ Provide support to family
☐ Active grieving stage	☐ Observations:_____	
☐ Refuses spiritual support		

16) OTHER (including mitigating factors impacting treatment, i.e., history of alcoholism, etc.)
Current Palliative Treatment ☐ Radiation Therapy Plan_____
☐ Chemo Therapy Plan_____
☐ Other _____

Contacted attending physician on _11/3/00_ . Physician participated in and approved the hospice plan of care.
Esophageal CA

ADMISSION NOTE:
☑ Reviewed Hospice Services & Philosophy E_____   ☑ Reviewed Consent Forms By _
☐ Pt has Advance Directives ☐ YES ☑ NO   ☑ Pt has signed DNR DNI
☐ Pt has not signed DNR DNI
☑ Emergency plan discussed, 24 on call number reviewed
Recommended Level of Care: ☑ Routine home care   ☐ Inpatient care   ☐ Continuous home care   ☐ Respite care

Plan of care developed by RN with input and agreement from the following team members:

Team members: ☑ Primary MD ☑ Medical Director ☑ MSW ☑ Care Coordinator ☑ Chaplain

RN Signature_____   Date _11/3/00_

Patient/Caregiver/Family Signature_____   Date _11-3-2000_

Initial IDT Conference _11/3/00_   Patient Care Coordinator_____

IDT Follow-up conference _11/7/00_

Social Worker_____   Chaplain_____

Hospice Medical Director_____   Other_____

Format/xxxbl rev 3/1/2000

Name: _____
SS #: _____
Facility: _____
Date: _____

Discipline:
- [x] Nursing
- [ ] MSW
- [ ] Spiritual Care
- [ ] Bereavement
- [ ] Music Therapy
- [ ] Massage Therapy
- [ ] Telephone
- [x] Visit

Problem(s): List all that apply from care plan/pathway

1. Comfort
2.
3.
4.
5.
6.

Narrative Notes: BP: 120/80 Pulse: 60-? Resp: 24 Temp: _____ Wt: _____

Pain Assessment (0/10): 0 By [x] Pt [ ] Other _____

Pt denied any problems or discomfort but he was
concerned about having to clear secretions before
eating everytime he takes anything in - worried
about if secretions increase. Will check ē case mgr ē
pharmacist to see appropriateness of scope patch or
ō Atropine drops for these type of secretions. Wife
appeared quite agitated that pt was discussing
a surgical procedure ē me to ↓ secretions & she
vented a bit ending ē how she "despised" the pt's dr
& also shared some of her experience as a nurse that
left her ē a negative feeling about nursing. Tried to
support her & allay her frustration. Asked her to
stop saying her feelings about his dr because she
had stated it several x's ē the acknowledgement that it
probably wasn't the best thing to say in front of the pt.
Checked ē pharmacist _____ who felt scope patch or
Atropine gtts would be appropriate to try. Passed info on in case →

HHA Supervision: [ ] Indirect [ ] Direct

	GOOD	FAIR	POOR
Aide Appearance	—	—	—
Relationship to Patient	—	—	—
Reliability/Punctuality	—	—	—
Task Completion	—	—	—
Task Observed	—	—	—

HHA Name: _____

Care Plan Update: [ ] Current Care Plan meeting needs   [ ] Care Plan changes _____

Changes to Service Agreement:

Discipline	Frequency	Rate	Payor Source

Plan for Next Visit:
_____

Scheduled Doctor Visit: _____

Coordination of Care with: [ ] MD [ ] RN/PHN [ ] SW [ ] HHA [ ] Music [ ] Massage [ ] Spiritual Care

Patient/Caregiver Signature: _____

Hospice Team Member Signature: _____

White: Medical Records   Yellow: Patient Copy

Please review, sign, and return to: Verbal Orders For:

Hospice   MR #:

                                                         Episode ID:

                                                            Location:

                                                       Date Of Birth:

                                                                  SSN:

‖‖‖‖‖‖‖‖‖‖‖‖‖

Verbal Order #   2016600122   New order for SN - SKILLED NURSING VISITS:
                                         VERIFICATION OF POC FOR HOSPICE STANDING ORDERS FOR 90 DAYS FOR
 ̄ ̄e of Order: 11/03/2000   PAIN AND SYMPTOM MANAGEMENT AND FAMILY SUPPORT SN1TO 3XWX13W
                                         PRN VISITS AS NEEDED FOR UNANTICIPATED NEEDS
Time of Order: 02:28 PM

                           Verbal Order
Physician's   Employee _____   Date 11/06/2000
Order(s)
                           Physician _____   Date 1 16
Page 1 of 1

                                                          Entry Date: 11/04/2000

RESUSCITATION GUIDELINES

CHECK ALL BOXES THAT APPLY

CATEGORY	RECOMMENDED ACTION	MEDICAL RESPONSE WILL PROVIDE	MEDICAL RESPONSE NOT PROVIDED
[ ] CPR	Call 911	Full Treatment As Appropriate	
[ ] DNR (No CPR)	Call 911 Except for Cardiac Arrest	Active Treatment up to the Point of Cardiac Arrest	If in Cardiac Arrest: No Intubation No Ventilatory Assistance No Chest Compressions No Defibrillation
[X] Hospice or Comfort Care	Call M.D. or R.N. May Call Ambulance for Routine Transport May Call 911 for Urgent Needs	Comfort and Hygiene Care	If in Cardiac Arrest: No Intubation No Ventilatory Assistance No Chest Compressions No Defibrillation

Patient/Client Name

I understand this document identifies the level of care to be rendered in situations where death may be imminent. I make this request knowingly and I am aware of the alternatives. I expressly release, on behalf of myself and my family, all persons who shall in the future attend to my medical care of any and all liability whatsoever for acting in accordance with this request of mine. Furthermore, I direct these guidelines be enforced even though I may develop a diminished mental capacity at some future time. I am aware that I can revoke these guidelines at any time by simply expressing my request verbally or in writing to my caretaker, family, physician, or designated health care provider.

_11 - 3 - 2000_

_____ Date
Patient/Client or Authorized Signature "Relationship"

I have witnessed the above signature:

_____
Witness Signature

_____ 11/7/00
Physician's Signature   Address   Phone #   Date

THE ABOVE 3 SIGNATURES AND 2 DATES ARE REQUIRED FOR THIS FORM TO BE VALID AND ITS INTENT CARRIED OUT

See Reverse Side for Background Information

Patient: _____

Cust ID: _____

Service Agreement

Service	Refused Services	Anticipated Schedule (frequency/duration)	Primary Goal/Care Plan	Expected Payor ☑ Card Verified	Expected Patient Charges*
☑Skilled Nursing ☑RN ☑Visits ☐Hourly ☐LPN ☐Visits ☐Hourly	x̲	1-3 xwk	Comfort care	MDCR	$0
☐Medical Supplies					
☐Pharmacy	Y				
☐Rehab Services ☐PT ☐OT ☐ST					
☑Social Services		1-3xmo			
☑Chaplain ☐Volunteer ∅		1-3xmo			
☐Home Health Aide					
☐Visits ☐Hourly	X				
☐Supervisory Visits ☐RN ☐Therapist					

*I understand that the information on payment for services is a preliminary estimate which is based on the information I have provided to FHCH at the time of my admission for services. I understand that actual payment by my insurance company cannot be determined until home care bills have been submitted to them. I understand that I am responsible for all services. I understand that actual payment by my insurance company. A placement fee of $2,000.00 will be charged if I hire a FHCH employee within 90 days of receiving services. charges that are not reimbursed by my insurance company.

In the case of a change in condition, FHCH should call my Emergency Contact: _____   **Relationship:** wf   (H) _____ . (W) _____

Emergency Preparedness Plan - *a plan to ensure the safety of patients in the event of an environmental or agency emergency which may interrupt patient services from FHCH.*
  ☑*Non-essential Services* - A patient who has the ability and/or has caregivers available to provide care for a short period of time. This could include the ability to self-medicate, manage bowel and bladder needs, get nutrition, manage transfers and access 911/emergency services.

  ☐*Essential Services* - A patient with immediate needs who cannot safely forfeit care and requires health care intervention regardless of other conditions. Patients in this category may include: patients with no qualified caregiver available; patients who are on life sustaining equipment or life sustaining infusion therapy; insulin dependent diabetic patients who are unable to self-inject; patients with significant cognitive impairment.

Contingency Plan
List Essential Services by Discipline: ☐Skilled Nursing ☐Pharmacy ☐Home Health Aide   Patient able to access 911: ☐Yes ☐No
My Primary Caregiver for Essential Services is: _____   Relationship: _____ (H) _____ (W)

A representative from ████████ can be reached at ████ , 24 hours per day OR
I understand that emergency services will not be summoned during a life threatening emergency when there is a written physician's order for DNR/DNI in my record that reflect my
wishes according to the Adult Health Care Decisions Act and home death has been pre-arranged. I have had the opportunity to participate in the development of this service agreement.
I have read this agreement, understand it and agree to abide by its terms.

_____   _____   11-3-00
Signature (Patient or Authorized Representative)   Witness   Date

          White: Patient   Yellow: Chart   Pink: Home Chart   122013

Patient: _____

Cust ID# _____

Hospice Consent and Election

CONSENT FOR HOSPICE SERVICES

I, the undersigned patient, acknowledge that the information contained in this document has been explained to me and I voluntarily consent and elect admission and care by ███████████. I understand:

- Hospice has been explained to me, including the purpose, costs, probable risks and benefits of hospice services, including alternatives, along with the risks of declining services. I have been given an opportunity to ask any questions I have concerning hospice.
- I am aware that health care is not an exact science and I acknowledge that no guarantees or promises have been made to me as to the results of hospice. I have had the opportunity to discuss these matters with my physician and desire to receive hospice care.
- The goal of the hospice program is not to cure my terminal illness, but to provide comfort, to relieve symptoms such as pain or nausea, and to provide emotional and spiritual support to me and my family. Palliative care and symptom control are appropriate goals for my treatment rather than cure.
- The hospice program consists of services delivered primarily in my home according to a plan of care developed by an Interdisciplinary Group (IDG.) The IDG includes the services of nursing, social work, spiritual care, home health aide, dietary, volunteers, rehabilitation therapy and bereavement support for family and friends.
- My family and I are involved in making decisions about the amount and type of services to be provided. **Changes to my Plan of Care will be discussed with me in advance.** Home visits are provided on a scheduled basis but nursing consultation and visits are also available as needed twenty-four hours a day, seven days a week by calling: ████████████████████ or ████████████████
- The hospice program will assist with arranging short-term inpatient services when it is deemed necessary by the IDG for intensive symptom control requiring continuous professional observation that cannot be managed at home. Inpatient care must be provided at one of the facilities who have a contract with ███████ Hospice inpatient services are designed to stabilize my condition so that I can return home.
- The IDG will not take the place of my caregiver, but rather will provide support to my caregiver in caring for me. The Hospice Medical Director does not take the place of my attending physician, but rather provides consultation as requested by my attending physician or the IDG.
- The hospice medical record will contain information about me, my plan or care and my family/caregivers. This information will be kept confidential, but information about me will be exchanged with my caregiver and family in order to coordinate and manage the best possible plan of care.
- I may choose to receive hospice care from another hospice at any time. To transfer to another hospice, I must first confirm that the new hospice will admit me, and obtain the date of admission. I must then inform ██████ of my desire to change programs, the name of the new hospice, the date of admission to the new hospice, and the date of discontinuance of hospice care by ██████
- I understand that I have the option to withdraw from the Hospice Program at any time. I agree that if I withdraw from hospice, or refuse or cancel services and/or treatments without my doctor's authorization, I will make no claim against ██████ for harm or damages caused by my cancellation of services.
- If my care is paid for by Medicare, I may revoke the Hospice Medicare Benefit (HMB) at any time if I so choose. To revoke the HMB I must complete and sign a hospice revocation statement, which can be obtained from ██████ Upon revocation of the HMB, or upon cancellation and discharge from the hospice program of care, the benefits under Part A of Medicare, which I waive by this election, will be reinstated.
- ██████ has the right to discontinue hospice care and discharge me from the hospice program with reasonable notice under the following circumstances:

1. I move from the service area;
2. My condition improves so much that I no longer can be considered terminally ill;
3. I do not wish to adhere to my hospice plan of care, which in turn, compromises hospice standards and quality care;
4. Issues of my safety or hospice staff safety cannot be resolved;
5. Medicare or my insurance company discontinues the hospice benefit.
- I understand that ██████ is an Equal Opportunity Employer and does not engage in discriminatory practices with regard to employment or assignment.

10/2000 revised   forms\hospiceconsent.doc

WHITE: CLINICAL RECORD   YELLOW: PATIENT COPY

172717 10/00

CustID_____

I understand that ▓▓▓has periodic price increases for services. I will be notified in writing, no later than 30 days prior to any price increase becoming effective.

I agree not to independently employ, nor contract with any ▓▓▓personnel for a period of one hundred eighty (180) days following the completion of services provided under this agreement. I understand to do so will be in direct violation of this agreement and I will be financially liable for a Placement Fee of $3,000.00, payable upon demand.

PAYOR INFORMATION

Is patient entitled to any benefits under the Federal Black Lung Program (Circle) Yes (No)
Is the patient receiving Veterans Administration Benefits? (Circle) Yes (No)

MEDICARE List 9 digit number and letter............	WORKERS COMPENSATION Is the illness or injury work related and covered by W/C? [Circle] Y (N) If yes, complete this box:
Medicare # X ?	
MEDICAL ASSISTANCE (MA election form MUST BE SIGNED)	Date of Injury: _____
MA # _____	Claim # _____
PMAP Plan Name: _____	Employer: _____
PMAP # _____	Employer Phone: _____
Waiver Program: _____	W/C Carrier: _____
County Case Mgr Name: _____	W/C Phone: _____
Phone:	
INSURANCE/HMO Does patient have health insurance based on own or a spouse's current employment? [Circle] Y (N) If yes, complete:	**AUTO/LIABILITY INSURANCE** Can payment be made by an automobile or liability plan? [Circle] Y (N) If yes, complete:
Insurance/HMO Company: _____	Date of MVA or injury: _____
Phone: _____	Insurance Company: _____
Policy # _____ Group # _____	Phone # _____
Policy Holder: _____	Address: _____
Employer: _____	_____
	Policy # _____
	Claim # _____
PRIVATE PAY (Required for private pay only)	**CREDIT CARD BILLING INFORMATION** (Optional for private pay)
Bill to: _____	Card: (Circle) Visa Mastercard Am Ex Exp. Date: _____
Address: _____	Name of Cardholder: _____
	Signature: _____

ASSIGNMENT OF BENEFITS AND GUARANTEE OF ACCOUNT

I understand that I am personally responsible for all charges that are not reimbursed by my insurance company (except for Medicare or Medical Assistance) within 60 days. I understand that a reasonable degree of effort will be exercised to collect the benefits to which I may be entitled, but that ▓▓▓is not a guarantor of collection of such benefits. I authorize payment directly to ▓▓▓▓▓▓▓▓▓▓ and Hospice for all services/supplies rendered on my behalf. I request that this authorization remain in effect until revoked by me through written notice given to ▓▓▓Payment is due ten days after I receive the bill.

☒ **Medicare Authorization**
I certify that the information given by me in applying for payment under Title XVIII of the Social Security Act is correct. I authorize any holder of medical or other information about me to release to the Social Security Administration or its intermediaries or carriers any information needed for this or a related Medicare claim. I request that payment of authorized benefits be made on my behalf. I have Been advised to the extent to which payment for hospice care may be expected from Medicare

10/2000 revised

WHITE: CLINICAL RECORD   YELLOW: PATIENT COPY

Appendix Q

CustID_____

☐ **Insurance Authorization**
I hereby authorize payment directly to ████ for the insurance benefits allowed to me but not to exceed ████'s regular charges for these services. I understand that EXACT INSURANCE BENEFITS CANNOT BE DETERMINED UNTIL THE INSURANCE COMPANY RECEIVES THE CLAIM. ANY REMAINING PORTION OF THE BILL WILL BE MY RESPONSIBILITY. I further authorize the release of any medical information necessary to determine benefits.

TIME CARDS, SERVICE VERIFICATION AND BILLING
████ employees will request your signature on a document verifying the time and/or date of the service. Your signature verifies that the date of the service is accurate, and your bill will reflect this date of service. Some employees may also record time in and out, and will ask for your signature to verify the accuracy of the time. IF THE HOURS ARE NOT ACCURATE, DO NOT SIGN THE TIME CARD. Call our office and ask to speak to a supervisor. IF YOU SIGN THE TIME CARD, YOU OR YOUR INSURANCE COMPANY WILL BE RESPONSIBLE FOR PAYMENT OF THE HOURS RECORDED.

Employees may also ask to use your phone at the beginning and end of each shift or visit to electronically record their time in and out. These calls are placed to a toll-free number and will not affect your phone bill.

AUTHORIZATION FOR RELEASE OF INFORMATION AND MEDICAL RECORDS
I authorize ████ and Hospice to release information and appropriate clinical records:
- To hospice personnel involved with my case; for example, nurse, social worker, therapist, home health aides.
- To representatives of other health providers involved in my health care; for example, physicians, hospital/long term care personnel, other home care and hospice agencies.
- To regulatory and accreditation bodies, or to ████ quality/compliance team for the purpose of survey or inspection, to obtain and maintain certification, licensure and accreditation as ████ deems necessary.
- To Medicare, Medical Assistance or my insurance company for purpose of obtaining payment of my home care and hospice costs.
- In circumstances specified in statute where health record information may be released.
- To medical researchers for external medical or scientific research. By collecting information from medical records, researchers learn about new or better ways to diagnose and treat illnesses. Research results do not identify individuals by name or by any other personally identifying characteristics. This authorization does not expire but may be revoked or limited in writing by me at anytime. I may refuse to permit my medical record to be used for external research purposes by crossing through this paragraph and initialing in the left margin.
- I authorize my physician (physician name) _____ or other health care provider (name)_____ to release to ████ and Hospice my most recent history and physical, other medical records and a copy of any health care directives, if currently in my medical record.

I understand that ████ cannot prevent the redisclosure of information released as a result of this authorization; therefore, ████ is released from any and all liability from redisclosure.

A photocopy of this authorization shall be as valid as the original.

THE HOSPICE PROGRAM HAS BEEN FULLY EXPLAINED TO ME AND I HAVE BEEN GIVEN AMPLE OPPORTUNITY TO ASK ANY AND ALL QUESTIONS I HAVE CONCERNING THE PROGRAM. WITH THIS UNDERSTANDING, I ELECT TO RECEIVE HOSPICE CARE THROUGH ████ HOSPICE AND AUTHORIZE HOSPICE CARE TO BEGIN ON (date) _____11-3, 00_____.

11-3-00
Date | Signature of Patient or Responsible Party | *spouse- wife* If not signed by patient, give relationship of responsible party to patient.

pts wife — If not signed by patient, must give reason patient cannot sign | Witness

10/2000 revised

WHITE: CLINICAL RECORD   YELLOW: PATIENT COPY

432

CustID_____

Medicare Hospice Benefit Patients Only
I understand that the Hospice Medicare Benefit (HMB), a federal program that provides reimbursement for hospice care, is available so long as I am covered under Part A of Medicare and certified as being terminally ill. (A patient is considered terminally ill if the patient has a medical prognosis that his or her life expectancy is six months or less if the disease runs its normal course.) By electing to receive HMB through ██████, I waive all benefits available under Part A of Medicare for services that are related to the treatment of the terminal illness for which hospice care is elected, or a related condition, or for services that are equivalent to hospice care, except for services provided by:

* ██████;
* another hospice under arrangements made by ██████;
* my attending physician if that physician is not an employee of ██████ or receiving compensation from ██████ for those services. (My attending physician will continue to bill Medicare Part B for his/her services and I will continue to be responsible for the co-payments.)

Medicare Hospice Benefit Patients Only (continued)
Benefits available under Medicare Part A for services not related to my terminal illness are not waived. Medicare Part B coverage is not affected by this election and will continue uninterrupted.

There are special benefit periods in the HMB that apply to hospice care. The benefit periods may be used consecutively or at different times. The benefit periods are as follows:

First Benefit Period	90 days
Second Benefit Period	90 days
Subsequent Benefit Periods	60 days indefinitely

My election to receive hospice care is considered to continue through the initial benefit period and through the subsequent benefit periods without a break in care as long as I remain terminally ill and in the care of the hospice, and so long as I do not revoke the election.

* The HMB provides coverage for drugs that are related to promoting my comfort and relieving pain and symptoms related to the terminal illness. The drugs must be obtained from a ██████ Community Pharmacy.
* Medical tests or procedures must have prior approval by ██████ in order to be covered under the HMB.

I understand that the following services will be covered under the Medicare Hospice Benefit if certified as reasonable and necessary by the IDG, provided by a provider who has a contract with ██████, and authorized by ██████:

* **Routine home care** consisting of visits by the IDG (as defined above).
* **Continuous nursing and home health aide care at home** if required for short periods of crisis (only when authorized by the IDG.)
* **Inpatient Respite Care** to provide relief to caregivers. Up to five (5) consecutive days may be authorized by the IDG. Transportation to and from respite care is covered if in the patients Plan of Care.
* **Inpatient Care** if needed for acute symptom management.
* **Medical supplies** such as prescription drugs for management of my terminal illness when authorized and supplied by ██████.
* **Durable medical equipment** when authorized and supplied by ██████.
* **Transportation** when authorized by ██████ for transfer to an inpatient acute care setting, and provided by a contracted transportation company.

CONSENT TO TEST MY BLOOD
In the event a health care worker sustains exposure to my blood or body fluids, I give permission for a sample of my blood to be tested for infectious disease.

HOME CARE/HOSPICE PATIENT BILL OF RIGHTS
I have received the Home Care Patient Bill of Rights, it has been reviewed and explained to my satisfaction in terms I could understand, and my questions have been answered. I understand my rights, including the right to register a complaint without fear of retribution. I understand how to make a complaint and who to contact to register a complaint about care, treatment or services (found at the end of the Bill of Rights.)

HEALTH CARE DIRECTIVES (also called ADVANCE DIRECTIVES)
I have been provided with a brochure entitled *Powerful Choices*, which explains my rights under Minnesota law to make decisions regarding my health care, and summarizes ██████ policy regarding the implementation of health care directives.

TERMS OF AGREEMENT
I understand that the information on the Service Agreement (types of service, rates for service, payer source, and my financial responsibility) is a preliminary estimate which is based upon the information I have provided to ██████ at the time of my admission for services. I understand that actual payment by my insurance company cannot be determined until hospice bills have been submitted to them. If it becomes necessary for ██████ to obtain the services of an attorney to collect my account, I agree to pay such reasonable court and attorney fees as established by the court.

10/2000 revised

WHITE: CLINICAL RECORD   YELLOW: PATIENT COPY

Appendix R

Software Product Matrix

The following pages contain the results of the 2000 annual market update completed by Home Care Automation Report (HCAR). Every year since 1994, HCAR has asked vendors serving the home health industry to provide snapshots of their software features and news on recent company and product developments.

Company Name	Business Lines					System Features																Data Capture			
	Traditional Care	Hospice	Private Duty	IV Therapy	HME	Billing UB92	Billing HCFA 1500	Benchmarking	Care Planning	Clinical Records	Data Exchange	Electronic Claims	Electronic Remittance	Financial/Accounting	Hospital Interface	Human Resources	Medicare Cost Report	Medications Database	OASIS	Report Writer	Scheduling	Imaging/Scanning	Point-of-Care	Telephony	NAHC Booth
3M Home Health Care www.3M.com/hhs 800-447-3377	X	X	X		X	X	X	X	X	X	X	X	X	X	X	X	X	X	X	X	X	X	X	X	613
Advanced Information Management www.almcares.com 920-996-2380	X	X	X		X	X	X	X	X	X	X	X	X	X	X		X	X	X	X	X	X	X		
Alpha Site 925-460-0703	X		X			X	X		X	X	X	X			X	X		X		X	X				
August Systems www.august-systems.com 509-468-2988	X	X	X			X	X	X	X	X	X			X	X		X		X	X	X	X			
AutoData Systems www.autodata.com 800-662-2192	X	X	X					X	X	X				X	X			X	X			X			
Axiom Internet Commerce www.axiominternet.com 818-346-2779	X	X	X	X		X	X	X	X	X	X	X	X	X	X	X	X		X	X	X		X		
BeyondNow Technologies www.beyondnow.com 913-385-0212	X	X	X	X	X	X	X	X	X	X	X	X	X	X	X	X	X		X	X	X	X			
C3 800-243-9583	X	X	X	X																	X		X	X	
Campana Systems www.campana.com 800-463-2688			X			X	X	X	X	X	X	X	X	X	X	X	X	X	X	X	X	X			
Capstone Computing 419-866-5503	X	X	X			X	X		X	X	X		X		X		X		X	X	X				
CareFacts Information Systems www.carefacts.com 651-636-3890	X	X	X	X	X	X	X	X	X	X	X	X	X	X	X	X	X		X	X	X	X	X	X	
CareKeeper Software www.carekeeper.com 770-392-1542	X	X	X			X	X	X	X	X	X	X	X	X	X	X	X		X	X	X				1009
Cerner Corporation www.cerner.com 816-221-1024	X	X	X			X	X	X	X	X	X	X	X	X	X	X	X		X	X	X	X	X	X	
CHAMP Software www.champsoftware.com 507-625-7449	X		X			X	X	X	X	X	X	X	X		X	X	X		X	X	X		X		
ClaimPulse www.claimpulse.com 225-709-2199							X	X				X	X								X				
Clinical Pharmacy Systems 630-832-5966					X	X	X	X	X	X	X	X		X			X				X				
Comprehensive Health Systems www.pms5.com 800-445-8649	X	X			X	X	X	X	X	X	X	X	X	X	X	X	X		X	X	X	X			
Computer Applications Unlimited www.cau.com 717-541-0651	X		X	X	X	X		X	X	X		X	X	X					X	X					
Computer Outsourcing Services www.infocrossing.com 201-840-4700	X	X	X	X																				X	

Vendors in **Bold** provided update information for this survey.

Software Product Matrix

Company Name	Traditional Care	Hospice	Private Duty	IV Therapy	HME	Billing UB92	Billing HCFA 1500	Benchmarking	Care Planning	Clinical Records	Data Exchange	Electronic Claims	Electronic Remittance	Financial/Accounting	Hospital Interface	Human Resources	Medicare Cost Report	Medications Databases	OASIS	Report Writer	Scheduling	Imaging/Scanning	Point-of-Care	Telephony	NAHC Booth
Creative Healthcare Strategies / www.chsidata.com / 888-460-9046	X	X	X	X	X																				
DataMed Technologies / www.datamedtech.com / 818-563-3633	X					X	X	X	X	X	X	X	X	X			X		X	X	X	X			
Delta Health Systems / www.deltahealth.com / 814-944-1651	X	X	X	X		X	X	X	X	X	X	X	X	X		X	X		X	X	X	X	X		901
Dial-n-Document / www.dialndocument.com / 606-431-5640	X	X	X	X	X				X	X	X			X			X		X	X		X	X	X	
Dixon Kanary & Co. / www.dixonkanary.com / 800-544-5188	X															X									
eClickMD.com / www.eclickmd.com / 888-660-5465	X	X	X	X				X	X	X	X									X	X	X			431
eHomecare.com / www.ehomecare.com / 908-874-9570	X	X	X			X	X	X	X	X	X	X	X	X	X	X	X		X	X	X	X			1339
Emerald Data Systems / 800-321-7544	X	X	X		X	X	X	X	X	X	X	X	X						X	X		X			
Encounter Technology Solutions / www.encountertechnology.com / 404-881-8311	X								X	X	X						X		X	X	X	X	X		1039
Fastrack Healthcare Systems / www.fastrk.com / 516-349-9136	X	X	X	X		X		X	X	X	X	X	X	X	X	X	X		X	X	X	X	X		
FGA Software Solutions / www.fgainc.com / 800-682-5749	X	X	X			X		X	X	X	X	X	X	X	X	X	X		X	X	X	X			514
Golden Rule Software / www.grule.com / 800-408-5503	X			X			X	X	X	X	X	X	X	X			X		X	X	X	X			525
Hann's On Software / www.hannsonsoftware.com / 707-823-6089				X			X	X	X	X	X	X	X	X			X		X	X	X	X			
Health Care Data / www.hcdinc.com / 760-943-8087	X	X	X	X	X	X	X	X	X	X	X	X	X	X	X	X	X		X	X	X	X	X		612
Health Magic / www.healthmagic.com / 803-748-9444		X	X	X		X	X	X	X	X	X	X	X	X			X		X	X	X	X		X	
Healthcare Automation / www.halhomecare.com / 401-732-8980	X	X	X	X		X	X	X	X	X	X	X	X	X			X		X	X	X	X		X	
Healthcare Synergy / www.2synergy.com / 562-866-2444	X	X	X	X		X	X	X	X	X	X	X	X			X			X	X	X	X	X		626
HealthWyse / www.healthwyse.com / 877-777-9973	X	X	X	X		X	X	X	X	X	X	X	X	X	X	X	X		X	X	X	X			
Home Care Information Systems / www.hcis.com / 732-936-3000	X	X	X	X		X	X	X	X	X	X	X	X	X	X	X	X		X	X	X	X	X		713
Home Care Resources / www.homecare2000.com / 954-472-2333	X	X	X			X	X	X	X	X	X	X	X	X	X	X			X	X		X			

Vendors in **Bold** provided update information for this survey.

Company Name	Traditional Care	Hospice	Private Duty	IV Therapy	HME	Billing UB92	Billing HCFA 1500	Benchmarking	Care Planning	Clinical Records	Data Exchange	Electronic Claims	Electronic Remittance	Financial/Accounting	Hospital Interface	Human Resources	Medicare Cost Report	Medications Database	OASIS	Report Writer	Scheduling	Imaging/Scanning	Point-of-Care	Telephony	NAHC Booth
Home Health Gold www.homehealthgold.com 207-872-4544	X							X												X		X			
Homecare Software Systems www.hcsw.com 800-657-2050	X	X	X	X			X		X		X	X	X	X			X		X	X	X				
Horizon Healthware www.hcsw.com 919-676-8090	X	X	X		X	X	X		X	X	X	X	X	X			X	X	X	X	X		X		
IMA Technologies Corporation www.casetrakker.com 800-458-1114	X	X	X			X				X	X	X	X												
InfoSys www.infosysusa.com 800-978-4636	X	X	X	X	X	X	X	X	X	X	X	X	X	X	X	X	X	X	X	X	X	X	X	X	1125
Keynote Systems www.keynotesystems.com 716-564-1332	X		X			X	X		X		X	X	X	X	X		X			X	X				
Lewis Computer Services www.lewis.com 225-709-2000	X	X	X	X		X	X	X		X	X	X	X	X	X		X	X	X	X	X	X	X		1100
Lighthouse Infomatics www.lighthouse-infomatics.com 530-790-2500	X	X	X	X				X		X			X						X	X					525
Logicon www.home-adv.com 800-297-2180	X	X	X	X	X				X	X											X			X	
Management By Information www.mbimbi.com 501-661-0386	X			X	X	X	X		X	X	X	X	X	X		X	X		X	X	X				
McKesson HBOC www.hboc.com 417-874-4000	X		X			X	X		X	X	X	X	X	X	X		X	X	X	X	X		X	X	701
Medical Bar-Code Systems www.medbarcode.com 615-646-7199	X	X	X									X													
NewTech Care Systems www.homehealthplace.com 800-989-7290	X		X			X	X		X	X	X	X	X	X	X	X	X	X	X	X	X				
NoteTime www.notetime.com 610-645-9797	X		X												X				X	X	X		X	X	
Nnovative Data Systems www.ndsinc.net 757-365-4358	X		X			X	X	X	X	X	X	X	X	X			X		X	X	X	X	X	X	
OMS2 Software www.pmplus.com 800-279-9949	X	X		X		X	X	X	X	X	X	X	X	X	X	X	X		X	X	X				
Outcome Concept Systems www.ocsys.com 888-325-3396	X		X	X	X			X											X	X		X		X	
PathNotes www.pathnotes.com 940-898-8672	X	X	X					X	X	X									X	X					
Patient Care Technologies www.ptct.com 404-235-7828	X		X	X		X	X		X	X	X	X	X	X	X	X	X	X	X	X	X	X	X	X	1201
Picker Business Systems www.masterpak.com 860-721-0050	X	X	X			X	X			X	X	X	X	X			X			X					

Vendors in **Bold** provided update information for this survey.

Company Name	Traditional Care	Hospice	Private Duty	IV Therapy	HME	Billing UB92	Billing HCFA 1500	Benchmarking	Care Planning	Clinical Records	Data Exchange	Electronic Claims	Electronic Remittance	Financial/Accounting	Hospital Interface	Human Resources	Medicare Cost Report	Medications Database	OASIS	Report Writer	Scheduling	Imaging/Scanning	Point-of-Care	Telephony	NAHC Booth
PPS Eval.com / www.ppseval.com / 225-927-3064	X	X						X	X					X											
Pro Business Systems / www.pbscorp.com / 800-239-1498	X	X	X	X	X	X	X	X	X	X	X	X	X	X	X	X	X	X	X	X	X	X	X	X	1100
Prodata / 800-776-3282	X	X	X	X	X	X	X	X	X	X	X	X	X	X	X	X	X	X	X	X	X	X	X	X	736
Professional Computer Consultants / www.time-track.com / 800-632-7045			X			X	X				X			X	X	X			X	X	X	X	X	X	
Provider Solutions / www.providersolutions.com / 800-850-0018	X	X	X		X	X	X	X	X		X	X			X	X	X		X	X	X	X	X		
RemitData / www.remitdata.com / 901-312-4163	X	X				X						X													
Resource Management Systems / 414-774-8582	X	X	X	X		X	X			X	X	X	X	X	X	X				X	X			X	
Sandata / www.sandata.com / 800-544-7263	X	X	X	X		X	X	X	X	X	X	X	X	X	X	X	X		X	X	X	X		X	913
ScanHealth / www.scanhealth.com / 800-682-2559	X		X			X	X	X	X	X	X	X	X	X	X	X	X		X	X	X		X		835
Select Data / www.selectdata.com / 714-974-4445	X	X	X	X	X	X	X	X	X	X	X	X	X	X	X	X	X		X	X	X	X	X		1035
Simione Central / www.simcen.com / 800-441-2331	X	X	X	X	X	X	X	X	X	X	X	X	X	X	X	X	X		X	X	X	X	X	X	501
Software Innovations / 800-466-4790	X	X	X	X	X	X	X	X	X	X	X	X	X	X	X		X		X	X	X	X	X		
Specialized Clinical Services / www.spclin.com / 714-259-0106			X	X	X	X	X	X	X	X	X	X	X	X						X	X			X	
STATLinc Computer Systems / www.nursenetwork.com / 561-689-7100	X					X	X		X	X	X	X			X	X	X			X	X	X			
Strategic Healthcare Programs / www.strategichp.com / 805-963-9446	X	X								X						X			X				X		
Stratis Business Systems / www.stratisinc.com / 561-274-4240	X	X	X			X	X	X	X	X	X	X	X	X	X	X	X		X	X	X			X	
The Anesis Group / www.anesis.com / 423-531-0303	X	X	X			X	X	X	X	X	X	X	X	X	X	X	X		X	X	X				
Thornberry Ltd. / www.thornberryltd.com / 717-431-3070	X	X						X	X	X	X						X		X	X	X		X		
United Wisconsin ProServices / www.proservices.uwz.com / 414-226-6112	X	X				X	X	X	X	X	X	X	X	X	X	X	X		X	X	X		X	X	512
Voice Log / www.voicelog.net / 913-901-9090	X	X				X	X		X	X	X	X							X	X			X	X	

Vendors in Bold provided update information for this survey.

Appendix S

Sample Forms for Maintenance, Disclosure, and Redisclosure of Health Information

The following maintenance, disclosure, and redisclosure forms have been modified for use in home care and hospice programs. The forms are designed to be used strictly as models and not for other purposes. Readers must review each sample against final HIPAA privacy regulations once the regulations are released.

Exhibit 1

Employee/Independent Contractor/Student/Volunteer Nondisclosure Agreement

[Name of home care/hospice organization] has a legal and ethical responsibility to safeguard the privacy of all patients/families and protect the confidentiality of their health information. In the course of my employment/assignment at [name of organization], I may come into possession of confidential patient/family information, even though I may not be directly involved in providing patient services.

I understand that such information must be maintained in the strictest confidence. As a condition of my employment/assignment, I hereby agree that, unless directed by my supervisor, I will not at any time during or after my employment/assignment with [name of organization] disclose any patient information to any person whatsoever or permit any person whatsoever to examine or make copies of any patient/family reports or other documents prepared by me, coming into my possession, or under my control, or use patient/family information, other than as necessary in the course of my employment/assignment.

In the course of my work when patient/family information must be discussed with other healthcare practitioners or when clinical records copies must be maintained outside of the organization's office(s), I will use discretion to ensure that conversations cannot be overheard and that record copies cannot be observed by others who are not involved in the care of the patient/family.

I understand that violation of this agreement may result in corrective action, up to and including discharge.

_____
Signature of Employee/Student/Volunteer

_____
Date

Note: This sample form is for discussion purposes only. Not for use without advice of legal counsel. Adapted from Mary D. Brandt's *Release and Disclosure: Guidelines Regarding Maintenance and Disclosure of Health Information,* AHIMA © 1997.

Exhibit 2

Employee/Independent Contractor/Student/Volunteer Nondisclosure Acknowledgement

I have been asked by [name of home care/hospice organization] to reaffirm my commitment made at the time of my employment/assignment to protect the confidentiality of health information. I understand that [name of organization] reminds its employees and volunteers of their confidentiality obligations on a periodic basis to help ensure compliance, due to the significance of this issue. By my signature below, I acknowledge that I made the commitment set forth below at the time of my employment/assignment, I confirm my past compliance with it, and I reaffirm my continued obligation to it:

[Name of organization] has a legal and ethical responsibility to safeguard the privacy of all patients/families and protect the confidentiality of their health information. In the course of my employment/assignment at [name of organization], I may come into possession of confidential patient/family information, even though I may not be directly involved in providing patient/family services.

I understand that such information must be maintained in the strictest confidence. As a condition of my employment/assignment, I hereby agree that, unless directed by my supervisor, I will not at any time during or after my employment/assignment with [name of organization] disclose any patient/family information to any person whatsoever or permit any person whatsoever to examine or make copies of any patient/family reports or other documents prepared by me, coming into my possession, or under my control, or use patient/family information, other than as necessary in the course of my employment/assignment.

In the course of my work when patient/family information must be discussed with other healthcare practitioners or when clinical record copies must be maintained outside of the organization's office(s), I will use discretion to ensure that conversations cannot be overheard and that records cannot be observed by others who are not involved in the care of the patient/family.

I understand that violation of this agreement may result in corrective action, up to and including discharge.

_____
Signature of Employee/Student/Volunteer

_____
Date

Note: This sample form is for discussion purposes only. Not for use without advice of legal counsel. Adapted from Mary D. Brandt's *Release and Disclosure: Guidelines Regarding Maintenance and Disclosure of Health Information,* AHIMA © 1997.

Exhibit 3

Sample Business Partner Contract

This agreement is made effective as of [date], by and between [client and client address] and [contractor and contractor address]. In this Agreement, the party who is contracting to receive services shall be referred to as [client acronym], and the party who will be providing the services shall be referred to as [contractor acronym].

The parties agree as follows:

Description of Services: Commencing [date], [contractor] will provide the following services (collectively, the "Services"):

[Spell out specific services, any required due dates, and any required outcome measures, such as:

1. *Review policies, procedures, and systems relative to health information privacy and security for compliance with federal and state law and regulation and standards of practice*

2. *Review policies, procedures and systems relative to electronic signatures for compliance with federal and state law and regulation and standards of practice*

3. *Provide a written assessment identifying any shortcomings or opportunities for improvement and suggested methodologies for bringing existing practice into compliance with federal and state law or existing standards of practice]*

Performance of Services: The manner in which the Services are to be performed and the specific hours to be worked by [contractor] shall be determined by [contractor]. [Client] will rely on [contractor] to work as many hours as may be reasonably necessary to fulfill [contractor's] obligations under this agreement.

Price and Payment Terms: [Client] will pay a fee to [contractor] for the Services in the amount of [dollar amount]. This fee shall be payable [method of payment, i.e., in a lump sum upon completion of the service, based on an hourly rate billed at the end of the month and payable within 30 days]. Upon termination of this Agreement, payments under this paragraph shall cease, however, [contractor] shall be entitled to payments for periods or partial periods that accrued prior to the date of termination and for which [contractor] has not yet been paid.

Term/Termination: This Agreement shall terminate automatically upon completion by [contractor] of the Services required by this Agreement. Either party may terminate this agreement with or without cause by submitting a 30-day written notice.

Relationship of Parties: It is understood by the parties that [contractor] is an independent contractor and not an employee of [client]. [Client] will not provide fringe benefits, including health insurance, holidays, paid vacation, or any other employee benefit, for the benefit of [contractor].

Confidentiality: [Contractor] recognizes that [client] has patient health information and other proprietary information (collectively, "Information") which are valuable, special, and unique assets of [client]. [Contractor] will not divulge, disclose, or communicate in any manner any Information to any third party without prior written consent. [Contractor] will protect the Information and treat it as strictly confidential. [Contractor] will abide by the requirements of 42 CFR, Part 164.506, Standards for Privacy of Individually Identifiable Health Information: Proposed Rule. A violation of this paragraph shall be a material violation of this agreement.

Legal Fees and Court Costs: In the event any legal action is taken to enforce this agreement or any portion thereof, the party that prevails in that suit shall be entitled to recover from the other, reasonable attorney fees plus the cost of said suit.

Notices: All notices required or permitted under this Agreement shall be in writing and shall be deemed delivered when delivered in person or deposited in the United States mail, postage prepaid, addressed as follows:

[Client Contact Name and Address]

[Contractor Contact Name and Address]

Such address may be changed from time to time by either party by providing written notice to the other in the manner set forth above.

Entire Agreement: This Agreement contains the entire agreement of the parties and there are no other promises or conditions in any other agreement whether oral or written. This Agreement supersedes any prior written or oral agreements between the parties.

Amendment: This Agreement may be modified or amended if the amendment is made in writing and is signed by both parties.

Severability: If any provision of this Agreement shall be held to be invalid or unenforceable for any reason, the remaining provisions shall continue to be valid and enforceable. If a court finds that any provision of this Agreement is invalid or unenforceable, but that by limiting such provision, it would become valid and enforceable, then such provision shall be deemed to be written, construed, and enforced as so limited.

Waiver of Contractual Right: The failure of either party to enforce any provision of this Agreement shall not be construed as a waiver or limitation of that party's right to subsequently enforce and compel strict compliance with every provision of this Agreement.

Applicable Law: This Agreement shall be governed by the laws of the State of [state].

Signature Party
Receiving Service _____

Signature Party
Providing Service_____

Note: This sample form was developed for discussion purposes only. It should not be used without review by legal counsel to ensure compliance with state and local laws. From Practice brief: Letters of agreement/contracts (updated). 2001 (June). *Journal of the American Health Information Management Association* 72(6).

Exhibit 4

Statement of Accompanying Disclosures

As the recipient of this information, you are prohibited from using this information for any purpose other than the stated purpose. You may disclose this information to another party only:

- With written authorization from the patient or his or her legal representative;

- As required by state law; or

- If urgently needed for the patient's continued care.

You must destroy this information after its stated need has been fulfilled.

If this disclosure contains information relating to alcohol or drug abuse education, training, treatment, rehabilitation, or research, the following shall apply:

This information has been disclosed to you from records whose confidentiality is protected by Federal law. Federal regulations (42CFR Part 2) prohibit you from making any further disclosure of it without the specific written consent of the person to whom it pertains, or as otherwise permitted by such regulations. A general authorization for the release of medical or other information is NOT sufficient for this purpose.

Note: This sample form is for discussion purposes only. Not for use without advice of legal counsel. Adapted from Mary D. Brandt's *Release and Disclosure: Guidelines Regarding Maintenance and Disclosure of Health Information,* AHIMA © 1997.

Exhibit 5

Facsimile Cover Letter

[sending facility name]

[address]

[city, state, zip code]

[telephone number]

[facsimile number]

DATE:_____TIME:_____NUMBER OF PAGES: _____

TO: _____
      (name of authorized receiver)

_____
      (name and address of authorized receiver's facility)

TELEPHONE:_____FAX:_____
      (of receiver)   (of receiver)

FROM: _____
      (name of sender)

TELEPHONE:_____FAX: _____
      (of sender)   (of sender)

*****CONFIDENTIALITY NOTICE*****

The documents accompanying this telecopy transmission contain confidential information, belonging to the sender, that is legally privileged. This information is intended only for the use of the individual or entity named above. The authorized recipient of this information is prohibited from disclosing this information to any other party and is required to destroy the information after its stated need has been fulfilled.

If you are not the intended recipient, you are hereby notified that any disclosure, copying, distribution, or action taken in reliance on the contents of these documents is strictly prohibited. If you have received this telecopy in error, please notify the sender immediately to arrange for return of these documents.

COMMENTS:

Note: This sample form is for discussion purposes only. Not for use without advice of legal counsel. Adapted from Mary D. Brandt's *Release and Disclosure: Guidelines Regarding Maintenance and Disclosure of Health Information,* AHIMA © 1997.

Appendix T

Listing of HHRGs, HIPPS Codes, and Weights

HHRG Description	Case Mix Description by Domains	HIPPS Code	Weight	Fallback HIPPS Code	Fallback Code Weight
C0F0S0—all computed	Clinical = Min, Functional = Min, Service = Min	HAEJ1	0.5265	na	na
2nd position derived		HAEJ2	0.5265	na	na
3rd position derived		HAEJ3	0.5265	na	na
4th position derived		HAEJ4	0.5265	na	na
2nd & 3rd derived		HAEJ5	0.5265	na	na
3rd & 4th derived		HAEJ6	0.5265	na	na
2nd & 4th derived		HAEJ7	0.5265	na	na
All derived		HAEJ8	0.5265	na	na
C0F0S1	Clinical = Min, Functional = Min, Service = Low	HAEK1	0.6074	na	na
2nd position derived		HAEK2	0.6074	na	na
3rd position derived		HAEK3	0.6074	na	na
4th position derived		HAEK4	0.6074	na	na
2nd & 3rd derived		HAEK5	0.6074	na	na
3rd & 4th derived		HAEK6	0.6074	na	na
2nd & 4th derived		HAEK7	0.6074	na	na
All derived		HAEK8	0.6074	na	na
C0F0S2	Clinical = Min, Functional = Min, Service = Mod	HAEL1	1.4847	HAEJ1	0.5265
2nd position derived		HAEL2	1.4847	HAEJ2	0.5265
3rd position derived		HAEL3	1.4847	HAEJ3	0.5265
4th position derived		HAEL4	1.4847	HAEJ4	0.5265
2nd & 3rd derived		HAEL5	1.4847	HAEJ5	0.5265
3rd & 4th derived		HAEL6	1.4847	HAEJ6	0.5265
2nd & 4th derived		HAEL7	1.4847	HAEJ7	0.5265
All derived		HAEL8	1.4847	HAEJ8	0.5265
C0F0S3	Clinical = Min, Functional = Min, Service = High	HAEM1	1.7364	HAEK1	0.6074
2nd position derived		HAEM2	1.7364	HAEK2	0.6074
3rd position derived		HAEM3	1.7364	HAEK3	0.6074
4th position derived		HAEM4	1.7364	HAEK4	0.6074
2nd & 3rd derived		HAEM5	1.7364	HAEK5	0.6074
3rd & 4th derived		HAEM6	1.7364	HAEK6	0.6074
2nd & 4th derived		HAEM7	1.7364	HAEK7	0.6074
All derived		HAEM8	1.7364	HAEK8	0.6074

HHRG Description	Case Mix Description by Domains	HIPPS Code	Weight	Fallback HIPPS Code	Fallback Code Weight
C0F1S0	Clinical = Min, Functional = Low, Service = Min	HAFJ1	0.6213	na	na
2nd position derived		HAFJ2	0.6213	na	na
3rd position derived		HAFJ3	0.6213	na	na
4th position derived		HAFJ4	0.6213	na	na
2nd & 3rd derived		HAFJ5	0.6213	na	na
3rd & 4th derived		HAFJ6	0.6213	na	na
2nd & 4th derived		HAFJ7	0.6213	na	na
All derived		HAFJ8	0.6213	na	na
C0F1S1	Clinical = Min, Functional = Low, Service = Low	HAFK1	0.7022	na	na
2nd position derived		HAFK2	0.7022	na	na
3rd position derived		HAFK3	0.7022	na	na
4th position derived		HAFK4	0.7022	na	na
2nd & 3rd derived		HAFK5	0.7022	na	na
3rd & 4th derived		HAFK6	0.7022	na	na
2nd & 4th derived		HAFK7	0.7022	na	na
All derived		HAFK8	0.7022	na	na
C0F1S2	Clinical = Min, Functional = Low, Service = Mod	HAFL1	1.5796	HAFJ1	0.6213
2nd position derived		HAFL2	1.5796	HAFJ2	0.6213
3rd position derived		HAFL3	1.5796	HAFJ3	0.6213
4th position derived		HAFL4	1.5796	HAFJ4	0.6213
2nd & 3rd derived		HAFL5	1.5796	HAFJ5	0.6213
3rd & 4th derived		HAFL6	1.5796	HAFJ6	0.6213
2nd & 4th derived		HAFL7	1.5796	HAFJ7	0.6213
All derived		HAFL8	1.5796	HAFJ8	0.6213
C0F1S3	Clinical = Min, Functional = Low, Service = High	HAFM1	1.8313	HAFK1	0.7022
2nd position derived		HAFM2	1.8313	HAFK2	0.7022
3rd position derived		HAFM3	1.8313	HAFK3	0.7022
4th position derived		HAFM4	1.8313	HAFK4	0.7022
2nd & 3rd derived		HAFM5	1.8313	HAFK5	0.7022
3rd & 4th derived		HAFM6	1.8313	HAFK6	0.7022
2nd & 4th derived		HAFM7	1.8313	HAFK7	0.7022
All derived		HAFM8	1.8313	HAFK8	0.7022
C0F2S0	Clinical = Min, Functional = Mod, Service = Min	HAGJ1	0.7249	na	na
2nd position derived		HAGJ2	0.7249	na	na
3rd position derived		HAGJ3	0.7249	na	na
4th position derived		HAGJ4	0.7249	na	na
2nd & 3rd derived		HAGJ5	0.7249	na	na
3rd & 4th derived		HAGJ6	0.7249	na	na
2nd & 4th derived		HAGJ7	0.7249	na	na
All derived		HAGJ8	0.7249	na	na
C0F2S1	Clinical = Min, Functional = Mod, Service = Low	HAGK1	0.8058	na	na
2nd position derived		HAGK2	0.8058	na	na
3rd position derived		HAGK3	0.8058	na	na
4th position derived		HAGK4	0.8058	na	na
2nd & 3rd derived		HAGK5	0.8058	na	na
3rd & 4th derived		HAGK6	0.8058	na	na

HHRG Description	Case Mix Description by Domains	HIPPS Code	Weight	Fallback HIPPS Code	Fallback Code Weight
2nd & 4th derived		HAGK7	0.8058	na	na
All derived		HAGK8	0.8058	na	na
C0F2S2	Clinical = Min, Functional = Mod, Service = Mod	HAGL1	1.6831	HAGJ1	0.7249
2nd position derived		HAGL2	1.6831	HAGJ2	0.7249
3rd position derived		HAGL3	1.6831	HAGJ3	0.7249
4th position derived		HAGL4	1.6831	HAGJ4	0.7249
2nd & 3rd derived		HAGL5	1.6831	HAGJ5	0.7249
3rd & 4th derived		HAGL6	1.6831	HAGJ6	0.7249
2nd & 4th derived		HAGL7	1.6831	HAGJ7	0.7249
All derived		HAGL8	1.6831	HAGJ8	0.7249
C0F2S3	Clinical = Min, Functional = Mod, Service = High	HAGM1	1.9348	HAGK1	0.8058
2nd position derived		HAGM2	1.9348	HAGK2	0.8058
3rd position derived		HAGM3	1.9348	HAGK3	0.8058
4th position derived		HAGM4	1.9348	HAGK4	0.8058
2nd & 3rd derived		HAGM5	1.9348	HAGK5	0.8058
3rd & 4th derived		HAGM6	1.9348	HAGK6	0.8058
2nd & 4th derived		HAGM7	1.9348	HAGK7	0.8058
All derived		HAGM8	1.9348	HAGK8	0.8058
C0F3S0	Clinical = Min, Functional = High, Service = Min	HAHJ1	0.7629	na	na
2nd position derived		HAHJ2	0.7629	na	na
3rd position derived		HAHJ3	0.7629	na	na
4th position derived		HAHJ4	0.7629	na	na
2nd & 3rd derived		HAHJ5	0.7629	na	na
3rd & 4th derived		HAHJ6	0.7629	na	na
2nd & 4th derived		HAHJ7	0.7629	na	na
All derived		HAHJ8	0.7629	na	na
C0F3S1	Clinical = Min, Functional = High, Service = Low	HAHK1	0.8438	na	na
2nd position derived		HAHK2	0.8438	na	na
3rd position derived		HAHK3	0.8438	na	na
4th position derived		HAHK4	0.8438	na	na
2nd & 3rd derived		HAHK5	0.8438	na	na
3rd & 4th derived		HAHK6	0.8438	na	na
2nd & 4th derived		HAHK7	0.8438	na	na
All derived		HAHK8	0.8438	na	na
C0F3S2	Clinical = Min, Functional = High, Service = Mod	HAHL1	1.7212	HAHJ1	0.7629
2nd position derived		HAHL2	1.7212	HAHJ2	0.7629
3rd position derived		HAHL3	1.7212	HAHJ3	0.7629
4th position derived		HAHL4	1.7212	HAHJ4	0.7629
2nd & 3rd derived		HAHL5	1.7212	HAHJ5	0.7629
3rd & 4th derived		HAHL6	1.7212	HAHJ6	0.7629
2nd & 4th derived		HAHL7	1.7212	HAHJ7	0.7629
All derived		HAHL8	1.7212	HAHJ8	0.7629
C0F3S3	Clinical = Min, Functional = High, Service = High	HAHM1	1.9728	HAHK1	0.8438
2nd position derived		HAHM2	1.9728	HAHK2	0.8438
3rd position derived		HAHM3	1.9728	HAHK3	0.8438
4th position derived		HAHM4	1.9728	HAHK4	0.8438

HHRG Description	Case Mix Description by Domains	HIPPS Code	Weight	Fallback HIPPS Code	Fallback Code Weight
2nd & 3rd derived		HAHM5	1.9728	HAHK5	0.8438
3rd & 4th derived		HAHM6	1.9728	HAHK6	0.8438
2nd & 4th derived		HAHM7	1.9728	HAHK7	0.8438
All derived		HAHM8	1.9728	HAHK8	0.8438
C0F4S0	Clinical = Min, Functional = Max, Service = Min	HAIJ1	0.9305	na	na
2nd position derived		HAIJ2	0.9305	na	na
3rd position derived		HAIJ3	0.9305	na	na
4th position derived		HAIJ4	0.9305	na	na
2nd & 3rd derived		HAIJ5	0.9305	na	na
3rd & 4th derived		HAIJ6	0.9305	na	na
2nd & 4th derived		HAIJ7	0.9305	na	na
All derived		HAIJ8	0.9305	na	na
C0F4S1	Clinical = Min, Functional = Max, Service = Low	HAIK1	1.0114	na	na
2nd position derived		HAIK2	1.0114	na	na
3rd position derived		HAIK3	1.0114	na	na
4th position derived		HAIK4	1.0114	na	na
2nd & 3rd derived		HAIK5	1.0114	na	na
3rd & 4th derived		HAIK6	1.0114	na	na
2nd & 4th derived		HAIK7	1.0114	na	na
All derived		HAIK8	1.0114	na	na
C0F4S2	Clinical = Min, Functional = Max, Service = Mod	HAIL1	1.8887	HAIJ1	0.9305
2nd position derived		HAIL2	1.8887	HAIJ2	0.9305
3rd position derived		HAIL3	1.8887	HAIJ3	0.9305
4th position derived		HAIL4	1.8887	HAIJ4	0.9305
2nd & 3rd derived		HAIL5	1.8887	HAIJ5	0.9305
3rd & 4th derived		HAIL6	1.8887	HAIJ6	0.9305
2nd & 4th derived		HAIL7	1.8887	HAIJ7	0.9305
All derived		HAIL8	1.8887	HAIJ8	0.9305
C0F4S3	Clinical = Min, Functional = Max, Service = High	HAIM1	2.1404	HAIK1	1.0114
2nd position derived		HAIM2	2.1404	HAIK2	1.0114
3rd position derived		HAIM3	2.1404	HAIK3	1.0114
4th position derived		HAIM4	2.1404	HAIK4	1.0114
2nd & 3rd derived		HAIM5	2.1404	HAIK5	1.0114
3rd & 4th derived		HAIM6	2.1404	HAIK6	1.0114
2nd & 4th derived		HAIM7	2.1404	HAIK7	1.0114
All derived		HAIM8	2.1404	HAIK8	1.0114
C1F0S0	Clinical = Low, Functional = Min, Service = Min	HBEJ1	0.6221	na	na
2nd position derived		HBEJ2	0.6221	na	na
3rd position derived		HBEJ3	0.6221	na	na
4th position derived		HBEJ4	0.6221	na	na
2nd & 3rd derived		HBEJ5	0.6221	na	na
3rd & 4th derived		HBEJ6	0.6221	na	na
2nd & 4th derived		HBEJ7	0.6221	na	na
All derived		HBEJ8	0.6221	na	na
C1F0S1	Clinical = Low, Functional = Min, Service = Low	HBEK1	0.703	na	na
2nd position derived		HBEK2	0.703	na	na

HHRG Description	Case Mix Description by Domains	HIPPS Code	Weight	Fallback HIPPS Code	Fallback Code Weight
3rd position derived		HBEK3	0.703	na	na
4th position derived		HBEK4	0.703	na	na
2nd & 3rd derived		HBEK5	0.703	na	na
3rd & 4th derived		HBEK6	0.703	na	na
2nd & 4th derived		HBEK7	0.703	na	na
All derived		HBEK8	0.703	na	na
C1F0S2	Clinical = Low, Functional = Min, Service = Mod	HBEL1	1.5803	HBEJ1	0.6221
2nd position derived		HBEL2	1.5803	HBEJ2	0.6221
3rd position derived		HBEL3	1.5803	HBEJ3	0.6221
4th position derived		HBEL4	1.5803	HBEJ4	0.6221
2nd & 3rd derived		HBEL5	1.5803	HBEJ5	0.6221
3rd & 4th derived		HBEL6	1.5803	HBEJ6	0.6221
2nd & 4th derived		HBEL7	1.5803	HBEJ7	0.6221
All derived		HBEL8	1.5803	HBEJ8	0.6221
C1F0S3	Clinical = Low, Functional = Min, Service = High	HBEM1	1.832	HBEK1	0.703
2nd position derived		HBEM2	1.832	HBEK2	0.703
3rd position derived		HBEM3	1.832	HBEK3	0.703
4th position derived		HBEM4	1.832	HBEK4	0.703
2nd & 3rd derived		HBEM5	1.832	HBEK5	0.703
3rd & 4th derived		HBEM6	1.832	HBEK6	0.703
2nd & 4th derived		HBEM7	1.832	HBEK7	0.703
All derived		HBEM8	1.832	HBEK8	0.703
C1F1S0	Clinical = Low, Functional = Low, Service = Min	HBFJ1	0.7169	na	na
2nd position derived		HBFJ2	0.7169	na	na
3rd position derived		HBFJ3	0.7169	na	na
4th position derived		HBFJ4	0.7169	na	na
2nd & 3rd derived		HBFJ5	0.7169	na	na
3rd & 4th derived		HBFJ6	0.7169	na	na
2nd & 4th derived		HBFJ7	0.7169	na	na
All derived		HBFJ8	0.7169	na	na
C1F1S1	Clinical = Low, Functional = Low, Service = Low	HBFK1	0.7978	na	na
2nd position derived		HBFK2	0.7978	na	na
3rd position derived		HBFK3	0.7978	na	na
4th position derived		HBFK4	0.7978	na	na
2nd & 3rd derived		HBFK5	0.7978	na	na
3rd & 4th derived		HBFK6	0.7978	na	na
2nd & 4th derived		HBFK7	0.7978	na	na
All derived		HBFK8	0.7978	na	na
C1F1S2	Clinical = Low, Functional = Low, Service = Mod	HBFL1	1.6752	HBFJ1	0.7169
2nd position derived		HBFL2	1.6752	HBFJ2	0.7169
3rd position derived		HBFL3	1.6752	HBFJ3	0.7169
4th position derived		HBFL4	1.6752	HBFJ4	0.7169
2nd & 3rd derived		HBFL5	1.6752	HBFJ5	0.7169
3rd & 4th derived		HBFL6	1.6752	HBFJ6	0.7169
2nd & 4th derived		HBFL7	1.6752	HBFJ7	0.7169
All derived		HBFL8	1.6752	HBFJ8	0.7169

HHRG Description	Case Mix Description by Domains	HIPPS Code	Weight	Fallback HIPPS Code	Fallback Code Weight
C1F1S3	Clinical = Low, Functional = Low, Service = High	HBFM1	1.9269	HBFK1	0.7978
2nd position derived		HBFM2	1.9269	HBFK2	0.7978
3rd position derived		HBFM3	1.9269	HBFK3	0.7978
4th position derived		HBFM4	1.9269	HBFK4	0.7978
2nd & 3rd derived		HBFM5	1.9269	HBFK5	0.7978
3rd & 4th derived		HBFM6	1.9269	HBFK6	0.7978
2nd & 4th derived		HBFM7	1.9269	HBFK7	0.7978
All derived		HBFM8	1.9269	HBFK8	0.7978
C1F2S0	Clinical = Low, Functional = Mod, Service = Min	HBGJ1	0.8205	na	na
2nd position derived		HBGJ2	0.8205	na	na
3rd position derived		HBGJ3	0.8205	na	na
4th position derived		HBGJ4	0.8205	na	na
2nd & 3rd derived		HBGJ5	0.8205	na	na
3rd & 4th derived		HBGJ6	0.8205	na	na
2nd & 4th derived		HBGJ7	0.8205	na	na
All derived		HBGJ8	0.8205	na	na
C1F2S1	Clinical = Low, Functional = Mod, Service = Low	HBGK1	0.9014	na	na
2nd position derived		HBGK2	0.9014	na	na
3rd position derived		HBGK3	0.9014	na	na
4th position derived		HBGK4	0.9014	na	na
2nd & 3rd derived		IIBGK5	0.9014	na	na
3rd & 4th derived		HBGK6	0.9014	na	na
2nd & 4th derived		HBGK7	0.9014	na	na
All derived		HBGK8	0.9014	na	na
C1F2S2	Clinical = Low, Functional = Mod, Service = Mod	HBGL1	1.7787	HBGJ1	0.8205
2nd position derived		HBGL2	1.7787	HBGJ2	0.8205
3rd position derived		HBGL3	1.7787	HBGJ3	0.8205
4th position derived		HBGL4	1.7787	HBGJ4	0.8205
2nd & 3rd derived		HBGL5	1.7787	HBGJ5	0.8205
3rd & 4th derived		HBGL6	1.7787	HBGJ6	0.8205
2nd & 4th derived		HBGL7	1.7787	HBGJ7	0.8205
All derived		HBGL8	1.7787	HBGJ8	0.8205
C1F2S3	Clinical = Low, Functional = Mod, Service = High	HBGM1	2.0304	HBGK1	0.9014
2nd position derived		HBGM2	2.0304	HBGK2	0.9014
3rd position derived		HBGM3	2.0304	HBGK3	0.9014
4th position derived		HBGM4	2.0304	HBGK4	0.9014
2nd & 3rd derived		HBGM5	2.0304	HBGK5	0.9014
3rd & 4th derived		HBGM6	2.0304	HBGK6	0.9014
2nd & 4th derived		HBGM7	2.0304	HBGK7	0.9014
All derived		HBGM8	2.0304	HBGK8	0.9014
C1F3S0	Clinical = Low, Functional = High, Service = Min	HBHJ1	0.8585	na	na
2nd position derived		HBHJ2	0.8585	na	na
3rd position derived		HBHJ3	0.8585	na	na
4th position derived		HBHJ4	0.8585	na	na
2nd & 3rd derived		HBHJ5	0.8585	na	na
3rd & 4th derived		HBHJ6	0.8585	na	na

HHRG Description	Case Mix Description by Domains	HIPPS Code	Weight	Fallback HIPPS Code	Fallback Code Weight
2nd & 4th derived		HBHJ7	0.8585	na	na
All derived		HBHJ8	0.8585	na	na
C1F3S1	Clinical = Low, Functional = High, Service = Low	HBHK1	0.9394	na	na
2nd position derived		HBHK2	0.9394	na	na
3rd position derived		HBHK3	0.9394	na	na
4th position derived		HBHK4	0.9394	na	na
2nd & 3rd derived		HBHK5	0.9394	na	na
3rd & 4th derived		HBHK6	0.9394	na	na
2nd & 4th derived		HBHK7	0.9394	na	na
All derived		HBHK8	0.9394	na	na
C1F3S2	Clinical = Low, Functional = High, Service = Mod	HBHL1	1.8168	HBHJ1	0.8585
2nd position derived		HBHL2	1.8168	HBHJ2	0.8585
3rd position derived		HBHL3	1.8168	HBHJ3	0.8585
4th position derived		HBHL4	1.8168	HBHJ4	0.8585
2nd & 3rd derived		HBHL5	1.8168	HBHJ5	0.8585
3rd & 4th derived		HBHL6	1.8168	HBHJ6	0.8585
2nd & 4th derived		HBHL7	1.8168	HBHJ7	0.8585
All derived		HBHL8	1.8168	HBHJ8	0.8585
C1F3S3	Clinical = Low, Functional = High, Service = High	HBHM1	2.0684	HBHK1	0.9394
2nd position derived		HBHM2	2.0684	HBHK2	0.9394
3rd position derived		HBHM3	2.0684	HBHK3	0.9394
4th position derived		HBHM4	2.0684	HBHK4	0.9394
2nd & 3rd derived		HBHM5	2.0684	HBHK5	0.9394
3rd & 4th derived		HBHM6	2.0684	HBHK6	0.9394
2nd & 4th derived		HBHM7	2.0684	HBHK7	0.9394
All derived		HBHM8	2.0684	HBHK8	0.9394
C1F4S0	Clinical = Low, Functional = Max, Service = Min	HBIJ1	1.0261	na	na
2nd position derived		HBIJ2	1.0261	na	na
3rd position derived		HBIJ3	1.0261	na	na
4th position derived		HBIJ4	1.0261	na	na
2nd & 3rd derived		HBIJ5	1.0261	na	na
3rd & 4th derived		HBIJ6	1.0261	na	na
2nd & 4th derived		HBIJ7	1.0261	na	na
All derived		HBIJ8	1.0261	na	na
C1F4S1	Clinical = Low, Functional = Max, Service = Low	HBIK1	1.107	na	na
2nd position derived		HBIK2	1.107	na	na
3rd position derived		HBIK3	1.107	na	na
4th position derived		HBIK4	1.107	na	na
2nd & 3rd derived		HBIK5	1.107	na	na
3rd & 4th derived		HBIK6	1.107	na	na
2nd & 4th derived		HBIK7	1.107	na	na
All derived		HBIK8	1.107	na	na
C1F4S2	Clinical = Low, Functional = Max, Service = Mod	HBIL1	1.9843	HBIJ1	1.0261
2nd position derived		HBIL2	1.9843	HBIJ2	1.0261
3rd position derived		HBIL3	1.9843	HBIJ3	1.0261
4th position derived		HBIL4	1.9843	HBIJ4	1.0261

HHRG Description	Case Mix Description by Domains	HIPPS Code	Weight	Fallback HIPPS Code	Fallback Code Weight
2nd & 3rd derived		HBIL5	1.9843	HBIJ5	1.0261
3rd & 4th derived		HBIL6	1.9843	HBIJ6	1.0261
2nd & 4th derived		HBIL7	1.9843	HBIJ7	1.0261
All derived		HBIL8	1.9843	HBIJ8	1.0261
C1F4S3	Clinical = Low, Functional = Max, Service = High	HBIM1	2.236	HBIK1	1.107
2nd position derived		HBIM2	2.236	HBIK2	1.107
3rd position derived		HBIM3	2.236	HBIK3	1.107
4th position derived		HBIM4	2.236	HBIK4	1.107
2nd & 3rd derived		HBIM5	2.236	HBIK5	1.107
3rd & 4th derived		HBIM6	2.236	HBIK6	1.107
2nd & 4th derived		HBIM7	2.236	HBIK7	1.107
All derived		HBIM8	2.236	HBIK8	1.107
C2F0S0	Clinical = Mod, Functional = Min, Service = Min	HCEJ1	0.7965	na	na
2nd position derived		HCEJ2	0.7965	na	na
3rd position derived		HCEJ3	0.7965	na	na
4th position derived		HCEJ4	0.7965	na	na
2nd & 3rd derived		HCEJ5	0.7965	na	na
3rd & 4th derived		HCEJ6	0.7965	na	na
2nd & 4th derived		HCEJ7	0.7965	na	na
All derived		HCEJ8	0.7965	na	na
C2F0S1	Clinical = Mod, Functional = Min, Service = Low	HCEK1	0.8774	na	na
2nd position derived		HCEK2	0.8774	na	na
3rd position derived		HCEK3	0.8774	na	na
4th position derived		HCEK4	0.8774	na	na
2nd & 3rd derived		HCEK5	0.8774	na	na
3rd & 4th derived		HCEK6	0.8774	na	na
2nd & 4th derived		HCEK7	0.8774	na	na
All derived		HCEK8	0.8774	na	na
C2F0S2	Clinical = Mod, Functional = Min, Service = Mod	HCEL1	1.7548	HCEJ1	0.7965
2nd position derived		HCEL2	1.7548	HCEJ2	0.7965
3rd position derived		HCEL3	1.7548	HCEJ3	0.7965
4th position derived		HCEL4	1.7548	HCEJ4	0.7965
2nd & 3rd derived		HCEL5	1.7548	HCEJ5	0.7965
3rd & 4th derived		HCEL6	1.7548	HCEJ6	0.7965
2nd & 4th derived		HCEL7	1.7548	HCEJ7	0.7965
All derived		HCEL8	1.7548	HCEJ8	0.7965
C2F0S3	Clinical = Mod, Functional = Min, Service = High	HCEM1	2.0065	HCEK1	0.8774
2nd position derived		HCEM2	2.0065	HCEK2	0.8774
3rd position derived		HCEM3	2.0065	HCEK3	0.8774
4th position derived		HCEM4	2.0065	HCEK4	0.8774
2nd & 3rd derived		HCEM5	2.0065	HCEK5	0.8774
3rd & 4th derived		HCEM6	2.0065	HCEK6	0.8774
2nd & 4th derived		HCEM7	2.0065	HCEK7	0.8774
All derived		HCEM8	2.0065	HCEK8	0.8774
C2F1S0	Clinical = Mod, Functional = Low, Service = Min	HCFJ1	0.8914	na	na
2nd position derived		HCFJ2	0.8914	na	na

HHRG Description	Case Mix Description by Domains	HIPPS Code	Weight	Fallback HIPPS Code	Fallback Code Weight
3rd position derived		HCFJ3	0.8914	na	na
4th position derived		HCFJ4	0.8914	na	na
2nd & 3rd derived		HCFJ5	0.8914	na	na
3rd & 4th derived		HCFJ6	0.8914	na	na
2nd & 4th derived		HCFJ7	0.8914	na	na
All derived		HCFJ8	0.8914	na	na
C2F1S1	Clinical = Mod, Functional = Low, Service = Low	HCFK1	0.9723	na	na
2nd position derived		HCFK2	0.9723	na	na
3rd position derived		HCFK3	0.9723	na	na
4th position derived		HCFK4	0.9723	na	na
2nd & 3rd derived		HCFK5	0.9723	na	na
3rd & 4th derived		HCFK6	0.9723	na	na
2nd & 4th derived		HCFK7	0.9723	na	na
All derived		HCFK8	0.9723	na	na
C2F1S2	Clinical = Mod, Functional = Low, Service = Mod	HCFL1	1.8496	HCFJ1	0.8914
2nd position derived		HCFL2	1.8496	HCFJ2	0.8914
3rd position derived		HCFL3	1.8496	HCFJ3	0.8914
4th position derived		HCFL4	1.8496	HCFJ4	0.8914
2nd & 3rd derived		HCFL5	1.8496	HCFJ5	0.8914
3rd & 4th derived		HCFL6	1.8496	HCFJ6	0.8914
2nd & 4th derived		HCFL7	1.8496	HCFJ7	0.8914
All derived		HCFL8	1.8496	HCFJ8	0.8914
C2F1S3	Clinical = Mod, Functional = Low, Service = High	HCFM1	2.1013	HCFK1	0.9723
2nd position derived		HCFM2	2.1013	HCFK2	0.9723
3rd position derived		HCFM3	2.1013	HCFK3	0.9723
4th position derived		HCFM4	2.1013	HCFK4	0.9723
2nd & 3rd derived		HCFM5	2.1013	HCFK5	0.9723
3rd & 4th derived		HCFM6	2.1013	HCFK6	0.9723
2nd & 4th derived		HCFM7	2.1013	HCFK7	0.9723
All derived		HCFM8	2.1013	HCFK8	0.9723
C2F2S0	Clinical = Mod, Functional = Mod, Service = Min	HCGJ1	0.9949	na	na
2nd position derived		HCGJ2	0.9949	na	na
3rd position derived		HCGJ3	0.9949	na	na
4th position derived		HCGJ4	0.9949	na	na
2nd & 3rd derived		HCGJ5	0.9949	na	na
3rd & 4th derived		HCGJ6	0.9949	na	na
2nd & 4th derived		HCGJ7	0.9949	na	na
All derived		HCGJ8	0.9949	na	na
C2F2S1	Clinical = Mod, Functional = Mod, Service = Low	HCGK1	1.0758	na	na
2nd position derived		HCGK2	1.0758	na	na
3rd position derived		HCGK3	1.0758	na	na
4th position derived		HCGK4	1.0758	na	na
2nd & 3rd derived		HCGK5	1.0758	na	na
3rd & 4th derived		HCGK6	1.0758	na	na
2nd & 4th derived		HCGK7	1.0758	na	na
All derived		HCGK8	1.0758	na	na

HHRG Description	Case Mix Description by Domains	HIPPS Code	Weight	Fallback HIPPS Code	Fallback Code Weight
C2F2S2	Clinical = Mod, Functional = Mod, Service = Mod	HCGL1	1.9532	HCGJ1	0.9949
2nd position derived		HCGL2	1.9532	HCGJ2	0.9949
3rd position derived		HCGL3	1.9532	HCGJ3	0.9949
4th position derived		HCGL4	1.9532	HCGJ4	0.9949
2nd & 3rd derived		HCGL5	1.9532	HCGJ5	0.9949
3rd & 4th derived		HCGL6	1.9532	HCGJ6	0.9949
2nd & 4th derived		HCGL7	1.9532	HCGJ7	0.9949
All derived		HCGL8	1.9532	HCGJ8	0.9949
C2F2S3	Clinical = Mod, Functional = Mod, Service = High	HCGM1	2.2048	HCGK1	1.0758
2nd position derived		HCGM2	2.2048	HCGK2	1.0758
3rd position derived		HCGM3	2.2048	HCGK3	1.0758
4th position derived		HCGM4	2.2048	HCGK4	1.0758
2nd & 3rd derived		HCGM5	2.2048	HCGK5	1.0758
3rd & 4th derived		HCGM6	2.2048	HCGK6	1.0758
2nd & 4th derived		HCGM7	2.2048	HCGK7	1.0758
All derived		HCGM8	2.2048	HCGK8	1.0758
C2F3S0	Clinical = Mod, Functional = High, Service = Min	HCHJ1	1.0329	na	na
2nd position derived		HCHJ2	1.0329	na	na
3rd position derived		HCHJ3	1.0329	na	na
4th position derived		HCHJ4	1.0329	na	na
2nd & 3rd derived		HCIIJ5	1.0329	na	na
3rd & 4th derived		HCHJ6	1.0329	na	na
2nd & 4th derived		HCHJ7	1.0329	na	na
All derived		HCHJ8	1.0329	na	na
C2F3S1	Clinical = Mod, Functional = High, Service = Low	HCHK1	1.1139	na	na
2nd position derived		HCHK2	1.1139	na	na
3rd position derived		HCHK3	1.1139	na	na
4th position derived		HCHK4	1.1139	na	na
2nd & 3rd derived		HCHK5	1.1139	na	na
3rd & 4th derived		HCHK6	1.1139	na	na
2nd & 4th derived		HCHK7	1.1139	na	na
All derived		HCHK8	1.1139	na	na
C2F3S2	Clinical = Mod, Functional = High, Service = Mod	HCHL1	1.9912	HCHJ1	1.0329
2nd position derived		HCHL2	1.9912	HCHJ2	1.0329
3rd position derived		HCHL3	1.9912	HCHJ3	1.0329
4th position derived		HCHL4	1.9912	HCHJ4	1.0329
2nd & 3rd derived		HCHL5	1.9912	HCHJ5	1.0329
3rd & 4th derived		HCHL6	1.9912	HCHJ6	1.0329
2nd & 4th derived		HCHL7	1.9912	HCHJ7	1.0329
All derived		HCHL8	1.9912	HCHJ8	1.0329
C2F3S3	Clinical = Mod, Functional = High, Service = High	HCHM1	2.2429	HCHK1	1.1139
2nd position derived		HCHM2	2.2429	HCHK2	1.1139
3rd position derived		HCHM3	2.2429	HCHK3	1.1139
4th position derived		HCHM4	2.2429	HCHK4	1.1139
2nd & 3rd derived		HCHM5	2.2429	HCHK5	1.1139
3rd & 4th derived		HCHM6	2.2429	HCHK6	1.1139

HHRG Description	Case Mix Description by Domains	HIPPS Code	Weight	Fallback HIPPS Code	Fallback Code Weight
2nd & 4th derived		HCHM7	2.2429	HCHK7	1.1139
All derived		HCHM8	2.2429	HCHK8	1.1139
C2F4S0	Clinical = Mod, Functional = Max, Service = Min	HCIJ1	1.2005	na	na
2nd position derived		HCIJ2	1.2005	na	na
3rd position derived		HCIJ3	1.2005	na	na
4th position derived		HCIJ4	1.2005	na	na
2nd & 3rd derived		HCIJ5	1.2005	na	na
3rd & 4th derived		HCIJ6	1.2005	na	na
2nd & 4th derived		HCIJ7	1.2005	na	na
All derived		HCIJ8	1.2005	na	na
C2F4S1	Clinical = Mod, Functional = Max, Service = Low	HCIK1	1.2814	na	na
2nd position derived		HCIK2	1.2814	na	na
3rd position derived		HCIK3	1.2814	na	na
4th position derived		HCIK4	1.2814	na	na
2nd & 3rd derived		HCIK5	1.2814	na	na
3rd & 4th derived		HCIK6	1.2814	na	na
2nd & 4th derived		HCIK7	1.2814	na	na
All derived		HCIK8	1.2814	na	na
C2F4S2	Clinical = Mod, Functional = Max, Service = Mod	HCIL1	2.1588	HCIJ1	1.2005
2nd position derived		HCIL2	2.1588	HCIJ2	1.2005
3rd position derived		HCIL3	2.1588	HCIJ3	1.2005
4th position derived		HCIL4	2.1588	HCIJ4	1.2005
2nd & 3rd derived		HCIL5	2.1588	HCIJ5	1.2005
3rd & 4th derived		HCIL6	2.1588	HCIJ6	1.2005
2nd & 4th derived		HCIL7	2.1588	HCIJ7	1.2005
All derived		HCIL8	2.1588	HCIJ8	1.2005
C2F4S3	Clinical = Mod, Functional = Max, Service = High	HCIM1	2.4105	HCIK1	1.2814
2nd position derived		HCIM2	2.4105	HCIK2	1.2814
3rd position derived		HCIM3	2.4105	HCIK3	1.2814
4th position derived		HCIM4	2.4105	HCIK4	1.2814
2nd & 3rd derived		HCIM5	2.4105	HCIK5	1.2814
3rd & 4th derived		HCIM6	2.4105	HCIK6	1.2814
2nd & 4th derived		HCIM7	2.4105	HCIK7	1.2814
All derived		HCIM8	2.4105	HCIK8	1.2814
C3F0S0	Clinical = High, Functional = Min, Service = Min	HDEJ1	1.1973	na	na
2nd position derived		HDEJ2	1.1973	na	na
3rd position derived		HDEJ3	1.1973	na	na
4th position derived		HDEJ4	1.1973	na	na
2nd & 3rd derived		HDEJ5	1.1973	na	na
3rd & 4th derived		HDEJ6	1.1973	na	na
2nd & 4th derived		HDEJ7	1.1973	na	na
All derived		HDEJ8	1.1973	na	na
C3F0S1	Clinical = High, Functional = Min, Service = Low	HDEK1	1.2782	na	na
2nd position derived		HDEK2	1.2782	na	na
3rd position derived		HDEK3	1.2782	na	na
4th position derived		HDEK4	1.2782	na	na

HHRG Description	Case Mix Description by Domains	HIPPS Code	Weight	Fallback HIPPS Code	Fallback Code Weight
2nd & 3rd derived		HDEK5	1.2782	na	na
3rd & 4th derived		HDEK6	1.2782	na	na
2nd & 4th derived		HDEK7	1.2782	na	na
All derived		HDEK8	1.2782	na	na
C3F0S2	Clinical = High, Functional = Min, Service = Mod	HDEL1	2.1556	HDEJ1	1.1973
2nd position derived		HDEL2	2.1556	HDEJ2	1.1973
3rd position derived		HDEL3	2.1556	HDEJ3	1.1973
4th position derived		HDEL4	2.1556	HDEJ4	1.1973
2nd & 3rd derived		HDEL5	2.1556	HDEJ5	1.1973
3rd & 4th derived		HDEL6	2.1556	HDEJ6	1.1973
2nd & 4th derived		HDEL7	2.1556	HDEJ7	1.1973
All derived		HDEL8	2.1556	HDEJ8	1.1973
C3F0S3	Clinical = High, Functional = Min, Service = High	HDEM1	2.4073	HDEK1	1.2782
2nd position derived		HDEM2	2.4073	HDEK2	1.2782
3rd position derived		HDEM3	2.4073	HDEK3	1.2782
4th position derived		HDEM4	2.4073	HDEK4	1.2782
2nd & 3rd derived		HDEM5	2.4073	HDEK5	1.2782
3rd & 4th derived		HDEM6	2.4073	HDEK6	1.2782
2nd & 4th derived		HDEM7	2.4073	HDEK7	1.2782
All derived		HDEM8	2.4073	HDEK8	1.2782
C3F1S0	Clinical = High, Functional = Low, Service = Min	HDFJ1	1.2922	na	na
2nd position derived		HDFJ2	1.2922	na	na
3rd position derived		HDFJ3	1.2922	na	na
4th position derived		HDFJ4	1.2922	na	na
2nd & 3rd derived		HDFJ5	1.2922	na	na
3rd & 4th derived		HDFJ6	1.2922	na	na
2nd & 4th derived		HDFJ7	1.2922	na	na
All derived		HDFJ8	1.2922	na	na
C3F1S1	Clinical = High, Functional = Low, Service = Low	HDFK1	1.3731	na	na
2nd position derived		HDFK2	1.3731	na	na
3rd position derived		HDFK3	1.3731	na	na
4th position derived		HDFK4	1.3731	na	na
2nd & 3rd derived		HDFK5	1.3731	na	na
3rd & 4th derived		HDFK6	1.3731	na	na
2nd & 4th derived		HDFK7	1.3731	na	na
All derived		HDFK8	1.3731	na	na
C3F1S2	Clinical = High, Functional = Low, Service = Mod	HDFL1	2.2504	HDFJ1	1.2922
2nd position derived		HDFL2	2.2504	HDFJ2	1.2922
3rd position derived		HDFL3	2.2504	HDFJ3	1.2922
4th position derived		HDFL4	2.2504	HDFJ4	1.2922
2nd & 3rd derived		HDFL5	2.2504	HDFJ5	1.2922
3rd & 4th derived		HDFL6	2.2504	HDFJ6	1.2922
2nd & 4th derived		HDFL7	2.2504	HDFJ7	1.2922
All derived		HDFL8	2.2504	HDFJ8	1.2922
C3F1S3	Clinical = High, Functional = Low, Service = High	HDFM1	2.5021	HDFK1	1.3731
2nd position derived		HDFM2	2.5021	HDFK2	1.3731

HHRG Description	Case Mix Description by Domains	HIPPS Code	Weight	Fallback HIPPS Code	Fallback Code Weight
3rd position derived		HDFM3	2.5021	HDFK3	1.3731
4th position derived		HDFM4	2.5021	HDFK4	1.3731
2nd & 3rd derived		HDFM5	2.5021	HDFK5	1.3731
3rd & 4th derived		HDFM6	2.5021	HDFK6	1.3731
2nd & 4th derived		HDFM7	2.5021	HDFK7	1.3731
All derived		HDFM8	2.5021	HDFK8	1.3731
C3F2S0	Clinical = High, Functional = Mod, Service = Min	HDGJ1	1.3957	na	na
2nd position derived		HDGJ2	1.3957	na	na
3rd position derived		HDGJ3	1.3957	na	na
4th position derived		HDGJ4	1.3957	na	na
2nd & 3rd derived		HDGJ5	1.3957	na	na
3rd & 4th derived		HDGJ6	1.3957	na	na
2nd & 4th derived		HDGJ7	1.3957	na	na
All derived		HDGJ8	1.3957	na	na
C3F2S1	Clinical = High, Functional = Mod, Service = Low	HDGK1	1.4766	na	na
2nd position derived		HDGK2	1.4766	na	na
3rd position derived		HDGK3	1.4766	na	na
4th position derived		HDGK4	1.4766	na	na
2nd & 3rd derived		HDGK5	1.4766	na	na
3rd & 4th derived		HDGK6	1.4766	na	na
2nd & 4th derived		HDGK7	1.4766	na	na
All derived		HDGK8	1.4766	na	na
C3F2S2	Clinical = High, Functional = Mod, Service = Mod	HDGL1	2.354	HDGJ1	1.3957
2nd position derived		HDGL2	2.354	HDGJ2	1.3957
3rd position derived		HDGL3	2.354	HDGJ3	1.3957
4th position derived		HDGL4	2.354	HDGJ4	1.3957
2nd & 3rd derived		HDGL5	2.354	HDGJ5	1.3957
3rd & 4th derived		HDGL6	2.354	HDGJ6	1.3957
2nd & 4th derived		HDGL7	2.354	HDGJ7	1.3957
All derived		HDGL8	2.354	HDGJ8	1.3957
C3F2S3	Clinical = High, Functional = Mod, Service = High	HDGM1	2.6056	HDGK1	1.4766
2nd position derived		HDGM2	2.6056	HDGK2	1.4766
3rd position derived		HDGM3	2.6056	HDGK3	1.4766
4th position derived		HDGM4	2.6056	HDGK4	1.4766
2nd & 3rd derived		HDGM5	2.6056	HDGK5	1.4766
3rd & 4th derived		HDGM6	2.6056	HDGK6	1.4766
2nd & 4th derived		HDGM7	2.6056	HDGK7	1.4766
All derived		HDGM8	2.6056	HDGK8	1.4766
C3F3S0	Clinical = High, Functional = High, Service = Min	HDHJ1	1.4337	na	na
2nd position derived		HDHJ2	1.4337	na	na
3rd position derived		HDHJ3	1.4337	na	na
4th position derived		HDHJ4	1.4337	na	na
2nd & 3rd derived		HDHJ5	1.4337	na	na
3rd & 4th derived		HDHJ6	1.4337	na	na
2nd & 4th derived		HDHJ7	1.4337	na	na
All derived		HDHJ8	1.4337	na	na

HHRG Description	Case Mix Description by Domains	HIPPS Code	Weight	Fallback HIPPS Code	Fallback Code Weight
C3F3S1	Clinical = High, Functional = High, Service = Low	HDHK1	1.5147	na	na
2nd position derived		HDHK2	1.5147	na	na
3rd position derived		HDHK3	1.5147	na	na
4th position derived		HDHK4	1.5147	na	na
2nd & 3rd derived		HDHK5	1.5147	na	na
3rd & 4th derived		HDHK6	1.5147	na	na
2nd & 4th derived		HDHK7	1.5147	na	na
All derived		HDHK8	1.5147	na	na
C3F3S2	Clinical = High, Functional = High, Service = Mod	HDHL1	2.392	HDHJ1	1.4337
2nd position derived		HDHL2	2.392	HDHJ2	1.4337
3rd position derived		HDHL3	2.392	HDHJ3	1.4337
4th position derived		HDHL4	2.392	HDHJ4	1.4337
2nd & 3rd derived		HDHL5	2.392	HDHJ5	1.4337
3rd & 4th derived		HDHL6	2.392	HDHJ6	1.4337
2nd & 4th derived		HDHL7	2.392	HDHJ7	1.4337
All derived		HDHL8	2.392	HDHJ8	1.4337
C3F3S3	Clinical = High, Functional = High, Service = High	HDHM1	2.6437	HDHK1	1.5147
2nd position derived		HDHM2	2.6437	HDHK2	1.5147
3rd position derived		HDHM3	2.6437	HDHK3	1.5147
4th position derived		HDHM4	2.6437	HDHK4	1.5147
2nd & 3rd derived		HDHM5	2.6437	HDHK5	1.5147
3rd & 4th derived		HDHM6	2.6437	HDHK6	1.5147
2nd & 4th derived		HDHM7	2.6437	HDHK7	1.5147
All derived		HDHM8	2.6437	HDHK8	1.5147
C3F4S0	Clinical = High, Functional = Max, Service = Min	HDIJ1	1.6013	na	na
2nd position derived		HDIJ2	1.6013	na	na
3rd position derived		HDIJ3	1.6013	na	na
4th position derived		HDIJ4	1.6013	na	na
2nd & 3rd derived		HDIJ5	1.6013	na	na
3rd & 4th derived		HDIJ6	1.6013	na	na
2nd & 4th derived		HDIJ7	1.6013	na	na
All derived		HDIJ8	1.6013	na	na
C3F4S1	Clinical = High, Functional = Max, Service = Low	HDIK1	1.6822	na	na
2nd position derived		HDIK2	1.6822	na	na
3rd position derived		HDIK3	1.6822	na	na
4th position derived		HDIK4	1.6822	na	na
2nd & 3rd derived		HDIK5	1.6822	na	na
3rd & 4th derived		HDIK6	1.6822	na	na
2nd & 4th derived		HDIK7	1.6822	na	na
All derived		HDIK8	1.6822	na	na
C3F4S2	Clinical = High, Functional = Max, Service = Mod	HDIL1	2.5596	HDIJ1	1.6013
2nd position derived		HDIL2	2.5596	HDIJ2	1.6013
3rd position derived		HDIL3	2.5596	HDIJ3	1.6013
4th position derived		HDIL4	2.5596	HDIJ4	1.6013
2nd & 3rd derived		HDIL5	2.5596	HDIJ5	1.6013
3rd & 4th derived		HDIL6	2.5596	HDIJ6	1.6013

HHRG Description	Case Mix Description by Domains	HIPPS Code	Weight	Fallback HIPPS Code	Fallback Code Weight
2nd & 4th derived		HDIL7	2.5596	HDIJ7	1.6013
All derived		HDIL8	2.5596	HDIJ8	1.6013
C3F4S3	Clinical = High, Functional = Max, Service = High	HDIM1	2.8113	HDIK1	1.6822
2nd position derived		HDIM2	2.8113	HDIK2	1.6822
3rd position derived		HDIM3	2.8113	HDIK3	1.6822
4th position derived		HDIM4	2.8113	HDIK4	1.6822
2nd & 3rd derived		HDIM5	2.8113	HDIK5	1.6822
3rd & 4th derived		HDIM6	2.8113	HDIK6	1.6822
2nd & 4th derived		HDIM7	2.8113	HDIK7	1.6822
All derived		HDIM8	2.8113	HDIK8	1.6822

Source: Health Care Financing Administration, 2000.

Appendix U

Excerpts from the January 1999 Special Fraud Alert

The Importance of Physician Certification for Medicare

The Medicare program only pays for health care services that are medically necessary. In determining what services are medically necessary, Medicare primarily relies on the professional judgment of the beneficiary's treating physician, since he or she knows the patient's history and makes critical decisions, such as admitting the patient to the hospital; ordering tests, drugs, and treatments; and determining the length of treatment. In other words, the physician has a key role in determining both the medical need for, and utilization of, many healthcare services, including those furnished and billed by other providers and suppliers.

Congress has conditioned payment for many Medicare items and services on a certification signed by a physician attesting that the item or service is medically necessary. For example, physicians are routinely required to certify to the medical necessity for any service for which they submit bills to the Medicare program.

Physicians also are involved in attesting to medical necessity when ordering services or supplies that must be billed and provided by an independent supplier or provider. Medicare requires physicians to certify to the medical necessity for many of these items and services through prescriptions, orders, or, in certain specific circumstances, Certificates of Medical Necessity (CMNs). These documentation requirements substantiate that the physician has reviewed the patient's condition and has determined that services or supplies are medically necessary.

Two areas where the documentation of medical necessity by physician certification plays a key role are (i) home health services and (ii) durable medical equipment (DME). Through various OIG audits, we have discovered that physicians sometimes fail to discharge their responsibility to assess their patients' conditions and need for home health care. Similarly, the OIG has found numerous examples of physicians who have ordered DME or signed CMNs for DME without reviewing the medical necessity for the item or even knowing the patient.

Physician Certification for Home Health Services

Medicare will pay a Medicare-certified home health agency for home health care provided under a physician's plan of care to a patient confined to the home. Covered services may include skilled nursing services, home health aide services, physical and occupational therapy and speech-language pathology, medical social services, medical supplies (other than drugs and biologicals), and DME.

As a condition for payment, Medicare requires a patient's treating physician to certify initially and recertify at least every 62 days (2 months) that:

- The patient is confined to the home;

- The individual needs or needed (i) intermittent skilled nursing care; (ii) speech or physical therapy or speech-language pathology services; or (iii) occupational therapy or a continued need for occupational therapy (payment for occupational therapy will be made only upon an initial certification that includes care under (i) or (ii) or a recertification where the initial certification included care under (i) or (ii));

- A plan of care has been established and periodically reviewed by the physician; and

- The services are (were) furnished while the patient is (was) under the care of a physician.

The physician must order the home health services, either orally or in writing, prior to the services being furnished. The physician certification must be obtained at the time the plan of treatment is established or as soon thereafter as possible. The physician certification must be signed and dated prior to the submission of the claim to Medicare. If a physician has any questions as to the application of these requirements to specific facts, the physician should contact the appropriate Medicare fiscal intermediary or carrier.

Physician Orders and Certificates of Medical Necessity for Durable Medical Equipment, Prosthetics, Orthotics, and Supplies for Home Use

DME is equipment that can withstand repeated use, is primarily used for a medical purpose, and is not generally used in the absence of illness or injury. Examples include hospital beds, wheelchairs, and oxygen delivery systems. Medicare will cover medical supplies that are necessary for the effective use of DME, as well as surgical dressings, catheters, and ostomy bags. However, Medicare will only cover DME and supplies that have been ordered or prescribed by a physician. The order or prescription must be personally signed and dated by the patient's treating physician.

DME suppliers that submit bills to Medicare are required to maintain the physician's original written order or prescription in their files. The order or prescription must include:

- The beneficiary's name and full address;

- The physician's signature;

- The date the physician signed the prescription or order;

- A description of the items needed;

- The start date of the order (if appropriate); and

- The diagnosis (if required by Medicare program policies) and a realistic estimate of the total length of time the equipment will be needed (in months or years).

For certain items or supplies, including supplies provided on a periodic basis and drugs, additional information may be required. For supplies provided on a periodic basis, appropriate information on the quantity used, the frequency of change, and the duration of need should be included. If drugs are included in the order, the dosage, frequency of administration, and, if applicable, the duration of infusion and concentration should be included.

Medicare further requires claims for payment for certain kinds of DME to be accompanied by a CMN signed by a treating physician (unless the DME is prescribed as part of a plan of care for home health services). When a CMN is required, the provider or supplier must keep the CMN containing the treating physician's original signature and date on file.

Generally, a CMN has four sections:

- Section A contains general information on the patient, supplier, and physician. **Section A may be completed by the supplier.**

- Section B contains the medical necessity justification for DME. This cannot be filled out by the supplier. **Section B must be completed by the physician, a nonphysician clinician involved in the care of the patient, or a physician employee.** If the physician did not personally complete section B, the name of the person who did complete section B and his or her title and employer must be specified.

- Section C contains a description of the equipment and its cost. **Section C is completed by the supplier.**

- Section D is the treating physician's attestation and signature, which certifies that the physician has reviewed sections A, B, and C of the CMN and that the information in section B is true, accurate, and complete. **Section D must be signed by the treating physician.** Signature stamps and date stamps are not acceptable.

By signing the CMN, the physician represents that:

- He or she is the patient's treating physician, and the information regarding the physician's address and unique physician identification number (UPIN) is correct;

- The entire CMN, including the sections filled out by the supplier, was completed **prior** to the physician's signature; and

- The information in section B relating to medical necessity is true, accurate, and complete to the best of the physician's knowledge.

Improper Physician Certifications Foster Fraud

Unscrupulous suppliers and providers may steer physicians into signing or authorizing improper certifications of medical necessity. In some instances, the certification forms or statements are completed by DME suppliers or home health agencies and presented to the physician, who then signs the forms without verifying the actual need for the items or services. In many cases, the physician may obtain no personal benefit when signing these unverified orders and is only accommodating the supplier or provider. While a physician's signature on a false or misleading certification made through mistake, simple negligence, or inadvertence will not result in personal liability, the physician may unwittingly be facilitating the perpetration of fraud on Medicare by suppliers or providers. When the physician knows the information is false or acts with reckless disregard as to the truth of the statement, such physician risks criminal, civil, and administrative penalties.

Sometimes, a physician may receive compensation in exchange for his or her signature. Compensation can take the form of cash payments, free goods, or any other thing of value. Such cases may trigger additional criminal and civil penalties under the anti-kickback statute.

The following are examples of inappropriate certifications uncovered by the OIG in the course of its investigations of fraud in the provision of home health services and medical equipment and supplies:

- A physician knowingly signs a number of forms provided by a home health agency that falsely represent that skilled nursing services are medically necessary in order to qualify the patient for home health services.

- A physician certifies that a patient is confined to the home and qualifies for home health services, even though the patient tells the physician that her only restrictions are due to arthritis in her hands, and she has no restrictions on her routine activities, such as grocery shopping.

- At the prompting of a DME supplier, a physician signs a stack of blank CMNs for transcutaneous electrical nerve stimulator (TENS) units. The CMNs are later completed with false information in support of fraudulent claims for the equipment. The false information purports to show that the physician ordered and certified to the medical necessity for the TENS units for which the supplier has submitted claims.

- A physician signs CMNs for respiratory medical equipment, falsely representing that the equipment was medically necessary.

- A physician signs CMNs for wheelchairs and hospital beds without seeing the patients, then falsifies his medical charts to indicate that he treated them.

- A physician accepts anywhere from $50 to $400 from a DME supplier for each prescription he signs for oxygen concentrators and nebulizers.

Potential Consequences for Unlawful Acts

A physician is not personally liable for erroneous claims due to mistakes, inadvertence, or simple negligence. However, knowingly signing a false or misleading certification or signing with reckless disregard for the truth can lead to serious criminal, civil, and administrative penalties including:

- Criminal prosecution;
- Fines as high as $10,000 per false claim plus treble damages; or
- Administrative sanctions including: exclusion from participation in Federal health care programs, withholding or recovery of payments, and loss of license or disciplinary actions by state regulatory agencies.

Physicians may violate these laws when, for example:

- They sign a certification as a "courtesy" to a patient, service provider, or DME supplier when they have not first made a determination of medical necessity;
- They knowingly or recklessly sign a false or misleading certification that causes a false claim to be submitted to a Federal health care program; or
- They receive any financial benefit for signing the certification (including free or reduced rent, patient referrals, supplies, equipment, or free labor).

Even if they do not receive any financial or other benefit from providers or suppliers, physicians may be liable for making false or misleading certifications.

Source: Health Care Financing Administration. 1999 (January 12). Notices. *Federal Register* 64(7):1814–6.

Glossary

485:   HCFA form number for the plan of care.

1500:   The claim form, in either paper or electronic version, used by most noninstitutional healthcare providers and suppliers to bill Medicare. Published as form HCFA-1500.

Admission date: Within the home health prospective payment system, the date of first service or first service in a period of continuous care.

Assessment: The systematic collection and review of patient-specific data.

Benchmarking: Comparing data against a predetermined reference point. Benchmarking may be internal or external.

Claim: A bill for services rendered.

Continuous quality improvement (CQI):   Term used to describe an ongoing cycle of improvement in healthcare processes.

Customer: External or internal recipient of services.

Data: Raw facts, figures, and observations.

Data accuracy: The extent to which data are free of identifiable errors.

Data analysis: The process of translating data into information that can be used by an application.

Data collection: The process by which data are accumulated.

Data element: Smallest unique subset of a database.

Data reliability: The stability, repeatability, or precision of data.

Data validity: Verification of correctness.

Database: A collection of related data elements that are stored together for multiple applications.

Database management: Access and control of data by passwords or other techniques.

Degaussing: The process of removing or rearranging the magnetic field of a disk, rendering the data unrecoverable.

Durable medical equipment (DME): Includes the retail sale of items such as eyeglasses, hearing aids, and surgical appliances and supplies; bulk and cylinder oxygen; and equipment rental. Also known as home medical equipment (HME).

Durable medical equipment regional carrier (DMERC): A fiscal intermediary designated to process DME claims. A carrier is contracted by Medicare to process durable medical equipment, prosthetics, and orthotics (DMEPOS) claims submitted by Part B providers within a defined region. A carrier has many contract-specific obligations. Chief among them is to administer the rules of the program, maintain program integrity, and report statistical information required for analysis to the statistical analysis durable medical equipment regional carrier (SADMERC).

Episode: The sixty-day unit of payment for the home health prospective payment system.

Grouper: A software module that groups information for payment classification for the home health prospective payment system from the OASIS assessment tool to form HHRGs and HIPPS codes.

HCFA Common Procedural Coding System (HCPCS): Coding system designed to promote uniform reporting and statistical data collection of medical procedures, supplies, products, and services.

HCFA form-1450: HCFA's version of the UB-92.

Health Care Financing Administration (HCFA): The federal agency administering the Medicare program and the federal portions of Medicaid and the child health programs.

Health Insurance Portability and Accountability Act (HIPAA): Federal legislation passed in 1996 that includes provisions on the confidentiality and security of health information.

Health insurance prospective payment system (HIPPS): Procedural coding used in form locator 44 of the Form HCFA-1450 (UB-92) for HH PPS. Eight HIPPSs are assigned to each HHRG for HH PPS.

Health insurance query for HHAs (HIQH): On-line transaction providing information on HH PPS episodes for specific Medicare beneficiaries for HHAs and hospices.

Health record: Compilation of pertinent information about a patient's past and present illness(es) and treatment(s). Also called patient record.

Home health (HH): Medical and nonmedical services provided to patients and their families in their homes or places of residence. Also known as home care.

Home health agency (HHA): Providers offering one or more home care services. Providers may be certified, noncertified, home care staffing companies, or home care equipment companies.

Home health resources group (HHRG): The eighty home health episode rates.

Hospice: Provider of palliative medical care to the terminal patient and psychosocial and spiritual support to the patient and patient's family.

Indicator: A measure to determine an organization's performance over time.

Information: Facts, statistics, and observations processed in a formal, intelligent way for a specific purpose.

Information system: Specific data-processing applications.

Line item: Service- or item-specific detail of claims.

Low-utilization payment adjustment (LUPA):   An episode of four or fewer visits, paid by national, standardized per-visit rates instead of HHRGs.

Measure: Quantifiable data about a function or process.

Measurement: The systematic process of data collection, repeated over time or at a single point in time.

National standard per-visit rates: Rates for six home health disciplines based on historical claims data. Used in the payment of low-utilization payment adjustments and the calculation of outliers.

No-RAP low-utilization payment adjustments: Claim submitted for an episode when the home health agency is aware from the outset that the episode will require four visits or less.

Outcome: The result of the performance of a function or process.

Outcomes and Assessment Information Set (OASIS):   The home health assessment instrument required by the Health Care Financing Administration.

Outlier: An addition to a full episode payment, when the cost of the estimated service exceeds a fixed loss threshold.

Patient/client: The person and/or the family receiving service.

Patient status code: Describes patient status at discharge or end of period in form locator 22 of the HCFA-1450 form (UB-92).

Partial episode payment (PEP) adjustment: A reduced episode payment that may be based on the number of service days in an episode.

Performance improvement (PI):   The continuous study and adaptation of a healthcare organization's functions and processes to increase desired outcomes.

Plan of care (POC):   A physician-established plan required by Medicare home health services for homebound beneficiaries.

Population: The universe of data under investigation from which a sample will be taken.

Pricer: The software module in a Medicare claim processing system that is used in pricing claims under the prospective payment system.

Prosthetics and orthotics (P/Os):   An artificial extremity, augmentation device, or mechanical appliance for orthopedic use.

Prospective payment system (PPS):   A Medicare payment for medical care that is based on predetermined payment rates or periods and linked to the anticipated intensity of services delivered and beneficiary condition.

Regional home health intermediaries (RHHI):   Five fiscal intermediaries nationally designated to process Medicare home health and hospice claims. Contract-specific obligations include administering the rules of the program, maintaining program integrity, and reporting statistical information required for analysis to the Health Care Financing Administration.

Reliability: The extent of agreement among different raters. An example of a reliability question would be "Can different care providers collect OASIS information on the same patient and get the same HHRG?"

Request for anticipated payment (RAP): The first of two HCFA forms 1450 (UB-92) used at the opening of a prospective payment system episode to receive one of two split-percentage payments. The RAP is not a claim according to Medicare statutes.

Revenue code: Payment codes for services or items placed in form locator 42 of the form HCFA-1450 (UB-92).

Risk adjustment: Patient condition or circumstance that positively or negatively influences the outcome.

Sample: A portion of the population from which a conclusion can be drawn.

Significant change in condition (SCIC) adjustment: A single episode payment under multiple home health resource groups, each prorated to the number of service days delivered.

Source of admission code: Form locator 20 on the form HCFA-1450 (UB-92).

Statistical significance: Probability that the observed difference is due to chance.

Type of bill (TOB): Coding representing the nature of each form HCFA-1450 (UB-92) claim.

UB-92: The claim or bill form in either paper or electronic version used by most institutional providers.

Validity: Substantiated data.

Additional Resources

American Health Information Management Association (AHIMA) Web site.
  www.ahima.org/journal/practice.brief.html
    This address provides access to the following AHIMA Practice Briefs:
    • Facsimile Transmission of Health Information (July/August 1996)
    • Electronic Signatures (October 1998)
    • Managing Health Information Relating to Infection with the Human Immunodeficiency Virus (HIV) (May 1999)
    • E-mail Security (February 2000)
    • Transfer of Patient Health Information across the Continuum (November/December 2000)

American Society of Health-System Pharmacists. 1992. *Example Patient Medical Chart.* Bethesda, Md.: American Society of Health-System Pharmacists.
    This publication includes an actual health record.

Brassard, Michael, and Diane Ritter. 1994. T*he Memory Jogger II: A Pocket Guide of Tools for Continuous Improvement and Effective Planning.* Methuen, Mass.: GOAL/QPC.
    The case study examples within this guide demonstrate how to improve the workings of an organization (also available on CD-ROM).

Briggs Corportation. 1995. *Home Care Clinical Documentation System.* Des Moines, Iowa: Briggs Corporation.
    This system offers forty-four forms that provide a standardized, consistent, regulatory-compliant documentation system.

Cofer, Jennifer, and Jean Clark. 2000. *Information Management: The Compliance Guide to the JCAHO Standards.* 3rd ed. Marblehead, Mass.: Opus Communications.
    This text aids the reader in understanding JCAHO information management standards.

Frye, Carla B. 1994. *Monitoring a Pharmacist's Care Plan.* Bethesda, Md.: American Society of Health-System Pharmacists.
    This work serves as a continuing education module for pharmacists that covers patient monitoring and documentation of this monitoring.

Goodwin, D. R. 1992. Critical pathways in home health care. *Journal of Nursing Administration* 22(2):35–40.

Giuliano, K. K., and C. R. Poirier. 1991. Nurse case management: critical pathways to desirable outcomes. *Nursing Management* 22(3):52–55.

Health Care Financing Administration (HCFA) Web site.
  www.hcfa.gov/medicare/hhmain.htm
    This address provides specifications for the HH PPS grouper.
  www.hcfa.gov/pubforms/p2192toc.htm
    This address provides relevant HCFA manuals.
  www.hcfa.gov/stat/pufiles.htm
    This address provides the Health Care Financing Administration's durable medical equipment fee schedule.

Joint Commission on Accreditation of Healthcare Organizations. 1993. *The Measurement Mandate: On the Road to Performance Improvement in Health Care.* Oakbrook Terrace, Ill.: JCAHO.
  This book provides detailed information on the concept of measurement.

Jones, William N., and Suzanne Campbell. 1994. *Designing and Recommending a Pharmacist's Care Plan.* Bethesda, Md.: American Society of Health-System Pharmacists.
  This book is a continuing education module for pharmacists that focuses on formulating and documenting a pharmacist's care plan.

Juran, Joseph, and Godfrey A. Blanton. 1998. *Juran's Quality Handbook.* 5th ed. New York City: McGraw-Hill.
  This book explains the processes behind quality management.

Lewis-Beck, Michael S. 1995. *Data Analysis: An Introduction.* Thousand Oaks, Calif.: Sage Publications.
  This short text can be helpful for the beginning researcher.

Marrelli, Tina M. 2001. *Handbook of Home Health Standards and Documentation Guidelines for Reimbursement.* 4th ed. St. Louis: Mosby-Year Book.
  Written for the home care nurse, this handbook provides information on the documentation of care.

Marrelli, T. M., and L. S. Hilliard. 1995. *Home Care and Clinical Paths: Effective Care Planning Across the Continuum.* St. Louis: Mosby-Year Book.
  This book explains and demonstrates clinical paths for the home care nurse and manager.

Mason, Nancy, and Leslie A. Shimp. 1993. *Building a Pharmacist's Patient Data Base.* Bethesda, Md.: American Society of Health-System Pharmacists.
  This continuing education module for pharmacists focuses on developing and documenting a patient database.

Massanari, R. M. 1994. Transforming data into usable information: generating rate-based information. *Journal of the American Health Information Management Association* 65(6):48–52.

McFadden, Fred R., Jeffrey A. Hoffner, and Mary B. Prescott. 1998. *Modern Database Management.* 5th ed. New York City: Addison-Wesley Publishing.
  This textbook provides information on database management.

Norman, Geoffrey R., and David L. Streiner. 1998. *PDQ Statistics.* 2nd ed. Philadelphia: B. C. Decker.
  This work provides a short, simple introduction to statistics.

Omdahl, Diane. 2001. *The Beacon Guide to Medicare Service Delivery.* Edition 5.7. Mequon, Wis.: Beacon Health.

Saba, V. K. 1992. *Develop and Demonstrate a Method for Classifying Home Health Patients to Predict Resource Requirements and to Measure Outcomes.* Springfield, Va.: National Technical Information Service, U.S. Department of Commerce, PB92-177013/AS.
  This publication presents the final report on the Health Care Financing Administration-funded project to develop a home healthcare classification system.

Scholtes, Peter R., Brian L. Joiner, and Barbara J. Streibel. 1996. *The Team Handbook.* 2nd revised ed. Madison, Wis.: Oriel.

Shepherd, Michele F. 1992. *Reviewing Patient Medical Charts.* Bethesda, Md.: American Society of Health-System Pharmacists.
> This continuing education module for pharmacists focuses on how to understand the patient record and locate information in the record.

Shimp, Leslie A., and Nancy Mason. 1993. *Constructing a Patient's Drug Therapy Problem List.* Bethesda, Md.: American Society of Health-System Pharmacists.
> This continuing education module for pharmacists focuses on identification and resolution of medication-related problems and their documentation.

Streiner, David L., and Geoffrey R. Norman. 1998. *PDQ Epidemiology.* 2nd ed. Philadelphia: B. C. Decker.
> This work provides a short, simple introduction to epidemiology.

Index

Medication administration, 37
Message authentication, 121
Microfiche, 92
Microfilming inactive records, 91–92
Middle digit filing system, 88
Minor, definitions of, 128
Mobile work forces, automated solutions for,
    108–11

NAHC. *See* National Association for Home
    Care
NANDA. *See* North American Nursing
    Diagnosis Association
National Association for Home Care (NAHC)
    data set used by, 3, 99–100
    estimates of spending for home care of, 3
    survey of agencies, *ix*
    untimely physician orders as major cause
        of claim denials according to, 53
National Center for Health Statistics survey
    summary of home care, 2
National Medical Expenditure Survey, 3
Needs assessment for computerization, 104–5
Negligence risk from inadequate transmission
    of information, 17
Network security system, 121
NIC. *See* Nursing Intervention Classification
NOC. *See* Nursing Outcome Classification
Nondisclosure agreement for home care and
    hospices, individuals who should sign,
    124
North American Nursing Diagnosis
    Association (NANDA), 24, 25
Numbering of records, 83–84
Numeric record filing system, 88, 89
Nurse supervision of home health aide, 38
Nursing care, involvement of HIM profes-
    sionals in, 23–26
Nursing diagnoses, 23–24
Nursing Intervention Classification (NIC), 24,
    25
Nursing note for continuous care, 39
Nursing Outcome Classification (NOC), 24,
    25
Nursing process, health record documentation
    and, 24, 26

OASIS. *See* Outcome and Assessment
    Information Set
OBQI. *See* Outcome-based quality
    improvement
OBQM. *See* Outcome-based quality
    management
OBRA. *See* Omnibus Budget Reconciliation
    Act of 1986
Occupational therapy under HH PPS, 143
Office of Inspector General (OIG)
    compliance program of, 49, 97
    fraud alert, 147–48
    monitoring of Medicare beneficiary access
        to HHAs monitored by, 28

OIG. *See* Office of Inspector General
Older Americans Act as source of home care
    funding, 47
Omnibus Budget Reconciliation Act of 1986
    (OBRA)
    patient rights mandated by, 21
    prospective payment system mandated by
        BBA and, 1–2
Open-shelf file shelving, 89–90
Optical storage-based document imaging
    system, 92
ORYX initiative of JCAHO, 11, 69–71
    paperwork for, 107–8
Outcome and Assessment Information Set
    (OASIS)
    added by HCFA to *Conditions of Partici-
        pation* in 1999, 61
    added to uniform data set, 3
    assessment of data items for, 31, 142
    A2 and B1 versions of, 4, 62
    to capture outcome data, 11
    collection of data items for, 30
    comprehensive assessments created with
        data from, 141
    confidentiality of data for, 79–80, 129–30
    data collection for home health using, 46,
        110
    documentation burdens for providers
        under, 15–16
    electronic submission of data for, 46
    home care assessment and outcome moni-
        toring supported by, 62
    monthly report of data for, 16
    paperwork for, 107–8
    as part of information system, 4
    patient assessment using data items of,
        30–31
    patient's rights under, 30
    for payment of services in HH PPS, 96
    performance measures of, 101
    principal diagnosis for, 94, 95
    software for data submission of, 118
    Statement of Patient Privacy Rights of, 80
    as subject to Federal Privacy Act of 1974,
        21–22, 79–80
    to support home confinement status, 44
    uses of, 4
    Web site of, 30
Outcome data, service bureaus to access, 108
Outcome-based quality improvement (OBQI),
    4
Outcome-based quality management (OBQM)
    case-mix and adverse event reports for,
        63–65
    paperwork for, 107–8
Outcome-Based Quality Management reports,
    2
Outguides to mark location of records leaving
    storage area, 90
Outlier payments under HH PPS, 140,
    141–42